INTRODUCTION TO

# ELECTRIC CIRCUITS

# INTRODUCTION TO

# ELECTRIC CIRCUITS

by **HERBERT W. JACKSON**

*Head of the Electronic Technology Department*
*Ryerson Institute of Technology*

**PRENTICE-HALL, INC.**

*Englewood Cliffs, N. J.*

*Library of Congress Catalog Card Number: 59-14511*




*First printing*........*September, 1959*
*Second printing*........*August, 1960*
*Third printing*..........*March, 1961*
*Fourth printing*........*August, 1962*

PRINTED IN THE UNITED STATES OF AMERICA

48133-C

# PREFACE

THIS BOOK has been written especially for those studying electric circuit theory at the Technical Institute and Junior College level. Electrical and electronics technicians are required to possess a knowledge of direct and alternating current theory well beyond the factual information level of the skilled craftsman. However, whereas the engineering student is trained to accept a mathematical derivation as satisfactory proof of a principle, the technician chooses this particular field of endeavor because he finds that he needs to *visualize* what goes on in a circuit in order to understand it. Because this book is devoted to developing an *understanding* of the principles of electric circuit behavior, it is titled an *"Introduction to Electric Circuits."*

The objective of this approach is to develop the student's understanding of circuit theory by discovering why electric circuits must behave as they do. Much space is devoted to developing the fundamental ideas step by step, each step based on a preceding step, progressing from the simple ideas to the more complex concepts, even to the extent of sometimes calling attention to the obvious. Where there is a choice of approach in defining a principle, the one that best fits this pattern of development is selected. If more conventional forms do not suit this technique, they are omitted. The detailed and deliberate, step by step progress of the early chapters increases in pace as the plot develops and the student's understanding of the basic principles grows. This treatment will partly compensate for the absence of an instructor in the case of those readers who have the ambition to advance their technical education by home study.

From the technician's point of view, mathematics must be treated as an essential tool required in applying an understanding of circuit theory to the solution of practical problems. Therefore it is necessary to assume a knowledge of algebra to the extent of the transposition of equations and the solution of simultaneous and the general quadratic equations. Keeping in mind the readers using this book for home study, any mathematical processes beyond basic algebra are introduced as required. A complete chapter is devoted to vector algebra to assist readers not familiar with this aid to circuit solutions.

Each basic idea as developed is related to practice by numerical examples with step by step solutions. Examples have been selected from both power and communications applications. Each chapter contains extensive problem assignments. These problems are designed to illustrate the application of theory and to test for comprehension of the principles involved. In most cases they cannot be solved by simply inserting numbers into equations. The problems are grouped into pairs; answers appear at the back of the book to odd-numbered problems The review questions for each chapter are worded so that they cannot be answered by copying verbatim from the text. They ask the student "how" or "why" the principles he has learned apply to a given situation.

In order to keep the student's attention directed to the understanding of fundamental principles and their application to the behavior of direct and alternating current circuits, reference to electric and electronic equipment is made only to the extent that it serves to illustrate a point in question. Notwithstanding the practical approach to circuit theory, every effort has been made to develop the basic concepts in such a manner that they comply with the most recent American Institute of Electrical Engineers and Institute of Radio Engineers standards. Both the mks units of the engineer and the English practical units of the skilled craftsman are used throughout, with numerous problems requiring conversion from the one system to the other, to develop an appreciation of their relative magnitudes and applications. There is sparse reference to the now practically obsolete cgs system of units. Although electric current in metallic conductors is developed as an electron flow, both electronics and electrical technicians are expected to be acquainted with conventional current direction. This has been introduced in marking circuit diagrams associated with the solution of network problems.

The complete text covers all of the circuit theory that electrical and electronics technicians are usually required to understand in order to progress to courses involving the application of this fundamental theory to the understanding of equipment operation. This course has been presented for several years in the first year of a technical institute curriculum for electrical and electronics technicians. As such it has required about five hours per week. The material has also been used in a two semester course with all technical students receiving an introduction to electricity during the first semester, the electrical and electronics students carrying on into circuits and networks in the second semester. The same material, slightly streamlined, is used in extension classes.

I should like to acknowledge the suggestions and assistance received from members of the staff of the Electrical and Electronic Technology departments of the Ryerson Institute of Technology. The contributions of A. R. Low, head of the Mathematics and Physics department, and J. T. Koski, head of the Electrical Technology department, to this book are greatly appreciated. Thanks are also due to I. L. Kosow, head of the Electrical Technology department of the Staten Island Community College, for many helpful suggestions made when reviewing the manuscript.

H. W. JACKSON

# CONTENTS

# Chapter 1

# INTRODUCTION

~~~~~~~~~~~~~~~~~~~~~~~~~~~~~~~~~~~~~~~~~~~~~~~

## 1. On Studying Electric Circuits

When a person first attempts to read a book in a foreign language, for example in French, armed only with a French-English dictionary, it is difficult for him to appreciate the content fully, because of the conscious effort required in translating the individual words. A prior study of the basic rules of the grammar of the language, along with sufficient vocabulary practice, would be a more logical approach to the task. Similarly, basic electric circuit theory constitutes the language by which the operation of electric and electronic apparatus is described. Therefore a study of the basic laws of this language along with sufficient practice to minimize the conscious effort required in its application are prerequisites to any serious study of electric and electronic equipment.

To carry the analogy one step further, translation by searching through the dictionary for the desired word and substituting the equivalent English word will do little to assist in understanding the material being translated. Therefore the student is warned not to think of electric circuit theory and this text as a dictionary of formulas by which one may arrive at the correct numerical solution simply by selecting the right formula and inserting given data. In electric circuits, a formula is merely a convenient way of expressing a definition of the behavior of the circuit. Since the task at hand is to *understand* circuit behavior, the student should not apply a formula unless he is satisfied that he fully understands the definition it represents. In this respect electric circuit theory has an advantage over language study in that every definition can be readily and logically developed from a preceding step.

In preparing this text, the important laws, definitions, and formulas have been made to stand out from the descriptive material, so that the

1

student should find it unnecessary to repeat any of this information in notebook form. However it is suggested that the solutions to the problem and question assignments be kept in a notebook. It is advisable to develop the habit of solving electric circuit problems in a logical, step by step manner and recording these steps neatly. Since a considerable amount of numerical calculation is involved, the student is advised to become proficient in the use of the slide rule. Full instructions are supplied with most good quality rules.

## 2. Energy

The Earth would be a dead planet if it were not for the abundance of energy in its many forms and the ease with which it can be converted from one form to another. Heat, light, sound, and mechanical energy are forms with which man is directly concerned since they contribute to his comfort. When man could not obtain sufficient heat energy directly from the sun, he discovered a means of converting the chemical energy of various forms of fuel into heat by combustion. In early history when man had need for mechanical energy, he had to produce it by his own muscular effort or that of his domestic animals. In search of laborsaving devices to conserve his own energy, he found a way to convert the energy of falling water, which in itself was of no direct use to him, into useful mechanical energy through the invention of the water wheel.

Electricity is a form of energy which may be compared with the hydraulic energy of water. In its natural state it was no more than a scientific curiosity in the nineteenth century. But once man found a means of *converting* vast amounts of natural energy into an electrical form and then *converting* it at will into heat, light, mechanical, or other useful forms of energy, electricity became his greatest servant.

## 3. The Nature of Electricity

Let us consider for a moment some of the energy conversions taking place in a modern aircraft. The original source of energy was the radiant energy from the sun which formed the petroleum used as fuel. The chemical energy of the fuel is converted first into heat and then into mechanical energy in the main engines of the aircraft. The majority of this mechanical energy is required to propel the aircraft, but some of the mechanical energy is needed to move the control surfaces and to raise and lower the undercarriage of the aircraft.

Although it would be possible to convey some of the mechanical energy from the engines to the undercarriage in mechanical form via a system of shafts, gears, belts, and pulleys, it would not be very practical to do so. One solution to the problem is to drive a hydraulic pump from one of the main engines and to convey the energy by means of a fluid under pressure to a hydraulic motor located at the point where the mechanical energy is required. With this system, all the moving shafts, gears, pulleys, and belts are replaced by two stationary copper tubes. Another solution is to drive an electric generator from one of the main engines and to convey the energy in electrical form to an electric motor located at the point where the mechanical energy is required. Both systems are used in modern aircraft.

Since the hydraulic fluid can be seen, felt, smelled, and even tasted by the human senses, it is easy for us to visualize the action of the fluid as the medium for conveying energy. The medium by which the energy is conveyed in electrical form cannot be detected directly by the human senses and therefore is more difficult to appreciate. Since both the hydraulic and the electric energy-conveying systems in the aircraft perform the same function, we shall use the hydraulic analogy to help us in formulating an idea of the nature of the electric medium.

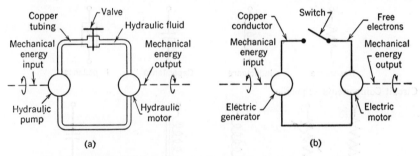

**Fig. 1.1.** (a) Hydraulic, and (b) electrical systems for conveying mechanical energy from one location to another.

If the fluid were drained from the copper tubing of the hydraulic system of Fig. 1.1(a), the motor could not operate and no energy would be conveyed by the system. The molecules of the fluid form the **medium** by which energy is conveyed. Yet in doing so, they undergo no change in composition. Energy is conveyed simply by forcing the medium to flow under pressure through the motor. The pump maintains this pressure at the expense of the mechanical energy driving the pump. Similarly the solid copper conductors of the electric system of Fig. 1.1(b) must contain some form of particle which, while undergoing no change itself, is forced under pressure to flow around the circuit. From the foregoing discussion we may think of electricity not so much as a form of energy in its natural state, but thus:

> **Electricity** may be thought of as a medium by which energy can be conveniently conveyed from one location to another.

The apparatus for conveying energy in electrical form or, for the purposes of this text, the representation of such apparatus by graphic

# Table I. Standard Graphic Symbols Used In This Text

**Sources of emf—General**

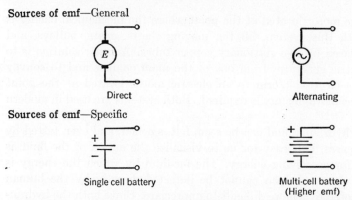

Direct

Alternating

**Sources of emf—Specific**

Single cell battery

Multi-cell battery
(Higher emf)

*Note:* The + and − signs need not be drawn since it is standard for the longer stroke to represent the positive terminal and the shorter stroke the negative terminal of a battery.

**Circuit Elements—General**

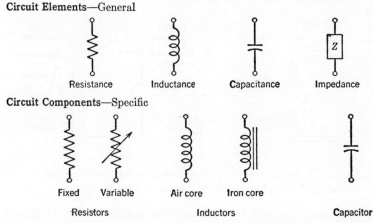

Resistance    Inductance    Capacitance    Impedance

**Circuit Components—Specific**

Fixed    Variable    Air core    Iron core

Resistors    Inductors    Capacitor

*Note:* An arrow drawn obliquely through any of these symbols represents a variable component.

Switch    Lamp    Voltmeter    Ammeter

**Interconnecting Conductors**

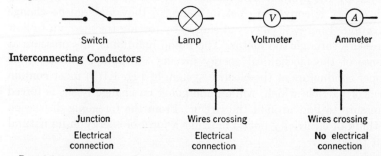

Junction | Wires crossing | Wires crossing

Electrical connection | Electrical connection | **No** electrical connection

In a circuit diagram, these conductors are assumed to be ideal conductors. Any resistance, inductance, or capacitance possessed by practical conductors in an actual circuit will be represented by the appropriate symbol in the circuit diagram.

## Layout of Circuit Diagrams

Circuit diagrams are drawn in such a manner that the flow of energy is from left to right. Graphic symbols and interconnecting wiring should be drawn either vertically or horizontally. Oblique lines are to be avoided.

symbols as in Fig. 1.1(b) is called an **electric circuit.** Since a sketch can show the exact interconnection of the various components much more clearly than a description in words, we shall follow the accepted practice of drawing a **circuit diagram** for each of the electric circuits we discuss. To keep these circuit diagrams as simple and as clear as possible, we represent the various circuit elements by standard graphic symbols rather than by pictorial sketches. Although there have been some variations in symbols in the past, the graphic symbols used in this text are presently accepted as standard by both the American Institute of Electrical Engineers and the Institute of Radio Engineers. The interpretation of these symbols is shown in Table I, and the student should refer back to this table whenever a symbol is first encountered in studying the text.

## 4. The Free Electron

There are very few students nowadays who do not know that all matter is made up of atoms and that each atom has a nucleus around which electrons revolve in a manner similar to that in which the planets of the solar system follow orbits around the sun. The electrons of every atom are identical and physicists have measured their effective mass and charge. The atoms of one element differ from those of another in terms of the mass of the nucleus and the number of orbital electrons.

Since a force of attraction exists between an orbital electron and a nucleus, in order for the electron to maintain a fixed orbit, it must move at a constant velocity around the orbit to develop the required centrifugal force to balance this attraction exactly. And since an electron has a certain mass, the moving electron must possess a kinetic energy proportional to its mass and the square of its velocity. ($W = \frac{1}{2} mv^2$) Therefore, to occupy a certain orbit, an electron must possess a definite amount of energy. We can therefore discuss electron orbits in terms of the **energy levels** of the electrons in them.

A closer study of the atom reveals that the electrons do not revolve about the nucleus in a random manner. They must do so in distinct energy levels. Only two electrons can occupy any one orbit and therefore only two electrons can possess exactly the same energy. However, the spacing between energy levels is such that, when considering the chemical properties of various atoms, it is to our advantage to group several closely spaced energy levels together into **electron shells,** as shown in Fig. 1.2. The gap in energy level between one shell and the next is much greater than the gaps between energy levels within a shell.

The maximum number of electrons which each shell can contain is the same for all atoms, and in general, these shells must fill up from the center outward as the atomic weight of the element increases. The first shell can contain two electrons, the second eight, the third eighteen, and so on to a seventh shell for such elements as uranium. Elements such as helium with its two orbital electrons, and neon with ten orbital electrons, have no tendency to combine chemically with other elements since they possess completely filled shells. Hydrogen with only one electron tries to combine chemically with other elements in such a manner that it can either gain or lose an electron to complete its first shell, thus becoming stable. Even in its uncombined form, a molecule of hydrogen gas consists of two

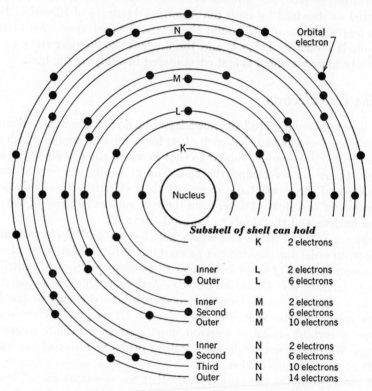

**Fig. 1.2.** Location of orbital electrons in the first four energy levels of an atom.

hydrogen atoms, each sharing its one orbital electron with the other to give both atoms a complete shell, thus becoming a stable substance, as shown in Fig. 1.3. This action is called **covalent bonding**.

Copper atoms have twenty-nine electrons revolving about each nucleus. After the first three shells are filled up $(2 + 8 + 18 = 28)$, there is one lone electron left to take its position in the fourth shell which is capable of holding thirty-two electrons. Since it is all by itself in the N shell, this electron travels in a much larger orbit than the twenty-eight tightly held electrons in the first three shells. As Fig. 1.4 indicates, this orbit is so great that as the twenty-ninth electron passes an adjacent copper atom, it is almost midway between two nuclei. As a result of being in this position of balanced attraction, this electron is *free* to move to the fourth shell of the adjacent atom and in turn to be replaced by an electron from another similar atom. Thus in a seemingly solid piece of copper there are millions upon millions of **free electrons** drifting from atom to atom. It would appear from Fig. 1.4 that it is possible to have as many free electrons in a piece of copper as there are atoms. Knowing the mass of a copper atom, we can then estimate that

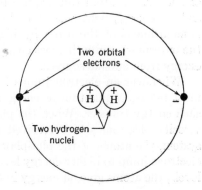

Fig. 1.3. A hydrogen molecule.

there are somewhere in the neighborhood of 1.4 million, million, million, million ($1.4 \times 10^{24}$) free electrons in a cubic inch of copper.

It is the **free electrons** in the copper conductors of Fig. 1.1(b) which form the energy conveying medium which is the electrical equivalent of the hydraulic fluid of Fig. 1.1(a).

Since atomic structure is such that the orbital electrons can exist only at certain specific energy levels, it is impossible to add just a little

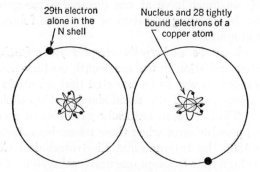

Fig. 1.4. Two adjacent copper atoms.

energy to an electron, thereby increasing its velocity and the radius of its orbit just a bit. If an orbital electron accepts any energy from an outside source, it must accept just the right amount to allow it to jump to the next higher (further from the nucleus) energy level. Not only is the kinetic energy of the electron increased as it travels at a greater velocity in the higher energy level, but also the potential energy is increased since it has been moved against the force of attraction between the orbital electron and the nucleus. The amount of energy required to move an electron from one energy level to the next higher level is called a **quantum** of energy. An atom can acquire this energy from such external sources as heat energy, light energy, and even mechanical energy in the form of bombardment of the atom by high-velocity electrons. The electrons in the outermost orbits (highest energy levels) are the ones that acquire this energy from outside sources.

Whenever an electron jumps back to a lower energy level, the atom must release a quantum of energy. A fluorescent lamp is an example of such energy transfer. When the phosphor coating is bombarded by high-velocity electrons which received their kinetic energy from the electric system, the atoms of the phosphor take on energy as some of the orbital electrons jump to higher energy levels. As they jump back to their original levels, the atoms give off energy in the form of light.

## 5. The mks System of Units

Back in 1883 Lord Kelvin observed, "I often say that when you can measure what you are speaking about, and express it in numbers, you know something about it; but when you cannot measure it, when you cannot express it in numbers, your knowledge is of a meagre and unsatisfactory kind." The full significance of this remark will be appreciated when we realize that the scientists of Lord Kelvin's time had no knowledge of atomic structure and the free electron. To apply this philosophy to our study of electric circuits, we must have at our disposal a recognized system of measuring units. In selecting a system of units, the following conditions should be kept in mind.

*The system should be universally accepted for scientific work.* Since international communication in the nineteenth century was by no means as extensive as today, it was to be expected that scientists working independently in various parts of the world should set up their own systems of measurement. This situation naturally gave rise to a certain amount of confusion and possible error when these researchers started to compare notes. In June 1935 the International Electrotechnical Commission decided that it was high time to adopt one universal system of standard units for scientific measurement. The system adopted at that time is the mks system based on the meter as the basic unit of length, the kilogram as the basic unit of mass, and the second as the basic unit of time.

*The system should be developed so that practically all units can be derived from a minimum number of elemental units.* In this manner, the number of primary standards which must be maintained is kept to a minimum. This approach has the additional advantage of helping us to understand the relationship among the various units as we develop them in later chapters. The mks standard meter and kilogram are preserved at the International Bureau of Weights and Measures at Sèvres in France. The meter is marked off on a platinum-iridium bar. Being a fundamental unit, it had to be arbitrarily selected in the first instance. The length marked off on the bar was to represent as closely as could be calculated at that time one ten millionth of the distance from the Earth's equator to the pole at sea level. Similarly, although the primary standard kilogram is preserved in the form of a platinum-iridium cylinder, it represents one thousand times the mass of one cubic centimeter of pure water at 4°C. The universally accepted unit of time is the second which is defined as 1/86,400 of a mean solar day. With these three elemental units specified, all other units required in the mks system may be derived.

*The unit of energy must be the same for both electrical and mechanical measurement* since the majority of electric energy is generated at the expense of mechanical energy. This permits calculations in the one system of energy to be readily related to the other system. The unit of energy is the **joule.** Its derivation will be dealt with in a later chapter.

*In deriving a unit of measurement,* **single** *unit should be formed by combining* **one** *unit of each of two or more units already defined.* To students who have grown up with a metric system of units, such a statement is redundant. But to students from English speaking areas of the world who have learned that a cubic foot of water weighs 62.38 pounds (etc. ad infinitum), this will be a welcome relief.

*Whenever it is more convenient to express a measurement in a larger or smaller* **size** *of unit than the basic unit, the ratio between unit sizes should be on a decimal basis.* Although the length of a certain electric conductor may be expressed as 696 inches, it is much easier to visualize the magnitude of this measurement if it is expressed as 58 feet. Similarly in the mks system of units, a size of unit suitable to the magnitude of the quantity being measured is desirable. Again the English speaking student will be happy to escape from the nondecimal 12 in. = 1 ft and 3 ft = 1 yd system in common use. By simply having to shift a decimal point to change unit size rather than having to actually multiply or divide by some conversion factor which changes for each situation, an appreciable advantage in time saved and errors prevented is achieved.

There are two schools of thought on expressing larger or smaller magnitudes of a unit in the mks system. Research people favor **scientific notation** in which the decimal point is shifted to leave one significant digit to the left of the decimal point and the result is then multiplied by the appropriate power of ten to equal the original number. Using scientific notation makes it unnecessary to change the basic unit name.

EXAMPLE 1: Express 839,000 meters in scientific notation.

*Solution:* Shifting the decimal point five places to the left and multiplying by $10^5$ gives

$$839,000 \text{ meters} = 8.39 \times 10^5 \text{ meters}$$

EXAMPLE 2: Express 1/200 second in scientific notation.

*Solution:* The first step is to divide the fraction out into decimal form:

$$\frac{1}{200} \text{ sec} = 0.005 \text{ sec}$$

The decimal point is now shifted three places to the right and the result is multiplied by $10^{-3}$, giving

$$\frac{1}{200} \text{ sec} = 5.0 \times 10^{-3} \text{ sec}$$

Engineering personnel prefer to use a suitable prefix on the basic unit to indicate the shift of the decimal point. The metric system of units is equipped with a list of prefixes to permit shifting the decimal point one place at a time. However, for engineering purposes, a shift of three places (a thousand to one ratio) at a time is quite satisfactory. These prefixes and their meanings are shown in Table II.

#### Table II

| Prefix | Meaning | | Abbreviation* |
|--------|---------|---|---------------|
| mega- | one million | or $10^6$ | M |
| kilo- | one thousand | or $10^3$ | k |
| milli- | one thousandth | or $10^{-3}$ | m |
| micro- | one millionth | or $10^{-6}$ | $\mu$ |

\* To avoid possible confusion between *mega-* and *milli-* when abbreviated, it is preferred that *mega-* be written in full. The abbreviation for *micro* is the Greek letter $\mu$ (mu).

EXAMPLE 3:

$$1 \text{ kilometer} = 1000 \text{ meters}$$
$$1 \text{ microsec} = 0.000,001 \text{ sec}$$

EXAMPLE 4: Express 839,000 meters in a more convenient size of unit.

*Solution:* Shifting the decimal point three places to the left gives a figure 839 of a unit which must then be one thousand times as large as a meter. Therefore

$$839,000 \text{ meters} = 839 \text{ kilometers}$$

EXAMPLE 5: Express 1/200 second in a more convenient size of unit.

*Solution:* Again the first step is to divide the fraction out into decimal form.

$$\frac{1}{200} \text{ sec} = 0.005 \text{ sec}$$

If the decimal point is now shifted three places to the right to give a figure of 5.0, the required unit of time must be one thousandth as large as a second. Therefore

$$\frac{1}{200} \text{ sec} = 5.0 \text{ millisec}$$

In practice not all prefixes are applicable to every unit. For example, the term *megameter* is not used. An exception to the use of metric prefixes is for units of time larger than the second. In this case the minute and the hour are universally accepted. The student will become familiar with those prefixes in common usage by studying the examples and problems throughout the text. With the prefix method of changing unit size, it is imperative that the correct unit size be written either in full or in abbreviated form with the numerical answer. Omitting the units in Examples 4 and 5 will illustrate this point.

## 6. Conversion of Units

Unfortunately the English speaking areas of the world do not use the metric system for everyday measurement. Therefore the student is faced with the additional chore of converting the common units, dimensions in particular, to the mks system which is used for electrical measurement and calculation purposes. The conversion factors for the basic units of length and mass are given in Table III. At this point it is not necessary to memorize more than these two fundamental conversion factors since other units can be derived from these as required.

**Table III**

1 meter = 39.37 inches
1 kilogram = 2.205 pounds

When first faced with conversion of units, students often have trouble deciding whether to multiply or divide by the conversion factor. Some texts state the conversion data in the form shown in Table IV.

**Table IV**

To find inches, multiply meters by 39.37
To find pounds, multiply kilograms by 2.205

However this problem will resolve itself if the student interprets Table III thus: It takes 39.37 inches to make one meter. Therefore the inch is a smaller unit than the meter and the number of inches in a given length will be greater than the number of meters.

EXAMPLE 6: Express 2.0 m in inches.

*Solution:* Since the inch is smaller than the meter, there will be more inches than there are meters. Therefore 2.0 must be *multiplied* by the conversion factor of 39.37. Therefore

$$2.0 \text{ m} = 2.0 \times 39.37 \text{ in.} = 78.74 \text{ in.}$$

EXAMPLE 7: Express 4 lb in kilograms.

*Solution:* Since the kilogram is a larger unit than the pound, there will be fewer kilograms than there are pounds. Therefore 4 must be *divided* by the conversion factor. Therefore

$$4 \text{ lb} = \frac{4}{2.205} \text{ kg} = 1.814 \text{ kg}$$

This same line of thought applies to changing the prefix of a unit in the mks system of units.

## Problems

1. The distance between two towns is 25 km (kilometers). Express this in meters, using scientific notation.

2. A coulomb is an electrical unit of quantity representing

$$6,240,000,000,000,000,000 \text{ electrons.}$$

Express this in scientific notation.

3. The mass of an electron is

$$0.000,000,000,000,000,000,000,000,000,899,9 \text{ g (grams).}$$

Express this in scientific notation.

4. The effective diameter of an electron is

$$0.000,000,000,000,2 \text{ cm (centimeters).}$$

Express this in scientific notation.

5. Express 1650 g in kilograms.

6. Express 850 mm (millimeters) in meters.

7. Express 1/60 sec in milliseconds.

8. Express 0.000067 km in millimeters.

9. Express 0.04 m$^2$ (square meters) in square centimeters.

10. Express the cross-sectional area of an electric conductor whose diameter is 4.0 cm in square millimeters.

11. Express 1/4 cu ft in cubic inches.

12. Express $4.08 \times 10^7$ cc (cubic centimeters) in cubic meters.

13. Derive the conversion factor for miles into kilometers.

14. Derive the conversion factor for ounces into grams.

15. Derive the conversion factor for square feet into square meters.

16. Derive the conversion factor for cubic centimeters into cubic inches.

17. Express a velocity of 50 mph (miles per hour) in meters/second.

18. Express a velocity of 50 ft/sec in kilometers/hour.

19. An electric conductor with a square cross section has a cross-sectional area of 0.016 cm$^2$. State the dimensions of the cross section in inches.

20. How many free electrons are there in an electric conductor of pure copper with a diameter of 0.006 in. and a length of 50 ft?

## Review Questions

1. What is meant by the term *energy*?

2. What is the significance of the law of conservation of energy?

3. Describe a device for converting heat energy into mechanical energy.

4. Explain the statement: "Electricity may be thought of more as a medium by which energy can be conveyed from one location to another, rather than as a form of energy in itself."

5. What is the significance of the "shell" concept of atomic structure in determining whether an element is likely to be a good electric conductor?

6. Argon has an atomic number of 18 (18 orbital electrons). With reference to the "shell" structure of an atom, discuss the probable chemical activity of argon.

7. Silver has an atomic number of 47. Show how the "shell" structure of an atom supports the observation that silver is an excellent electric conductor.

8. What do the letters mks represent?

9. What advantage has a system of units, most of which can be derived from a few basic units?

10. What is meant by "scientific notation" in expressing a numerical quantity?

11. How does the engineering method of expressing numerical quantities differ from the scientific method?

12. In the mks system of units, the wavelength of light waves is expressed in millimicrons. What relationship would exist between the millimicron and the meter?

13. Why is it important for the unit to be written with the numerical solutions to problems?

14. Which is the larger unit, the kilometer or the mile?

15. Use a reference handbook to determine the conversion factor for liters into gallons. Which is the larger unit?

# Chapter 2

# CURRENT AND VOLTAGE

~~~~~~~~~~~~~~~~~~~~~~~~~~~~~~~~~~~~~~~~~~~~~~~~~~~~~~~~~~~~~~

## 1. Hydraulic Analogy

Again we may refer to the hydraulic system by which some of the mechanical energy developed by the main engines of an aircraft is conveyed to the landing gear in Fig. 1.1(a), to provide us with a clue to what we must look for in the equivalent electric circuit of Fig. 1.1(b). In setting up the hydraulic system, one of the factors that the designer will have to know is the quantity of the hydraulic fluid in the system. As we have already noted, this information will have to be expressed in suitable numerical units. Using the English units with which we are familiar, the gallon would be a suitable unit for measuring the **quantity of the hydraulic medium.**

We shall also have to know the **rate of flow of the medium.** In hydraulic systems this is expressed in terms of *quantity* and *time*. Rate of flow can be defined as the quantity of the hydraulic medium passing a certain point in the copper tubing in a given interval of time. Thus gallons per minute and cubic feet per second (cfs) become suitable units of measurement of flow without devising a special unit. For the present analogy, the only other factor we need to know about the hydraulic system is the **pressure** that the pump is applying to the medium to force it to flow through the system. Our first step in investigating the electric circuit of Fig. 1.1(b) is to determine what constitutes the quantity of the electric medium, rate of flow of the electric medium, and electric pressure, and to derive suitable units for expressing these quantities numerically.

## 2. Conductors and Insulators

We have already determined that the *free electrons* which roam from atom to atom with very little opposition in copper conductors form the

14

electric medium. Therefore to be classed as an electric **conductor,** a material must have a very large number of free electrons per unit volume. It also follows that the greater the number of free electrons per unit volume, the better that material will be as an electric conductor. All metals have their atoms arranged so that, like copper, free electrons can drift from atom to atom. We have estimated that a cubic inch of copper contains approximately $1.4 \times 10^{24}$ free electrons. Silver is the best electric conductor since it contains 5% more free electrons per unit volume than copper. Although aluminum has only 60% as many free electrons per unit volume as copper, it is becoming a popular conductor material since it is lighter and less expensive than copper. Even though some metal alloys have less than 1% of the number of free electrons that copper has, this still represents in the order of $10^{22}$ free electrons per cubic inch, which allows them to be classed as reasonably good electric conductors.

Unlike the metals, there are many materials whose atoms have to arrange themselves into a structure somewhat similar to that of the hydrogen atoms of Fig. 1.3. In such structures, *all* electrons are held tightly in a fixed pattern and theoretically there would be no free electrons in such a material. A material with no free electrons could not act as an electric conductor and would therefore be classed as a perfect **insulator.** If we could surround the electric conductors of Fig. 1.1(b) with such a material, the free electrons in the copper could not cross the boundary into the insulating material and would be restricted to flowing along the length of the conductor.

Some of you may remember the natural rubber inner tubes used in car tires a few years ago. It was necessary to add air every few days in order to maintain the pressure since some of the air molecules were able to leak through the walls of the inner tube. Practical electric insulators behave in much the same manner. Some free electrons from the conductor can leak through the insulation because there are quite a few free electrons (due to thermal agitation breaking valence bonds, and other factors) in even the best of insulating materials. Polystyrene, which is considered to be a very good electric insulator, has over $10^{12}$ free electrons per cubic inch. Although this may appear to be a large number, compared with copper it is extremely small and the leakage of the electric medium through polystyrene is negligible for practical purposes. Although air has considerably more free electrons per unit volume than polystyrene, this number is still very small compared with the metallic conductors. Though not an ideal insulator, air is widely used since it is not expensive.

Since there are no perfect insulators, those materials which have a very small number of free electrons per unit volume compared with metallic conductors are classed as practical insulators. Mica, glass, rubber, plastic, ceramic, silk, cotton, paper, and oil are a few of the common electrical insulating materials. All materials cannot be classified at the extreme ends of the scale as good conductors or good insulators. There is an important group of materials in the center of the scale which, compared with copper, are poor conductors but which, compared with rubber, are poor insulators. This group of materials includes carbon, germanium, and silicon. The atoms of these materials are bound together into crystal structures which permit only a few free electrons for every million atoms at room temperature. These materials are classified as **semiconductors.** Semiconductors have from $10^{15}$ to $10^{20}$ free electrons per cubic inch. Practical application of these materials is developing rapidly.

The valve in the hydraulic system of Fig. 1.1(a) prevents the flow of the medium by placing a barrier between two sections of the tubing through which the medium cannot pass. The electric switch of Fig. 1.1(b) can perform the same function by inserting air between two sections of the electric conductor. This is accomplished by simply breaking the electric circuit at a suitable point. Thus *opening* an electric switch performs the same function as *closing* a hydraulic valve.

If the pressure developed by the pump in the hydraulic system is increased, a point will be reached where the walls of the tubing are no longer able to withstand the pressure. They then rupture, allowing the fluid to escape. The same situation can exist in an electric circuit. If sufficient pressure or stress is applied to the insulating sheath around a conductor, electrons can be torn free from their orbits. This provides additional free electrons within the insulating material to form a path for the leakage of the electric medium through the insulator resulting in a *rupture* or *breakdown* of the insulator at that point. Just as the thickness of the walls of the tubing in the hydraulic system governs the breakdown pressure, the breakdown pressure in an electric circuit will depend on the thickness of the insulating sheath around a conductor. And just as copper tubing in a hydraulic system can withstand a greater pressure than plastic tubing, some insulating materials can withstand a much greater electric pressure for a given thickness than others. Air rates fairly poorly in this respect. The only advantage of air as an insulator is that it is cheap.

## 3. Quantity of the Electric Medium

If we tried to measure the quantity of the hydraulic medium in terms of the actual molecules of the fluid, we would have an unmanageably large figure to cope with. Therefore a more practical size of unit such as the gallon is used. Similarly, although the electron is the basic particle forming the electric medium, a practical unit of electric quantity must represent a good many billions of electrons.

The **coulomb** is the basic unit of electric quantity.

Physicists have determined that

a **coulomb** represents a quantity of $6.24 \times 10^{18}$ electrons.

In physics, equations are used to state definitions and data in concise and precise form. Therefore all variable quantities must have letter symbols to represent them in these equations.

The letter symbol for **electric quantity** is $Q$.

EXAMPLE 1: If there are $2.40 \times 10^{19}$ free electrons in a certain piece of copper wire, how many coulombs does this represent?

*Solution:*

$$Q = \frac{2.40 \times 10^{19}}{6.24 \times 10^{18}} = 3.85 \text{ coulombs}$$

In dealing with electric circuits, the term **charge** is often used in preference to the term **quantity of the electric medium. Charge** is used in the same sense that a **quantity** of dynamite placed under a tree stump is referred to as a **charge** of dynamite; and that the guests at a banquet are instructed to **charge** their glasses with a **quantity** of a suitable beverage. The term **charge** therefore implies not just any quantity, but a quantity of some energy-conveying medium.

## 4. Flow of the Electric Medium

The designer of the hydraulic system of Fig. 1.1(a) will be concerned with the rate of flow of the medium since this will determine the size of the tubing he needs and the rate at which energy can be conveyed by the medium. Similarly we will be directly concerned with the rate of flow of the electric medium in all studies of electric circuits. Our main interest in the coulomb at this point is in establishing a unit to express the flow of the electric medium. Although not in common usage in referring to the hydraulic system, in electric circuits the term **current** is used to express **rate of flow of the medium.** Thus

> **electric current** is the **rate of flow** of the electric medium. The letter symbol for electric current is $I$.*

As already noted, no special unit is required to express the rate of hydraulic flow. Gallons per second is a quite satisfactory way of indicating the flow. Similarly it is quite correct to express electric current in **coulombs per second.** It is unfortunate that it is not common practice to do so, since this automatically draws our attention to the nature of electric current. Although unnecessary, a special unit of electric current, the **ampere,** has been established to perpetuate the memory of one of the pioneer electrical physicists, André Marie Ampere. In order to satisfy the specifications we laid down for electrical units of measurement,

> **one ampere** is the **rate of flow** of the electric medium when one coulomb of free electrons passes a certain point in an electric circuit in one second.

---

* $I$ is said to stand for *I*ntensity of the electron flow. The letter symbol $C$ is reserved to represent capacitance.

Therefore **amperes** and **coulombs per second** are synonymous, and in using the ampere as a unit of electric current, we must keep reminding ourselves that current is a *rate of flow* in coulombs per second. The ampere is the first of the *derived* units we have encountered so far and this derivation can be conveniently stated in equation form:

$$I = \frac{Q}{t} \tag{2.1}$$

where $I$ is current in amperes, $Q$ is quantity in coulombs, and $t$ is time in seconds.

> EXAMPLE 2: What is the current in an electric circuit when 75 coulombs of electrons pass a certain point in the circuit in half a minute?
>
> *Solution:*
>
> $$I = \frac{Q}{t} = \frac{75}{30} = 2.5 \text{ amp}$$

Since we will find that a systematic solution of electrical problems will greatly assist in understanding electric circuits, let us take the time to identify the individual steps that were performed in solving Example 2.

*Step I.* Note that the problem states two pieces of information and asks for one. Express the relationship between the given data and the required information in equation form. Place the symbol for the unknown quantity on the left of the *equals* sign and the given data (in their proper relationship) on the right of the equals sign.

*Step II.* Substitute the given data into the equation using the *basic* units of the quantities expressed on the right-hand side of the equation. If necessary convert the given data into the basic units represented by the equation.

*Step III.* Perform the numerical computation (using slide rule).

*Step IV.* Express the answer in the proper units using prefixes if necessary, to obtain the most convenient *size* of unit. Some students prefer to underline the final answer to make it stand out from intermediate steps in the solution.

> EXAMPLE 3: How long will it take 4.0 millicoulombs of electrons to pass through a fuse in an electric circuit if the current is 50 amp?
>
> *Solution:* Since
>
> $$I = \frac{Q}{t}, \qquad \therefore \quad t = \frac{Q}{I}$$
>
> $$\therefore \quad t = \frac{0.004}{50} = 0.00008 \text{ sec} = 80 \text{ } \mu\text{sec}$$

## 5. Electron Velocity

Since we are not in the habit of expressing electric current in coulombs per second, we must keep reminding ourselves that the ampere is a *rate* unit. Nevertheless we must be careful not to confuse **rate of flow** with the **velocity** of the free electrons in the conductor. Let us again refer to the hydraulic system to discover a method whereby we can determine the velocity of the free electrons.

EXAMPLE 4: If the flow in a copper tube whose inside cross-sectional area is 2.0 sq in., is found to be 0.05 cfs, what is the velocity of the fluid?

*Solution:*

$$0.05 \text{ cu ft} = 0.05 \times 1728 = 86.4 \text{ cu in.}$$

With a cross-sectional area of 2.0 sq in., 86.4 cu in. will occupy a length along the tube of 86.4/2 = 43.2 in.

Therefore in order for the 0.05 cu ft of fluid to pass a given point in one sec, the fluid will have to move along the tube at a **velocity** of 43.2 in./sec or 3.6 ft/sec.

Similarly, since we know the number of free electrons in 1 cu in. of copper, if we know the current and the cross-sectional area of the conductor, we can find the effective velocity at which the electrons move along the wire.

EXAMPLE 5: What is the effective velocity of the electron flow in a copper conductor having a cross-sectional area of 0.005 sq in. if the current is 10 amp?

*Solution:* One coulomb = $6.24 \times 10^{18}$ electrons. One cu in. of copper contains $1.4 \times 10^{24}$ free electrons. Therefore one coulomb of free electrons in copper occupies

$$\frac{6.24 \times 10^{18}}{1.4 \times 10^{24}} = 4.46 \times 10^{-6} \text{ cu in.}$$

The rate of flow is 10 amp, which is 10 coulombs/sec. In copper this is

$$10 \times 4.46 \times 10^{-6} = 4.46 \times 10^{-5} \text{ cu in./sec}$$

With a cross-sectional area of 0.005 sq in., $4.46 \times 10^{-5}$ cu in. will occupy a length of

$$\frac{4.46 \times 10^{-5}}{0.005} = 8.9 \times 10^{-3} \text{ in. of conductor}$$

Since the 10 coulombs which occupy a length of $8.9 \times 10^{-3}$ in. along the length of the conductor must pass a given point in one second, the average velocity of the electrons along the length of the conductor will be $8.9 \times 10^{-3}$ in./sec, or

$$v = 8.9 \text{ thousandths of an inch per second}$$

Because of this very low velocity, the effective electron flow along the length of a conductor is sometimes referred to as an electron **drift**. There is no practical advantage in knowing the velocity of this electron drift at the moment. We have made these calculations to emphasize the distinction between **velocity** and **current**.

## 6. Electric Pressure

As we have already noted, in order for current to flow in an electric circuit, some form of pressure must be applied to the medium. Although a hydraulic analogy will not give us an exact comparison, it will get us started in the right direction. Let us consider what happens in the hydraulic model of Fig. 2.1. If the level of the water is the same in both tanks, no flow will take place when the valve is opened. If we consider one particular drop of water in the connecting pipe, the pressure on it from both directions is the same, so it will flow neither to the right nor to the left. If, however, some mechanical energy is supplied to the pump, it

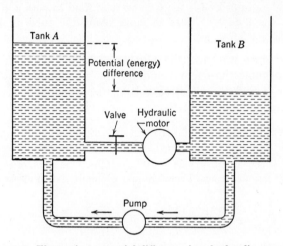

**Fig. 2.1.** Illustrating potential difference in a hydraulic system.

will remove water from tank $B$ and place it in tank $A$. This involves converting mechanical energy into static energy of position by raising a certain quantity of water to a higher elevation in tank $A$ than it was in tank $B$. This potential energy that has been imparted to the water in tank $A$ will apply a greater pressure on the water in the interconnecting pipe than the lower level of water in tank $B$. This unbalance of pressures or **potential energy difference** will cause water to flow from tank $A$ to tank $B$ through the interconnecting pipe and hydraulic motor as the flow attempts to reduce the potential energy difference to zero.

Now let us consider what is going on inside a piece of copper wire lying on a table. Each atom of copper possesses 29 orbital electrons. As discussed in Chapter 1, the 29th electron is able to move from atom to atom with very little effort. But as soon as the 29th electron leaves an atom, the atom is deficient one electron and exerts a force of *attraction* on the electrons of the neighboring atoms in order to regain its proper complement of orbital electrons. However, if a free electron from some other atom moves into the orbital pattern of a neutral copper atom which has its full number of 29 electrons, there is now one excess electron in the atom, and the atom exerts a force of *repulsion* to get rid of the surplus electron in order to regain its balanced complement of electrons. It does not matter which electron is expelled, since all electrons are identical. Unlike the drop of water in Fig. 2.1, which moved as a result of unbalance in pressure applied to it, there are two forces that can be exerted on free electrons to make them move in a desired direction. They are *repelled* by a surplus of electrons and *attracted* by a deficiency of electrons.

In order to avoid having to use *deficiency of electrons* and *excess of electrons* as electrical terms, it was arbitrarily decided to label these two opposite forces as **positive** (+) **charge** for deficiency of electrons and **negative** (−) **charge** for excess of electrons. Remember that we use the term **charge** to signify a quantity of electrons with potential energy implied. Applying the term quantity or charge to a surplus of electrons presents no problem, but it is rather difficult to visualize *quantity* referring to a *deficiency* of electrons. We can think of a deficiency of electrons as representing holes in the orbital structure of atoms where electrons are removed. These holes are just as real as the hole that appears in the ground when a fence post is removed. And since an electron must be placed in each hole in the original atom structure to cancel out the positive charge, positive charge (deficiency of electrons) can therefore be thought of as possessing physical characteristics that are equal (but opposite in sign) to those of an electron. Since all electrons are alike, it follows that the free electrons which constitute the electric medium can also represent a negative charge.

In the hydraulic model of Fig. 2.1, we obtain a flow of the medium through the motor by having the pump lower the potential energy level in tank *B* and raise the level in tank *A*, thereby creating a **potential** energy **difference.** Similarly if we could remove some free electrons from one end of a piece of copper wire and introduce them into the other end, the remainder of the free electrons would be repelled by the negative charge and attracted by the positive charge, and a current would flow in the wire as the electrons try to return all atoms to a neutral state, each with its proper complement of electrons. As the flow through the hydraulic motor in Fig. 2.1 attempts to return the difference in level between the two tanks to zero, the pump continues to raise the level in tank *A* above that in tank *B* and a continuous flow results.

## 7. Batteries

A simple method of maintaining a potential difference between the two ends of an electric conductor is shown in Fig. 2.2. When hydrogen with its one orbital electron combines with chlorine, which has 17 orbital electrons, to form hydrochloric acid, the chlorine borrows the one electron from the hydrogen to complete a full subshell in its atomic structure. (Check this by referring to Fig. 1.2.) In doing so the hydrogen becomes deficient an electron as indicated by the + sign in Fig. 2.2, and the chlorine takes with it a surplus electron. The chemical makeup of hydrogen chloride and zinc chloride is such that energy must be expended to transfer a chlorine atom from a zinc chloride molecule to a hydrogen chloride molecule. Therefore energy must be released when the chlorine atom moves from a hydrogen chloride molecule to a zinc chloride molecule.

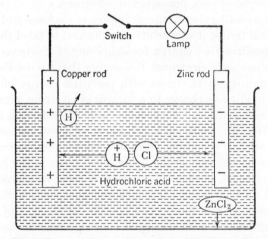

**Fig. 2.2.** Producing an electric potential difference with a simple chemical cell.

In the chemical cell of Fig. 2.2, the chlorine in the acid will combine with zinc atoms from the zinc rod to form zinc chloride. During this process, the surplus electron that the chlorine borrowed from the hydrogen is deposited on the zinc rod, thus building up a surplus of electrons or a negative charge on the zinc rod. As each chlorine ion* combines with the zinc, the hydrogen ion which loaned the electron to the chlorine ion can now go in search of a source of free electrons to regain its normal state as an atom of hydrogen. The copper rod represents such a source, and as the hydrogen ions rob the copper of free electrons, a positive charge builds up on the copper rod. The number of electrons taken from the copper rod by the hydrogen is equal to the number of electrons deposited on the zinc rod by the chlorine. We may think of the loss of chemical energy as zinc is converted into zinc chloride in terms of a pump building up a potential difference between the copper and zinc rods by seemingly pumping electrons from the copper to the zinc.

If the switch is left open, the chemical action can proceed until suffi-

---

* A charged atom with either a surplus or deficiency of electrons from its normal complement is called an **ion**.

cient potential difference is established between the copper and the zinc that the negatively charged chlorine ions do not have sufficient chemical attraction to reach the zinc against this electric pressure. The formation of zinc chloride will then cease. When the switch is closed, there will be a flow of free electrons through the conductors and the lamp as the electrons in the conductors are repelled by the negative charge on the zinc rod and attracted by the positive charge on the copper rod. This flow is attempting to return the potential difference in the circuit to zero. But as soon as the potential difference drops the least bit, chemical action recommences, depositing electrons on the zinc rod and removing them from the copper rod. The result will be a steady flow of free electrons (electric current) as the tendency for the electric load (lamp) to lower the potential difference is offset by the action of the cell to raise the potential difference to a level determined by the two particular metals used in the cell. This steady flow of current in one direction around the loop is referred to as **direct current** (d-c).

Any device which develops an electric pressure by converting some other form of energy into electric energy can be classed as a **generator.** A device for developing an electric potential difference at the expense of *chemical* energy is referred to as a **battery.** As the term implies, a battery originally meant a *group* of chemical cells, but common usage allows us to refer to the simple chemical cell of Fig. 2.2 as a single-cell battery. Because of the nature of the electrolyte in this cell, it can also be classed as a *wet*-cell battery.

As long as the switch is closed in Fig. 2.2, energy is taken from a chemical form and conveyed by the electric current to the lamp where it is converted into light energy and heat energy. While this energy transfer is taking place, the combining of chlorine ions with the zinc dilutes the acid and eats away the zinc rod. In time then this battery can no longer maintain a potential difference. We have noted that when the switch is opened, chemical action will cease when the potential difference builds up to a level at which the chlorine ion is no longer able to reach the zinc atoms. If we raise the potential difference above this level by connecting some other electric generator to the battery, it is possible to separate the chlorine ions from the zinc chloride, thus **recharging** the battery at the expense of electric energy from the external generator. However, recharging this type of battery in this manner is not economically practical. It is cheaper to replace the used up acid and zinc rod. Cells that are discarded when their chemical energy is exhausted are called **primary** cells.

We have taken the time to consider the electrochemical action of the simple wet cell because it clearly illustrates the nature of electric pressure and how a potential difference may be produced. However, the practical restrictions of this cell limit its use to laboratory experiments. The liquid nature of the **electrolyte** means that the battery is not readily portable.

Another disadvantage results from the release of hydrogen gas at the copper rod as the hydrogen ions recover their missing electrons from the copper. After the switch in Fig. 2.2 has been closed for a few minutes, the copper is blanketed with hydrogen bubbles. Since hydrogen gas is an electric insulator (see Fig. 1.3) this layer of hydrogen bubbles prevents hydrogen ions from getting to the copper rod. This appreciably limits the current in the circuit. This action is called **polarization.**

The familiar **dry cell** battery of Fig. 2.3 overcomes these two disadvantages by virtue of its construction. The negative electrode consists of the zinc container. The electrolyte must still be wet in order to permit positive and negative ions to migrate to their respective electrodes. But in the so-called dry battery, the electrolyte, which consists of a solution of

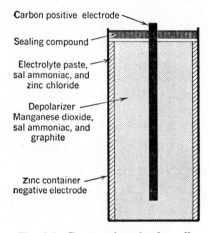

Carbon positive electrode

Sealing compound

Electrolyte paste, sal ammoniac, and zinc chloride

Depolarizer Manganese dioxide, sal ammoniac, and graphite

Zinc container negative electrode

**Fig. 2.3.** Construction of a dry cell.

sal ammoniac and zinc chloride, is mixed with a suitable binder to form a paste. This overcomes one disadvantage of the wet cell.

Although the chemical action is not quite as simple as that of the metal-acid wet cell, the net results are the same. Surplus electrons are added to the zinc by the electrolyte, and hydrogen ions rob the carbon rod of electrons, thus building up a positive charge on the carbon. Again a film of hydrogen bubbles tries to form on the positive electrode. But the majority of the space in a dry cell is packed with a **depolarizer.** The active ingredient in the depolarizer is manganese dioxide, which combines with the hydrogen as it is released, thus preventing polarization from taking place. Some of the electrolyte material and graphite (which is an electric conductor) are mixed with the depolarizer to effectively increase the surface area of the positive electrode. Since hydrogen gas is not allowed to form, the dry cell can be sealed to make the dry battery completely portable. Like the simple wet cell, the dry battery is classed as a primary cell.

As Fig. 2.3 indicates, most of the space in the conventional dry cell is taken up by the depolarizer. If we could select an electrochemical action that does not result in polarization of the positive terminal, we would be able to construct a very tiny battery with a performance at least as good as the dry cell. The recently developed mercury cell is an example of such construction. Zinc, in this case, forms the positive electrode. The negative electrode consists of mercuric oxide and graphite and the electrolyte is potassium hydroxide. The mercury cell is about the size of a dime. It too is a primary cell.

One particular wet cell worthy of note at this point is the lead-acid storage battery shown in Figs. 2.4 and 2.5. The chemical action is such that no gas is liberated as it discharges its chemical energy, and therefore

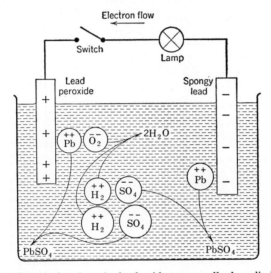

**Fig. 2.4.** Chemical action of a lead-acid storage cell when discharging.

polarization does not occur. This, along with the ability to convert chemical energy into electric energy very rapidly, allows this battery to maintain an appreciable potential difference between its terminals even when the current through the circuit approaches 100 amp. The high rate of energy conversion possible with the lead-acid battery makes it particularly useful for industrial applications. In this case recharging the battery by converting surplus electric energy back into energy stored in chemical form is economically feasible. A cell which is recharged in this manner is called a **secondary cell.** The ability of the lead-acid battery to store energy in chemical form accounts for its common classification as a **storage battery.** The electric system of an automobile is a good example of the charge and discharge cycle of the lead-acid storage battery. When starting the car, energy stored in chemical form is converted to electric energy to operate the starter motor. Then when the car is being driven down the highway, surplus electric energy from the generator (obtained at the expense of mechanical energy from the engine which in turn came from the chemical energy of the fuel, etc.) reverses the chemical action in the battery to store up energy for the next time the car has to be started.

The electrolyte of the lead-acid cell consists of sulfuric acid diluted with water. The positive electrode consists of lead peroxide supported by a grid of lead-antimony alloy. The negative plate consists of a similar grid packed with pure lead in a spongy form. In solution the sulfuric acid forms sulfate ($SO_4$) ions which borrow an electron from each of the two hydrogen atoms in the acid molecule. These sulfate ions are chemically very active and combine with the lead in *both* plates to form lead sulfate. Since lead

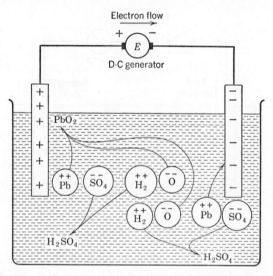

**Fig. 2.5.** Chemical action of a lead-acid storage cell when charging.

sulfate is insoluble, each of the electrodes will receive two electrons. However the combining of two molecules of acid to form one molecule of lead sulfate at each plate leaves four hydrogen ions on their own to look for their missing electrons. They can obtain these by combining with the oxygen that is made available when the lead in the lead peroxide of the positive plate forms lead sulfate. In the over-all action, for two molecules of acid, two electrons were deposited on the negative plate, and although two electrons were deposited at the positive plate, *four* electrons were taken from it as the hydrogen combined with the oxygen to form additional water. Therefore the net effect at the positive plate is the loss of two electrons. As the battery discharges through the lamp in Fig. 2.4 the chemical action continues to reduce both plates to lead sulfate, and the acid becomes weaker and weaker as hydrogen sulfate disappears and water is produced. As the battery discharges, electrons will flow from the negative terminal through the lamp and the switch to the positive terminal.

In order to recharge the battery, the chemical action must be reversed. First the hydrogen and oxygen ions in the water must be separated. This is done by connecting an external d-c generator which can take electrons from the positive plate of the battery to the negative terminals of the battery via the generator. This current flow outside the battery is in the opposite direction from the discharge current in Fig. 2.4. As a result of this removal of electrons from the positive terminal and adding of electrons to the negative terminal, the potential difference between the two plates in Fig. 2.5 is raised above that normally created by the chemical action of the battery itself. This additional potential difference attracts the oxygen ions to the positive plate and takes their surplus electrons away from them. Robbed of these surplus electrons the oxygen becomes very active and unites with the lead of the lead sulfate to re-form the lead peroxide on the positive plate. The external generator must now use up energy to move the two electrons it took from the oxygen ion around to the negative plate.

The recombination of the oxygen from two molecules of water and one molecule of lead sulfate frees four hydrogen ions and one sulfate ion. Two of the hydrogen ions will combine with the one sulfate ion to form a molecule of sulfuric acid. The other two are attracted to the negative plate where they will regain the two missing electrons. This allows the hydrogen to become active and combine with sulfate from non-ionized lead sulfate at the negative plate, thus forming another molecule of sulfuric acid and depositing pure spongy lead on the negative plate.

## 8. The Volt

In both the hydraulic and the electric systems, the pressure that forces the medium to flow is not an absolute quantity. Rather it is the potential energy difference, or simply **potential difference,** between two points in the system. In the hydraulic system of Fig. 2.1, this can be represented by the elevation (in feet) of the level in tank *A* above that in tank *B*. Since an equivalent dimension is not available in the electric system, we must find another way of determining the magnitude of the potential difference. In the hydraulic system the amount of energy imparted to the medium by the pump will be the product of the quantity of water passing through the pump (mass) and the average increase in elevation after passing through the pump. Therefore the difference in elevation or potential difference can be expressed in terms of the energy imparted per unit quantity of the medium. Similarly then, the unit of electric potential difference may be stated in terms of the amount of energy imparted to a unit quantity of electrons (which form the electric medium). Energy is imparted to electrons when they are forced to move *away from* a positive charge and *toward* a negative charge, as is the case in the hydrochloric acid in the chemical cell of Fig. 2.2. Therefore in an electric system,

> **Potential difference** (PD) may be defined as the rise (or fall) in potential energy per unit quantity of electrons moved. The letter symbol for potential difference is $E$ or $V$.*

As stated in Chapter 1, the electrical unit of energy in the mks system of units must be the same as the mechanical unit of energy. Therefore

> the **joule** is the basic unit of electric **energy.** The letter symbol for electric energy is $W$.

As we have already decided in defining potential difference, the basic unit of potential difference shall be a unit derived from the basic units of **energy** and **quantity**.

The **volt** is the basic unit of **potential difference.**

And from the definition of potential difference,

> **one volt** is the potential difference between two points in an electric circuit when the energy involved in moving **one coulomb** of electrons from the one point to the other is **one joule.**

This relationship may be expressed in equation form as

$$E \text{ (or } V) = \frac{W}{Q} \qquad (2.2)$$

*where* $E$ (or $V$) is the potential difference in volts, $W$ is energy in joules, and $Q$ is quantity of electrons in coulombs.

> EXAMPLE 6: During the chemical action in the wet cell of Fig. 2.2, 50 coulombs of electrons are effectively transferred from the copper to the zinc by the release of 55 joules of energy. What is the potential difference between the two rods?
>
> *Solution:*
>
> $$E = \frac{W}{Q} = \frac{55}{50} = 1.1 \text{ v}$$
>
> EXAMPLE 7: A current of 0.3 amp flowing through the filament of a radio tube releases 9.45 joules of heat energy in 5 sec. What is the PD across the filament of the tube?
>
> *Solution:* Since $I = Q/t$, therefore
>
> $$Q = It = 0.3 \times 5 = 1.5 \text{ coulombs}$$
> $$V = \frac{W}{Q} = \frac{9.45}{1.5} = 6.3 \text{ v}$$

## 9. Electromotive Force and Voltage Drop

It is rather unfortunate that the term potential difference or PD is not commonly used in discussing electric circuits. It is a very descriptive term

---

* The distinction between $E$ and $V$ is discussed in the next section.

in that its wording suggests the very nature of electric pressure. It also reminds us that *two* particular points in a circuit must be stated before the potential *difference* can be stated. In both the hydraulic and electric circuits of Figs. 2.1 and 2.2, we noted that there are two kinds of potential difference. There is the potential *rise* that takes place in the pump or battery (chemical cell), and the potential *fall* that takes place in the hydraulic motor or the lamp. Numerically the potential fall must equal the potential rise, and therefore the same unit of measurement can apply to both rise and fall.

As there is a certain tendency on the part of human beings to be lazy, it was soon discovered that one could avoid having to distinguish between potential rise and potential fall in an electric circuit by substituting the term **voltage.** Voltage simply means something that can be measured in volts. Since this applies to both potential rise and potential fall, the distinction between them disappears. Along with the indiscriminate use of the term voltage, the distinction between the symbols $E$ and $V$ has disappeared in many electrical books.

Although we cannot ignore the general term **voltage,** we shall endeavor to retain the distinction between potential rise and potential fall by selecting more modern terminology for each of these quantities. Since the potential rise developed in the battery of Fig. 2.2 is the electric pressure that forces electrons to flow when the switch is closed, potential rise may then be called an **electron moving force** or **electromotive force.** Electromotive force is usually abbreviated to **emf** (ee-em-eff).

The letter symbol for **emf** is $E$.

The potential drop which occurs as the electrons flow through the lamp in an effort to return the PD in the system to zero is usually referred to nowadays as **voltage drop.**

The letter symbol for **voltage drop** is $V$.

Another means of distinguishing between emf and voltage drop or PD (potential drop) is to define them thus:

> **emf** is the work per unit charge done by a generator (battery) on the electric charges.

> **PD** is the work per unit charge done by the electric charges in moving from one point in an electric circuit to another. (Refer to Equation 2.2.)

That there is indeed a distinction between emf and voltage drop is illustrated by Fig. 2.6. When the switch is closed, both voltmeters show the same reading as the flow of current through the lamp creates a **voltage drop** across the lamp equal to the **emf** of the battery. When the switch is open the voltmeter across the battery terminals still registers the presence of the emf developed by the chemical action in the battery. But the voltmeter across the lamp terminals reads zero. The voltage drop appears across the lamp only when electrons are flowing through it in an attempt to return the potential difference in the circuit to zero. Since our primary interest in studying electric circuits is to develop an understanding of what is going on, we shall note the distinction between emf and voltage drop by using the symbols $E$ for emf and $V$ for voltage drop as applicable in equations throughout this text. (Note Examples 6 and 7.)

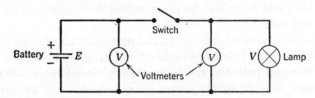

**Fig. 2.6.** Illustrating the distinction between emf and voltage drop in a simple electric circuit.

It is also worth noting at this point the prepositions which can be used with the terms current and voltage. Remembering that current is the rate of flow of electrons, we speak of current *in* or *through* a conductor or other circuit component. To talk about "current *across* the lamp" would be meaningless. Since we are not accustomed to using the term potential difference, we must remind ourselves that there is no such thing as "voltage *at* a certain point." Electromotive force and voltage drop must be measured *between* two points or *from* one point *with respect to* another or *across* a certain circuit element. Talking about "voltage *through* a component" would therefore be meaningless.

## 10. Conventional Current Direction

Our present-day knowledge of atomic structure provides fairly conclusive evidence that electric current in a metallic conductor consists of a flow of free electrons around the circuit. In the portion of the circuit outside the generator (battery), the free electrons must flow from the negative terminal of the battery through the lamp to the positive terminal of the source of emf. (Counterclockwise in the circuit of Fig. 2.6 when the switch is closed.) Inside a generator, since energy is being imparted to the electrons, they are forced to move from the positive terminal to the negative terminal. (Note Fig. 2.2.) However, in the days when the mathematical conventions for current direction were being established so that network rules and laws could be stated, there was no way of determining the exact nature of electric current in a metallic conductor. However, Michael Faraday was well aware of the effect of passing electric current through a salt solution. From the observations of this process, which is known as **electrolysis,** a conventional current direction was established.

Figure 2.7 shows an **electrolytic cell** or electroplating bath consisting of a silver (Ag) **electrode** and a steel (Fe) electrode in the form of a spoon dipped into a solution of silver nitrate ($AgNO_3$). This current carrying solution is called an **electrolyte**. The silver electrode is connected to the positive terminal of the battery and is called the **anode**. The spoon is connected to the negative terminal of the source of emf and is called the

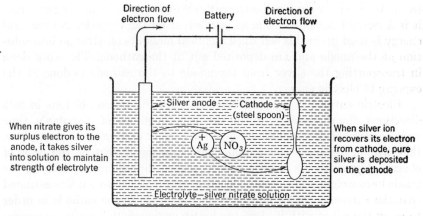

**Fig. 2.7.** A simple electrolytic cell.

**cathode.** Faraday discovered that as current was allowed to flow through the cell, silver disappeared from the anode and the same amount of silver was added to the cathode. With no knowledge of the electron, Faraday was able to state his first law of electrolysis from his observations.

> **The mass of a substance liberated by the anode and deposited on the cathode varies directly with the quantity ($Q$) of electricity passing through the cell.**

In fact the principle of electrolysis has formed the basis for the international standard for the ampere, which is the current that will deposit silver at the rate of 0.001118 grams per second with an apparatus similar to that of Fig. 2.7.

Our present-day knowledge of the **dissociation** of a salt as it goes into solution and the mechanics of electric conduction in liquids enables us to see how the silver is transported from the anode to the cathode by the flow of electric current. In forming a silver nitrate molecule, the silver lends its valence electron to the nitrate radical. ($Ag^+NO_3^-$) Since the anode is connected to the positive terminal of the source of emf, the source removes some free electrons from the anode rod by attraction, leaving the anode with a positive charge. The anode rod in turn is able to attract the nitrate radicals with their negative charges which are due to the electrons they borrowed from the silver ions in the solution. As the $NO_3^-$ gives up its surplus electron to the positively charged anode, it becomes chemically active and takes an atom of silver from the anode into solution with it, thus maintaining the strength of the electrolyte.

Since the cathode is connected to the negative terminal of the source, surplus electrons from the source are forced into it by repulsion, placing a negative charge on the cathode. This negative charge attracts the silver ions which are positively charged because of their missing valence electron. As the silver ion touches the cathode and regains its missing electron, it is deposited out of solution as pure silver on the cathode. No *chemical* energy is used up in this cell since identical amounts of silver go into solution at the anode and are deposited out at the cathode. The work done in transporting the silver from the anode to the cathode is done at the expense of electric energy.

Electric current in an electrolyte requires the motion of ions in *both* directions simultaneously. Since the experimenters of Faraday's time were unaware of this dual direction of the **current carriers** in an electrolyte, they had to assume a conventional direction for current on the basis of observable results. As electric current passes through an electrolyte, the anode loses weight and the cathode gains weight. Therefore it was assumed that the current must be flowing from the anode to the cathode in order to carry the silver with it. Lacking better evidence, this positive to negative direction became the accepted convention in electrical physics and all the laws and rules about electric circuits are based on this conventional current direction. Although we now believe the energy-carrying medium in metallic conductors to be the free electrons which actually flow in the opposite direction to the conventional direction, there is no need to scrap the original conventional direction for marking current on electric circuit diagrams. Conventional direction and electron flow are merely two different points of view on the one basic electric energy transferring phenomenon. Several different concepts of current are quite compatible. In dealing with electrolytes, current is carried by ions moving in *both* directions simultaneously. If we are dealing with electron tubes, we find it necessary to think in terms of electron flow to explain their operation. To explain the operation of the semiconductor materials of transistors, we must return to the concept of *two* types of current carriers moving in opposite directions. But since the laws and rules of electric circuits were based on the conventional direction, we shall use conventional current direction to mark electric circuit diagrams in this text.

## Problems

1. What is the quantity of free electrons in 1 cu in. of copper?
2. What is the quantity of free electrons in 1 cu in. of aluminum?
3. What is the quantity of free electrons in a piece of copper wire 0.001 in. in diameter and 1 ft long?

4. What is the quantity of free electrons in a silver bar with a 1.0 cm square cross section and a length of 1.0 m?

5. What is the current through a switch in an electric circuit if it takes 6 sec for 30 coulombs of electrons to pass through it?

6. What is the current through a vacuum tube if it takes 1 min for a coulomb of electrons to arrive at its plate?

7. How many coulombs of electrons pass through the lamp in Fig. 2.2 in 1 min if the current is a steady 300 ma?

8. How many coulombs of electrons pass from the copper rod to the zinc rod (effectively) in the battery in Fig. 2.2 in 1/60 sec if the current is a steady 1/2 amp?

9. How long will it take 8 coulombs of electrons to pass through the switch in Fig. 2.2 if the current is 250 ma?

10. How long will it take for $10^{20}$ chlorine ions to combine with the zinc if the current through the lamp in Fig. 2.2 is a steady 300 ma?

11. If the conductors used in Fig. 2.2 are pure copper with a diameter of 0.002 in., what is the average velocity of the electron drift if the current is a steady 300 ma?

12. What would the average velocity be if pure aluminum conductors of the same diameter were substituted in Problem 11?

13. If it takes 5 joules of chemical energy to move 20 coulombs of electrons between the positive and negative terminals of a battery, what is the emf between its terminals?

14. What PD must be developed across the terminals of a lamp in order for a flow of 0.05 coulomb from one terminal to the other to release 6 joules of energy?

15. What energy is required to move 5 millicoulombs of electrons through a PD of 60 v?

16. What quantity of electrons will move from the positive terminal to the negative terminal (effectively) of a battery whose emf is 1.5 v during the conversion of $\frac{1}{4}$ joule of chemical energy?

17. How much energy is involved in maintaining a 0.5 amp current through a battery for 0.5 min if the PD between the battery terminals is 1.1 v?

18. How long will a steady 250 ma current have to flow through a flashlight lamp with a 3 v drop between its terminals for 6 joules of energy to be transferred to the lamp?

19. What current must be flowing through a load in an electric circuit if energy is being delivered to the load at the rate of 18 joules/sec with a 120 v drop across its terminals?

20. At what rate is chemical energy being converted in a battery whose emf is 3 v if a lamp connected to the battery draws a steady 150 ma current?

## Review Questions

1. What is the distinction between the *rate of flow* and the *velocity* of a fluid in a pipe?

2. Is the velocity of the free electrons in the circuit of Fig. 2.6 zero when the switch is open? Explain.

3. What change in electron motion takes place when the switch in the circuit of Fig. 2.6 is closed?

4. Distinguish between *current* and *electron drift velocity* in an electric circuit.

5. Why is the term *drift* appropriate for describing electric current in a metallic conductor?

6. Why is the flow of electric current restricted to the electric conductors in the circuit of Fig. 2.6?

7. State two characteristics of a good electric insulating material.

8. What is the relationship between *free electrons* and a metal's ability to act as an electric conductor?

9. Why does opening the switch in the circuit of Fig. 2.6 interrupt the flow of electric current?

10. What are the cause and the result of a ruptured insulator?

11. What is the magnitude of the negative charge on a single electron in coulombs?

12. Although not in common usage, the ampere-second is a unit of electrical measurement. In the measurement of what electrical property would it be used?

13. What is meant by a positively charged electric conductor?

14. Explain the forces acting on a free electron located midway between a positively and a negatively charged conductor.

15. Explain how the copper rod in the simple battery of Fig. 2.2 became positively charged.

16. Explain how the silver anode in the circuit of Fig. 2.7 became positively charged.

17. When the switch in the circuit in Fig. 2.2 is closed, light energy is produced by the lamp. Where does this energy come from originally in this circuit?

18. Discuss, using numerical examples, how the particular arrangement of the symbols in the equation $E = W/Q$ satisfies the definition of the *volt*.

19. With reference to Fig. 2.2, explain the distinction between *emf* and *voltage drop*.

20. What is the basic difference between electric conduction in a liquid and in a metallic conductor?

# Chapter 3

# RESISTANCE

~~~~~~~~~~~~~~~~~~~~~~~~~~~~~~~~~~~~~~~~~~~~~~~~~~~~~~~~~~~~~~~~~~~~~~~~~~~~~~~~~~~~~~~~~~

## 1. Ohm's Law of Constant Proportionality

We have noted in Chapter 2 that when the switch in the simple electric circuit of Fig. 3.1 is closed, current will flow through the lamp as the system tries to return the potential difference created by the chemical action of the battery to zero. However, since the chemical action continues, the potential difference becomes a constant emf and the current therefore continues to flow at a constant rate. The magnitude of the emf in this case is dependent on the pair of metals used in the battery. We now want to find out just what governs the magnitude of the current.

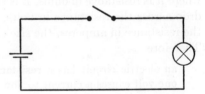

Fig. 3.1. A simple electric circuit.

Over a hundred years ago, Georg Simon Ohm discovered that every time he closed the switch in a circuit such as that of Fig. 3.1, the current became the same constant value. He also discovered that, providing the temperature of the conductor did not change, doubling the emf doubled the current and tripling the emf tripled the current. In other words,

**for a given circuit, the ratio of the applied emf to the current is a constant.**

This became known as **Ohm's law of constant proportionality.** It can be expressed in equation form thus:

$$\frac{E}{I} = k \tag{3.1}$$

where $E$ is the applied emf in volts, $I$ is the resulting current in amperes, and $k$ is a numerical constant.

Carrying this discovery a step further, it was found that changing the conductors or the lamp to some other size resulted in a different value for the numerical constant. If the current is 1 amp when the emf is 10 v, the constant becomes 10/1 or simply 10; and if the current is 0.5 amp when the emf is 10 v, the constant becomes 10/0.5, or 20. From these results Ohm concluded that this constant $E/I$ ratio for a given circuit is therefore a property of that circuit. And since, for a given emf, the value of the constant *increases* as the current *decreases*, this constant can be thought of as representing the *opposition of the circuit to the flow of current*. This property then should be given a name which suggests *opposition*, such as **resistance.** Therefore

> **resistance** is the opposition of an electric circuit to the flow of current through that circuit. The letter symbol for resistance is $R$.

Therefore we can substitute the symbol $R$ for the constant $k$ in Equation (3.1). Since resistance is an electrical property, we require a unit of measurement for it. Although it would be quite proper to express resistance in terms of **volts per ampere,** it was decided to honor Ohm's original discovery by making the **ohm** the **unit of electric resistance.** Since Equation (3.1) has now become:

$$R = \frac{E}{I} \quad \text{or} \quad R = \frac{V}{I} \tag{3.2}$$

where $R$ is resistance in ohms, $E$ is the applied emf in volts, $V$ is the voltage drop across the resistance in volts, and $I$ is the resulting current through the resistance in amperes, the size of the ohm is automatically established. Therefore

> an electric circuit has a **resistance** of **one ohm** when an applied **emf of one volt** causes a current to flow at the rate of **one ampere.**

Few people nowadays recall the original wording of Ohm's law of constant proportionality which allowed us to define resistance and to establish a unit of resistance. As a result, Ohm's law is usually stated simply by the equation

$$R = \frac{E}{I}.$$

EXAMPLE 1: What is the resistance of a lamp if a current of 150 ma flows through the lamp when an emf of 6.0 v is applied to its terminals?
*Solution:*

$$R = \frac{E}{I} = \frac{6.0}{0.15} = 40 \text{ ohms}$$

## 2. The Nature of Resistance

We have established that free electrons are the current carriers in a metallic conductor. When no emf is applied to a conductor, these free electrons can move around in a random manner from the outer shell of one atom to the outer shell of another. But there is *no* net drift along the length of the conductor. However, when we apply an electromotive force between the ends of a conductor (by connecting it to the terminals of a battery for example) the free electrons are attracted by the deficiency of electrons at one end of the conductor and repelled by the surplus of electrons at the other end. Therefore, in addition to their basic velocity, the free electrons begin to acquire a velocity component along the length of the conductor. Since an electron possesses a certain mass, as it accelerates, potential energy is converted into kinetic (mechanical) energy. When a battery is used as the source of emf, the energy which is transferred to the free electrons comes from the chemical energy used up as the battery maintains the potential (energy) difference between its terminals.

Before the accelerating free electron gets very far in its journey along the length of the conductor, it collides with an atom of the conductor material. This collision results in a considerable reduction in the speed of the electron. As a result, some of the kinetic energy gained by the electron is transferred to the atom with which it collided in the form of heat energy (just as vigorous hand clapping results in a transfer of mechanical energy to heat energy). After the collision, the free electron is again urged by the electromotive force to accelerate and acquire more kinetic energy. Again it will collide with an atom of conductor material and give up some of its kinetic energy in the form of heat. Therefore the progress of the electrons which constitute the current carriers in a metallic conductor is characterized by alternate acceleration (during which interval potential energy from the source of emf is transferred to the electron in kinetic form) and sudden deceleration (at which time some of the kinetic energy of the electron is transferred to the atoms of the conductor material in the form of heat). This accounts for the very low *net* velocity of the current carriers that we noted in Section 2.5.

These many collisions, which constitute an *opposition to the flow of current*, account for the property of electric conductors known as **resistance**. The consequence of resistance in an electric circuit is the transfer of energy taken from the source of emf into heat energy whenever current if forced to flow in conductors possessing this property.

Resistance is a desirable property in such circuit components as lamps and electric stove elements, in which we are interested in producing heat energy. In circuit elements such as the conductors connecting the lamp to the battery in Fig. 3.1, resistance is an undesirable property. Not only is some of the energy in the system wasted in the form of heat in the conductors, but if heat is developed at a greater rate than the conductors can dissipate it or pass it on to the surrounding air, the temperature of the conductors can rise to the point where they become a fire hazard.

Resistance is often inserted into an electric circuit as a means of limiting current flow. For example, if we wish to dim the lamp in the circuit of Fig. 3.1, we can connect a circuit element possessing appreciable resistance in *series* with the lamp and the battery as shown in Fig. 3.2. Now the free electrons have to flow through both the lamp and the added resistance in completing their journey from the negative terminal of the battery to the positive terminal. Since this additional resistance produces heat when current flows through it, rather than connecting the lamp to the battery with conductors possessing higher resistance it is preferable to lump the extra resistance into a single electric component termed a **resistor,** which has been designed to dissipate the heat adequately without damage to either itself or nearby objects.

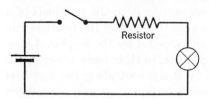

**Fig. 3.2.** Using a resistor to limit current.

## 3. Factors Governing the Resistance of Metallic Conductors

In stating his law of constant proportionality, Ohm had to add the provision that the temperature must be kept constant. Therefore temperature must have some effect on the resistance of an electric conductor. We can readily check this in the laboratory by measuring the $E/I$ ratio (resistance) of a lamp operating at the rated value of applied emf (white hot) and then measuring the $E/I$ ratio when the emf is reduced to 10% of the rated value and the filament gives off practically no light. We shall investigate the exact manner in which temperature affects the resistance of a metallic conductor a little later in this chapter. For the moment we shall assume temperature to remain constant at normal room temperature (20°C).

Returning for the moment to the hydraulic system of Chapter 1, we find that the flow of the hydraulic fluid causes energy to be converted into heat as atoms of fluid in contact with the walls of the tubing alternately pick up energy from the pump as they are accelerated by pump pressure, and then convert this energy into heat as they are slowed down by friction with the tube walls. Increasing the length of the pipes will reduce the flow of the hydraulic medium for a given pump pressure since the length of the path over which friction is converting kinetic energy into heat has been increased. Therefore the opposition to the flow is proportional to the length of the pipes. We can see also that a greater flow for a given pressure will occur if the cross-sectional area of the pipe is increased. Therefore the opposition to the flow is inversely proportional to the cross-sectional area.

Similarly, if we cut two lengths of wire from the same reel, one being twice the length of the other, in order for electrons to make the complete trip through the longer wire, they will have twice as many opportunities to collide with atoms of the conductor material. Therefore the opposition of the longer wire to the flow of current is twice as great as that of the shorter wire. Therefore

the **resistance** of an electric conductor is **directly proportional** to its length.

If we select a wire size which has double the cross-sectional area of another wire size and cut equal lengths of each, the wire with the larger cross section would have the same cross-sectional area as two pieces of the wire with the smaller cross section connected in *parallel*. Since each of the two smaller diameter wires in parallel will pass the same current when connected to a single source of emf, the two parallel connected wires pass twice the current of one wire. And since $R = E/I$, double current with no change in emf represents half as much resistance. Since doubling the cross-sectional area of a single conductor is the same as using two of the smaller diameter wires in parallel, doubling the cross-sectional area cuts the resistance in half. Therefore

the **resistance** of an electric conductor is **inversely proportional** to its cross-sectional area.

We noted in Chapter 2 that some materials possess more free electrons per unit volume than others and that the greater the number of free electrons per unit volume, the better conductor that material becomes. The greater the number of current carriers in a conductor of certain dimensions, the smaller the percentage of the total energy that is carried by any one electron. Therefore the amount of energy that is converted into heat by collision with atoms of conductor material is proportionately reduced. Therefore a silver wire has a lower resistance than a copper wire with the same dimensions, and the copper wire has a lower resistance than an aluminum wire with the same dimensions. Therefore

the **resistance** of an electric conductor is dependent on the type of **conductor material**.

## 4. Specific Resistance or Resistivity

Since we know that the resistance of a conductor is directly proportional to its length, if we are given the resistance of unit length of wire, we can readily calculate the resistance of any length of wire of that particular material having the same diameter. Similarly, since we know that the resistance of a conductor is inversely proportional to its cross-sectional area, if we are given the resistance of a length of wire with unit cross-sectional area, we can calculate the resistance of a similar length of wire of the same material with any cross-sectional area. Combining both of these statements we find that if we know the resistance of a given conductor, we can calculate the resistance for any dimensions of a conductor of the same material at the same temperature.

EXAMPLE 2: A piece of wire one foot long with a cross-sectional area of $10^{-5}$ sq in. has a resistance of 0.75 ohm. What is the resistance of 100 ft of wire of the same material with a cross-sectional area of $3 \times 10^{-5}$ sq in.?

*Solution:* From the relationships stated above, we can write the equation

$$\frac{R_2}{R_1} = \frac{l_2}{l_1} \times \frac{A_1}{A_2} \tag{3.3}$$

$$\therefore \quad R_2 = 0.75 \times \frac{100}{1} \times \frac{1 \times 10^{-5}}{3 \times 10^{-5}} = 25 \text{ ohms}$$

From Example 2 we will note that a convenient way of showing the effect of the type of material on the resistance of a given conductor is to state the resistance of a standard conductor with unit length and unit cross-sectional area made from that material.

The **resistance** of a unit length and cross section conductor of a certain material is called the **specific resistance** or **resistivity** of that material. The letter symbol for specific resistance is the Greek letter $\rho$ (rho).

Since the mks unit for both length and cross section is the meter, the mks standard conductor must take the form of a cube with each of its edges one meter in length. The specific resistance of a certain electric conducting material will therefore be the resistance between opposite faces of the one meter cube and will be expressed in **ohm-meters.**

A standard conductor in the shape of a one meter cube bears little resemblance to practical electric conductors. Therefore it is not surprising that, for engineering purposes, we set aside the mks ohm-meter of the physicist in favor of a practical unit for specific resistance based on English dimensional units. Because of the shape of practical electric conductors, the inch is too small a unit to express length conveniently but too large to use for cross section. Therefore in expressing the length of electric conductors we shall use the **foot** as the unit of length and the **mil** (1/1000 inch) as the unit of diameter. On this basis then,

the **specific resistance** of a material is the resistance of a wire of that material at a stated temperature with a circular cross section of one mil diameter and a length of one foot. Therefore the practical unit of specific resistance is ohms for a "mil-foot" conductor at a specified temperature (usually 20°C).

Note that although we have switched to English units for dimensions, temperature is specified in centigrade degrees. Table I gives the specific resistances for some of the more common conducting materials.

Before we set forth the procedure for calculating the resistance of a given conductor, we need to consider the method used in dealing with the

**Table I.** SPECIFIC RESISTANCE OF SOME COMMON
ELECTRIC CONDUCTOR MATERIALS

| Conductor Material | Specific Resistance (ohms for a mil-foot section at 20°C) |
|---|---|
| Silver | 9.9 |
| Copper (annealed) | 10.37 |
| Aluminum | 17 |
| Tungsten | 33 |
| Nickel | 47 |
| Iron (pure) | 58 |
| Nichrome II | 660 |

cross-sectional area of *round* wires. We have learned that the area of a circle is expressed by the equation:

$$A = \pi r^2 = \frac{\pi}{4} d^2$$

*where A* is the area in **square** measure, $\pi = 3.14$ (the ratio of the circumference to diameter of a circle), $r$ is radius, and $d$ is diameter. The penalty we have to pay for using *square* measure to express the area of a *circle* is that the constant $\pi$ has to be included in all numerical computations.

EXAMPLE 3: What is the cross-sectional area of a wire 3 mils in diameter?

*Solution:*

$$A = \frac{\pi}{4} d^2 = \frac{3.14 \times 3 \times 3}{4} = 7.065 \text{ sq mils}$$

Since $\pi/4$ is a constant, the area is always directly proportional to the square of the diameter. Let us therefore select a new area unit and call it the *circular* mil (as opposed to the *square* mil) and define it thus:

The **circular mil** is the area of a circle whose diameter is one mil.

Therefore

$$A = d^2 \tag{3.4}$$

where $A$ is the area of a circle in circular mils and $d$ is the diameter of the circle in mils. Since the majority of electric conductors have a circular cross section, the use of circular measure saves us the extra work and possible error of multiplying $d^2$ by $\pi/4$.

From our previous investigation of the manner in which specific resistance, length, and cross-sectional area affect the resistance of a given conductor, we can set up an equation for calculating the resistance of any electric conductor at room temperature.

$$R = \rho \times \frac{l}{d^2} \tag{3.5}$$

where $R$ is the resistance of the conductor in ohms, $l$ is the length of the conductor in feet, $d$ is the diameter of the conductor in mils ($d^2$ is the area of the cross section in circular mils), and $\rho$ is the specific resistance of the material in ohms for a mil-foot section at 20°C.

EXAMPLE 4: What is the resistance of 500 ft of aluminum wire having a diameter of 10 mils?

Solution: From Table I, $\rho$ for aluminum is 17 ohms for a mil-foot section at 20°C.

$$R = \rho\frac{l}{d^2} = 17 \times \frac{500}{10 \times 10} = 85 \text{ ohms}$$

## 5. Wire Tables

In the interest of standardization, North American wire manufacturers use cross-sectional dimensions which conform to the American Wire Gauge (AWG) sizes as given in Table II. Note that the larger the gauge number, the smaller the diameter of the conductor. Although the wire tables in reference handbooks include columns which show area, ohms per thousand feet, pounds per thousand feet, feet per pound, etc., for copper at 20°C for each gauge number, Table II shows only the diameter for each wire size. The reason for doing so is that we wish to become acquainted with the use of Equation (3.5). A column in the wire table showing ohms per thousand feet for each wire size provides a means of by-passing the equation showing the basic factors governing resistance altogether.

Table II. DIAMETERS OF AMERICAN WIRE GAUGE CONDUCTOR SIZES

| AWG number | Diameter in mils | AWG number | Diameter in mils | AWG number | Diameter in mils |
|---|---|---|---|---|---|
| 0000 | 460.0 | 12 | 80.81 | 27 | 14.20 |
| 000 | 409.6 | 13 | 71.96 | 28 | 12.64 |
| 00 | 364.8 | 14 | 64.08 | 29 | 11.26 |
| 0 | 324.9 | 15 | 57.07 | 30 | 10.03 |
| 1 | 289.3 | 16 | 50.82 | 31 | 8.928 |
| 2 | 257.6 | 17 | 45.26 | 32 | 7.950 |
| 3 | 229.4 | 18 | 40.30 | 33 | 7.080 |
| 4 | 204.3 | 19 | 35.89 | 34 | 6.305 |
| 5 | 181.9 | 20 | 31.96 | 35 | 5.615 |
| 6 | 162.0 | 21 | 28.46 | 36 | 5.000 |
| 7 | 144.3 | 22 | 25.35 | 37 | 4.453 |
| 8 | 128.5 | 23 | 22.57 | 38 | 3.965 |
| 9 | 114.4 | 24 | 20.10 | 39 | 3.531 |
| 10 | 101.9 | 25 | 17.90 | 40 | 3.145 |
| 11 | 90.74 | 26 | 15.94 | | |

EXAMPLE 5: Using the data in Table II, what is the resistance at 20°C of 200 ft of AWG #14 copper wire?

*Solution:*

Diameter of AWG #14 wire $d = 64.1$ mils.

Area of AWG #14 wire $d^2 = 64.1 \times 64.1 = 4109$ circular mils.

$$R = \rho \frac{l}{d^2} = 10.37 \times \frac{200}{4109} = 0.505 \text{ ohms}$$

It is worth while noting that in setting up the AWG wire table, the cross-sectional dimensions were chosen so that each decrease of one gauge number represents a 25% increase in cross-sectional *area*. On this basis, a decrease of *three* gauge numbers represents an increase in cross-sectional area of $1.25 \times 1.25 \times 1.25 =$ approx 2:1. Similarly a change of ten wire gauge numbers represents a 10:1 change in cross-sectional area. Also, since doubling the cross-sectional area cuts the resistance in half, a decrease of three wire gauge numbers cuts the resistance of the conductor of a given length in half. Therefore if we memorize the dimensions for any one wire gauge number, we can approximate the dimensions of any other wire gauge number. For this purpose AWG 10 wire is quite convenient.

| | | | |
|---|---|---|---|
| AWG gauge number | 10 | diameter (mils) 100 (approx) | |
| ohms/thousand feet | 1 | area (circular mils) 10,000 | |
| (copper at 20°C) | | | |

## Problems

1. What is the resistance of a circuit which draws a 2.5 amp current from a 120 v source of emf?

2. What resistance is required to limit the current in a circuit to 2 amp when the applied emf is 30 v?

3. What is the resistance of a stove element when a 5 amp current through it causes a 110 v voltage drop across it?

4. If a current of 0.15 amp through the resistor in Fig. 3.2 causes a 1.0 v drop across it, what is its resistance?

5. What current will flow through a 20 ohm resistor connected across a 100 v source of emf?

6. What current through a 250 ohm resistor will cause a voltage drop of 75 v across the resistor?

7. A 12 ohm heating element has a voltage drop of 98 v across it. What current is flowing through the heater?

8. What current will flow in a circuit whose total resistance is 17 ohms when it is connected to a 117 v source of emf?

9. What emf must be applied to a 15 ohm resistor to make it pass a 3 amp current?

10. What is the voltage drop across a 125 ohm resistor when 0.2 amp current flows through it?

11. What voltage drop is produced by a 1.6 amp current flowing through a 56 ohm resistor?

12. What emf is required to cause current to flow at the rate of 0.35 amp in a circuit whose total resistance is 124 ohms?

13. A 15 $\mu$a current through a resistor in a radio receiver causes a 30 mv drop across it. What is its resistance?

14. What is the resistance of an ammeter whose full scale reading is 10 amp with a 30 mv drop across the meter?

15. What value of cathode bias resistor is required for an amplifier tube in order to produce a 7 v drop across the resistor when the cathode current through the resistor is 12 ma?

16. What value of resistor will draw a 32 ma current when connected to a 2.5 kv source of emf?

17. A fuse in the plate power supply of an amplifier has a resistance of 0.02 ohm. What current through the fuse will develop a 500 $\mu$v drop across it?

18. What current will flow when a 50 $\mu$v source of emf is connected to a 5 megohm resistor?

19. What current will flow through a 2.2 kilohm resistor connected across a 480 mv source of emf?

20. What screen grid current must flow through a 6.8 kilohm screen grid voltage dropping resistor to produce an 80 v drop across the resistor?

21. What emf must be applied to a 220 kilohm bleeder resistance in a piece of electronic equipment if the bleeder current is to be 20 $\mu$a?

22. What $IR$ drop is produced by the 6 ma plate current of an amplifier tube passing through a 15 kilohm plate load resistor?

23. What will be the voltage drop across a radio frequency choke in the plate circuit of an amplifier tube if the choke has a resistance of 2.7 ohms and the plate current through it is 13 ma?

24. The operating coil of a relay which is designed to energize with a current of 24 ma through the coil, has a resistance of 3.7 kilohms. What is the minimum applied emf which will energize the relay?

*Note:* Normal room temperature is assumed in Problems 25 to 40.

25. Using the data in Table I, determine the resistivity of copper in ohm-meters.

26. Using the data in Table I, determine the specific resistance of aluminum in ohm-meters.

27. The specific resistance of carbon is $3.0 \times 10^{-5}$ ohm-meters at 20°C. Express this in ohms per mil-foot.

28. Given the resistivity of constantan as $4.9 \times 10^{-7}$ ohm-meters at 20°C, what is the specific resistance of constantan expressed in ohms per mil-foot?

29. A copper conductor with a diameter of 0.1 in. has a resistance of 1.0 ohm per thousand feet. What is the resistance of 200 ft of copper wire with a diameter of 40 mils?

30. An aluminum wire 50 mils in diameter and 50 feet in length has a resistance of 0.34 ohm. What length of 40 mil diameter aluminum wire will have a resistance of 3.0 ohms?

31. Using the data of Table I, what is the resistance of a copper conductor 80 mils in diameter and 20 ft long?

32. What length of silver wire 20 mils in diameter has a resistance of 0.04 ohm?

33. What is the resistance of a copper bar with a rectangular cross section of $2 \times 4$ cm and a length of $1\frac{1}{2}$ meters?

34. What is the resistance of an aluminum conductor 4 mm in diameter and 40 m in length?

35. What is the resistance of one mile of #12 AWG copper wire?

36. What length of #24 AWG nickel wire has a resistance of 0.5 ohm?

37. A relay coil requires 484 ft of copper wire. If its resistance is to be approx 50 ohms, what AWG wire size is required?

38. A coil of #24 AWG copper wire wound in a single layer on a cylindrical form so that the mean diameter of each turn is 2.0 in., has a resistance of 1.6 ohms. How many turns of wire are there in the coil?

39. A stranded cable consists of eight #18 AWG copper wires. Twisting the wires to form the cable requires the length of each conductor to be 3% longer than the length of the cable in its final form. What is the resistance of one mile of this cable?

40. What size of solid copper conductor will have the same resistance per thousand feet as a stranded cable consisting of six #16 AWG aluminum wires? Allow an increase of 3% in the length of the individual aluminum conductors for twisting in forming the cable.

## 6. Effect of Temperature on Resistance

We have already noted that temperature will have some effect on the resistance of an electric conductor, but so far we have not had to consider it, since we have assumed that the temperature remained constant at 20°C. By checking the effect of temperature on the $E/I$ ratio (resistance) of a conductor as previously suggested, we find that for most conducting materials, the resistance increases linearly with an increase in temperature over normal temperature ranges. In Fig. 3.3, if $R_1$ is the resistance of a certain conductor at temperature $T_1$, then $R_2$ is its resistance at temperature $T_2$. The straight line $CF$ represents the

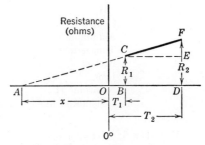

Fig. 3.3. Effect of temperature on resistance.

manner in which the resistance varies for temperatures between $T_1$ and $T_2$. The *slope* of the line $CF$ is dependent on the type of material. Some alloys have been developed (e.g., constantan) for which the line $CF$ is almost horizontal. Temperature has very little effect on the resistance of such materials. There are a few materials (e.g., carbon) which have a *negative* temperature effect, i.e., the resistance *decreases* as the temperature *increases*.

Since $CF$ in Fig. 3.3 is a straight line, we can project it to the left to cut the base line (zero ohms) at point $A$, thus producing two similar triangles $ABC$ and $ADF$. Since these triangles are similar we can show that

$$\frac{DF}{BC} = \frac{AD}{AB} = \frac{AO + OD}{AO + OB}$$

Substituting the electrical properties that these geometric dimensions represent gives

$$\frac{R_2}{R_1} = \frac{x + T_2}{x + T_1} \tag{3.6}$$

where $R_1$ is the resistance of the conductor at temperature $T_1$, $R_2$ is the resistance of the conductor at temperature $T_2$, $T_1$ and $T_2$ are the temperatures of the conductor in degrees centigrade, and $x$ is a constant which depends on the type of material used in the conductor.

From examination of Fig. 3.3, we may call $x$ the temperature (degrees centigrade below zero) at which the resistance of a particular material *apparently* becomes zero. This value of $x$ remains constant for any given material. Table III gives the numerical value of $x$ for some of the common electric conductor materials.

**Table III.** VALUES OF $x$ FOR SOME COMMON ELECTRIC
CONDUCTOR MATERIALS (see Fig. 3.3)

| Conductor material | $x$ (in $-°C$) |
|---|---|
| Silver | $-243$ |
| Copper | $-234.5$ |
| Aluminum | $-236$ |
| Tungsten | $-202$ |
| Nickel | $-147$ |
| Iron | $-180$ |
| Nichrome II | $-6,250$ |
| Constantan (55% Cu, 45% Ni) | $-125,000$ |

EXAMPLE 6: A copper conductor has a resistance of 12 ohms at 20°C. What is its resistance at 100°C?

*Solution:*

$$\frac{R_2}{R_1} = \frac{x + T_2}{x + T_1} \quad \text{or} \quad R_2 = R_1 \frac{x + T_2}{x + T_1}$$

$$\therefore \quad R_2 = 12 \frac{234.5 + 100}{234.5 + 20} = \frac{12 \times 334.5}{254.5} = 15.77 \text{ ohms}$$

EXAMPLE 7: A precision resistor made of constantan wire has a resistance of 10,000 ohms at 20°C. What is its resistance when its temperature rises 20°C?

*Solution:*

$$R_2 = R_1 \frac{x + T_2}{x + T_1} = 10,000 \frac{125,000 + 40}{125,000 + 20}$$

$$R_2 = 10,001.6 \text{ ohms.}$$

In addition to being able to calculate the effect that temperature has on resistance, we can use the change in resistance of a certain material to calculate the temperature in locations where it is difficult to place a thermometer.

EXAMPLE 8: The copper winding of an electric motor which has been standing for several hours in a room at 20°C has a resistance of 0.20 ohm. When the motor has been in use for some hours the resistance of the winding is found to be 0.22 ohm. Calculate the temperature rise of the winding.

*Solution:*

$$\frac{R_2}{R_1} = \frac{x + T_2}{x + T_1}$$

$$\frac{0.22}{0.20} = \frac{234.5 + T_2}{234.5 + 20}$$

$$\therefore \quad T_2 = (1.1 \times 254.5) - 234.5 = 45.45°C$$

$$\therefore \quad \text{temperature rise} = T_2 - T_1 = 25.45°C$$

## 7. Temperature Coefficient of Resistance

Although the method we have just derived is quite adequate for calculating the effect of temperature on resistance, it does not lend itself to setting down a formula which shows how to calculate the resistance of any conductor, given its length, cross-sectional area, material, and temperature. So let us return to geometric construction on Fig. 3.3 to derive an alternate method of showing the effect of temperature on the resistance of an electric conductor. The line $CE$ is drawn parallel to the base line. Since specific resistance $(\rho)$ is usually stated for a temperature of 20°C, we shall let $T_1$ represent 20°C.

Since triangle $ABC$ is similar to triangle $CEF$, we can show that

$$\frac{FE}{BC} = \frac{CE}{AB} \quad \text{or} \quad \frac{FE}{R_1} = \frac{\Delta T}{x + 20}$$

where $\Delta T$ is the difference in temperature (centigrade degrees) between $T_2$ and 20°C. Therefore

$$FE = R_1 \left( \frac{\Delta T}{x + 20} \right)$$

Since $CE$ and $BD$ are parallel,

$$R_2 = R_1 + FE$$

$$\therefore \quad R_2 = R_1 + R_1 \left(\frac{\Delta T}{x + 20}\right) = R_1 \left(1 + \frac{\Delta T}{x + 20}\right)$$

If we now call $1/(x + 20)$ the **temperature coefficient of resistance** (at 20°C) and represent it by the Greek letter $\alpha$ (alpha),

$$R_2 = R_1 (1 + \alpha \Delta T) \tag{3.7}$$

where $R_2$ is the resistance of a conductor at any specified temperature, $R_1$ is its resistance at 20°C, $\alpha$ is the temperature coefficient of resistance at 20°C $[\alpha = 1/(x + 20)]$, and $\Delta T$ is the difference (centigrade degrees) between the specified temperature and 20°C.

Since $R_1$ represents the resistance of a given conductor at 20°C.

$$R_1 = \rho \frac{l}{d^2} \tag{3.5}$$

Therefore the **general equation** for the resistance of an electric conductor becomes

$$R = \rho \frac{l}{d^2} (1 + \alpha \Delta T) \tag{3.8}$$

where $R$ is the resistance of the conductor in ohms, $\rho$ is the specific resistance of the material in ohms for a mil-foot section at 20°C, $l$ is the length in feet, $d$ is the diameter in mils (thousandths of an inch), $\alpha$ is the temperature coefficient (ohmic change per degree per ohm at 20°C), and $\Delta T$ is the difference between the operating temperature and 20°C (in centigrade degrees).

Since the temperature coefficient $(\alpha_{20°}) = 1/(x + 20)$ and $x$ is dependent on the type of material, then temperature coefficient of resistance represents the manner in which each ohm of resistance of that material changes for each degree change in temperature from the reference temperature of 20°C. A table of temperature coefficients can be calculated from the relationship we have already stated between $\alpha$ and $x$.

**Table IV.** Temperature Coefficient of Resistance of Some Common Electric Conductor Materials at 20°C

| Conductor material | $\alpha 20°$ |
|---|---|
| Silver | 0.0038 |
| Copper | 0.00393 |
| Aluminum | 0.0039 |
| Tungsten | 0.0045 |
| Nickel | 0.006 |
| Iron | 0.0055 |
| Nichrome II | 0.00016 |
| Constantan | 0.000008 |
| Carbon | −0.0005 |

EXAMPLE 9: What is the resistance of 1000 ft of #20 AWG copper wire at 40°C?

*Solution:*

From Table I,    $\rho = 10.37$
From Table II,    $d = 32$
From Table IV, $\alpha = 0.00393$

$$R = \rho \frac{l}{d^2} (1 + \alpha \, \Delta T)$$

$$= \frac{10.37 \times 1000}{32 \times 32} (1 + 0.00393 \times 20)$$

$$\therefore \quad R = 10.9 \text{ ohms}$$

If the required temperature is below 20°C, $\Delta T$ will be a *negative* quantity and Equation (3.8) becomes effectively:

$$R = \rho \frac{l}{d^2} (1 - \alpha \, \Delta T)$$

## 8. Nonlinear Resistors

Most electric conductor materials behave in the manner discovered by Georg Ohm in establishing his law of constant proportionality; that is, doubling the applied emf causes the current to double, tripling the applied voltage triples the current, and so on. This relationship can be shown graphically as in Fig. 3.4. The straight line graph represents a constant value of resistance. As shown, the smaller the resistance, the steeper the slope of the linear graph. A resistor that maintains this constant $E/I$ ratio is known as a **linear** resistor. As current through a resistor is increased, electric energy is converted into heat at an increased rate, resulting in a rise in the temperature of the resistor. As indicated in Table IV, this increase in tem-

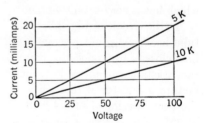

Fig. 3.4. Graph of a linear resistor.

perature causes a slight *increase* in the resistance of most conductor materials. But the percentage change in resistance over the usual temperature ranges encountered in practice is small enough in the case of the common electric conductor materials that the deviation of their resistance graphs from the straight lines of Fig. 3.4 is hardly perceptible. Therefore copper and aluminum are classed as linear resistors. Special alloys with almost zero temperature coefficient (such as *constantan*) have been developed for making the precision resistors used in measuring equipment in order to ensure a linear resistance characteristic.

The tungsten filament of an incandescent lamp and the heaters of radio tubes are examples where the temperature range from room temperature to the operating temperature is such that there is considerable change in resistance. A 60 watt lamp operating from a 120 v source of emf has a white hot resistance of 240 ohms to limit the current through it to $I = E/R = 120/240 = 0.05$ amp. But when the lamp is turned off, the cold resistance is only about 18 ohms. Therefore at the instant the lamp is turned on, before the filament has had a chance to heat up, the *inrush* current will be $I = E/R = 120/18 = 6.6$ amp. Fortunately the mass of the lamp filament is small enough that it can reach white heat in less than a millisecond. Therefore the current surge is of very short duration, as shown in Fig. 3.5. If the heating elements of electric stoves had the same temperature coefficient as tungsten, the surge would be much more serious since these elements take several seconds to reach red heat. Therefore stove elements are manufactured from some alloy such as Nichrome II which has a very small temperature coefficient.

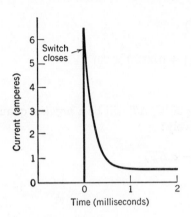

**Fig. 3.5.** The inrush current of an incandescent lamp.

In the circuit of Fig. 3.2, the resistor in series with the lamp (or vacuum tube heaters) would prevent a high surge of current when the switch is first closed. But once the lamp has heated up we would like to remove the resistance to allow it to operate normally. Perhaps we could manufacture a resistor with such a high *negative* temperature coefficient that the heat developed in it by the flow of current after the switch is closed would lower its resistance to a small enough value that it would effectively be out of circuit once the initial warm-up is completed. Such resistors are available under various trade names for use in limiting the initial surge which occurs when radio, television, and other electronic apparatus is first switched on. These resistors have a resistance of over 100 ohms at room temperature, but with a current of approximately 1 amp through them, their resistance drops to less than 1 ohm in from ten to fifteen seconds.

Certain metallic oxides mixed into a ceramic binder exhibit this remarkably high negative temperature characteristic. In addition to their application in inrush surge limiting resistors, tiny beads of these materials can be calibrated in terms of resistance vs. temperature to become sensitive temperature measuring devices. These tiny nonlinear resistors are called **thermistors.** A decrease in temperature of less than 20C° will more than double their resistance.

A study of the graph of the nonlinear resistance characteristic of Fig. 3.6 would seem to indicate a material with a pronounced negative temperature coefficient. Actually temperature has little effect on the resistance of **thyrite,** which is a trade name for carborundum crystals in a clay binder. In this case the resistance decreases considerably when the *voltage* applied between the two sides of a thyrite wafer is increased beyond a certain value. As Fig. 3.6 indicates, this decrease in resistance is such that many times the normal current can flow through the thyrite without appreciable increase in the voltage drop across it. Therefore connecting a thyrite resistor in parallel with a piece of electric apparatus provides this portion of the circuit with a means of coping with a sudden surge in

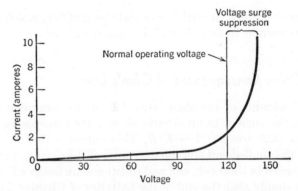

Fig. 3.6. A typical thyrite resistor characteristic.

total circuit current without appreciably affecting the voltage across and the current through the protected piece of equipment. Thyrite was developed primarily for lightning arrestors on power transmission lines.

Some resistors are manufactured in such a manner as to take advantage of a large positive temperature coefficient. Figure 3.7 shows the $E/I$ characteristic of a material with such a temperature coefficient. As the voltage drop across the resistor is doubled from 8 to 16 v, the accompanying increase in temperature is sufficient to almost double the resistance. This in turn results in practically no increase in current as the voltage drop is doubled. This particular nonlinear resistor is called a **current regulator** or **ballast** resistor. When it is connected in series with the heaters of radio tubes, it will help to maintain a reasonably constant current through them in spite of variations in the source emf. This protection increases the life of certain tubes considerably.

There are other examples of nonlinear resistance characteristics which are more properly included in a study of electronics. These include the

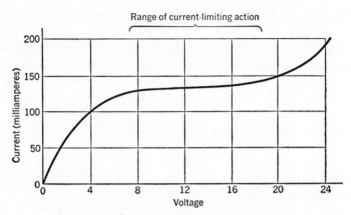

Fig. 3.7. A typical ballast resistor characteristic.

flow of electric current through a gas and the **rectifier,** which is a device that permits current to flow through it more readily in one direction than in the other.

## 9. Some Other Consequences of Ohm's Law

At the beginning of the chapter we set out to determine the factors that govern the current in an electric circuit. By transposing the Ohm's law formula (3.2) we get: $I = E/R$. This indicates that current is dependent on the applied emf and the resistance of the circuit. In the electric circuits discussed in this book, emf and resistance are *independent* variables. This means simply that the emf of the batteries of Chapter 2 depends on the two particular metals used and is essentially *independent* of the resistance and the current. Similarly the resistance depends only on such controllable physical factors as length, diameter, type of material, and temperature. Current, on the other hand, is the *dependent* variable. Whenever the switch is closed in the circuits we have discussed, the current *must* automatically take on a value which will satisfy the relationship

$$I = \frac{E}{R}$$

*where* $I$ is the current that must flow in the circuit (in amperes), $E$ is the emf applied to the circuit (in volts), and $R$ is the resistance of the circuit (in ohms).

In the circuit of Fig. 2.6 we noted that the distinction between the emf of the battery and the voltage drop across the resistor was that when the switch is open, the emf is still present but the voltage drop across the resistor becomes zero. In fact a voltage can appear across a resistor *only* when current flows through it. Transposing Ohm's law once more gives us

$$V = IR$$

where $I$ is the current through a resistor (in amperes), $R$ is the resistance of the resistor (in ohms), and $V$ is the resulting voltage drop across the resistor (in volts). Because of this relationship, it is quite common to hear *voltage drop* across a resistance referred to as an **IR drop.**

## Problems

41. A length of copper telephone line has a resistance of 24 ohms at 20°C. What is its resistance on a hot summer day when its temperature rises to 36°C?

42. What is the resistance of an aluminum conductor at −20°C if its resistance at +30°C is 1.25 ohms?

43. What is the resistance of 80 ft of #24 AWG copper wire at 60°C?

44. What length of #22 AWG Nichrome II wire has a resistance of 48 ohms at 200°C?

45. If the resistance/temperature graph for brass is extended in a straight line till the resistance is zero, the corresponding temperature would be −480°C. What is the temperature coefficient of brass at 20°C?

46. The temperature coefficient of platinum at 20°C is 0.003 per degree per ohm. Find the temperature $x$ at which the resistance of platinum would become zero if the resistance/temperature graph were extended as a straight line.

47. An incandescent lamp draws a 1.0 amp current from a 110 v source of emf to raise the temperature of its tungsten filament to 2800°C. What is its resistance at normal room temperature?

48. By how many degrees must the temperature of a nickel rod be changed to increase its resistance to 105% of its resistance at normal room temperature?

49. A certain conductor has a resistance of 10 ohms at 20°C and 11.35 ohms at 50°C. Considering only those materials listed in Tables III and IV, of what material is this conductor made?

50. An electric motor is to be operated at a distance of 800 ft from a 120 v source of emf. The current drawn by the motor is 8.0 amp. This current raises the temperature of the conductors feeding the motor to 40°C. What is the maximum AWG wire size number that can be used without the voltage drop in the conductors exceeding more than 10% of the applied emf?

## Review Questions

1. Why can Ohm's law be described in terms of "constant proportionality"?

2. Why does the $E/I$ ratio of an electric circuit indicate its ability to oppose electric current flow rather than its ability to permit current flow?

3. If there were no such unit as the *ohm*, how could you express the resistance of an electric circuit?

4. If resistance is the *opposition* to the flow of current, energy must be expended in forcing free electrons to move *against* this opposition. Where does this energy come from? Where does it go?

5. What relationship exists between the resistance of a given conductor and the number of free electrons in the conductor?

6. An electric fuse consists of a small strip of metal with a low melting temperature. The current in the protected electric circuit flows through this strip of metal. Which will have the greater resistance, a 10 amp fuse or a 20 amp fuse? Explain.

7. The National Electrical Code limits the current through #14 AWG house wiring to 15 amp. What is the reason for doing so? Is it possible for a current of greater than 15 amp to flow through #14 wire?

8. A resistor made of Nichrome wire wound on a ceramic form has the same resistance and is passing the same current as the filament of an incandescent lamp, yet the temperature of the lamp filament is many times that of the Nichrome resistor. Explain.

9. Why does shortening the length of a given conductor decrease its resistance?

10. Why is resistance inversely proportional to the square of the diameter of a conductor?

11. What is meant by a mil-foot section of wire?

12. Given an accurate resistance measuring device, how would you go about determining the resistivity of a sample of an unknown alloy?

13. Why is it possible to express the cross-sectional area of a round conductor without involving $\pi$?

14. What is the conversion factor for converting ohm-meters to ohms per circular mil-foot?

15. Prepare the mks equivalent of Table I.

16. Knowing the diameter and resistance per thousand feet of #10 AWG copper wire, how would you estimate the resistance of 200 ft of #16 AWG copper wire without the aid of wire tables?

17. Draw a graph of the type shown in Fig. 3.3 for carbon, using the data given in Table IV. What would the temperature $x$ be for carbon?

18. In checking the temperature rise of the copper field winding of an electric motor by measuring its resistance, before the motor was started, its resistance (at room temperature) was 50 ohms. After thirty minutes of operation, its resistance was 53 ohms. A half hour later its resistance was 54.3 ohms, and after a further thirty minutes had elapsed, the field coil resistance was 54.7 ohms. It took three hours in all for the resistance to settle at a steady value of 55 ohms. Plot a graph of temperature rise against time for this heat run. Explain the reasons for the shape of the graph.

19. Draw a graph similar to Fig. 3.4 for a resistor having a fairly pronounced negative temperature coefficient. Would such a resistor be useful as a current regulator? Explain.

20. Find the temperature coefficient of copper at 0°C. From our derivation of temperature coefficient, discuss why the temperature coefficient should be different when 0°C is specified rather than 20°C.

# Chapter 4

# WORK AND POWER

~~~~~~~~~~~~~~~~~~~~~~~~~~~~~~~~~~~~~~~~~~~~~~~~~~~~~~~~~~~~~~~

## 1. Energy and Work

In mechanics, energy and work are defined thus:

**Work** is the accomplishment of motion against the action of a force which tends to oppose the motion. **Energy** is the capacity to do work.

From the definition of energy it is apparent that energy and work are closely related. The distinction between energy and work can be shown by referring to specific examples. Referring back to the hydraulic model of Fig. 2.1, the pump is *moving* the water into Tank *A against the force* of gravity which tries to maintain the same level in both tanks. Therefore *work* is being accomplished by the pump. This work is being done at the expense of the mechanical *energy* applied to the pump. Since the work being done by the pump raises the water in Tank *A* to a higher level than that in Tank *B*, the result of the *work* is the storing up of *energy* in the hydraulic system. If the pump is stopped and the valve is opened, the potential difference between the two tanks causes water to flow through the hydraulic motor against the mechanical opposition of the motor to rotation. Therefore the *energy* that was stored in the higher water level is converted into *work* as the medium flows against the opposition of the hydraulic motor. From the sequence of events in this example, we may think of **work as being the process of transforming energy from one form into another.**

If we apply the mechanical definition of work to the electric circuit of Fig. 3.1, *work* is accomplished by moving electrons through the lamp against the *resistance* of the filament of the lamp. This *work* is accomplished at the expense of the chemical *energy* of the battery and the result of work being done is a transformation of energy to the heat energy which lights the lamp.

From our observations in these two examples, we can appreciate a basic law about energy—the law of conservation of energy. This law states that energy can be transformed from one form into another but that the total energy after transformation must exactly equal the total energy going into the transformation. Hence *energy* and *work* are numerically equal and the same unit of measurement and letter symbol may be used for both.

The letter symbol for both energy and work is $W$.

## 2. The Joule

We have already found it necessary to refer to the **joule** in Chapter 2 in order to establish the exact magnitude of the **volt** as the basic unit of PD. In Chapter 1 we decided that the unit of electric energy should be the same as the unit of mechanical energy to provide us with a common denominator for solving problems involving the conversion of mechanical energy to electric energy and vice versa. In the mks system of units, the **joule** is the mechanical energy required to move an object *one* meter against a force of *one* newton. The equivalent amount of electric energy is also called a **joule.** Therefore

The **joule** is the basic unit of electric energy or work.

Since work represents the conversion of energy from one form into another, we need to know the equivalent of an electric **joule** in terms of the more common forms of energy which are conveyed by electrical means. The two forms of energy with which we are likely to be concerned are mechanical energy and heat, both in English units. The English unit of mechanical energy is the foot-pound. The foot-pound is the mechanical energy required to move an object one foot against a force of one pound. The English unit of heat energy is the British thermal unit (Btu). The Btu is the heat energy required to raise the temperature of one pound of water by one Fahrenheit degree. The conversion factors are given in Table I.

**Table I.** Electric, Mechanical, and Heat Energy Conversion Factors

$$1 \text{ ft-lb} = 1.356 \text{ joules}$$
$$1 \text{ Btu} = 1054.8 \text{ joules}$$

EXAMPLE 1: How much electric energy must be supplied to an electric motor to raise an elevator weighing 4 tons a distance of 120 ft? Assume that 10% of the electric energy supplied to the motor is lost in the form of heat.
*Solution:*

Mechanical work, $W = 120 \times 4 \times 2000 = 960{,}000$ ft-lb

Electric energy going toward raising the elevator,

$$W = 960,000 \times 1.356 = 1,301,760 \text{ joules}$$

Since this represents only 90% of the electric energy supplied to the motor, the total electric energy required is

$$W_T = \frac{1,301,760}{0.9} = 1,446,400 \text{ joules}$$

EXAMPLE 2: A teakettle contains 2 pounds of water at room temperature (68°F). If 20% of the electric energy supplied to the stove element under the kettle is lost by radiation and in heating the kettle itself, how much electric energy must be supplied to the element to bring the water to the boiling point?
*Solution:*

$$\text{Heat energy, } W = 2 \times (212 - 68) = 288 \text{ Btu}$$

Electric energy going toward raising the temperature of the water,

$$W = 288 \times 1054.8 = 303,780 \text{ joules}$$

Since this represents only 80% of the electric energy supplied to the stove element, the total electric energy required is

$$W_T = \frac{303,780}{0.8} = 380,000 \text{ joules}$$

## 3. Efficiency

Examples 1 and 2 suggest that in converting energy from one form into another, some of the input energy is converted to a form of energy that is not useful in performing the work which the equipment was set up to do. This wasted energy is usually in the form of heat. Some of this heat comes from mechanical friction, some of it from current flow in an electric resistance, and some of it is lost by radiation as in Example 2. Not only does this wasted energy cost money to supply but the equipment has to be designed to dissipate the wasted heat energy safely.

The ability of an energy converting device (such as the electric motor of Example 1 and the electric stove element of Example 2) to convert as much of the input energy as possible into *useful* work is specified in terms of its **efficiency.**

**Efficiency** is the ratio of useful output energy to total input energy.

Efficiency is usually expressed as a percentage. For example, the efficiency of the system in Example 1 is 90%.

EXAMPLE 3: What is the efficiency of an electric hoist if 60,000 joules of electric energy have to be supplied to the motor in order to raise an 800 lb weight through 50 ft?

*Solution:*

$$\text{Mechanical work, } W = 50 \times 800 = 40{,}000 \text{ ft-lb}$$
$$= 40{,}000 \times 1.356 = 54{,}240 \text{ joules}$$
$$\text{Efficiency} = \frac{54{,}240}{60{,}000} \times 100\% = 90.4\%$$

## 4. Power

By using a suitable train of gears that will multiply mechanical force by dividing down its speed by the same factor, a small electric motor could be used to raise the elevator in Example 1. But in doing so it would take about five minutes for the elevator to move through the 120 ft. This might be satisfactory for a freight elevator but a passenger elevator would have to be supplied with a much larger motor so that the required amount of mechanical work could be accomplished in a much shorter time. Therefore in energy conversion systems, the *rate* of doing work is just as important as the amount of work done. Since we have decided to think of electricity as a medium for conveying energy, *rate of doing work* is probably more important than the amount of work done and is given the name **power.**

**Power** is the *rate* of doing work.
The letter symbol for power is $P$.

Since the **joule** is the basic unit of work and the **second** is the basic unit of time, it would be quite satisfactory to express power in **joules per second.** Expressing power in joules per second automatically calls our attention to the fact that power is the *rate* of doing work. But it was decided to honor James Watt for his work in converting heat energy into mechanical energy with his steam engine by calling the unit of electric power the **watt.** Therefore

The **watt** is the common unit of electric power.

The magnitude of the watt is automatically established in terms of joules and seconds:

**One watt** is the rate of doing work when one joule of work is done in one second.

Expressing this in equation form:

$$P = \frac{W}{t} \tag{4.1}$$

where $P$ is power in watts, $W$ is work in joules, and $t$ is time in seconds. Since the term *watt* does not suggest the idea of *rate* as does the term *joules per second,* we must keep reminding ourselves when calculating power that *watts* are exactly the same as *joules per second* and that *power* is the *rate* of doing work.

EXAMPLE 4: At what rate must electric energy be supplied to the electric hoist in Example 3 if the weight must be raised through 50 ft in 1 min?

*Solution:*

$$P = \frac{W}{t} = \frac{60,000}{60} = 1000 \text{ w} \quad \text{or} \quad 1 \text{ kw}$$

Equation (4.1) is the basic equation which defines power and establishes the magnitude of the watt. But it does not provide the most convenient method of determining power in electric circuits. By means of the following algebraic substitution, we can develop a more useful relationship for calculating electric power:

From the defining Equation (2.2) for potential difference,

$$E = \frac{W}{Q} \quad \therefore \quad W = QE$$

And from the defining Equation (2.1) for current,

$$I = \frac{Q}{t} \quad \therefore \quad t = \frac{Q}{I}$$

Substituting for $W$ and $t$ in Equation (4.1) gives

$$P = \frac{W}{t} = \frac{QE}{Q/I} = QE \times \frac{I}{Q} = E \times I$$

$$\therefore \quad P = EI \tag{4.2}$$

where $P$ is power in watts, $E$ is emf in volts (or $V$ is voltage drop in volts), and $I$ is current in amperes. Also, since $E = IR$ (from Ohm's law Equation 3.2), substituting in Equation (4.2) gives

$$P = IR \times I$$

$$\therefore \quad P = I^2R \tag{4.3}$$

where $P$ is power in watts, $I$ is current through the resistance in amperes, and $R$ is resistance in ohms. And since $I = V/R$ (from Ohm's law Equation 3.2), substituting in Equation (4.2) gives

$$P = \frac{V^2}{R} \tag{4.4}$$

where $P$ is power in watts, $V$ is voltage drop across the resistance in volts, and $R$ is resistance in ohms.

EXAMPLE 5: A lamp draws a 2 amp current when connected to a 120 v source of emf. What is the power rating of the lamp?

*Solution:*

$$P = EI = 120 \times 2 = 240 \text{ w}$$

EXAMPLE 6: A 10 kilohm resistor is connected into a circuit where the current through it is 50 ma. What is the minimum safe power rating for a resistor to be used in this circuit?

*Solution:*

$$P = I^2R = 0.05 \times 0.05 \times 10{,}000 = 25 \text{ w}$$

*Note:* Since the current is **squared,** it is very important to change milliamperes into the basic unit, **amperes,** before carrying out the arithmetic operations.

EXAMPLE 7: What is the highest voltage that can be applied to a 5 kilohm, 2 w resistor without exceeding its heat dissipating capability?

*Solution:*

$$P = \frac{E^2}{R} \quad \therefore \quad E^2 = PR \quad \text{and} \quad E = \sqrt{PR}$$

$$\therefore \quad E = \sqrt{2 \times 5000} = 100 \text{ v}$$

## 5. The Horsepower

Before the invention of the steam engine, many industries used the horse as a source of mechanical energy. Therefore when James Watt tried to sell his steam engine to industry, he had to be able to compare it to the power developed by a horse. By observing an average horse operating a winch for raising water, he established the horsepower (hp) as 33,000 ft-lb of work *per minute*. On this basis he was then able to state the power developed by his steam engine in horsepower. As time went by and the electric motor replaced the steam engine, the same situation prevailed. To sell an electric motor to industry, it was necessary to be able to compare it to the steam engine it was replacing by rating its mechanical power *output* in horsepower.

Since electric motors are still rated in horsepower, we must determine the electrical equivalent of the mechanical horsepower.

Since 1 hp = 33,000 ft-lb per min,

$$\therefore \quad 1 \text{ hp} = \frac{33{,}000}{60} = 550 \text{ ft-lb per sec}$$

And since 1 ft-lb = 1.356 joules,

$$1 \text{ hp} = 550 \times 1.356 = 746 \text{ joules per sec}$$

$$\therefore \quad \textbf{1 hp = 746 w}$$

EXAMPLE 8: What horsepower electric motor is required to raise a 4 ton elevator 120 ft in 1 min?

*Note:* Electric motors are rated in terms of their mechanical power **output.**

*Solution:*

$$W = 120 \times 4 \times 2000 = 960{,}000 \text{ ft-lb}$$

$$P = 960{,}000 \text{ ft-lb per min}$$

$$\therefore \quad P = \frac{960{,}000}{33{,}000} = 29.09 \text{ hp}$$

EXAMPLE 9: If the motor in Example 8 has an efficiency of 90%, at what rate must electric energy be supplied to the motor?

*Solution:*

Power output, $P = 29.09 \times 746 = 21{,}700$ w

Power input, $P = \dfrac{21{,}700}{0.9} = 24{,}110$ w, or 24.11 kw

*Note:* Efficiency can also be treated as the ratio of **power** output to **power** input.

## 6. The Kilowatt-hour

If we examine the answers to the examples we have worked out in this chapter, we will note that a comparatively small amount of work results in a large numerical value when the answer is expressed in joules. Therefore the *basic* unit of electric energy, the *joule*, is considered to be too small a unit for practical purposes such as computing a monthly electric power bill. We can develop a more practical unit for electric energy by transposing the basic equation for power:

Since $\qquad P = \dfrac{W}{t} \quad \therefore \quad W = Pt$

If $P$ is power in *watts* and $t$ is time in *seconds*, then $W$ must be work in *watt-seconds* or *joules*.

But if $P$ is power in *kilowatts* and $t$ is time in *hours*, then $W$ must be work in *kilowatt-hours*.

*Note*: Kilowatt-hours = kilowatts **times** hours (not kilowatts/hour).

The **kilowatt-hour** is the practical unit of electric work or energy.

The kilowatt-hour is defined by the equation

$$W = Pt \tag{4.5}$$

where $W$ is work or energy in kilowatt-hours, $P$ is power in kilowatts, and $t$ is time in hours.

Since 1 kw = 1000 w   and   1 hr = 3600 sec,

$$1 \text{ kwhr} = 1000 \times 3600 = 3.6 \times 10^6 \text{ joules.}$$

EXAMPLE 10: At 2¢ per kwhr, how much will it cost to leave a 60 w lamp burning for 5 days?

*Solution:*

$$W = Pt = 0.06 \times (24 \times 5) = 7.2 \text{ kwhr}$$
$$\text{Cost} = 7.2 \times 2 = 14.4\cancel{c}$$

## 7. Interrelationship of Basic Electrical Units

If we gather together all the basic equations which define the basic electrical units which we have discussed so far, we will find that if we know three such circuit parameters as voltage, current, and elapsed time, we can determine any of the other parameters such as resistance, work, and power. This is achieved by a process of algebraic substitution in the defining equations as we did to develop a practical equation for power. Table II shows some of the more useful derived equations. The student should derive each of the equations shown in this table from the basic defining equations as an aid to understanding and remembering the interrelationship among the basic electrical units. It will be noted that not all

**Table II.** INTERRELATIONSHIP OF BASIC ELECTRICAL UNITS

| Function | Defining Equation | Useful Derived Equations | Derivation |
|---|---|---|---|
| Voltage | $E = W/Q$ | $E = IR$ | Transpose equation (3.2) |
|  |  | $E = P/I$ | Transpose equation (4.2) |
|  |  | $E = \sqrt{PR}$ | Transpose equation (4.4) |
| Current | $I = Q/t$ | $I = E/R$ | Transpose equation (3.2) |
|  |  | $I = P/E$ | Transpose equation (4.2) |
|  |  | $I = \sqrt{P/R}$ | Transpose equation (4.3) |
| Resistance | $R = E/I$ | $R = E^2/P$ | Transpose equation (4.4) |
|  |  | $R = P/I^2$ | Transpose equation (4.3) |
| Power | $P = W/t$ | $P = EI$ | Equation (4.2) |
|  |  | $P = I^2R$ | Equation (4.3) |
|  |  | $P = E^2/R$ | Equation (4.4) |
| Work and energy | Unit taken from mechanics | $W = Pt$ | Equation (4.5) |

*Note:* $V$ may be substituted for $E$ in the equations above.

possible combinations are shown. Only those which are useful in solving and understanding electric circuits have been included. The symbol $V$ may be substituted for $E$ in this table where the attention is directed toward voltage drop rather than emf in a particular circuit.

## Problems

1. How many joules of energy are required to raise a 5 ton elevator 150 ft?

2. How many joules of energy are required to pump 500 gal of water to the surface from a well which is 16 ft deep? (1 gal, U.S. liquid measure, of water weighs 8.347 lb.)

3. How many joules of energy are required to raise the temperature of 1 gal of water by 60°F?

4. How many joules of heat energy must be developed by an electric stove to heat 1 qt of water from 68°F to 188°F assuming that the container and radiation account for $\frac{1}{3}$ of the heat energy produced by the stove element?

5. If $2.5 \times 10^6$ joules of electric energy are supplied to the motor operating the elevator in Problem 1, what is the efficiency of the system?

6. With the friction of the pipes and the pump bearings, the over-all efficiency of the pump in Problem 2 is 86%. What mechanical energy is expended in raising the 500 gal to the surface?

7. What is the electric power input to the motor in Problems 1 and 5 if the elevator is raised the 150 ft in 15 sec?

8. What mechanical horsepower is required to raise the elevator in Problem 7?

9. What horsepower motor is required to operate the pump in Problem 6 if water is to be pumped at the rate of 1000 gal per hour?

10. How long would it take a $\frac{1}{3}$ hp motor to raise the 500 gal of water in Problem 6?

11. How long will it take to raise the temperature of 1 gal of water by 60°F if energy is imparted to the water at the rate of 1 kw?

12. What power rating must the stove element in Problem 4 have if the temperature of the quart of water is to be raised from 68°F to 188°F in 4 min?

13. What is the power rating of a toaster which draws a 5 amp current from a 120 v source of emf?

14. What is the power rating of a soldering iron which has a 110 v drop between its terminals when the current through it is 1.2 amp?

15. At what rate is electric energy converted into heat in the heater of a vacuum tube that is rated at 6.3 v, 0.6 amp?

16. A 4 ma screen grid current through a screen grid dropping resistor causes a voltage drop across the resistor of 120 v. What is the minimum "wattage" rating this resistor must have?

17. At what rate must a 75 ohm resistor be able to dissipate heat if the current through it is 2.5 amp?

18. At what rate must a resistor convert electric energy into heat if 6000 joules of heat are produced in 10 min?

19. What power rating must a 100 ohm resistor have to pass a current of 20 ma without overheating?

20. What wattage rating must a 10 kilohm resistor have to safely pass a current of 250 ma?

21. What wattage rating would you select for a 560 ohm cathode bias resistor which has to pass a current of 36 ma?

22. At what rate is electric energy being converted into heat in a 1.5 ohm motor starting resistor when the starting current through it is 60 amp?

23. The armature winding of an electric motor has a resistance of 0.2 ohm. At what rate is electric energy being used up by this particular motor loss when the armature current is 40 amp?

24. How many Btu of heat are produced in the motor winding in Problem 23 in one hour?

25. What is the maximum current that a 20 kilohm, 10 w resistor can handle without overheating?

26. What is the maximum emf that can be safely applied to the resistor in Problem 25?

27. What voltage drop will there be across a 1 kw stove element whose resistance when hot is 40 ohms?

28. What voltage drop will there be across a 75 ohm, 3 w Christmas tree lamp?

29. A certain voltmeter has a resistance of 150 kilohms. While it is measuring a source of emf, it draws energy from the source at the rate of 96 mw. What is the emf of the source?

30. If the 600 ma heater of a "series string" television tube must produce heat at the rate of 3 w, what is the voltage drop across the heater?

31. What current will an electric motor draw from a 250 v source if it is developing mechanical energy at the rate of 5 hp at 90% efficiency?

32. What mechanical work can be done by a 75% efficient electric motor drawing 2 amp from a 120 v source for 8 hr?

33. What is the minimum value of resistance that can be placed across the terminals of a 120 v source of emf if the power drawn from the source is not to exceed 0.48 kw?

34. An electric heater produces heat at the rate of 50 Btu per min when the current through it is 10 amp. What is its resistance?

35. What is the total rate of energy conversion into heat in a triode vacuum tube if the heater is rated at 0.3 amp, 6.3 v and the plate current is 20 ma when the plate to cathode voltage is 200 v?

36. In an automobile electric system, the following devices are simultaneously drawing energy from the storage battery whose emf is 6.0 v: (a) two 6 w tail light lamps; (b) two parking lamps with a hot resistance of 12 ohms each; (c) a radio drawing a 6.0 amp current; and (d) the heater fan motor which develops $\frac{1}{20}$ hp at 80% efficiency. What is the total rate at which the battery is supplying electric energy?

37. How much electric energy is used by a 750 w water heater in 24 hr?

38. If the over-all efficiency of a radio transmitter is 48%, how much electric energy is required to produce a power output of 50 kw from 7:00 A.M. to midnight?

39. How much will it cost to operate a 4000 ohm electric clock from a 110 v power line for one year if electric energy costs $2\frac{1}{2}$¢ per kwhr?

40. How much electric energy did Mr. Jones use in May if:
    (a) Electric energy costs 3¢ per kwhr.
    (b) The meter reading at the end of May was 574,267 kwhr.
    (c) He receives a bill from the power company every two months.
    (d) The meter reading at the end of February was 573,067 kwhr.
    (e) His bill for March and April was $24.00.

## Review Questions

1. What is the distinction between *work* and *energy?*
2. Why is the joule not commonly used in calculating electric energy?
3. What is the significance of the unit *watt-second* found in some textbooks?
4. Why is the amount of energy represented by a joule quite small?
5. Why is the joule used as the basic unit for electric energy even though it is not used in practice?
6. Why would a 5 hp motor with a 90% efficiency be physically smaller than a 5 hp motor with a 60% efficiency?
7. Why is it possible to express efficiency in terms of the ratio of output *power* to input *power* even though efficiency is defined as the ratio of output *energy* to input *energy?*
8. Why must electric kettles be equipped with thermostatic switches to open the circuit when the kettle boils dry?
9. Some small heaters consist of an electric heating coil and a small fan. It is noted that the heating element is brighter when the fan is turned off. Explain.
10. Is the heater coil in Question 9 drawing more current when the fan is turned off? Explain.
11. How would you apply the observations of Question 9 to the miniaturization of an aircraft radio?
12. Two 1000 ohm resistors are wound from Nichrome wire on ceramic tubes. One is rated at 5 w and the other at 50 w. Compare the two resistors for conductor size, over-all dimensions, and temperature at rated dissipation.
13. A 35 w soldering iron is used to solder miniature radio components, whereas a 150 w iron is needed to solder a lead to the radio chassis. Explain. What would be the effect of using the 150 w iron on the miniature components?
14. Why can power be expressed in terms of voltage and resistance when power is a *rate* unit but neither voltage nor resistance are?
15. Why is it customary to find larger electric motors used on passenger elevators than freight elevators although the freight elevators are the heavier?
16. What is wrong with the wording of the question: "How much power is consumed by a toaster drawing 3 amp from a 110 v source of emf?"

17. What is wrong with the wording of the question: "How many Btu are there in a horsepower?"

18. Starting with the conversion factor for foot-pounds to joules, find the number of horsepower equivalent to a kilowatt.

## Review Problems: Interrelationship of Basic Electrical Units

*Note:* The purpose of these short drill problems is to help the student to recognize the relationships that must exist among the basic electrical units. At the same time, solving for the numerical relationships provides drill in the use of the slide rule. Each of these problems should be solved by the method outlined with Example 2 in Chapter 2. These problems should be attempted without constant reference to Table II of Chapter 4.

41. What voltage drop is produced across a 42 ohm resistor by a 2.4 amp current through it?

42. At what rate is electric energy converted into heat in the resistor in Problem 41?

43. How long will it take the resistor in Problem 41 to convert 2 kwhr of energy?

44. What emf must be applied to a 34 ohm resistor to make it dissipate energy at the rate of 180 w?

45. What is the power rating of a 72 ohm heater which passes a 6 amp current?

46. How long will it take the heater in Problem 45 to consume 9400 joules of electric energy?

47. How many coulombs of electrons pass through the heater in Problem 46?

48. What current is flowing in a 17 ohm resistor while it is dissipating energy at the rate of 520 w?

49. What is the resistance of a load which draws 1.4 amp from a 24 v source?

50. What current will a 40 w lamp draw from a 117 v source?

51. What resistance will dissipate energy at the rate of 50 w when connected to a 110 v source?

52. What voltage must be applied to a 555 w heater to make it pass a 12 amp current?

53. What current will a 45 ohm resistor pass while it is producing heat at the rate of $\frac{1}{2}$ hp?

54. What voltage must be applied to a 27 ohm resistor to make it convert $1\frac{1}{2}$ kwhr in 7 hr?

55. What is the efficiency of a motor with a 1 kw input and a 1 hp output?

56. What voltage drop is created by a 6.8 ma plate current flowing through a 27 kilohm plate load resistor?

57. What voltage is developed across a 300 ohm resistance by a power input to the resistance of 50 $\mu$w?

58. What value of cathode resistance is required to obtain a voltage drop of 7 v when the cathode current is 18 ma?

59. What power rating must the resistor in Problem 58 have?

60. What current will flow when a 20 $\mu$v signal is applied to a 75 ohm load?

61. What power is fed to the load in Problem 60?

62. What current will a 4 kw load draw from a 220 v source?

63. If an automobile starter motor develops $1\frac{1}{4}$ hp at 80% efficiency, what current does it draw from a 12 v battery?

64. How much work can a fully charged 12 v storage battery accomplish if it is rated at 80 ampere-hours?

65. What is the resistance of a voltmeter which reads 120 v when it has a 40$\mu$a current passing through it?

66. How long will it take for 2.8 coulombs of electrons to pass through the meter in Problem 65?

67. What is the resistance of the copper bus bars feeding an aluminum refining cell if a 4000 amp current through them causes a 620 mv drop across them?

68. How much electric energy is lost as heat in the bus bars of Problem 67 in 8 hr?

69. What is the resistance of an ammeter shunt if it is designed to have a 5 mv drop across it with a 9.99 amp current through it?

70. What must be the resistance of a 15 amp fuse if heat must be developed at the rate of 4.3 w to melt it?

Chapter 5

# SERIES AND PARALLEL
# RESISTANCES

~~~~~~~~~~~~~~~~~~~~~~~~~~~~~~~~~~~~~~~~~~~~~~~~~~~~~~~~~~~~~

### *1. Resistances in Series*

In the last two chapters we have been treating electric current as a numerical quantity expressed in amperes. At this point we should remind ourselves that current is defined as the *rate of flow* of the electric medium. The flow of the electric medium consists of free electrons moving through the circuit under the pressure produced by a source of emf. Keeping this in mind as we examine the simple series circuit of Fig. 5.1, another part of Ohm's law becomes apparent.

The **current** must be the same in all parts of a simple electric circuit.

Common sense tells us that there cannot be more electrons entering $R_1$ per second than leave $R_1$ in a second. Nor can more electrons enter $R_1$ per

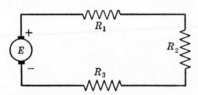

**Fig. 5.1.** A simple series circuit.

second than leave $R_2$ in the same period of time. Similarly the same number of electrons must pass through the source of emf or generator per second as pass through any other part of the series circuit in the same time interval. Since *electrons per second* can be expressed in *amperes*, the same current flows through all components of the simple series circuit of Fig. 5.1.

Since the truth of this statement is quite evident once we understand what constitutes an electric current, Ohm seldom receives credit nowadays for having been the first person to state this truth as a basic law of electric circuits. Since current is the same through all components in series, it becomes a convenient common denominator for dealing with series circuits. All characteristics of series circuits are based on the current being common to all components, beginning with the definition of a series circuit.

> Two or more electric components are considered to be **in series** if the *same* current flows through all these components.

Since the current in a series circuit is common to all components, it is not necessary to use any subscript with the letter symbol $I$ for the circuit of Fig. 5.1. Here $I$ represents the current through $R_1$, $R_2$, and $R_3$, and also the current through the source of emf and the wire connecting the components together.

In Chapter 3, we decided that current in simple electric circuits is a *dependent* variable. It depends on what emf is applied to the circuit and the total resistance of the circuit. Therefore in solving the simple series circuit of Fig. 5.1, we must be able to determine the total resistance of the circuit. Suppose that resistor $R_1$ is constructed of 20 ft of No. 20 AWG Nichrome wire, resistor $R_2$ is made from 10 ft of the same wire, and $R_3$ consists of 30 ft of the same resistance wire. Therefore for an electron to travel around the circuit from one terminal of the generator to the other, it must travel through $20 + 10 + 30 = 60$ ft of Nichrome wire. Since the resistance of an electric conductor is directly proportional to its length, and since the total length of resistance wire used in this example is the sum of the individual lengths, it follows that the total resistance of this circuit will be the sum of the individual resistances. Therefore

The **total resistance** of a series circuit is

$$R_T = R_1 + R_2 + R_3 + \text{etc.} \tag{5.1}$$

Once the total resistance of a series circuit has been determined, the common current on which all the characteristics of a series circuit are based can then be solved for by Ohm's law: $I = E/R_T$.

> EXAMPLE 1: What current will flow in a series circuit consisting of a 20 ohm, 10 ohm, and 30 ohm resistors connected to a 45 v source of emf?
>
> *Solution:*
> $$R_T = R_1 + R_2 + R_3 = 20 + 10 + 30 = 60 \text{ ohms}$$
> $$I = \frac{E}{R_T} = \frac{45}{60} = 0.75 \text{ amp}$$

As far as the source of emf is concerned, the current drawn from it will be exactly the same for a single 60 ohm resistor connected to its terminals as for the 20 ohms, 10 ohms, and 30 ohms in series. Therefore, if it will aid in solving a circuit,

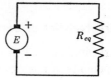

**Fig. 5.2.** Equivalent circuit of Fig. 5.1.

the total resistance may be thought of as being replaced by a single *equivalent* resistance ($R_{eq}$) and the circuit of Fig. 5.2 becomes the *equiva-*

*lent circuit* of the original circuit of Fig. 5.1. The solution we have used for Example 1 consists of reducing the original series circuit to a simple equivalent circuit and then solving for current by Ohm's law.

## 2. Kirchhoff's Voltage Law

Since the rules of algebra allow us to multiply both sides of an equation by the same quantity without changing the equality of the statement, let us multiply both sides of Equation (5.1) by $I$.

$$\therefore \quad IR_T = IR_1 + IR_2 + IR_3 + \text{etc.}$$

Since $\qquad I = \dfrac{E}{R_T} \qquad \therefore \quad IR_T = E \text{ (the applied emf)}$

and $\qquad IR_1 = V_1 \text{ (the voltage drop across resistor } R_1\text{)}$

$$\therefore \quad E = V_1 + V_2 + V_3 + \text{etc.} \tag{5.2}$$

Therefore in the series circuit, the sum of all of the voltage drops across the individual resistances must equal the applied emf.

Gustav Kirchhoff discovered that this applied to any complete electric circuit, whether a simple series circuit as in Fig. 5.1 or one loop of an elaborate network. This is known as Kirchhoff's voltage law and may be stated thus:

**Kirchhoff's voltage law:** In any complete electric circuit, the algebraic sum of the emf's must equal the algebraic sum of the voltage drops.

Kirchhoff's voltage law provides us with an alternate solution to Example 1. In this case the numerical work is essentially the same but only one step is involved as compared with the first method in which the first step was to replace the three separate resistances with a single equivalent resistance.

EXAMPLE 1A: What current will flow in a series circuit consisting of 20 ohm, 10 ohm, and 30 ohm resistances connected to a 45 v source of emf?

*Solution:*

$$E = IR_1 + IR_2 + IR_3$$
$$45 = 20I + 10I + 30I = 60I$$
$$\therefore \quad I = \frac{45}{60} = 0.75 \text{ amp}$$

## 3. Characteristics of Series Circuits

From Ohm's law, $I = V_1/R_1$ and since the current is the *same* through all components of a series circuit,

$$I = \frac{V_1}{R_1} = \frac{V_2}{R_2} = \frac{V_3}{R_3} = \frac{E}{R_T}$$

Taking any pair of these equal terms, e.g., $V_1/R_1 = V_2/R_2$, transposing gives $V_1/V_2 = R_1/R_2$. From this it follows that, in a series circuit, the ratio between any two voltage drops is the same as the ratio of the two resistances across which these voltage drops occur.

This knowledge is useful in solving for some specific information about a circuit without having to complete a detailed solution of the whole circuit.

EXAMPLE 2: A 20 kilohm resistor and a 15 kilohm resistor are connected in series to a 140 v source. What is the voltage drop across the 15 kilohm resistor?

*Note:* There is less chance of making an error in the solution of an electric circuit if as the first step in any solution we draw a fully labeled schematic diagram to work from.

*Long solution:*

$$R_T = R_1 + R_2 = 20 + 15 = 35 \text{ kilohms}$$

$$I = \frac{E}{R_T} = \frac{140}{35,000} = 0.004 \text{ amp} = 4 \text{ ma}$$

$$V_2 = IR_2 = 4 \times 10^{-3} \times 15 \times 10^3 = 60 \text{ v}$$

*Short solution:*

$$\frac{V_2}{E} = \frac{R_2}{R_T} \qquad \therefore \quad V_2 = E\frac{R_2}{R_T} = 140 \times \frac{15,000}{35,000} = 60 \text{ v}$$

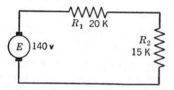     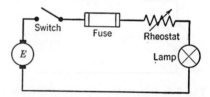

**Fig. 5.3.** Circuit diagram for Example 2.*     **Fig. 5.4.** Control components in series with a load.

Another characteristic of a series circuit that is based on the *same* current flowing through all components is that any change to *one* component of a series circuit will have an effect on the current through *all* of the components. Therefore such *control* components as switches to turn the current on and off, fuses to open the circuit if the current becomes excessive, and variable resistors (rheostats) to control the magnitude of the current must be connected in *series* with a load as in Fig. 5.4.

In order to be able to distinguish readily between series and parallel circuit characteristics, we must be thoroughly familiar with the characteristics of series circuits which we have just developed. Therefore we shall summarize these characteristics as follows:

1. The *current* is the same in all parts of a series circuit.
2. The *total resistance* is the sum of all the individual resistances.
   $$R_T = R_1 + R_2 + R_3 + \text{etc.}$$

* Although we prefer not to abbreviate *ohms* and *kilohms* in examples and problems, it is customary to use the Greek letter Ω (omega) as an abbreviation for *ohms* and the upper case letter K as an abbreviation for *kilohms* in schematic diagrams.

3. The applied emf is equal to the sum of all the individual voltage drops. $E = V_1 + V_2 + V_3 +$ etc.
4. The *ratio* between voltages is the same as the resistance ratio.
5. Any change to *any* component of a series circuit will affect the current through *all* components.

## 4. Internal Resistance

Up to this point we have not considered the possibility that the terminal voltage available from a practical source of emf such as a battery or a generator might change as the current drawn from the source changes. In many cases the change is so slight that it can be neglected. But in other cases, particularly in electronic circuits, the decrease in the terminal voltage of a source of emf as the current through it increases must be taken into consideration. An example of this change in terminal voltage is the way automobile headlights dim when the starter motor is drawing current from the car battery.

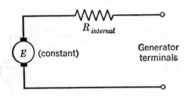

**Fig. 5.5.** Schematic representation of a practical source of emf.

A convenient way of representing this effect is to assume that the *practical* source of emf consists of (1) an *ideal* source which develops a constant emf at any current, and (2) a resistance connected in series with this ideal source and the actual terminals of the source as shown in Fig. 5.5. This resistance is known as the **internal resistance** of the source. In addition to causing the terminal voltage to drop as the current increases, this internal resistance can be used to calculate the loss of electric energy through conversion into heat within the practical generator.

If we can measure the voltage at the terminals of the practical generator without drawing any current from the source, there will be no voltage drop across the internal resistance (since $V_{int} = IR_{int}$ and $I =$ zero). Therefore the terminal voltage under these conditions is equal to the constant emf generated by the ideal source portion of the practical generator. From the method just described for determining the emf of the ideal source, this emf is referred to as the **open circuit voltage** of the source. The manner in which the internal resistance of a practical generator can be determined is illustrated by the following example.

EXAMPLE 3: When a voltmeter which draws negligible current is the only circuit connected to the terminals of a battery, it reads 6.0 v. When a 5 ohm resistor is connected to the battery terminals, the voltmeter reads 5.0 v. What is the internal resistance of the battery?

*Solution:* Since the open circuit voltage is 6.0 v, the voltage of the ideal source

(Fig. 5.6) is 6.0 v. And since the voltage drop across the 5 ohm load is 5.0 v, according to Kirchhoff's voltage law, the voltage drop across the internal resistance is

$$E = V_{int} + V_{load}$$

$$\therefore \quad V_{int} = E - V_{load} = 6.0 - 5.0 = 1.0 \text{ v}$$

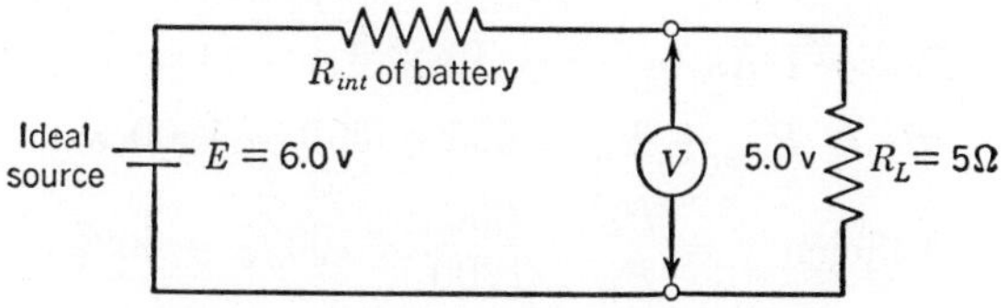

**Fig. 5.6.** Circuit diagram for Example 3.

From Ohm's law, the current in the circuit with the 5 ohm resistor connected is

$$I = \frac{V_L}{R_L} = \frac{5.0}{5} = 1 \text{ amp}$$

$$\therefore \quad R_{int} = \frac{V_{int}}{I} = \frac{1.0}{1} = 1 \text{ ohm}$$

*Alternate solution:*

$$\frac{R_{int}}{R_L} = \frac{V_{int}}{V_L}$$

$$\therefore \quad R_{int} = R_L \frac{V_{int}}{V_L} = 5 \times \frac{1}{5} = 1 \text{ ohm}$$

As we noted at the beginning of this section, in many practical sources of emf the effect of internal resistance is negligible. Therefore in solving the problems in this text, we shall consider the internal resistance of the source to be zero ohms if no specific value is stated.

## 5. Maximum Power Transfer

One effect of internal resistance in a source of emf is a decrease in generator terminal voltage as the current drawn from the source is increased. In order to determine what other effects internal resistance may have on electric circuit behavior, we can substitute various values of load resistance in the circuit of

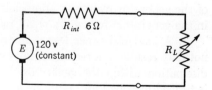

**Fig. 5.7.** Circuit diagram for Table I.

Fig. 5.7. The internal resistance remains constant for any value of load resistance. The calculations for one particular value of load resistance ($R_L = 6$ ohms) are as follows:

$$R_T = R_{int} + R_L = 6 + 6 = 12 \text{ ohms}$$

$$I = \frac{E}{R_T} = \frac{120}{12} = 10 \text{ amp}$$

$$V_L = IR_L = 10 \times 6 = 60 \text{ v}$$

$$P_L = I^2 R_L = 10 \times 10 \times 6 = 600 \text{ w}$$

$$P_{int} = I^2 R_{int} = 10 \times 10 \times 6 = 600 \text{ w}$$

$$P_T = P_{int} + P_L = 600 + 600 = 1200 \text{ w}$$

$$\text{Efficiency} = \frac{P_L}{P_T} = \frac{600}{1200} \times 100\% = 50\%$$

**Table I.** Effect of Connecting Various Load Resistances
to a Practical Generator

| $R_L$ | $R_{int}$ | $R_T$ | $I$ | $V_L$ | $P_L$ | $P_{int}$ | $P_T$ | % Eff. |
|---|---|---|---|---|---|---|---|---|
| | | $R_L + R_{int}$ | $E/R_T$ | $IR_L$ | $I^2R_L$ | $I^2R_{int}$ | $P_L + P_{int}$ | $P_L/P_T$ |
| 0 ohms | 6 ohms | 6 ohms | 20  amp | 0 v | 0 w | 2400 w | 2400 w | 0% |
| 2 | 6 | 8 | 15 | 30 | 450 | 1350 | 1800 | 25 |
| 3 | 6 | 9 | 13.3 | 40 | 533 | 1067 | 1600 | 33.3 |
| 6 | 6 | 12 | 10 | 60 | 600 | 600 | 1200 | 50 |
| 12 | 6 | 18 | 6.7 | 80 | 533 | 267 | 800 | 66.7 |
| 18 | 6 | 24 | 5 | 90 | 450 | 150 | 600 | 75 |
| ∞ | 6 | ∞ | 0 | 120 | 0 | 0 | 0 | 100 |

Table I contains the data we calculated for the circuit of Fig. 5.7 with a 6 ohm load resistance along with similar data for other values of load resistance. If we examine this data carefully we will find:

1. Maximum power output (into the load) is obtained when the load resistance is equal to the internal resistance of the generator. The efficiency under this condition is 50%.

2. A load resistance of from two to three times the internal resistance of the generator results in appreciable reduction in wasted power (as heat in the generator) for only a small reduction in power output.

3. A load resistance less than the internal resistance of the generator not only results in a reduction in power output but also causes a very high dissipation within the generator. In practice, this condition of operation is termed **overload** and must be avoided.

4. If we are interested more in *voltage* output than power output, (as in vacuum tube voltage amplifiers) the load resistance should be high in comparison to the internal resistance of the source. ($R_L \cong 5 \times R_{int}$)

5. Since $I = P/V$ and since $I$ is common, $P_T/E = P_L/V_L$; therefore $V_L/E = P_L/P_T$, and the terminal voltage is the same percentage of the open-circuit voltage as the percentage efficiency.

6. Similarly, since $I^2 = P/R$, then $P_T/R_T = P_L/R_L$, and therefore $R_L/R_T = P_L/P_T$ and the load resistance is the same percentage of the total resistance as the percentage efficiency.

## 6. Resistances in Parallel—Kirchhoff's Current Law

In dealing with parallel (or shunt) connected resistances, we will find a set of characteristics which in many respects are similar but opposite to those of series circuits. If we trace out the current flow in the simple parallel circuit of Fig. 5.8,* we will find that each of the resistors is connected directly across the generator terminals. Therefore $V_1 = V_2 = V_3 = E$. Since this voltage is common to all components in parallel, the subscript may be omitted. In keeping with our definition of a series circuit, we may define a parallel circuit thus:

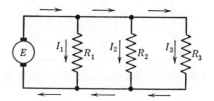

**Fig. 5.8.** A simple parallel circuit.

Two or more electric components are considered to be in **parallel** if the *same* voltage appears across all these components.

In solving the series circuit, we determined the total resistance in order to find the current in the circuit. In the **total current method** of solving parallel circuits, the steps are reversed. If we are given the emf of the source (assuming negligible internal resistance) and the values of each resistance in the circuit of Fig. 5.8, we can solve for the current in each branch as an individual circuit using Ohm's law. If we think of the current in each branch in terms of electrons per second flowing through the branch, it is apparent that the generator current must be the sum of the branch currents. Therefore in a simple parallel circuit,

$$I_T = I_1 + I_2 + I_3 + \text{etc.} \tag{5.3}$$

EXAMPLE 4: With reference to Fig. 5.8, $R_1$ is 40 ohms, $R_2$ is 30 ohms, $R_3$ is 20 ohms, and $E$ is 120 v. What single resistance would draw the same current from the source?

*Solution:*

$$I_1 = \frac{V_1}{R_1} = \frac{120}{40} = 3 \text{ amp}$$

$$I_2 = \frac{V_2}{R_2} = \frac{120}{30} = 4 \text{ amp}$$

* In working with circuits in which there is more than one path for current, it will help us to keep track of the various **branch** currents if we mark current direction on the schematic diagram with arrows. Note that we prefer to use the *conventional* current direction for this purpose.

$$I_3 = \frac{V_3}{R_3} = \frac{120}{20} = 6 \text{ amp}$$

$$I_T = I_1 + I_2 + I_3 = 3 + 4 + 6 = 13 \text{ amp}$$

$$\therefore \quad R_{eq} = \frac{E}{I_T} = \frac{120}{13} = 9.23 \text{ ohms}$$

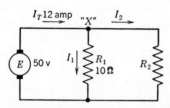

**Fig. 5.9.** Circuit diagram for Example 5.

Kirchhoff applied the total current principle of Equation (5.3), to any electric circuit, in the form of

**Kirchhoff's current law:** At any junction point in an electric circuit, the algebraic sum of the currents entering the point must equal the algebraic sum of the currents leaving the point.

EXAMPLE 5: What current is flowing in the $R_2$ branch of the circuit of Fig. 5.9?
*Solution:*

$$I_1 = \frac{V}{R_1} = \frac{50}{10} = 5 \text{ amp}$$

The current flowing into junction $X$ is $I_T$ and the currents flowing away from junction $X$ are $I_1$ and $I_2$. Therefore

$$I_T = I_1 + I_2 \quad \text{or} \quad I_2 = I_T - I_1$$

$$\therefore \quad I_2 = 12 - 5 = 7 \text{ amp}$$

## 7. Conductance

As the results in Examples 4 and 5 indicate, the total current must always be greater than the current through any branch of a parallel circuit. Therefore the equivalent resistance must always be *less* than the smallest of the branch resistances. Continuing this line of thought, the *more* resistors we place in parallel, the *smaller* the total resistance becomes. We will be able to appreciate the behavior of parallel circuits more readily if we turn our attention away from resistance and restate the above remark thus: The more resistors we place in parallel, the more readily the circuit can pass current since there are more parallel branches for current to flow through. Therefore, since resistance is a measure of the ability of a circuit to *oppose* the flow of current,

**Conductance** is a measure of the ability of an electric circuit to *pass* current. The letter symbol for **conductance** is $G$.

The **mho** (ohm spelled backward) is the basic unit of conductance.

Since conductance is simply the reciprocal point of view to resistance, the size of the mho can be defined by the equation

$$G = \frac{1}{R} \tag{5.4}$$

where $G$ is conductance of a circuit in mhos and $R$ is the resistance of the same circuit in ohms.

When we are given the voltage across a group of parallel branches, the total current method described in the preceding section is a convenient method of solving parallel circuits. Even if this voltage is not known, we can assume a suitable voltage in order to solve for the equivalent resistance. But in this case the concept of conductance offers a more straightforward approach to the solution of parallel circuits. If we divide both sides of Equation (5.3) by $E$ (or $V$ since they are the same for simple parallel circuits), we get

$$\frac{I_T}{E} = \frac{I_1}{V} + \frac{I_2}{V} + \frac{I_3}{V} + \text{etc.}$$

But $R = V/I$, and since $G = 1/R$, $G = I/V$

$$\therefore \quad G_T = G_1 + G_2 + G_3 + \text{etc.} \tag{5.5}$$

Therefore in parallel circuits, the total conductance is equal to the sum of the conductances of all the individual branches. Having determined the total conductance, the equivalent resistance is simply $R_{eq} = 1/G_T$.

EXAMPLE 4A: With reference to Fig. 5.8, $R_1$ is 40 ohms, $R_2$ is 30 ohms, and $R_3$ is 20 ohms. What single resistance would draw the same current from the source?

Solution:

$$G_T = G_1 + G_2 + G_3 = \frac{1}{40} + \frac{1}{30} + \frac{1}{20}$$

$$= 0.025 + 0.033 + 0.05 = 0.108 \text{ mho}$$

$$\therefore \quad R_{eq} = \frac{1}{G_T} = \frac{1}{0.108} = 9.25 \text{ ohms}$$

When only *two* resistances in parallel are involved, Equation (5.5) can be reduced to a convenient form for determining the equivalent resistance directly.

$$G_T = G_1 + G_2 = \frac{1}{R_1} + \frac{1}{R_2} = \frac{(R_1 + R_2)}{R_1 R_2}$$

$$\therefore \quad R_{eq} = \frac{R_1 R_2}{(R_1 + R_2)} \tag{5.6}$$

Therefore for *two* resistances in parallel, the equivalent resistance equals their product over their sum. This does *not* apply to more than two resistances as can be seen by trying to simplify Equation (5.5) with three or more terms. We must also note that, with the exception of the special case of two resistors in parallel, we have not attempted to set up an over-all equation for the equivalent resistance of parallel resistances. We prefer to treat parallel circuits by switching our thinking from the total resistance idea of series circuits to the total conductance concept for parallel circuits.

EXAMPLE 6: What is the equivalent resistance of a 1 kilohm and a 4 kilohm resistor in parallel?

*Solution:*

$$R_{eq} = \frac{R_1 R_2}{R_1 + R_2} = \frac{1000 \times 4000}{1000 + 4000} = \frac{4,000,000}{5000} = 800 \text{ ohms}$$

## 8. Conductivity

Resistivity was defined as a property of a conducting *material*, being the resistance of a unit length and cross section conductor of that material. Similarly then,

> The **conductivity** of a material is the conductance of a unit length and cross section conductor of that material. The letter symbol for **conductivity** is the Greek letter $\sigma$ (sigma).

Since conductance is the reciprocal of resistance, conductivity is the reciprocal of resistivity. Therefore

$$\sigma = \frac{1}{\rho} \tag{5.7}$$

Conductivity is expressed in **mhos per meter** or **mhos per mil-foot.**

## 9. Characteristics of Parallel Circuits

From Ohm's law, $V = IR$ and since $R = 1/G$, $V = I/G$, and since the voltage is the *same* across all components of a parallel circuit,

$$V = \frac{I_1}{G_1} = \frac{I_2}{G_2} = \frac{I_3}{G_3} = \frac{I_T}{G_T}$$

Taking any pair of these equal terms, e.g., $I_1/G_1 = I_2/G_2$ and transposing gives $I_1/I_2 = G_1/G_2 = R_2/R_1$. From this it follows that

In a **parallel circuit,** the ratio between any two branch currents is the *same* as the ratio of their conductances or the *inverse* of their resistance ratio.

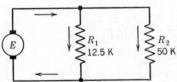

Fig. 5.10. Circuit diagram for Example 7.

EXAMPLE 7: The total current drawn by a 12.5 kilohm resistor ($R_1$) and a 50 kilohm resistor ($R_2$) in parallel is 15 ma. What is the current through the 50 kilohm resistor?

*Solution 1:*

$$I_1 + I_2 = 15 \text{ ma}$$

$$\frac{I_1}{I_2} = \frac{R_2}{R_1} = \frac{50,000}{12,500} = \frac{4}{1} \quad \therefore \quad I_1 = 4I_2$$

Substituting this value of $I_1$ in the first equation gives

$$4I_2 + I_2 = 15 \text{ ma} \quad \therefore \quad I_2 = \frac{15}{5} = 3 \text{ ma}$$

*Solution 2:*

$$R_{eq} = \frac{R_1 R_2}{R_1 + R_2} = \frac{12,500 \times 50,000}{12,500 + 50,000} = 10 \text{ kilohms}$$

$$V = I_T R_{eq} = 0.015 \times 10,000 = 150 \text{ v}$$

$$\therefore \quad I_2 = \frac{V}{R_2} = \frac{150}{50,000} = 3 \text{ ma}$$

*Note*: There is more than one way of solving most electric circuit problems. Although it is wise to try to understand the various methods, the student should select the method by which he can visualize what each step represents. It is much better to achieve accurate results by a longer method than to make an error in a short cut through not appreciating the significance of each step of the solution.

Another characteristic of parallel circuits is based on the internal resistance of the source of emf being negligible. If such is the case, altering the resistance of one branch will not affect the voltage across the other branches, and therefore will not affect the current through the other branches. Therefore changes in one branch of a parallel circuit have negligible effect on the other branches. In house wiring, each lighting circuit is connected in parallel with the others to the 117 v source of emf so that switching one circuit on or off does not affect the operation of the other circuits.

The characteristics of parallel circuits may be summarized as follows:

1. The *voltage* is the same across all components in a parallel circuit.
2. The *total conductance* is the sum of all the individual branch conductances. $G_T = G_1 + G_2 + G_3 +$ etc.
3. The total *current* is the sum of all the individual branch currents. $I_T = I_1 + I_2 + I_3 +$ etc.
4. The *ratio* between branch currents is the *same* as the conductance ratio and the *inverse* of the resistance ratio.
5. Each branch is essentially independent of any changes in the other branches providing the voltage across the parallel circuit is kept constant.

## 10. Series-Parallel Circuits

So far we have considered only simple series and simple parallel circuits. In practice, electric networks are seldom this simple. If we consider the circuit of Fig. 5.11 as a *whole*, it does not comply with the characteristics of either a series or a parallel circuit. But if we consider only $R_2$ and $R_3$, since they are connected between the same two junction points in the circuit, they will have the *same* voltage across them. Therefore $R_2$ and $R_3$ *do* fill the definition of a parallel circuit. If we are given the values for $R_2$ and $R_3$, we can use the rules of parallel circuits to solve for a single equivalent resistance. As far as the generator is concerned, the circuit of Fig. 5.12 is the same as the original circuit of Fig. 5.11. In Fig. 5.12, $R_1$ is in series with the equivalent resistance of $R_2$ and $R_3$ in parallel. Therefore we can solve the circuit of Fig. 5.12 by the rules of series circuits.

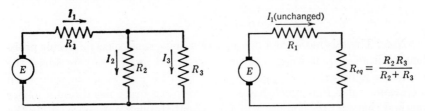

**Fig. 5.11.** A simple series-parallel circuit.     **Fig. 5.12.** Equivalent circuit of Fig. 5.11.

Another arrangement of series-parallel resistances is shown in Fig. 5.13(a). In this case $R_2$ and $R_3$ have the same current through them and therefore are in series and may be replaced by an equivalent resistor as in Fig. 5.13(b) which is equal to $R_2 + R_3$. We can now solve the simplified circuit of Fig. 5.13(b) by the rules for simple parallel circuits.

As these examples show, we may define a series-parallel circuit as one in which some portions of the circuit have the characteristics of simple series circuits and other portions have the characteristics of simple parallel circuits. Whenever two or more components of an electric network are in parallel, all the characteristics of parallel circuits must apply to these components. And whenever two or more components are in series, all the characteristics of series circuits must apply.

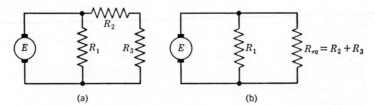

**Fig. 5.13.** (a) A series-parallel circuit; and (b) a simplified version.

Figures 5.12 and 5.13(b) suggest a method whereby some of the simpler series parallel networks may be solved; i.e., by substituting the equivalent resistance for portions of the circuit until the circuit is reduced to a simple series or parallel circuit. To assist in applying the characteristics of series and parallel circuits to resistance networks in general, we shall solve a few examples by completing tables of data similar to Table II in the following example.

EXAMPLE 8: Complete Table II with reference to the circuit diagram of Fig. 5.11.

**Table II**

| Component | Resistance | Voltage | Current | Power |
|:---:|:---:|:---:|:---:|:---:|
| $R_1$ | 12 ohms | | | |
| $R_2$ | 10 ohms | | | |
| $R_3$ | 40 ohms | | | |
| Totals | | 100 v | | |

*Solution:*

*Step I.* Draw a fully labeled schematic diagram for this particular circuit.

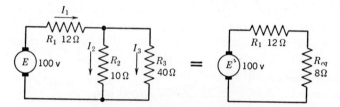

**Fig. 5.14.** Circuit diagram for Example 8.

*Step II.* Visual inspection of Fig. 5.14 shows that $R_2$ and $R_3$ are in parallel.

$$\therefore \quad R_{eq} = \frac{R_2R_3}{R_2 + R_3} = \frac{10 \times 40}{10 + 40} = 8 \text{ ohms}$$

With reference to Fig. 5.14, the total resistance becomes

$$R_T = R_1 + R_{eq} = 12 + 8 = 20 \text{ ohms}$$

Enter this answer in the appropriate blank of Table II.

*Step III.* From Ohm's law,

$$I_T = \frac{E}{R_T} = \frac{100}{20} = 5 \text{ amp}$$

*Step IV.* Since $R_1$ is directly in series with the generator,

$$I_1 = I_T = 5 \text{ amp}$$

*Step V.* From Ohm's law,

$$V_1 = I_1R_1 = 5 \times 12 = 60 \text{ v}$$

*Step VI.* From Kirchhoff's voltage law,

$$V_{eq} = E - V_1 = 100 - 60 = 40 \text{ v}$$

Returning now to the original circuit,

$$V_2 = V_3 = V_{eq} = 40 \text{ v}$$

*Step VII.* From Ohm's law,

$$I_2 = \frac{V_2}{R_2} = \frac{40}{10} = 4 \text{ amp}$$

$$I_3 = \frac{V_3}{R_3} = \frac{40}{40} = 1 \text{ amp}$$

As a check on our calculations, we can note that according to Kirchhoff's current law, $I_1 = I_2 + I_3$ for this circuit, which does check with our calculations.

*Step VIII.* Since $P = VI$,

$$P_1 = V_1 I_1 = \quad 60 \times 5 = 300 \text{ w}$$
$$P_2 = V_2 I_2 = \quad 40 \times 4 = 160 \text{ w}$$
$$P_3 = V_3 I_3 = \quad 40 \times 1 = \quad 40 \text{ w}$$
$$P_T = E I_T = 100 \times 5 = 500 \text{ w}$$

Again as a check, $P_T$ should equal $P_1 + P_2 + P_3$, which does check with our calculations.

Kirchhoff's laws provide us with an alternate method of solving series-parallel circuits, leaving them in their original form without reducing them to a simple series or parallel circuit by substituting "equivalent resistances."

*Kirchhoff's law solution to Example 8*

Referring to Fig. 5.14, from Kirchhoff's current law,

$$I_1 = I_2 + I_3$$

But from Ohm's law, $I_1 = V_1/R_1$ etc.

$$\therefore \quad \frac{V_1}{R_1} = \frac{V_2}{R_2} + \frac{V_3}{R_3} \quad \text{and} \quad \frac{V_1}{12} = \frac{V_2}{10} + \frac{V_3}{40}$$

Since $R_2$ and $R_3$ are in parallel, $V_2 = V_3$, and from Kirchhoff's voltage law,

$$V_2 = V_3 = E - V_1$$

Substituting in the preceding equation,

$$\frac{V_1}{12} = \frac{100 - V_1}{10} + \frac{100 - V_1}{40}$$

Multiplying through by the least common denominator (120) in order to clear the fractions,

$$10V_1 = 1200 - 12V_1 + 300 - 3V_1$$

Collecting the terms gives

$$25V_1 = 1500$$

from which    $V_1 = 60 \text{ v}$

$$\therefore \quad V_2 = V_3 = E - V_1 = 100 - 60 = 40 \text{ v}$$

The various currents may now be determined by Ohm's law: $I_1 = V_1/R_1$ etc.

The information given in Example 8 was such that we had a choice of methods in its solution. However, with the data given for Example 9, we cannot readily solve for the equivalent resistance, which would enable us to simplify the circuit to a simple series circuit. In this case we can again use Kirchhoff's laws to help us to set up algebraic equations from which we can obtain the required data.

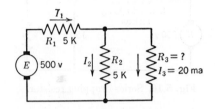

Fig. 5.15. Circuit diagram for Example 9.

EXAMPLE 9: A resistor passing a 20 ma current is in parallel with a 5 kilohm resistor. This combination is in series with another 5 kilohm resistor, the whole network being connected to a 500 v source of emf. What is the resistance of the resistor which is passing the 20 ma current?

*Solution:* From Kirchhoff's voltage law,

$$V_1 + V_2 = E$$

and since $V = IR$,

$$I_1 R_1 + I_2 R_2 = E$$

From Kirchhoff's current law,

$$I_2 = I_1 - 0.02$$

$$\therefore \quad R_1 I_1 + R_2(I_1 - 0.02) = E$$

Substituting given values for $R_1$, $R_2$, and $E$,

$$5000 I_1 + 5000(I_1 - 0.02) = 500$$

From which    $I_1 = 60$ ma. Therefore

$$I_2 = I_1 - 0.02 = 0.06 - 0.02 = 0.04 \text{ amp} \quad \text{or} \quad 40 \text{ ma}$$

Since $R_2$ and $R_3$ are in parallel,

$$\therefore \quad V_2 = V_3$$

But    $V_2 = I_2 R_2 = 0.04 \times 5000 = 200$ v

and then    $R_3 = \dfrac{V_3}{I_3} = \dfrac{200}{0.02} = 10$ kilohms

It is also possible to start the solution by substituting the appropriate $V/R$ in the Kirchhoff's current law equation, $I_1 = I_2 + 0.02$.

## 11. Voltage Dividers

The type of series parallel circuit we have been solving in the preceding section is widely used in electronic circuits where, for the sake of economy, the one source of emf must supply all the various direct voltages required by a piece of equipment. The **series dropping resistor** of Fig. 5.16 provides the simplest method of obtaining the required voltage drop across a certain circuit element. The advantage of the simple series dropping resistor is that the current drain on the power supply is no greater than the current required by the circuit element in question. But this circuit has the disadvantage that any change in load resistance will cause appreciable change in the current through the series dropping resistor and therefore in the voltage drop across it. This in turn will allow appreciable change in the voltage supplied to the load.

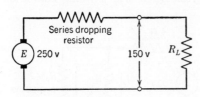

**Fig. 5.16.** Series dropping resistor.

EXAMPLE 10: The screen grid of one of the vacuum tubes in a piece of electronic equipment requires an operating voltage of 150 v with respect to the cathode. The screen grid current is 2 ma. If the supply voltage is 250 v, what value of series dropping resistor is required?

*Solution:* From Ohm's law, the screen grid circuit of the tube can be represented by a resistance as in Fig. 5.16.

$$R_L = \frac{V_L}{I_L} = \frac{150}{0.002} = 75 \text{ kilohms}$$

From Kirchhoff's voltage law, the voltage drop across the dropping resistor must be

$$V_{DR} = E - V_L = 250 - 150 = 100 \text{ v}$$

Since this is a simple series circuit,

$$I_{DR} = I_L = 2 \text{ ma}$$

$$\therefore \quad \text{Dropping resistance} = \frac{V_{DR}}{I_{DR}} = \frac{100}{0.002} = 50 \text{ kilohms}$$

To complete the design we must know what power rating the chosen resistor must possess.

$$P = VI = 100 \times 0.002 = 0.2 \text{ w}$$

EXAMPLE 11: Using the series dropping resistor determined in Example 10, what will the screen grid voltage become if the screen grid current drops to 1 ma?

*Solution:* Since the circuit (Fig. 5.16) is a simple series circuit, the current through the series dropping resistor will now become 1 ma. Therefore the voltage drop across the series dropping resistor will become

$$V_{DR} = IR_{DR} = 0.001 \times 50,000 = 50 \text{ v}$$

From Kirchhoff's voltage law,

$$V_L = E - V_{DR} = 250 - 50 = 200 \text{ v}$$

Therefore with only a simple series dropping resistance, a decrease in screen grid current from 2 ma to 1 ma causes the screen grid voltage to rise from 150 v to 200 v.

By adding an extra resistor referred to as the **bleeder** resistor which is designed to pass several times as much current as the load, the current through the series dropping resistor is now mainly dependent on this bleeder current. Therefore changes in load current will have only a slight effect on the voltage supplied to the load. The combination of a series dropping resistor and a bleeder resistor is called a **voltage divider.** (Fig. 5.17) The improved **voltage regulation** offered by the voltage divider is achieved at the expense of extra current drain from the power supply and extra heat produced in the voltage divider.

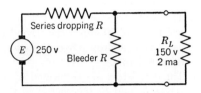

Fig. 5.17. Simple voltage divider.

> EXAMPLE 12: Allowing a bleeder current of 10 ma, design a voltage divider to supply a screen grid with 150 v at 2 ma from a 250 v source of emf.
>
> *Solution:* Since the bleeder resistor is in parallel with the load (Fig. 5.17), the voltage drop across it is 150 v. Therefore
>
> $$\text{Bleeder resistance} = \frac{V}{I} = \frac{150}{0.01} = 15 \text{ kilohms}$$
>
> $$\text{Power rating of bleeder} = VI = 150 \times 0.01 = 1.5 \text{ w}$$
>
> Voltage drop across series dropping resistor,
>
> $$V_{DR} = E - V_L = 250 - 150 = 100 \text{ v}$$
>
> $$I_{DR} = I_B + I_L = 10 + 2 = 12 \text{ ma}$$
>
> $$\therefore \quad \text{Series dropping resistance} = \frac{V_{DR}}{I_{DR}} = \frac{100}{0.012} = 8,333 \text{ ohms}$$
>
> $$\text{Power rating} = V_{DR}I_{DR} = 100 \times 0.012 = 1.2 \text{ w}$$

## Problems

Draw a fully labeled schematic diagram for each problem.

1. Given $R_1 = 5$ ohms, $R_2 = 10$ ohms, and $R_3 = 15$ ohms; what is the total resistance when they are connected in series?

2. What is the total resistance of a series circuit consisting of $R_1 = 47$ kilohms, $R_2 = 330$ kilohms, and $R_3 = 2.2$ kilohms?

3. If the series circuit of Problem 1 is connected to a 120 v source of emf, what is the voltage drop across each resistor?

4. What resistance must be connected in series with a vacuum tube heater rated at 150 ma with a hot resistance of 330 ohms in order to operate it safely from a 117 v source? What power rating must this resistor have?

5. A 6 v car radio draws a current of 6.5 amp. What resistance must be connected in series with it to operate it in a car with a 12 v battery? What "wattage" resistor is required?

6. An electric stove element is rated at 300 w when connected to a 110 v source. Assuming negligible change in resistance for any change in temperature, what will be the total rate of energy conversion when two of these elements are connected in series?

7. Three resistors are connected in series to a 120 v generator. The first has a resistance of 50 ohms, the second passes a current of 0.5 amp, and the third has a voltage drop across it of 50 v. Calculate the resistance of the second and third resistors.

8. Three resistors are connected in series to a 120 v source. The voltage drop across $R_1$ and $R_2$ together is 80 v, and the voltage drop across $R_2$ and $R_3$ together is 90 v. If the total resistance is 8 kilohms, what is the resistance of each of the three resistors?

9. A 10 kilohm, 20 w; an 80 kilohm, 100 w; and a 20 kilohm, 200 w resistor are connected in series. What is the maximum emf that can be applied to the network without exceeding the power rating of any resistor?

10. A Christmas tree light set for use with a 110 v source consists of eight 6 w lamps in series. What is the hot resistance of each lamp?

11. What resistance must be connected in series with a 100 ohm resistor for the 100 ohm resistor to dissipate heat at the rate of 30 w when the combination is connected to a 120 v source?

12. What resistance must be connected in series with a 100 ohm resistor for the unknown resistance to dissipate heat at the rate of 30 w when the combination is connected to a 120 v source?

13. A storage battery has an open circuit emf of 6 v and an internal resistance of 0.05 ohm.
(a) What is the terminal voltage of the battery when a 0.2 ohm load is connected to it?
(b) What power will be dissipated by a 0.5 ohm load?
(c) What is the efficiency of the system when a 0.15 ohm load is connected to the battery?
(d) What is the maximum power that a load can draw from this battery?

14. The generator of a lighting plant driven by a gasoline engine has an open circuit emf of 32 v and an internal resistance of 0.2 ohm. The generator is designed for a constant duty power output of 300 w.
(a) What value of load resistance will draw energy from the generator at the rate of 300 w?
(b) What is the efficiency of the generator under this condition?

15. The high-voltage power supply of a television receiver produces an open circuit emf of 15 kv. Its internal resistance is 2 megohms.
(a) What is the voltage at the high voltage anode of the picture tube when the anode current is 600 $\mu a$?
(b) What will the anode voltage be if the anode current is increased by 50%?
(c) What is the short-circuit current of this power supply?

16. A phonograph pickup develops an open circuit emf of 50 mv and has an internal resistance of 1200 ohms.
(a) What voltage will it develop across a 4 kilohm load resistance?
(b) What value of load resistance must be used to obtain a 75% efficiency?
(c) What is the maximum power output of the pickup?

17. A certain generator has a terminal voltage of 110 v when a 5.5 ohm load is connected to its terminals. The terminal voltage becomes 105 v when the load is 3.5 ohms. What is the internal resistance of the generator?

18. A 200 ohm resistor dissipates heat at the rate of 8 w when connected to a certain generator. If a 300 ohm resistor is connected in series with the 200 ohm resistor, the dissipation of the 200 ohm resistor becomes 2 w. What is the open-circuit voltage of the generator?

19. A generator whose internal resistance is 1 ohm feeds a load at the end of a line, each wire of which has a resistance of 2 ohms. The generator emf is adjusted to produce 120 v across the load at full load. If the total dissipation of the two wires is not to exceed 10% of the total generated power, what is the maximum power that can be delivered to the load?

20. An audio amplifier has an internal resistance at its output terminals of 4 ohms. The loudspeaker is connected at the end of a line, each wire of which has a resistance of 2 ohms. What resistance load must the loudspeaker present to obtain maximum power in the loudspeaker?

21. Given $R_1$ is 5 ohms, $R_2$ is 10 ohms, and $R_3$ is 15 ohms. What is the total current when they are connected in parallel to a 120 v source of emf?

22. What is the equivalent resistance of a parallel circuit consisting of $R_1 = 47$ kilohms, $R_2 = 330$ kilohms, and $R_3 = 2.2$ kilohms?

23. A circuit element having a conductance of 150$\mu$mho is connected in parallel with a branch having a conductance of 750 millimho. What is the equivalent resistance of the circuit?

24. Three lamps operating in parallel on a 110 v circuit are rated at 40 w, 60 w, and 100 w, respectively. What is the equivalent hot resistance of this load?

25. Three resistances in parallel pass a total current of 0.6 amp. The first resistor has a resistance of 400 ohms, the second passes a current of 60 ma, and third has a voltage drop across it of 150 v. Calculate the resistance of the second and third resistors.

26. If the three resistors in Problem 22 are each rated at $\frac{1}{2}$ watt, what is the maximum total current that the network can handle without overheating any resistor?

27. What resistance must be placed in parallel with a 15 kilohm resistor to reduce the equivalent resistance to 10 kilohms?

28. The equivalent resistance of three resistors in parallel is 2.5 kilohms. If $R_1$ is 10 kilohms and $R_2$ is 20 kilohms, what is the resistance of $R_3$?

29. The total current passed by a 10 kilohm, 15 kilohm, and a 20 kilohm resistors in parallel is 20 ma. What is the current through each branch?

30. A stranded power transmission cable consists of a central strand of #10 AWG steel ($\rho = 100$ ohms per mil-foot at 20°C) around which are twisted six strands of #10 AWG aluminum. The twisting of the aluminum conductors requires them to be 2% longer than the steel strand. What is the resistance of a mile of this cable at 20°C?

For Problems 31–36 draw fully labeled diagrams similar to Fig. 5.11 and prepare tables similar to Table II.

31. $E = 24$ v;  $R_1 = 4$ ohms;  $R_2 = 6$ ohms;  $R_3 = 12$ ohms.

32. $P_T = 300$ w;   $R_1 = 8$ ohms;   $R_2 = 5$ ohms;   $R_3 = 20$ ohms.

33. $E = 300$ v;   $R_1 = 8$ ohms;   $I_2 = 1$ amp;   $V_3 = 150$ v.

34. $E = 100$ v;   $P_T = 75$ w;   $R_2 = 100$ ohms;   $I_3 = 0.5$ amp.

35. $E = 180$ v;   $R_1 = 5$ ohms;   $R_2 = 15$ ohms;   $I_3 = 4$ amp.

36. $E = 250$ v;   $R_1 + R_2 = 10$ kilohms;   $V_2 = 100$ v;   $I_3 = 5$ ma.

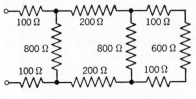

**Fig. 5.18.**

37. What is the equivalent resistance of the network of Fig. 5.18?

38. If the power input to the network of Fig. 5.18 is 150 w, what is the rate of dissipation of the 600 ohm resistor?

39. A 12 v generator has an internal resistance of 0.05 ohm. Two loads are connected in parallel to its terminals, one drawing a 12 amp current and the other dissipating energy at the rate of 200 w. What is the terminal voltage of the generator with this load?

40. When the automatic gain control voltage of a radio receiver is measured with a vacuum-tube voltmeter whose input resistance is 10 meg, it reads 4.5 v. When an ordinary voltmeter whose input resistance is 10 kilohms is also connected across the AGC voltage source, both meters read 0.40 v. What is the internal resistance of the AGC voltage source?

41. Calculate the screen grid voltage using the voltage divider designed in Example 12 when the screen grid current drops to 1 ma. Compare this with the result obtained in Example 11.

42. Design a voltage divider to supply 100 v at 25 ma from a 250 v source of emf if the total drain on the source is to be 100 ma.

43. What bleeder resistance is required to complete a voltage divider to give 300 v at 20 ma from a 500 v source if the series dropping resistor is 4 kilohms?

44. Design a voltage divider to deliver 100 v at 1 ma from a 240 v source of emf so that a 100% increase in load current causes only a 5% reduction in load voltage.

45. Fig. 5.19 shows the focus control of a cathode ray tube. In the one extreme position, the focus anode voltage is to be 600 v, at which the current drawn by the focus anode is 8 $\mu$amp. At the other extreme, the focus anode voltage is to be 1200 v for a current of 12 $\mu$amp. Find the resistance of $R_1$ and the focus control.

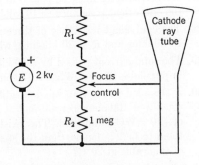

**Fig. 5.19.**

46. Design a voltage divider to supply 100 v at 10 ma and 250 v at 25 ma from a 400 v d-c supply with a bleeder current ($I_3$ in Fig. 5.20) of 50 ma.

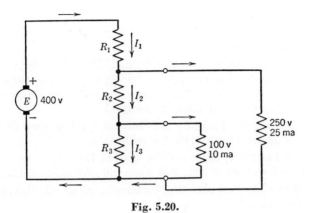

**Fig. 5.20.**

47. Calculate the resistances and wattage ratings of the sections of the voltage divider of Fig. 5.21 for the following conditions:

$$
\begin{aligned}
\text{plate current} \quad &= \quad 18 \text{ ma} \\
\text{control grid voltage} \quad &= \quad -5 \text{ v (with respect to cathode)} \\
\text{control grid current} \quad &= \quad 0 \text{ ma} \\
\text{screen grid voltage} \quad &= +150 \text{ v (with respect to cathode)} \\
\text{screen grid current} \quad &= \quad 2 \text{ ma} \\
\text{total drain on source} \quad &= \quad 50 \text{ ma}
\end{aligned}
$$

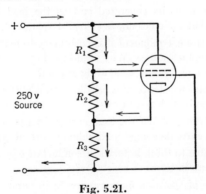

**Fig. 5.21.**

48. A voltage divider consists of a 10 kilohm resistor with an adjustable tap. The tap is set so that it feeds 80 v at 5 ma to a load when the voltage divider is connected across a 200 v source. What is the resistance of the bleeder portion of this voltage divider?

## Review Questions

1. How would you justify the statement that the current is the same in all parts of a simple series circuit?

2. How would you justify the statement that the total resistance of a series circuit is the sum of all the individual resistances?

3. Kirchhoff's voltage law may be stated thus: "The voltage between any two points in an electric network is the same via any path between those two points." Prove this statement numerically by considering the two ends of $R_2$ in Fig. 5.1 using the values given in Example 1.

4. Prove that in a series circuit, the ratio between any two power dissipations is the same as the ratio between the two resistances.

5. A lamp rated at 120 v, 100 w and one rated at 120 v, 25 w are connected in series to a 120 v source of emf. Which one will glow more brightly? Explain.

6. Explain the visible effect when the 25 w lamp in Question 5 is (a) open circuit; and (b) short circuit.

7. What disadvantage does the "series string" type of Christmas tree lamp possess as compared to the 110 v parallel type of Christmas tree lamp?

8. How would you go about determining the internal resistance of a given flashlight battery?

9. Explain why the kitchen light becomes a bit dimmer when a toaster is turned on.

10. Generator $B$ develops three times the open circuit emf of generator $A$ but has three times as great an internal resistance. Each generator is developing the same power in its load. Which has the greater efficiency?

11. A generator is operated in such a manner that its terminal voltage is kept constant by increasing its generated emf as the load current is increased. Does this mean that the efficiency is 100%? Explain.

12. In operating electronic equipment it is customary to make the load resistance equal to the internal resistance. Why would we do this for electronic apparatus but not in the case of a power generating station?

13. Why must the total resistance of a parallel circuit always be less than that of the smallest of the branch resistances?

14. Show that the statement that the total current in a parallel circuit is the sum of all the branch currents confirms Kirchhoff's current law.

15. Why is it preferable to think in terms of conductance in working with parallel circuits rather than in terms of resistance?

16. If the two lamps of Question 5 are connected in parallel, explain the visible effect when the 25 w lamp is (a) open circuit; and (b) short circuit.

17. An electric stove element has a resistance of 50 ohms with a center-tap connection. Draw circuit diagrams to show three means of connecting it to a 110 v source to obtain three different rates of conversion of electric energy to heat.

18. Two 50 kilohm resistors are connected in series across a source of emf. If a voltmeter which has a resistance of 100 kilohms is connected first across one resistor and then the other and finally across both, the sum of the first two

readings does not equal the third reading. Is this third reading greater or less than the sum of the other two? Explain.

19. Write one Kirchhoff's current law and two Kirchhoff's voltage law equations for the circuit of Fig. 5.22

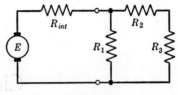

**Fig. 5.22.**

20. Why does a decrease in the bleeder resistance of a given voltage divider improve the voltage regulation of the output of the voltage divider?

# Chapter 6

# RESISTANCE NETWORKS

## 1. Networks With More Than One Source of emf

Many electric networks have two or more sources of emf within the one network. There are several methods of solving such networks. One method is to set up Kirchhoff's laws equations for the network and solve these equations by algebraic procedures. Perhaps the best way to outline the procedure involved in applying Kirchhoff's laws to such a network is to refer to a specific example of this type of solution.

EXAMPLE 1: An automobile generator with an internal resistance of 0.1 ohm develops an open circuit emf of 8.0 v. The storage battery has an internal resistance of 0.05 ohm and an open-circuit emf of 6.4 v. Both sources are connected in parallel to a 0.5 ohm load. Determine the generator current, battery current, and load current.

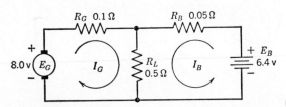

**Fig. 6.1.** Circuit diagram for Example 1.

*Solution:* The first step in all resistance network problems is to draw a detailed schematic diagram of the network. With more than one source of emf, it is very important to mark clearly the polarities of these sources. Since Kirchhoff's voltage law mentions the emf's and voltage drops around a complete loop, the second step is to mark current **tracing** loops through the network from the positive terminal of each source of emf to its negative terminal. Conventional direction is used for these loops. In any network solution, there must be sufficient tracing loops to include *all* components of the network. In this case two loops, $I_G$ and $I_B$, will meet this requirement.

The third step is to write a Kirchhoff's voltage law equation for each tracing loop, i.e., the algebraic sum of the emf's equals the algebraic sum of the voltage drops.

$$\therefore \quad \text{For the generator loop, } E_G = V_{R_G} + V_L$$

But from Ohm's law, any voltage drop across a resistance is always equal to the resistance times the current through it. Therefore

$$V_{R_G} = 0.1 I_G$$

Since the schematic diagram of Fig. 6.1 shows both the $I_G$ and the $I_B$ loops going in the *same* direction through the load, from Kirchhoff's current law, the load current is

$$I_L = I_G + I_B \quad \text{and} \quad V_L = 0.5(I_G + I_L)$$

$\therefore$   Kirchhoff's voltage law equation for the generator loop becomes

$$E_G = 0.1 I_G + 0.5(I_G + I_B)$$

or            $8.0 = 0.6 I_G + 0.5 I_B$            (1)

Similarly, Kirchhoff's voltage law equation for the battery loop becomes

$$E_B = 0.05 I_B + 0.5(I_G + I_B)$$

or            $6.4 = 0.5 I_G + 0.55 I_B$            (2)

Solving equations (1) and (2) simultaneously,

$$5 \times (1) \text{ gives } 40 \quad = 3 I_G + 2.5 I_B$$
$$6 \times (2) \text{ gives } \underline{38.4 = 3 I_G + 3.3 I_B}$$
subtracting,            $1.6 = \quad\quad -0.8 I_B$

from which            $I_B = -2 \text{ amp}$

The negative answer for $I_B$ simply tells us that the battery is not supplying current to the load as we had supposed in setting up the direction of the tracing loop for $I_B$. However, the numerical value is quite correct. In this example, the storage battery is *charging* at the rate of 2 amp. In order to avoid having to change our tracing directions in Fig. 6.1, we can carry on with the original tracing loops as long as we treat $I_B$ as a negative quantity. Substituting this value of $I_B$ in equation (1),

$$8 = 0.6 I_G + (0.5) \times (-2)$$

or            $8 = 0.6 I_G - 1$

from which       $I_G = 15 \text{ amp}$

$$I_L = I_G + I_B = 15 + (-2) = 13 \text{ amp}$$

EXAMPLE 2: A 110/220 v three-wire source (as shown in Fig. 6.2), having negligible internal resistance, feeds a 10 ohm load from one side of the source and a 15 ohm load from the other side of the source through three conductors each of which has a resistance of 1 ohm. What is the current in the common conductor?

*Solution:* After we have set up our tracing loops for this problem (as shown in Fig. 6.2), we will notice that the current in the common conductor is the *difference* between the two loop currents. In writing down the voltage drop across the common resistance for each Kirchhoff's voltage law equation, the current for the tracing loop in question is a *positive* quantity, and any current going *against* this tracing direction has a *negative sign*. Therefore the Kirchhoff's voltage law equation for the $I_1$ loop becomes

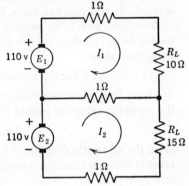

**Fig. 6.2.** Circuit diagram for Example 2.

$$E_1 = 1 \times I_1 + 10 \times I_1 + 1(I_1 - I_2)$$

or $$110 = 12I_1 - I_2 \tag{1}$$

Similarly, the Kirchhoff's voltage law equation for the $I_2$ loop becomes

$$E_2 = 1(I_2 - I_1) + 15 \times I_2 + 1 \times I_2$$

or $$110 = 17I_2 - I_1 \tag{2}$$

Solving equations (1) and (2) simultaneously, $12 \times$ (2) gives

$$1320 = -12I_1 + 204I_2$$

Equation (1)      $\underline{110 = \phantom{-}12I_1 - \phantom{20}I_2}$

Adding gives      $1430 = \phantom{-12I_1} 203I_2$

from which             $I_2 = 7.04$ amp

Substituting this value in equation (1),

$$110 = 12I_1 - 7.04$$

from which             $I_1 = 9.75$ amp

∴ The current in the common conductor is

$$9.75 - 7.04 = 2.71 \text{ amp}$$

## 2. The Superposition Theorem

It is possible to avoid the simultaneous equations of the Kirchhoff's laws method of solving the networks of the preceding section by applying the **superposition theorem.** This theorem is useful only for networks containing more than one source of emf and for determining the current through or voltage drop across *one* branch of these networks. However, in many cases, once the current through one branch of a network is known, the remainder of the network can be solved quite readily. We shall not worry about the proof of the superposition theorem which may be stated thus:

**The current that flows in any branch of a network** of resistors resulting from the simultaneous application of a number of emf's distributed in any manner throughout the network is the algebraic sum of the component currents in that branch that would be caused by each source of emf acting independently in turn while the others are replaced in the network by their respective internal resistances.

EXAMPLE 1A: An automobile generator with an internal resistance of 0.1 ohm develops an open circuit emf of 8.0 v. The storage battery has an internal resistance of 0.05 ohm and an open-circuit emf of 6.4 v. Both of these sources are connected in parallel to a 0.5 ohm load. What is the load current?

*Solution:* Since there are *two* sources of emf, there will be *two* component currents through the load resistance, and for the purpose of solving this example by the superposition theorem, the circuit of Fig. 6.1 can be redrawn as the two equivalent circuits of Fig. 6.3.

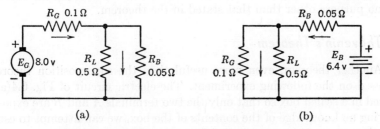

(a)                                                          (b)

**Fig. 6.3.** Equivalent circuit diagrams for Example 1A.

Solving first the circuit of Fig. 6.3(a),

$$R_T = R_G + \frac{R_L \times R_B}{R_L + R_B} = 0.1 + \frac{0.5 \times 0.05}{0.5 + 0.05} = 0.145 \text{ ohm}$$

$$I_T = \frac{E_G}{R_T} = \frac{8.0}{0.145} = 55 \text{ amp}$$

From the characteristics of parallel circuits,

$$\frac{I_B}{I_L} = \frac{R_L}{R_B} = \frac{0.5}{0.05} \qquad \therefore \quad I_B = 10I_L$$

and, since $I_B + I_L = 55$ amp,

$$I_L + 10I_L = 55 \text{ amp}$$

and the first component of the load current becomes

$$I_L = 5 \text{ amp}$$

Similarly, from the circuit of Fig. 6.3(b),

$$R_T = R_B + \frac{R_G \times R_L}{R_G + R_L} = 0.05 + \frac{0.1 \times 0.5}{0.1 + 0.5} = 0.133 \text{ ohm}$$

$$I_T = \frac{E_B}{R_T} = \frac{6.4}{0.133} = 48 \text{ amp}$$

Since $\qquad \dfrac{I_G}{I_L} = \dfrac{R_L}{R_G} = \dfrac{0.5}{0.1} \qquad I_G = 5I_L$

$$I_G + I_L = 48 \text{ amp} \qquad \therefore \quad 5I_L + I_L = 48$$

from which the second component of the load current becomes

$$I_L = 8 \text{ amp}$$

Since the direction of the load current in Fig. 6.3(b) is the same as in Fig. 6.3(a), the actual load current is $5 + 8 = 13$ amp.

*Note*: The component currents are only an aid to determining the real load current and do not represent the actual generator and battery currents, as can be seen by referring to Example 1. Therefore in using the superposition theorem, we must take care to use the component currents for no purpose other than that stated in the theorem.

## 3. Thévenin's Theorem

Another theorem, even more useful than the superposition theorem, is based on the following experiment. The electric circuit of Fig. 6.4(a) is placed in a sealed box so that only the two terminals $A$ and $B$ are exposed. Having no knowledge of the contents of the box, we can attempt to establish the nature of its contents with electric measuring instruments. First we connect a voltmeter that draws negligible current to terminals $A$ and $B$. The voltmeter will tell us that the box contains a source of emf, and since the voltmeter draws practically no current from this source, it shows the open-circuit voltage of the source. As we can check by solving the circuit of Fig. 6.4(a), we would read an open-circuit emf of 80 v. Therefore as far as we could tell without opening the box, it contains an 80 v source of emf as shown in Fig. 6.4(b). Next we short-circuit terminals $A$ and $B$ through an ammeter having negligible resistance. The ammeter reads 2 ma (as we can again check by solving the circuit of Fig. 6.4(a) with terminals $A$ and $B$ short-circuited). Therefore without knowledge of the contents, it would appear to us that the box contains an 80 v source of emf which will permit a 2 ma current to flow when its terminals are short-circuited. The source apparently has an internal resistance of

$$R = \frac{E}{I} = \frac{80}{0.002} = 40 \text{ kilohms}$$

as shown in Fig. 6.4(b).

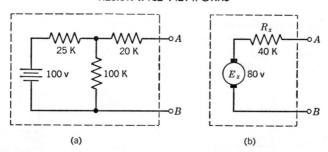

**Fig. 6.4.** (a) Original source of emf. (b) Thévenin equivalent source.

No matter how elaborate the network inside the sealed box may be, as long as it contains one or more sources of emf, all that we can determine about it without opening the box is that it is equivalent to a simple generator with a single internal resistance in series with it. Any load connected to terminals $A$ and $B$ of the equivalent circuit of Fig. 6.4(b) will draw exactly the same current with exactly the same voltage drop that it would have if it were connected to terminals $A$ and $B$ of the original circuit of Fig. 6.4(a). Rather than leave this simply as an experiment to show that any complex source of emf behaves just the same as the simple source of emf of Fig. 6.4(b), M. L. Thévenin stated the principle in the form of a theorem which provides us with a very useful method of simplifying electric networks to assist in their pencil and paper solution. Thévenin's theorem may be stated as follows:

> Any two-terminal network of fixed resistances and sources of emf may be replaced by a single source of emf having an equivalent emf equal to the open-circuit emf at the terminals of the original network and having an internal resistance equal to the resistance looking back into the network from the two terminals with all the sources of emf replaced by their internal resistances.

Thévenin's theorem can be applied to any of the resistance networks we have solved so far by treating one branch of the network as a *load* and the remainder of the network as a *two-terminal network containing one or more sources of emf*. Having decided which branch of the original network we are going to treat as a load, we *remove* it from the original network and place it in a Thévenin equivalent circuit and apply the rules set forth in the theorem to determine the remainder of the equivalent circuit. We can illustrate this procedure and at the same time assess its usefulness by applying Thévenin's theorem to some of the examples that we have already solved, using Kirchhoff's laws.

EXAMPLE 3: A resistor passing a 20 ma current is in parallel with a 5 kilohm resistor. This combination is in series with another 5 kilohm resistor, the whole network being connected to a 500 v source of emf. What is the resistance of the resistor which is passing the 20 ma current? (See Example 9 of Chapter 5)

*Solution:* Having first drawn a schematic diagram for the circuit as described in the example, we would select the unknown resistance passing the 20 ma current as the load and *remove* it from the original circuit as in Fig. 6.5(a) and place it in the Thévenin equivalent circuit of Fig. 6.5(b).

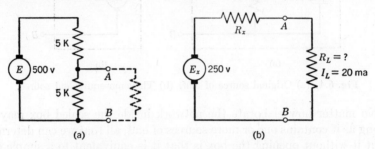

(a)                                    (b)

**Fig. 6.5.** Schematic diagram for first step of Example 3.

According to Thévenin's theorem, the emf ($E_x$) of the equivalent circuit will be the open-circuit voltage between terminals $A$ and $B$ of Fig. 6.5(a). This circuit is now simple enough that $E_x$ can be determined mentally by inspection of Fig. 6.5(a).

Since 500 v emf is applied to two 5 kilohm resistors in a simple series circuit, the open-circuit voltage between terminals $A$ and $B$ is $\frac{1}{2}$ of 500 v = 250 v. This answer is transferred to the Thévenin equivalent circuit of Fig. 6.5(b). The next step in following the instructions stated in Thévenin's theorem is to replace the source of emf in Fig. 6.5(a) by its internal resistance, which in this case is zero ohms. After doing this, the circuit of Fig. 6.5(a) becomes that of Fig. 6.6(a). The total resistance between terminals $A$ and $B$ can again be determined mentally in this example.

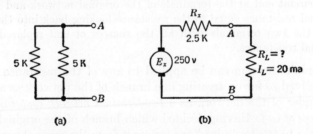

(a)                                    (b)

**Fig. 6.6.** Schematic diagram for second step of Example 3.

$$R_x = \frac{5 \times 5}{5 + 5} = 2.5 \text{ kilohms}$$

This answer is transferred to the Thévenin equivalent circuit of Fig. 6.6(b). The completed equivalent circuit can now be solved quite readily by Ohm's law.

$$R_T = \frac{E_x}{I} = \frac{250}{0.02} = 12.5 \text{ kilohms}$$

$$\therefore \quad R_L = R_T - R_x = 12.5 \text{ kilohms} - 2.5 \text{ kilohms} = 10 \text{ kilohms}$$

EXAMPLE 1B: An automobile generator with an internal resistance of 0.1 ohm develops an open circuit emf of 8.0 v. The storage battery has an internal resistance of 0.05 ohm and an open circuit emf of 6.4 v. Both of these sources are connected in parallel to a 0.5 ohm load. Find the load current.

*Solution:* Removing the load resistance from the original circuit of Fig. 6.1 leaves the circuit as shown in Fig. 6.7(a), which can be solved by one simple Kirchhoff's voltage law equation.

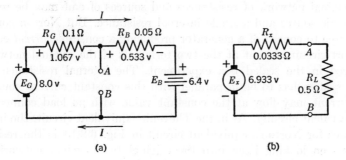

**Fig. 6.7.** Schematic diagram for Example 1B.

Since the two sources of emf are in opposition as far as current around the remaining loop is concerned, the tracing direction is established by the source with the greater emf. Therefore

$$E_G - E_B = IR_G + IR_B$$

$$8.0 - 6.4 = 0.1I + 0.05I$$

from which $\quad\quad I = 10.67$ amp, and

$$V_{R_G} = IR_G = 10.67 \times 0.1 = 1.067 \text{ v}$$

$$V_{R_B} = IR_B = 10.67 \times 0.05 = 0.533 \text{ v}$$

By inspection of Fig. 6.7(a), noting the polarities of the voltage drops carefully, the total voltage between terminals $A$ and $B$ becomes either

$$E_x = E_G - V_{R_G} = 8.0 - 1.067 = 6.933 \text{ v}$$

or $\quad\quad E_x = E_B + V_{R_B} = 6.4 + 0.533 = 6.933 \text{ v}$

If we short-circuit the generator and battery symbols of Fig. 6.7(a), leaving only their internal resistances, we will find that $R_G$ and $R_B$ are connected in parallel between terminals $A$ and $B$. Therefore, following the procedure set forth in Thévenin's theorem,

$$R_x = \frac{R_G \times R_B}{R_G + R_B} = \frac{0.1 \times 0.05}{0.1 + 0.05} = 0.0333 \text{ ohm}$$

The Thévenin equivalent circuit of Fig. 6.7(b) can now be solved by Ohm's law.

$$R_T = R_x + R_L = 0.0333 + 0.5 = 0.5333 \text{ ohm}$$

$$I_L = \frac{E_x}{R_T} = \frac{6.933}{0.5333} = 13 \text{ amp}$$

## 4. Norton's Theorem

Checking back over the "sealed box" example of Fig. 6.4, we will note that the method we used to determine the internal resistance for the Thévenin equivalent circuit experimentally differs from that stated in Thévenin's theorem. The method we used is based on **Norton's theorem.** Norton's and Thévenin's theorems are similar in that both state that any two-terminal network of resistances and sources of emf may be replaced by a single source and a single internal resistance. But Norton considers this source to consist of a generator producing a constant *current* equal to the short-circuit current at the two terminals of the original network as measured in the sealed box experiment. The internal resistance $R_x$ in such a system has to be in parallel with this constant current source (so that current may flow at the constant value with no load connected to the equivalent circuit). As in the Thévenin equivalent circuit, the internal resistance for Norton's equivalent circuit in Fig. 6.8(b) is the resistance that is seen looking back into the original two-terminal network from terminals $A$ and $B$ when all sources of emf within the network have been replaced by their internal resistances.

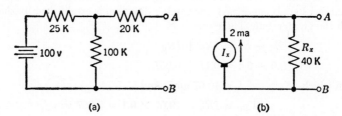

Fig. 6.8. (a) Original source of emf. (b) Norton equivalent source.

Applying Norton's theorem to the source of Fig. 6.8(a), we obtain a short-circuit current at the terminals $A$ and $B$ of 2 ma as previously determined. When the original source of emf is replaced by its internal resistance (zero ohms), the resistance looking back into terminals $A$ and $B$ appears as 40 kilohms. Therefore the Norton equivalent source becomes that shown in Fig. 6.8(b).

If a load is connected to the Thévenin equivalent source of Fig. 6.4(b), the load current from the simple series circuit becomes

$$I_L = \frac{E_x}{R_x + R_L} \tag{6.1}$$

From the Norton equivalent circuit of Fig. 6.8(b),

$$V = I_x R_T = I_x \frac{R_x R_L}{R_x + R_L}$$

But
$$I_L = \frac{V}{R_L} = \frac{I_x}{R_L} \cdot \frac{R_x R_L}{R_x + R_L}$$

$$\therefore \quad I_L = I_x \frac{R_x}{R_x + R_L} \tag{6.2}$$

In solving some electronic circuits (e.g., transistor equivalent circuits) it is more convenient to think of sources of emf in terms of the constant-current sources of Norton's theorem. However for this electric circuits course we shall confine our attention to the constant voltage type of source of the Thévenin equivalent circuit. Our interest in Norton's theorem at the moment is simply that it provides a laboratory method for determining the equivalent resistance for the Thévenin equivalent circuit.

## 5. Delta-Wye Transformation

Another useful type of transformation which replaces a given circuit with an equivalent circuit applies to the three-terminal resistance network of Fig. 6.9. If we can state the conditions under which the "wye" circuit of Fig. 6.9(a) is equivalent to the "delta" circuit of Fig. 6.9(b), we can substitute the wye for the delta and vice versa in circuit simplification.

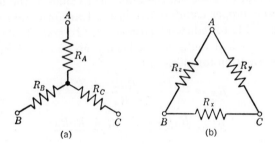

**Fig. 6.9.** (a) Y network (b) Δ network.

Ignoring terminal $C$ for the moment, the resistance between terminals $A$ and $B$ must be the same for both networks. For the wye circuit of Fig. 6.9(a), the circuit between $A$ and $B$ is a simple series circuit giving

$$R_{AB} = R_A + R_B$$

For the delta circuit of Fig. 6.9(b), there are two branches in parallel between terminals $A$ and $B$, giving

$$R_{AB} = \frac{R_Z(R_X + R_Y)}{R_Z + (R_X + R_Y)}$$

$$\therefore \quad R_A + R_B = \frac{R_X R_Z + R_Y R_Z}{R_X + R_Y + R_Z} \tag{1}$$

Similarly

$$R_B + R_C = \frac{R_X R_Y + R_X R_Z}{R_X + R_Y + R_Z} \qquad (2)$$

and

$$R_C + R_A = \frac{R_Y R_Z + R_X R_Y}{R_X + R_Y + R_Z} \qquad (3)$$

Subtracting (2) from (1) gives

$$R_A - R_C = \frac{R_Y R_Z - R_X R_Y}{R_X + R_Y + R_Z} \qquad (4)$$

Adding (3) and (4) gives

$$2R_A = \frac{2R_Y R_Z}{R_X + R_Y + R_Z}$$

from which

$$R_A = \frac{R_Y R_Z}{R_X + R_Y + R_Z} \qquad (6.3)$$

Similarly,

$$R_B = \frac{R_X R_Z}{R_X + R_Y + R_Z} \qquad (6.4)$$

and

$$R_C = \frac{R_X R_Y}{R_X + R_Y + R_Z} \qquad (6.5)$$

These are the delta to wye transformation equations. In using them we must be careful to associate the numerical values of the original delta circuit with their proper counterparts in the transformation formulas.

It is also possible to reduce equations (1), (2), and (3) algebraically to solve for the equivalent delta circuit from a given wye circuit. The wye to delta transformation formulas are

$$R_X = \frac{R_A R_B + R_B R_C + R_C R_A}{R_A} \qquad (6.6)$$

$$R_Y = \frac{R_A R_B + R_B R_C + R_C R_A}{R_B} \qquad (6.7)$$

$$R_Z = \frac{R_A R_B + R_B R_C + R_C R_A}{R_C} \qquad (6.8)$$

## 6. The Wheatstone Bridge

To complete our study of basic resistance networks, we shall solve the Wheatstone bridge circuit of Fig. 6.10 by the various methods we have discussed in this chapter. Since the bridge type circuit is widely used in electric and electronic measurement and control circuitry, we must be able to recognize and solve it in whatever form we may meet it. Although at first glance the bridge circuit may appear to be a simple series-parallel circuit (particularly if we redraw the resistors in a vertical position as in Fig. 6.11), no two resistors meet the requirements of either series or parallel circuits. Since there is only one source of emf, the superposition theorem is not applicable. We can, however, solve the bridge circuit by Kirchhoff's laws equations, Thévenin's theorem, or delta-wye transformation.

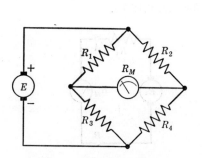

**Fig. 6.10.** Wheatstone bridge.

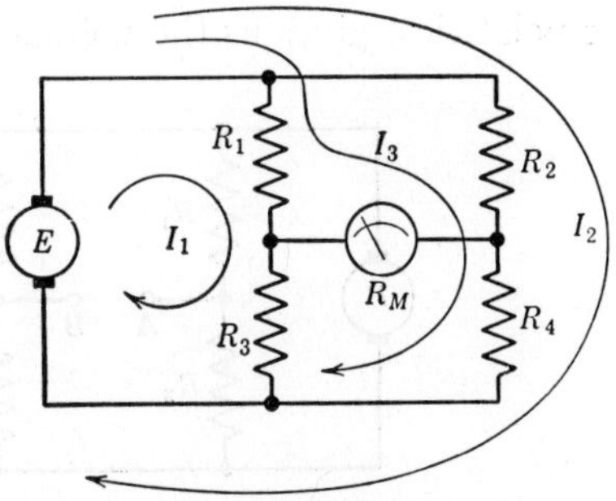

**Fig. 6.11.** Solving Wheatstone bridge by Kirchhoff's Laws.

*Solution by Kirchhoff's laws equations.* Three tracing loops, all starting from one terminal of the generator and going through the bridge network to the other generator terminal, are required to include all components of the circuit as marked in Fig. 6.11. If we guess the wrong direction for the tracing loop through the meter, $I_3$ will simply become a negative quantity as was the case in a previous example. Writing the Kirchhoff's voltage law equations for the three tracing loops, we get

From loop 1,    $E = R_1(I_1 + I_3) + R_3 I_1$

From loop 2,    $E = R_2 I_2 + R_4(I_2 + I_3)$

From loop 3,    $E = R_1(I_1 + I_3) + R_M I_3 + R_4(I_2 + I_3)$

Substituting the given values of resistance and emf, we can solve these three equations simultaneously for the three loop currents from which

| | |
|---|---|
| Total current | $= I_1 + I_2 + I_3$ |
| Meter current | $= I_3$ |
| Current through | $R_1 = I_1 + I_3$ |
| Current through | $R_2 = I_2$ |
| Current through | $R_3 = I_1$ |
| Current through | $R_4 = I_3 + I_2$ |

*Solution by Thévenin's Theorem.* If we are asked to find the current through only *one* branch of a bridge circuit (e.g., the meter current), Thévenin's theorem allows us to *remove* this branch from the original circuit as in Fig. 6.12(a) to a Thévenin equivalent circuit as in Fig. 6.12(b). The remaining circuit in Fig. 6.12(a) can then be solved by simple series-parallel circuit rules to find the values for the Thévenin equivalent circuit of Fig. 6.12(b). With the meter removed in Fig. 6.12(a), the voltage drop across each of the remaining resistors is readily determined. Tracing from terminal $A$ to terminal $B$ through these voltage drops (keeping track of the polarities) gives us the voltage $E_x$ for Fig. 6.12(b).

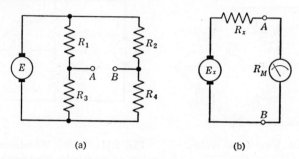

(a)                                        (b)

**Fig. 6.12.** Solving Wheatstone bridge by Thévenin's Theorem.

Assuming that the source of emf has negligible internal resistance, we can short-circuit the generator symbol of Fig. 6.12(a) to determine the internal resistance for the Thévenin equivalent circuit. Doing so places $R_1$ in parallel with $R_3$, and $R_2$ in parallel with $R_4$. These two parallel circuits are in series as far as terminals $A$ and $B$ are concerned. Therefore the equivalent resistance becomes

$$R_x = \frac{R_1 R_3}{R_1 + R_3} + \frac{R_2 R_4}{R_2 + R_4}$$

The meter current then becomes

$$I_M = \frac{E_x}{R_x + R_M}$$

The current through any other one branch of the bridge circuit can be determined in exactly the same manner.

*Solution by Delta-Wye Transformation.* By replacing $R_1$, $R_2$, and $R_M$ of the original bridge circuit of Fig. 6.13(a) (which form a delta) with

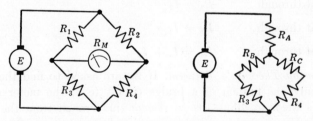

**Fig. 6.13.** Solving Wheatstone bridge by delta-wye transformation.

their equivalent wye circuit as in Fig. 6.13(b), the resulting circuit can be solved by the rules for simple series-parallel circuits. Since $R_3$ and $R_4$ have not been altered, the current through these two components in the transformed circuit will be the same as for the original circuit. Once these two currents are known, we can return to the original circuit to determine the remainder of the currents by Ohm's law.

## Problems

1. As the car slows down, the open-circuit emf of the generator in Example 1 becomes 7.0 v. What is the battery current?

2. What must the open circuit emf of the generator be in Example 1 for the battery current to be zero?

3. What will the current in the common lead in Example 2 become if another 15 ohm load is connected in parallel with the existing 15 ohm load?

4. In the original circuit of Fig. 6.2, the emf ($E_1$) of the one source is altered until the current in the common lead is zero. What is the required value of $E_1$?

5. Two batteries are connected in parallel to feed a 12 ohm load. Battery $A$ has an open circuit emf of 6.3 v and an internal resistance of 1.5 ohm. Battery $B$ has an open circuit emf of 6.0 v and an internal resistance of 2.1 ohms. Find the current drain from each battery.

6. What current will flow when the load is disconnected from the parallel connected batteries in Problem 5?

7. In the balance detecting circuit of Fig. 6.14, the voltmeter has a resistance of 100 kilohms. What is its reading?

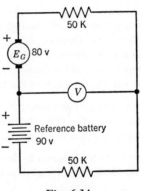

Fig. 6.14.

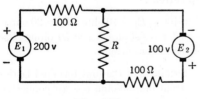

Fig. 6.15.

8. The current through the unknown resistor of the circuit of Fig. 6.15 is 0.5 amp. What is its resistance?

9. Find the load current in Problem 1, using the superposition theorem.

10. Find the current through the 10 ohm load in Example 2, using the superposition theorem.

11. Find the load current in Problem 5, using the superposition theorem.

12. Find the battery current in Problem 7, using the superposition theorem. Solve by Thévenin's theorem.

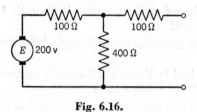

Fig. 6.16.

13. What resistance must be connected to the source shown in Fig. 6.16 to draw a 200 ma current through the unknown resistance?

14. What is the maximum power that can be developed in a load connected to the source of emf shown in Fig. 6.16 if the 400 ohm resistor is changed to 300 ohms?

15. What is the load current in Example 1B when the generator emf drops to 7.2 v?

16. What is the battery current in Example 1B when the generator emf drops to 6.8 v?

17. A trolley-bus is halfway along a section of trolley wire which is fed at one end from a 600 v source and at the other end from a 596 v source. The internal resistance of the sources can be neglected, but each trolley wire in the section has a resistance of 1.0 ohm. This trolley-bus is the only one in the section at the moment and it draws a current of 50 amp from the trolley wires. What is the voltage drop across the trolley-bus?

18. If the trolley-bus current in Problem 17 is still 50 amp when the bus is twice as far from the 600 v source as it is from the 596 v source, what current is drawn from the 596 v source?

19. Use Norton's theorem to determine the current that a 500 ohm load will draw from the source of emf shown in Fig. 6.16.

20. Use Norton's theorem to determine the voltage drop across the trolley-bus in Problem 17 when it is drawing a 60 amp current.

21. Given the following data for Fig. 6.10: $E = 100$ v, $R_1 = 10$ ohms, $R_2 = 20$ ohms, $R_3 = 30$ ohms, $R_4 = 40$ ohms, and the meter resistance $R_M = 50$ ohms. Use Kirchhoff's laws equations to determine the meter current.

22. What emf must be applied to the input terminals of the four-terminal lattice network of Fig. 6.17 to produce 1 amp current in a 50 ohm resistor connected to its output terminals? Use Kirchhoff's laws equations.

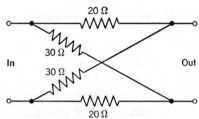

**Fig. 6.17.** Four terminal lattice network
for Problems 22 and 25.

NOTE: in schematic diagrams, when two
leads cross thus +, there is *no* electrical
connection at their junction. When two
leads cross thus +, there *is* an electrical
connection at their junction.

23. Given the following data for Fig. 6.10: $E = 200$ v, $R_1 = 10$ kilohms, $R_2 = 2.5$
kilohms, $R_3 = 5$ kilohms, $R_4 = 20$ kilohms, and $R_M = 25$ kilohms. Solve for
the meter current by Thévenin's theorem.

24. Use Thévenin's theorem to determine the current through a 500
ohm load connected to the output
of the bridged T attenuator of Fig.
6.18 when the input emf is 2 v.

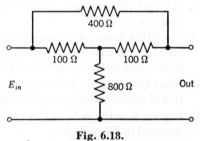

**Fig. 6.18.**

25. Use the delta-wye transformation to determine what emf must be applied to
the network of Fig. 6.17 in order to draw a 2 amp current from the source
when a 20 ohm load is connected to the output terminals of the network.

26. Use the delta-wye transformation to determine the current through a 300 ohm
load connected to the output of the bridged T attenuator of Fig. 6.18 when
the input voltage is 4 v.

## Review Questions

1. What precautions must be observed in writing Kirchhoff's voltage law equations for the circuit of Fig. 6.15?

2. What is the significance of a negative answer for $I_3$ in the circuit of Fig. 6.11?

3. Is it likely that either $I_1$ or $I_2$ in Fig. 6.11 would ever work out to be negative
answers? Explain.

4. If the tracing loops chosen in Fig. 6.11 do give a negative answer for $I_3$, show
with a sketch how you would redraw the tracing loops to produce a positive
answer for $I_3$.

5. What factor limits the application of the superposition theorem in network
solution?

6. What advantage does the superposition theorem have over Kirchhoff's laws equations in network solution?

7. Is it likely that we will encounter negative answers for component currents when applying the superposition theorem to a network problem? Explain.

8. Is it possible that we will have to *subtract* component currents when finding the real branch current when applying the superposition theorem? Explain.

9. What is meant by a "Thévenin equivalent circuit"?

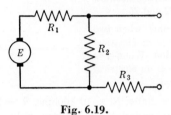

Fig. 6.19.

10. Draw a Thévenin equivalent circuit for the source of emf shown in Fig. 6.19 and express the equivalent emf ($E_x$) and the equivalent internal resistance ($R_x$) in terms of the components of the original circuit.

11. If a load ($R_L$) is connected to the original circuit of Fig. 6.19, derive a single equation for $I_L$.

12. Prove that the equation you derived for $I_L$ in the original circuit of Question 11 is equal to Equation (6.1) for the load current from the Thévenin equivalent source, thereby verifying Thévenin's theorem.

13. What feature of the Thévenin method of network solution simplifies the solution of networks containing more than one source of emf?

14. Explain how the polarities of the voltage drops across $R_G$ and $R_B$ were determined in Fig. 6.7(a).

15. Prove that the Thévenin equivalent resistance as found by the short-circuit method in the "sealed box" experiment is the same as that found by the procedure set forth in the statement of Thévenin's theorem.

16. What happens to the terminal voltage of a Norton equivalent circuit when a load resistor is connected to it?

17. Derive the wye to delta transformation Equation (6.6).

18. Figure 6.13 shows a method for solving a Wheatstone bridge by using a delta to wye transformation. Draw a diagram showing how the same bridge circuit can be solved by using a wye to delta transformation.

Chapter 7

# MAGNETIC CIRCUITS

## 1. Magnetism and Electricity

Although magnetism and electricity are often considered to be independent natural phenomena, in 1819 Hans Christian Oersted showed that electric currents and magnetic fields are closely associated. Modern theories of magnetism suggest that all magnetic properties stem from the exact manner in which the orbital electrons of some atoms move. As we have already discovered, electric current also consists of moving electrons. Since much of the apparatus used in practical electric circuits is dependent on magnetic properties in its operation, we must be able to identify these properties and express their magnitudes in suitable units.

In Chapter 1 we defined electricity as a medium for conveying energy from one location to another. Since an electric circuit is a means to this end, this particular concept of electricity is quite satisfactory for purposes of this course. As a study of electrostatics will reveal, there are other properties of electricity with which we are not concerned at the moment. Similarly the natural phenomenon of magnetism has several aspects that are not related to electric circuits. In this chapter we need consider only the characteristics of magnetic fields and the magnetic circuits which produce them.

## 2. The Nature of a Magnetic Field

If we bring a bar magnet close to a compass needle (which itself is a tiny magnet carefully pivoted at its center of gravity) as in Fig. 7.1, we will find that the compass needle will be deflected so that one end of the needle always points to one end of the bar magnet. As we move the bar magnet, the compass needle will follow this motion. Since the magnet itself does not come into contact with the compass needle, there must be some force associated with the bar magnet responsible for the deflection of the compass needle.

The space around the magnet in which this force can be detected is called a **magnetic field.**

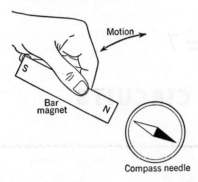

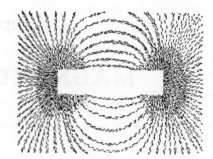

**Fig. 7.1.** Detecting the presence of a magnetic field.

**Fig. 7.2.** Pattern formed by sprinkling iron filings over a bar magnet.

Like the gravitational field which holds us to the Earth, a magnetic field contains no particles of matter, even of the infinitesimal magnitude of the electrons which form the current carrying medium of electric circuits. To assist us in visualizing the nature of a magnetic field, Michael Faraday suggested that we think of it as being made up of **magnetic lines of force.**

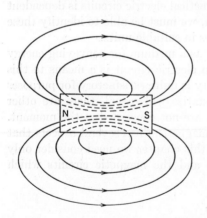

Even though these lines of force are fictitious, this concept has proved so useful in explaining magnetic properties that it has become the basis for establishing the standard units of measurement in magnetic circuits.

We can outline the magnetic field of a bar magnet by placing it under a piece of paper sprinkled with iron filings as in Fig. 7.2. We will note that the filings tend to gather around two areas, one at each end of the magnet. These areas where the effect of the magnetic field is concentrated are called the **poles** of the magnet. By applying Faraday's magnetic lines of force concept to the magnetic field detected by the iron filings in Fig. 7.2, we can sketch the magnetic field of a bar magnet in the form shown in Fig. 7.3.

**Fig. 7.3.** A diagram of the magnetic field around a bar magnet.

## 3. Characteristics of Magnetic Lines of Force

If we explore the magnetic fields of various shapes of magnets with a small compass needle as in Fig. 7.1 or iron filings as in Fig. 7.2, we will become aware of several important characteristics of magnetic lines of force. Since all the electromagnetic effects which we shall be studying can be traced directly to these characteristics, it is important that we learn them thoroughly at this point.

Magnetic lines of force possess **direction.**

Combining Figs. 7.3 and 7.1, we can say that the compass needle in Fig. 7.1 aligns itself with the magnetic lines of force. If we now bring the opposite pole of the bar magnet near the compass needle in Fig. 7.1, we will find that the compass needle will again align itself with the magnetic lines of force but it will now have the *opposite* end of the needle pointing at the pole of the bar magnet. For the compass needle to be able to distinguish one pole of the bar magnet from the other, we must think of the magnetic lines of force as possessing a positive direction. Since magnetic lines of force are mythical, this direction will have to be arbitrarily assigned. However, since the Earth itself has a magnetic field, we can identify the poles of a magnet more specifically. If we suspend the bar magnet by a thread tied around its center of gravity, it will act like a compass needle and align itself with the Earth's magnetic field. One pole of the magnet will always point north and is therefore referred to as the **North pole** of the magnet. Similarly the other pole is called the **South pole.** Having identified the poles of a magnet, we can now state that the positive direction of the magnetic lines of force in the region around a magnet shall be considered as being *from* the North pole of the magnet *toward* the South pole.

Magnetic lines of force always form **complete loops.**

They do not begin at the North pole of a magnet and end at the South pole but continue between South pole and North pole inside the magnet to form complete closed loops. We can show this by cutting the magnet of Fig. 7.4(a) in two. As we pull the two sections apart, we can detect the presence of the magnetic lines of force in the gap between the two halves. New North and South poles are formed on each side of the gap as shown in Fig. 7.4(b).

Magnetic lines of force represent a **tension along their length** which tends to make them as short as possible.

This effect would also be noticed as we separate the two halves of the magnet in Fig. 7.4(b). In pulling the two halves apart, we would be lengthening the lines of force and we would notice a definite attraction between the two pieces as the magnetic lines of force try to pull them to-

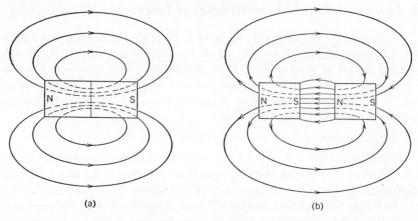

**Fig. 7.4.** Showing that magnetic lines of force form complete loops by continuing from South pole to North pole within the magnet.

gether again in an attempt to shorten the lines of force. The analogy of a magnetic field composed of rubber bands sometimes helps in grasping this idea.

Magnetic lines of force **repel** one another.

We can see this by examining the magnetic field around a bar magnet (Fig. 7.3). The magnetic lines of force tend to diverge as we move away from the poles rather than converge or even remain parallel. As a result of this mutual repulsion, **magnetic lines of force cannot intersect** but must always form individual closed loops.

The combination of these basic characteristics is responsible for the

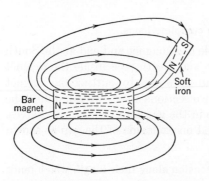

shape of the magnetic field of a magnet. The magnetic lines of force are kept in equilibrium by each line tending to shrink its loop length and at the same time being prevented from doing so by the repulsion of the next smaller line of force loop. The magnetic field around a uniform magnet will be symmetrical unless there are other magnetic materials within the field.

**Fig. 7.5.** Magnetic lines of force detour to include soft iron bar in their circuit.

If we place a piece of soft iron in the field of a magnet, we will find that some of the magnetic lines of force alter their normal paths to in-

clude the iron bar in their circuit as shown in Fig. 7.5. This is because iron is a better "conductor" of magnetic lines of force than air. The net result of the change in the pattern of the magnetic field is that the total number of lines of force is increased.

Therefore **magnetic fields always tend to arrange themselves** in such a manner that **the maximum number of lines of force** is set up.

The piece of soft iron in Fig. 7.5 exhibits the properties of a magnet while it is in the field of the main magnet. It takes on a South pole where the direction of the magnetic lines of force is toward the soft iron, and a North pole where their direction is away from the iron. The piece of soft iron has become a **temporary** magnet by **induction.** It will lose most of its magnetism when removed from the field of the main magnet.

## 4. Magnetic Field Around a Current-Carrying Conductor

So far we have discussed only the magnetic field around a permanent magnet. The disadvantage of this type of magnet is that we cannot turn the magnetic field on and off at will. However, Oersted discovered that a magnetic field is produced around an electric conductor whenever current flows through it. Since we can control an electric current quite readily, we therefore have a means of controlling the production of a magnetic field.

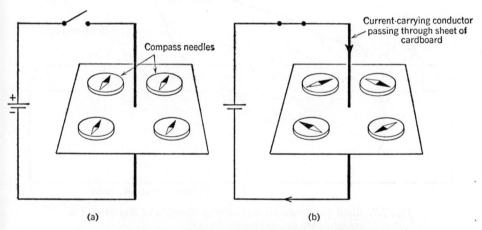

Fig. 7.6.  (a) With no current, compass needles all indicate Earth's magnetic field; (b) when current flows, compass needles indicate
circular magnetic lines of force around the conductor.

By exploring the magnetic field around a current-carrying conductor with iron filings or small compass needles as in Fig. 7.6, we find that the lines of force form concentric circles in a plane which is at right angles to the axis of the conductor. As the current increases from zero, a magnetic line of force loop of infinitesimal radius forms at the center of the conductor. As the current increases, the radius of the magnetic line of force increases and another loop forms at the center of the conductor. As the result of mutual repulsion of magnetic lines of force, this new loop forces the first line of force to expand still further. As long as the current is *increasing*, a whole series of closed loop magnetic lines of force *expand* outward from the center of the conductor. When the current becomes steady, the magnetic field becomes stationary. Because of the tendency for magnetic lines of force to shorten like rubber bands, they will be concentrated at the center of the conductor and spaced farther and farther apart as we move outward from the center of the conductor. When the current is turned off, this tension causes each line of force to collapse back toward the center of the conductor.

Although the magnetic field around a straight current-carrying conductor has no North and South poles, the individual lines of force must still have direction. This direction can be checked by the compass needle in Fig. 7.6(b). Reversing the direction of the current through the conductor causes all the compass needles to reverse their positions. The direction of the magnetic field around a straight current-carrying conductor is determined by the right hand rule illustrated in Fig. 7.7.

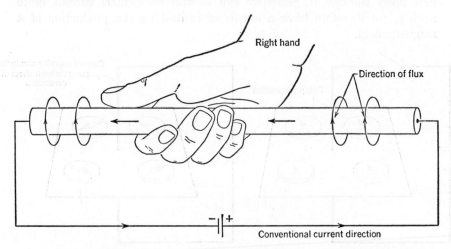

Right hand

Direction of flux

Conventional current direction

**Fig. 7.7.** Right hand rule for determining direction of flux around a straight current-carrying conductor.

**Grasp the conductor** (figuratively speaking) **with the right hand so that the thumb points in the conventional current direction; the fingers circling the conductor then point in the direction of the magnetic lines of force around the conductor.**

If we form the current-carrying conductor into a loop as in Fig. 7.8, we will note that the magnetic lines of force all pass through the center of the loop in the *same* direction. Since, for a given current, the total number of lines of force has not changed, we have strengthened the magnetic field by concentrating it into a smaller physical area.

We can concentrate the magnetic field of the conductor still further by winding the conductor around a cardboard tube as in Fig. 7.9 to form a **solenoid.** Since the current in the adjacent turns of the solenoid is traveling in the same direction around the circumference of the coil, the

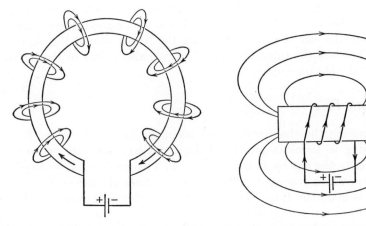

**Fig. 7.8.** Concentrating the magnetic field by forming the conductor into a loop.

**Fig. 7.9.** The magnetic field pattern of a current-carrying solenoid.

solenoid behaves as a single loop of a stranded conductor, each strand carrying a current equal to the actual solenoid current. This will result in a magnetic field around the solenoid having the pattern shown in Fig. 7.9. Since this magnetic field pattern is similar to that of the bar magnet of Fig. 7.3, we have produced an **electromagnet.**

The right-hand rule we use to find the direction of the flux around a straight wire can be adapted to a solenoid as illustrated in Fig. 7.10.

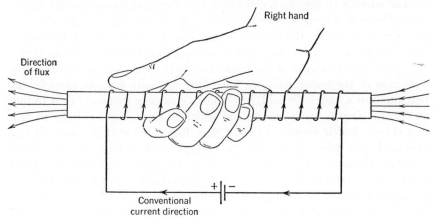

**Fig. 7.10.** Right hand rule for determining direction of flux through a current-carrying solenoid.

> Grasp the solenoid with the right hand so that the fingers follow the conventional current direction around the circumference of the solenoid; the thumb then points in the direction of the magnetic lines of force through the center of the solenoid.

Since we can think of the solenoid as an electromagnet, we can think of the end of the solenoid where the direction of the magnetic lines of force is away from the coil (Fig. 7.10) as being the North pole of the electromagnet. Therefore the thumb in this hand rule also points to the North pole end of the electromagnet.

## 5. Magnetic Flux

In describing the characteristics of magnetic lines of force, we have been thinking in terms of individual lines of force. However, when we wish to refer to the *number* of lines of force in a magnetic field, we require a single term which represents all the magnetic lines of force collectively. This term is **magnetic flux.** Therefore **magnetic flux** and **magnetic lines** (plural) **of force** are synonymous.

For current to flow in an electric circuit, the circuit must form a closed loop. Since magnetic lines of force must always form closed loops, we can refer to the path we can trace around these loops as a **magnetic circuit.** Although there is no *flow* associated with a magnetic circuit comparable to the motion of the electrons which constitute the current in an electric circuit, we will discover many similarities between current in an electric circuit and flux in a magnetic circuit.

Because of the close relationship between magnetism and electricity, in establishing a unit for magnetic flux, we should base it on already established electrical units. In Fig. 7.8 we noted that when we caused an electric current to flow in a clockwise direction around an electric circuit in the shape of a loop, we established a magnetic flux whose direction was into the page within the loop. Michael Faraday replaced the battery in Fig. 7.8 with a sensitive current-indicating **galvanometer** and then thrust a magnet into the center of the loop. As he did so he noticed a momentary deflection of the meter pointer. Therefore, not only does an electric current produce a magnetic field, but when we cause a magnetic field to link an electric circuit, we *induce* an emf which in turn causes current to flow in a closed electric circuit. Faraday also discovered that the induced emf appeared only when he moved the magnet with respect to the electric circuit, and that the faster he moved the magnet, the greater the deflection of the meter pointer. We shall pursue the consequences of this **electromagnetic induction** on the behavior of electric circuits further in Chapter 9. But for the moment Faraday's discovery gives us a means of specifying the basic unit of magnetic flux in terms of the emf induced into a single turn loop as we cause the flux *linking* (passing through the center of) the loop to build up from zero.

The **weber**\* is the mks unit of magnetic flux. If the flux linking a single turn coil builds up from zero at a rate which will induce an average emf of one volt in the coil, at the end of one second the flux linking the coil will have a magnitude of one weber.

For practical purposes in English-speaking countries, it is customary to express magnetic flux in terms of the individual magnetic lines of force which constitute magnetic flux. It is assumed that

$$1 \text{ weber} = 10^8 \text{ lines of force (maxwells)} \dagger$$

The letter symbol for **magnetic flux** is the Greek letter $\Phi$ (phi).

## 6. Magnetomotive Force

Just as an electric current cannot flow unless an electromotive force is applied to an electric circuit, magnetic lines of force cannot be established until a **magnetomotive force** is produced. With the electromagnet of Fig. 7.9, magnetic flux appeared when electric current flowed in the solenoid. Therefore magnetomotive force (mmf) must be a direct result of electric current. We can therefore establish a unit of mmf on the basis of the current flowing in a coil of wire. Since adding turns of wire to a solenoid produces the same effect as adding extra strands, each carrying the same current, to a single loop, the mmf will be directly proportional to both the current and the number of turns of wire in the coil.

The **ampere-turn** is the mks and English unit of magnetomotive force. The letter symbol for **mmf** is the script letter $\mathcal{F}$.

$$\mathcal{F} = NI \tag{7.1}$$

where $\mathcal{F}$ is the magnetomotive force in ampere-turns, $N$ is the number of turns of wire in the coil, and $I$ is the current through the coil in amperes.

## 7. Reluctance

For a given electric circuit, Ohm discovered a constant proportionality between the applied emf and the resulting current. He termed this constant the **resistance** of the electric circuit. Similarly for a given magnetic circuit (of nonferrous materials), there is a constant proportionality be-

---

\* The mks unit of flux was named in honor of Wilhelm Eduard Weber, who established many of the fundamental theories of magnetism.

† The older cgs system of units gave the line of force the name **maxwell** in honor of James Clerk Maxwell. Maxwells and lines of force are numerically synonymous.

tween the magnetomotive force and the resulting magnetic flux. This constant is called the **reluctance** of the magnetic circuit.

The letter symbol for **reluctance** is the script letter $\mathcal{R}$.

From the definition of reluctance,

$$\mathcal{R} = \frac{\mathcal{F}}{\Phi} \tag{7.2}$$

*where $\mathcal{R}$ is reluctance, $\mathcal{F}$ is magnetomotive force in ampere-turns, and $\Phi$ is flux in webers.*

Since it is not customary to calculate reluctance in the solution of magnetic circuits, a special unit for reluctance is not required. Reluctance can be expressed simply in terms of **ampere-turns per weber.**

## 8. Permeability

In dealing with parallel electric circuits, we found it more convenient to think in terms of the conductance of the circuit elements rather than in terms of their resistance. Similarly in dealing with magnetic circuits, we shall find it more convenient to think in terms of the ability of magnetic circuits to permit the setting up of magnetic lines of force rather than in terms of their opposition to magnetic flux.

**Permeance** is a measure of the ability of a magnetic circuit to permit the setting up of magnetic lines of force. The letter symbol for **permeance** is the script letter $\mathcal{P}$.

$$\mathcal{P} = \frac{1}{\mathcal{R}} \tag{7.3}$$

In comparing the magnetic properties of various materials, we would then compare the permeance of sections of each material with unit length and cross-sectional area. Permeance per unit length and cross-sectional area of a material is called its **permeability.** As such, **permeability** is a figure indicating the ability of a *material* to permit the setting up of magnetic lines of force; whereas **permeance** is a measure of the ability of a *given magnetic circuit* to permit the setting up of magnetic lines of force.

The letter symbol for **permeability** is the Greek letter $\mu$ (mu).

Unfortunately the letter symbol for the permeability of magnetic materials is the same as the prefix for *micro*. However, micro as a prefix is not required in dealing with magnetic circuits.

From the definition of permeability,

$$\mu = \mathcal{P}\frac{l}{A} = \frac{l}{\mathcal{R}A} \tag{7.4}$$

*where $\mu$ is the permeability in mks units, $\mathcal{P}$ is permeance $= 1/\mathcal{R}$, $\mathcal{R}$ is reluctance in ampere-turns per weber, $l$ is the length of the magnetic circuit in meters, and $A$ is the cross-sectional area in square meters.*

Although it is not customary to state a unit for permeability, we need to know its numerical value with respect to already defined units in order to convert from the mks value of permeability to the English value. Collecting the units in Equation (7.4) will show that we can express permeability in terms of **webers per ampere-turn for a one meter cube.** For practical purposes in English-speaking countries, the equivalent numerical value of permeability would be expressed in terms of **lines of force per ampere-turn for a one inch cube.**

## 9. Flux Density and Magnetizing Force

Permeability is a measure of the ability of a *material* to permit the setting up of magnetic lines of force. Equation (7.4) was set up so that permeability could be expressed in terms of permeance of a cube of that material having unit length and cross-sectional area. Therefore in thinking of permeability, we are not dealing with total flux. Rather we are interested in the *flux per unit cross-sectional area.*

Flux per unit cross-sectional area is called **flux density.** The **letter symbol** for flux density is **B.**

No special unit of flux density is used in the mks system. From the definition of flux density,

$$B = \frac{\Phi}{A} \tag{7.5}$$

*where* **B** *is flux density in* **webers per square meter,** **$\Phi$** *is total flux in a magnetic circuit in webers, and A is the cross-sectional area of the magnetic circuit in square meters.*

Again since permeability is based on a *cube* of the magnetic material, we are not concerned with the magnetomotive force required for the full length of the magnetic circuit. Rather we are interested in the magnetomotive force required to create a certain flux density in a unit length of the magnetic circuit.

Magnetomotive force per unit length is usually called the **magnetizing force.**

It is sometimes called **mmf gradient** or **magnetic intensity.**

The letter symbol for magnetizing force is **H.**

No special unit of magnetizing force is used in the mks system. From the definition of magnetizing force,

$$H = \frac{\mathfrak{F}}{l} \tag{7.6}$$

*where* **H** *is the magnetizing force in ampere-turns per meter,* $\mathfrak{F}$ *is the magnetomotive force in ampere-turns, and l is the length of the magnetic circuit in meters.*

Since $\qquad \mathcal{R} = \dfrac{\mathcal{F}}{\Phi}$ and $\therefore$ $\mathcal{P} = \dfrac{\Phi}{\mathcal{F}}$

substituting in Equation (7.4) gives

$$\mu = \frac{\Phi}{\mathcal{F}} \times \frac{l}{A} \quad \text{or} \quad \mu = \frac{\Phi}{A} \times \frac{l}{\mathcal{F}}$$

But $\qquad\qquad \dfrac{\Phi}{A} = B$ and $\dfrac{\mathcal{F}}{l} = H$

$$\therefore \quad \mu = \frac{B}{H} \tag{7.7}$$

*where $\mu$ is permeability, $B$ is flux density in webers per square meter, and $H$ is magnetizing force in ampere-turns per meter.*

In the English system of units, **flux density** is expressed in terms of **lines of force per square inch** and **magnetizing force** is expressed in terms of **ampere-turns per inch**.

## 10. Diamagnetic and Paramagnetic Materials

Since magnetic flux consists of imaginary lines of force, rather than drifting particles as in the case of electric current, there is no *insulator* for magnetic flux just as there is no insulator to prevent the gravitational force of the Earth from acting on a body. Magnetic lines of force can therefore pass through all substances and through empty space or a vacuum. Most substances have no more effect on a magnetic circuit than does free space. Such materials are **nonmagnetic** and have the same permeability as free space.

The permeability of free space in mks units is

$$\mu_v = 4\pi \times 10^{-7}$$

A few materials have a permeability slightly less than that of free space. They appear to offer a slight opposition to magnetic lines of force as compared with free space. Such materials are called **diamagnetic** materials. Silver, copper, and hydrogen show slight diamagnetic tendencies. A few materials have a permeability just slightly greater than that of free space. These materials are therefore very slightly magnetic. Such materials are called **paramagnetic** materials. Platinum, aluminum, and oxygen are inclined to be paramagnetic. In both cases these effects are so slight that, for practical purposes, both diamagnetic and paramagnetic substances can be assumed to have the same permeability as free space.

The magnetic properties of substances can be explained in terms of electromagnetism. We have already noted that electric current produces a magnetomotive force. Since electric current consists of moving electrons, the orbital electrons of every atom must be producing an mmf. In nonmagnetic materials, the orbital pattern is such that these individual mmf's completely cancel out, leaving zero net mmf for the atom. Such atoms therefore show no magnetic properties. Paramagnetic materials have a very slight net mmf due to the pattern of the orbital electrons. These atoms tend to line themselves up with any magnetic field, thus slightly increasing the over-all mmf and the resulting flux. Diamagnetic atoms show a slight net mmf, but when they are exposed to a magnetic field, their magnetic axes behave like the axis of a spinning top. The precessional motion of the magnetic axes of diamagnetic materials around the axis of a magnetic field has the same over-all effect as if these particular atoms had the ability to line themselves up in such a direction as to weaken the over-all magnetic field.

## 11. Ferromagnetic Materials

Some substances including iron and its compounds, and to a lesser extent, nickel and cobalt, have permeabilities many hundreds of times greater than that of free space. These substances are called **ferromagnetic** since iron is the major substance in this group. Apparently the pattern of the orbital electrons in the atoms of these materials is such that each atom has considerable net mmf. In an unmagnetized state, the atoms in a given piece of iron have a random orientation so that the net mmf for the piece of iron as a whole is zero. It is easy to visualize the atoms, which themselves are tiny magnets, rotating to line themselves up with a magnetic field in the case of liquids and gases. But the rotation of atoms and molecules of a solid requires further consideration. The magnetic properties of ferromagnetic solids are based on the manner in which the magnetic molecules within a piece of iron can align themselves with a magnetic field. This alignment process represents **magnetization** of the material.

It appears that the atoms of iron do not act independently as individual magnets. Since iron has a crystalline structure, groups of up to $10^{15}$ atoms, all aligned with their magnetic axes in the same direction, form magnetic **domains.** It seems that all atoms in a domain must rotate together when placed in a magnetic field. Iron crystals are shaped like cubes and each crystal contains many magnetic domains. These domains have their magnetic axes aligned with one of the edges of the cube rather than along one of the diagonals. In demagnetized iron crystals, one-third of the domains are aligned in each of the three planes which are parallel to the faces of the cube. Half of the domains in each plane have their magnetic axes in one direction and the other half are in the opposite direction.

If we place a single crystal of iron within a magnetic field of a solenoid in such a manner that the magnetic lines of force are parallel to one edge of the crystal, it is fairly easy for all the domains to align themselves with this magnetizing field. This greatly increases the number of lines of force which can be set up by the original mmf, and the permeability of the iron appears to be very high. If, however, the crystal is located so that a *diagonal* of the crystal is parallel to the magnetic lines of force, it is much more difficult for the domains to rotate into alignment with the flux since this is not one of their natural axes. The permeability now appears to be

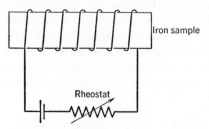

appreciably less although it is still many hundreds of times greater than that of free space, since the alignment of the domains along any axis will greatly increase the total flux.

**Fig. 7.11.** Magnetizing an iron sample.

In a typical sample of iron the orientation of the crystals is quite random. If we place this sample inside a solenoid, as in Fig. 7.11, and gradually increase the current in the coil, those crystals whose *faces* are parallel to the magnetic field will become magnetized first. Then as the magnetizing force increases, those crystals whose *diagonals* are parallel to the magnetic lines of force will become magnetized. If we increase the current through the solenoid to a point where all the domains are aligned with the magnetic field, any further increase in current can only increase the total flux by the same amount as if the iron were not present. The iron is now said to be completely **saturated** and its permeability has dropped to that of any nonmagnetic material. The current which is required to saturate a sample of iron within the solenoid depends on the type and grade of iron used.

The permeability of iron is also dependent on temperature. As the temperature is raised, a temperature known as the **Curie point** is reached where all magnetic properties disappear. This is thought to be brought about by thermal agitation becoming so great that the magnetic domains no longer exist and the individual molecules are not able to align themselves with a magnetic field in order to exhibit their magnetic properties.

## 12. Magnetization Curves

Rearranging Equation (7.7) gives

$$B = \mu H$$

Although magnetizing force is an independent variable over which we have direct control by varying the current in the solenoid which produces the mmf, the permeability of a given sample of iron varies considerably as the current in the coil is changed. The exact value of permeability depends on what percentage of the magnetic domains have aligned themselves with the magnetic field. This in turn is directly related to the flux density. Even though we can prepare a graph, as in Fig. 7.12, showing how the permeability of a given sample of iron is related to flux density, we are still faced with the problem indicated by the above equation. For a given magnetizing force, the flux density depends on the permeability, which in turn depends on the flux density. Such a situation results in a "cut-and-try" solution for flux density.

To avoid this situation, we can eliminate one of the dependent variables by disregarding permeability and concerning ourselves only with the manner in which the flux density of a certain type of iron varies with the applied magnetizing force. Since **B** and **H** as units of measurement were both based on a cube with *unit* dimensions, the **magnetization curve** (or simply **BH curve**) produced by plotting a graph of the manner in which **B** depends on **H**, is dependent only on the *type* of iron and not on its dimensions.

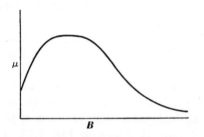

Fig. 7.12. The manner in which the per-      Fig. 7.13. **BH** curve for a typical cast
meability of cast steel varies                  steel sample.
with flux density.

On examining Fig. 7.13 we will note that the flux density increases slowly at first as the current in the energizing solenoid is gradually increased from zero. However, once the magnetizing force is sufficient to start aligning the magnetic domains in those iron crystals that are parallel to the magnetic lines of force, the flux density starts to rise quite steeply with any further increase in **exciting** current. This point where the steel sample begins to magnetize is indicated by the lower **knee** in the **BH** curve. Soft iron samples begin to magnetize with a very small magnetizing force and the magnetization curve for such samples shows practically no evidence of a lower knee.

At the point where all the domains of those crystals whose edges are parallel to the magnetic lines of force are aligned with the magnetic field, the **BH** curve enters an upper knee where the increase in flux density for a given increase in magnetizing force becomes progressively smaller. In this range of magnetizing force, the domains of those crystals of the sample which do not have an edge parallel to the magnetic lines of force are being aligned with the magnetic field. Since it is more difficult for these domains to change the orientation of their magnetic axes to coincide with the magnetic field, a greater increase in $H$ is required to bring about a certain increase in $B$. Finally for large values of magnetizing force, when all the domains are aligned with the magnetic field, the $BH$ curve becomes a straight line with a gradual slope which represents only the same increase in $B$ for a given increase in $H$ as for any nonmagnetic material.

It is difficult to mark the exact point on the $BH$ curve of Fig. 7.13 where saturation occurs. Theoretical saturation is when all the domains are finally aligned with the magnetic field. But this requires considerable magnetizing force for some types of iron. *Practical* saturation may be defined as the flux density beyond which it is *impractical* to magnetize a certain magnetic material. For some applications this point is the upper knee in the $BH$ curve where the steep, linear portion of the slope ends. In high-quality audio transformers, magnetizing force must be kept below this point, since any swing in $H$ past this point does not result in a linear transfer of the audio signal from a current waveform in the coil to a flux waveform in the magnetic circuit. To reduce the cost of power transformers, the amount of iron can be reduced if we design them so that their magnetic cores are magnetized to a point slightly beyond the upper knee of the $BH$ curve.

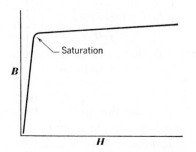

**Fig. 7.14.** *BH* curve for iron sample in which all crystals have the same orientation.

The random orientation of the iron crystals is responsible for the gradual saturation of most types of iron as shown in Fig. 7.13. If iron could be manufactured so that all the crystals have the *same* orientation, it follows that the flux density would rise very steeply with an increase in magnetizing force since all the magnetic domains would be acted upon in the same manner. At a certain definite value of magnetizing force, the iron will saturate as shown in Fig. 7.14, since *all* the domains line themselves up with the magnetic field at this particular value of magnetizing force. Such a type of iron is available for use in magnetic amplifiers, magnetic tapes for magnetic recording, and magnetic memory cores for electronic computers.

Although each different type of iron and steel will have its own particular $BH$ characteristics, we can solve the magnetic circuit problems in this chapter if we are given the flux density vs magnetizing force data for three commonly used magnetic materials; cast iron, cast steel, and sheet steel. This data may be supplied in table form as in Table I but it will be much easier to notice saturation and to interpolate for values not given in the table if we transfer the information to an accurate **BH** graph.

Table I. TABLE OF TYPICAL MAGNETIC PROPERTIES

| Magnetizing force | Flux density (webers per square meter) | | |
|---|---|---|---|
| (ampere-turns per meter) | Cast iron | Cast steel | Sheet steel |
| 200 | 0.07 | 0.36 | 0.64 |
| 400 | 0.18 | 0.65 | 1.00 |
| 600 | 0.26 | 0.87 | 1.17 |
| 800 | 0.32 | 1.00 | 1.29 |
| 1000 | 0.36 | 1.11 | 1.37 |
| 1400 | 0.42 | 1.25 | 1.45 |
| 1800 | 0.47 | 1.33 | 1.51 |
| 2200 | 0.51 | 1.39 | 1.55 |
| 2600 | 0.55 | 1.44 | 1.59 |
| 3000 | 0.59 | 1.48 | 1.62 |
| 3500 | 0.64 | 1.53 | 1.65 |
| 4000 | 0.68 | 1.57 | 1.68 |
| 4500 | 0.71 | 1.595 | 1.695 |
| 5000 | 0.74 | 1.62 | 1.71 |

In dealing with the specific resistance of electric conductors, we found it more practical to switch from the ohm-meters of the mks system of units to the ohms per mil-foot based on English units of length and cross section. Similarly, although the data in Table I is given in mks units, we can avoid having to convert the common units of length and cross section into metric units if we are given the magnetization curves plotted in terms of English units of flux density and magnetizing force as in Fig. 7.15.

## 13. Permeability from the BH Curve

As we noted in Fig. 7.12, the permeability of a ferromagnetic material is far from being a constant. It is very dependent on flux density. However, we can determine the permeability at a given flux density without being supplied with tables or graphs similar to Fig. 7.12. We can apply the relationship stated in Equation (7.7) to the **BH** curve which is supplied for a given type of magnetic material. The manner in which we apply this $\mu = B/H$ relationship to a **BH** curve will depend on the conditions under which the magnetic circuit is to be operated.

If the current in the energizing solenoid is to be kept constant, we can locate the appropriate value for magnetizing force and the resulting value of flux density on the **BH** curve as shown in Fig. 7.16(a). The **normal permeability** for this flux density is simply

$$\mu = \frac{B}{H}$$

In some magnetic circuits the magnetizing force will be varying between two points [$A$ and $B$ in Fig. 7.16(b)]. This situation occurs when a fluctuating direct current flows in the coil. In this case we are interested in the permeability over the limited operating range. This value of permeability is called the **incremental permeability** and is determined as shown in Fig. 7.16(b).

$$\mu_\Delta = \frac{\Delta B}{\Delta H} \tag{7.8}$$

*where $\mu_\Delta$ is the incremental permeability, $\Delta B$ is the difference between the maximum and minimum flux densities, $\Delta H$ is the difference between the maximum and minimum values of magnetizing force.*

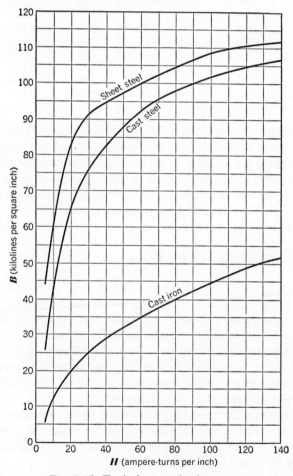

**Fig. 7.15.** Typical magnetization curves.

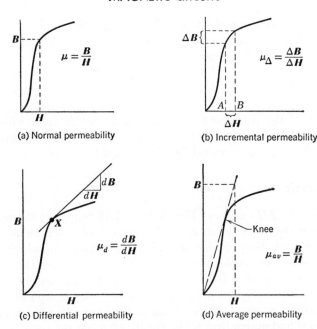

**Fig. 7.16.** Determining permeability from $BH$ curve.

If alternating current is passed through the solenoid, the magnetizing force will be constantly changing over wide limits. In this case we are likely to be concerned with the permeability as the magnetizing force *swings through* a certain value rather than as it maintains that value. This value of permeability is called the **differential permeability** for a particular point on the $BH$ curve. It can be determined from the *slope* of the magnetizing curve at the point in question. This can be calculated by drawing a tangent to the $BH$ curve at the desired point [point $X$ in Fig. 7.16(c)] and then constructing a right-angled triangle with the vertical side representing a certain increase in flux density, the horizontal side representing the equivalent increase in magnetizing force and the tangent forming the hypotenuse. Then $dB$ and $dH$ are determined in the same manner as for incremental permeability, and the differential permeability at point $X$ becomes

$$\mu_d = \frac{dB}{dH} \tag{7.9}$$

In some electronic circuits where the current is in the order of microamperes, the magnetizing force is so small that it is difficult to read the $B/H$ ratio from the magnetization curve. However, the value of permeability for very small values of $H$ and the associated values of $B$ is quite important and is called **initial permeability** ($\mu_0$). Initial permeability could also be defined as the differential permeability when the magnetizing force is zero.

We can simplify the problem of solving magnetic circuits in which the magnetizing force, consequently the permeability, is continually changing by determining an **average permeability** value for the type of iron being used. The average permeability is obtained by drawing a straight line through the origin of the **BH** graph and the upper knee of the curve as in Fig. 7.16(d). Because this line is *straight*, we may pick *any* point on this line to read off the corresponding values of **B** and **H** from which $\mu_{av}$ is determined. As long as the flux density in a magnetic circuit is kept below saturation, this average permeability is reasonably accurate.

## 14. Hysteresis

Although the **BH** curves of Figs. 7.13 to 7.16 represent the manner in which the flux density of an *unmagnetized* sample of iron rises as the value of **H** is increased, they do *not* represent the manner in which the flux density drops as the magnetizing force is decreased. When the current in the energizing solenoid is switched off, some of the magnetic domains do not return to their original orientation. Some types of iron have a very low **retentivity,** i.e., most of the domains do return to an orientation in which the **residual magnetism** is practically nil when the current is turned off. Such materials would be classed as **temporary magnets.** In some other types of iron a large percentage of the domains retain the orientation they were forced to take while in a strong magnetic field. These materials become **permanent magnets.**

Most magnetic materials have some retentivity. When the magnetizing force is returned to zero, the residual magnetism of the iron will produce an appreciable value of flux density. In order to get rid of this residual flux, it is necessary to pass some current through the solenoid in the *opposite* direction. The amount of *negative* magnetizing force required to demagnetize a particular sample of iron is called the **coercive force.**

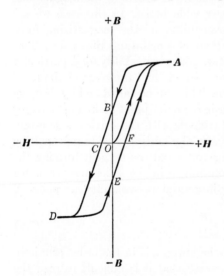

**Fig. 7.17.** Typical hysteresis loop.

Figure 7.17 shows the complete cycle of magnetization of a piece of iron as an *alternating* current is passed through the solenoid. Assuming that the sample started from an unmagnetized state, as the current is increased from zero to maximum in one direction through the solenoid (positive values of $H$), the flux density increases along the customary magnetizing curve $OA$. As the current is reduced to zero, the flux density decreases from saturation to a residual flux density at point $B$. In order to bring the flux density in the iron to zero, the current through the coil must be reversed and increased to a value represented by $OC$. As the current is now increased in this direction, the iron will again saturate at point $D$ with the magnetic domains all lined up in the opposite direction to that represented by point $A$. Again as the current is reduced to zero, the flux density in the iron will decrease only to point $E$. Again it is necessary to reverse the current direction to bring the flux density to zero at point $F$. Increasing the current to its maximum value in the positive direction completes the cycle by saturating the iron and returning the flux density to point $A$ in the graph of Fig. 7.17.

As shown in Fig. 7.17, when the magnetizing force is due to an alternating current, the flux density of ferromagnetic materials tends to *lag* the magnetizing force which creates it. This lagging of the magnetization of the iron behind the magnetizing force is called **hysteresis.** The graph which shows this lag as in Fig. 7.17 is called a **hysteresis loop.**

Since only ferromagnetic materials have residual magnetism, nonmagnetic materials show no hysteresis effect. For nonmagnetic materials, $B = \mu H$, where $\mu$ is a constant ($4\pi \times 10^{-7}$). Therefore the flux density is always directly proportional to the magnetizing force, regardless of its variation.

Hysteresis is due to some of the magnetic domains in a ferromagnetic material not wanting to return to their original orientation and having to be forced to do so by a certain amount of reversed magnetizing force (coercive force). Whenever motion is accomplished against an opposing force, an energy transfer must take place. This energy is taken from the source of alternating emf which is responsible for the magnetic domains having to change their orientation, and is transferred to the molecules of the ferromagnetic material in the form of heat. The higher the frequency of the alternating current in the solenoid, the more rapidly the magnetic domains have to change their alignment and therefore the greater the **hysteresis loss.**

The greater the retentivity of a particular type of iron, the greater the coercive force that is required to demagnetize it. This means an increased opposition by the magnetic domains to reorientation, which results in a greater transfer of energy into heat. Therefore hysteresis loss is also proportional to the retentivity of the iron. The iron selected for use in the magnetic circuits of transformers which are continually subject to an alternating mmf should have an absolute minimum retentivity if hysteresis loss is to be kept at a low value. Consideration of Fig. 7.17 will show us that as the residual flux density of a sample of iron increases, the area within the hysteresis loop increases. Therefore the area within the hysteresis loop for a given iron sample is a useful indication of its hysteresis loss.

## 15. Eddy Current

In Section 5 of this chapter we found that moving a magnetic field with respect to an electric conductor induced an emf into the conductor. This situation will exist inside a solenoid which is energized by an alternating current. If a metal core is placed inside the solenoid, any motion of the magnetic field will induce an emf in it. In electromagnetic induction the direction of the magnetic lines of force, the motion of the magnetic lines of force with respect to the electric conductor, and the flow of electric current are all at right angles to one another.

As the current in the solenoid is increased, more magnetic lines of force must be set up. This crowding of more lines of force into the existing space causes the lines of force already present to move along a radius from the axis of the solenoid. The direction of the lines of force themselves is parallel to the axis of the solenoid. The motion of these lines of force in and out along the various radii when an alternating current flows in the solenoid will then induce an emf into the metal core of the solenoid. As we have already noted, the current resulting from this induced emf must be at right angles to both the radius and the axis of the solenoid.

The only possible manner in which this can be achieved is for current to flow in a circle around the circumference of the metallic core as shown in Fig. 7.18. This current is called an **eddy current.** Eddy current is pro-

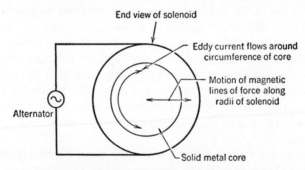

**Fig. 7.18.** Eddy current in a solid metal core.

duced in any core material which is an *electric* conductor. The core does not have to be a magnetic material. A brass core can become very hot due to eddy current produced as a result of a high-frequency alternating current in the solenoid. This heat comes from the customary $I^2R$ power loss as the eddy current flows through the resistance of the core material. Since the resistance of iron is comparatively high, the eddy current loss in a solid iron core would rule out its use with alternating mmf.

Eddy current loss can be greatly reduced by replacing the solid core with one made up of thin **laminations** which are insulated from each other with a thin coat of varnish. The laminations are oriented as shown in Fig. 7.19 so that the direction in which eddy current would have to flow is from

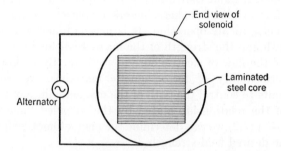

**Fig. 7.19.** Cross-section of a laminated core.

lamination to lamination through the varnish. Because of the high resistance of the varnish, the eddy current in a laminated core is very small and the accompanying eddy current power loss is in many cases negligible.

## 16. Magnetic Shielding

Although there is no insulator for magnetic lines of force, it is possible to shield a certain space such as a sensitive meter movement or a cathode ray tube from stray magnetic fields by enclosing this space in a cylinder of high permeability iron. As we noted in discussing the characteristics of magnetic lines of force, they will go out of their way to include the lower reluctance path through the iron as part of their circuit. This leaves the space within the cylinder comparatively free of magnetic lines of force as shown in Fig. 7.20.

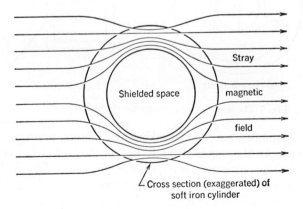

**Fig. 7.20.** Magnetic shielding.

## 17. Practical Magnetic Circuits

Since magnetic fields are produced around current-carrying electric conductors, it follows that magnetic fields are associated with practically all electric apparatus and that much of this apparatus (e.g., motors, generators, transformers, loudspeakers, meters, relays, etc.) is quite dependent on magnetic fields for its operation. It is just as important to be able to control the path and the strength of the magnetic fields in such devices as it is to control the flow of electric current in them. By making use of the very high permeability of ferromagnetic materials, we can construct **magnetic circuits** to control the path of the magnetic lines of force; and by application of the relationship stated by the so-called "magnetic Ohm's law" of Equation (7.2) we can determine the magnetomotive force required to develop the desired field strength.

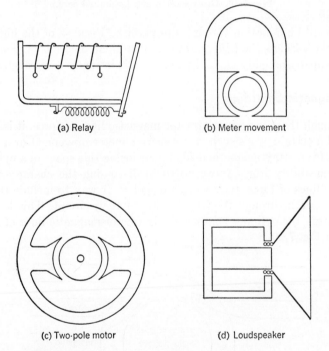

(a) Relay

(b) Meter movement

(c) Two-pole motor

(d) Loudspeaker

**Fig. 7.21.** Some typical magnetic circuit cross-sections.

In some instances, e.g., loudspeakers and meters, permanent magnets are used to supply the required mmf. But in most electric machines, the mmf is supplied by current-carrying coils of wire (solenoids, field windings, armatures, operating coils, etc.). In magnetic circuit design the shape, location, and strength of the desired magnetic field depend on the nature of the machine. The designer's task is to lay out a magnetic circuit so that the required magnetic field can be developed with the optimum compromise among structural size and strength, cost of materials, and cost of electric energy to produce the necessary mmf.

It is not the responsibility of the engineering technician to design magnetic circuits. Therefore we shall leave this chore to the design engineer. But it is the responsibility of the technician to *understand* the function of magnetic circuits. To accomplish this, we shall start with the specifications for the various magnetic circuits as set forth by the designer in the examples and problems of this chapter, and calculate the electric current required to produce the desired flux in the magnetic circuit or vice versa.

## 18. Long Air-Core Coils

In Fig. 7.9 we noted that the magnetic field around a coiled electric conductor resembled that of a bar magnet. If a solenoid having air or any other nonmagnetic material as a core is at least ten times as long as its

diameter, we can calculate fairly accurately the relationship between the flux at the center of the coil and the current through it.

As shown in Fig. 7.22, all the magnetic lines of force pass through the center of the coil and then complete their loops through the space outside the coil. Since the permeability of the air outside the coil is the same as that of the nonmagnetic core, about half of the lines of force do not travel the whole length of the core but leave and enter the

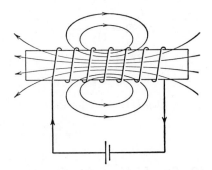

**Fig. 7.22.** Magnetic field around a long, air-core coil.

sides of the coil because of the tendency of magnetic lines of force to repel one another and to become as short as possible. Therefore our calculations will apply only to the center of the coil.

Figure 7.22 also shows that all the lines of force that are crowded into the small cross section at the center of the coil, complete their loops through a very large cross-sectional area outside the coil. Since the reluctance of a magnetic circuit is inversely proportional to its cross-sectional area, the reluctance of the portion of the magnetic path within the coil is much greater than that of the return portion outside the coil. Therefore it is reasonable to assume that **for long air-core coils, the total reluctance is approximately equal to the reluctance of the nonmagnetic core of the coil itself.**

Transposing Equation (7.4) gives

$$\mathfrak{R} = \frac{l}{\mu A} \tag{7.10}$$

where $\mathfrak{R}$ is the reluctance of the nonmagnetic core in ampere-turns per weber, $l$ is the length of the coil in meters, $\mu$ is the permeability of nonmagnetic materials ($4\pi \times 10^{-7}$ mks units), and $A$ is the inside cross-sectional area of the coil in square meters, **or** where $\mathfrak{R}$ is the reluctance of the nonmagnetic core in ampere-turns per line, $l$ is the length of the coil in inches, $\mu$ is the permeability of nonmagnetic materials (3.2 English units), and $A$ is the inside cross-sectional area of the coil in square inches.

EXAMPLE 1: An air-core coil 20 cm in length and 1 cm inside diameter has 1000 turns. What current must flow in the coil to develop a total flux of $10^{-6}$ weber at the center of the coil?

*Solution:*

*Step I.* Solve for the reluctance of the core.

$$\mathfrak{R} = \frac{l}{\mu A}$$

$$\therefore \quad \mathfrak{R} = \frac{0.2}{(4\pi \times 10^{-7})[\frac{1}{4}\pi \times (0.01)^2]} = 2.03 \times 10^9 \text{ AT/weber}^*$$

*Step II.* Solve for the magnetomotive force using Equation (7.2).

$$\mathfrak{F} = \Phi\mathfrak{R} = 10^{-6} \times 2.03 \times 10^9 = 2.03 \times 10^3 \text{ AT}$$

*Step III.* Solve for the current in the coil using Equation (7.1)

$$I = \frac{\mathfrak{F}}{N} = \frac{2.03 \times 10^3}{1000} = 2.03 \text{ amp}$$

## 19. Simple Magnetic Circuit

If we place an iron core in the coil of wire in Fig. 7.22, the high permeability of the iron will reduce the reluctance of the core well below that of the return path outside the core. Therefore we can no longer assume that the total reluctance is very nearly that of the core itself. In this case the reluctance of the return circuit outside the core is the major factor in determining the total reluctance of the magnetic circuit. This reluctance is considerably more difficult to calculate than that of the core with its finite dimensions. We usually avoid magnetic circuits in which the magnetic lines of force are allowed to find their own return path as best they can from one end of the core to the other.

By winding the coil completely around a ring-shaped core, forming a **toroid** type winding as shown in Fig. 7.23, the magnetic field is confined

---

* AT is the abbreviation for *ampere-turns*.

to a path completely within the coil for both nonmagnetic and magnetic core materials. Toroids with non-magnetic cores are solved in the same manner as Example 1.

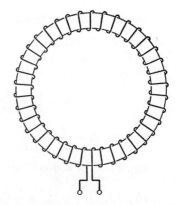

Fig. 7.23. Construction of a toroid winding.

EXAMPLE 2: The brass core in Fig. 7.23 has a circular cross section. The inside diameter of the core is 4 in. and the outside diameter is 6 in. If there are 2000 turns in the winding, what total flux will be produced by a 1 amp current in the coil?

*Solution:*

*Step I.* Some care is required in determining the correct values for the length and cross-sectional area of magnetic circuits. From the dimensions given it follows that the diameter of the cross section of the core is 1 in.

$$\therefore \quad A = \frac{\pi}{4} \times 1^2 = 0.785 \text{ sq in.}$$

The length of the magnetic circuit will be the *average* path length. In this example the inside circumference is $\pi \times 4$ in. and the outside circumference is $\pi \times 6$ in. The average of these two extreme path lengths is $\pi \times 5$ in.

$$\therefore \quad l = \pi \times 5 = 15.7 \text{ in.}$$

*Step II.* $\quad \mathcal{R} = \dfrac{l}{\mu A} = \dfrac{15.7}{3.2 \times 0.785} = 6.21 \text{ AT/line}$

*Step III.* $\quad \mathcal{F} = NI = 2000 \times 1 = 2000 \text{ AT}$

*Step IV.* $\quad \Phi = \dfrac{\mathcal{F}}{\mathcal{R}} = \dfrac{2000}{6.21} = 322 \text{ lines}$

If the core in Example 2 were made of cast steel, the problem would be more difficult to solve since the permeability of the steel would depend on the flux density, which is not known. However if, as is usually the case, we are given the flux required and are supplied with data from which we can determine the permeability for various flux densities, we can use much the same procedure to solve the magnetic circuit.

EXAMPLE 3: The cast steel core in Fig. 7.23 has a square cross section. The inside diameter of the ring is 4 cm and the outside diameter is 6 cm. If there are 2000 turns on the coil, what current must flow through it to develop a total flux of $10^{-4}$ weber?

*Solution 1:*

*Step I.* Determine the dimensions of the magnetic circuit.

Cross-sectional area: $A = 0.01 \times 0.01 = 10^{-4}$ sq m

*Average* path length: $l = \pi \times 0.05 = 0.157$ m

*Step II.* Determine flux density: $B = \dfrac{\Phi}{A} = \dfrac{10^{-4}}{10^{-4}} = 1$ weber/sq m.

*Step III.* Determine the permeability:

From Table I, a magnetizing force of 800 AT/meter is required to produce a flux density of 1 weber/sq m in cast steel.

$$\therefore \quad \mu = \frac{B}{H} = \frac{1}{800} = 1.25 \times 10^{-3} \text{ mks units}$$

*Step IV.* $\Re = \dfrac{l}{\mu A} = \dfrac{0.157}{1.25 \times 10^{-3} \times 10^{-4}} = 1.25 \times 10^{6}$ AT/weber

*Step V.* $\quad \mathcal{F} = \Phi\Re = 10^{-4} \times 1.25 \times 10^{6} = 125$ AT

*Step VI.* $\quad \therefore \quad I = \dfrac{\mathcal{F}}{N} = \dfrac{125}{2000} = 62.5$ ma

Actually the above procedure represents a rather roundabout way of solving magnetic circuits in which reference to *BH* tables or curves is involved. Once we have determined the flux density, the tables or graphs tell us how much magnetizing force is required for each unit length of the magnetic circuit. We can therefore solve for the mmf directly without going through Steps III and IV. Both permeability and reluctance are therefore completely bypassed in this method of solving magnetic circuits.

*Solution 2:*

*Step I.* Cross-sectional area: $A = 0.01 \times 0.01 = 10^{-4}$ sq m

*Average* path length: $l = 3.14 \times 0.05 = 0.157$ m

*Step II.* Flux density: $B = \dfrac{\Phi}{A} = \dfrac{10^{-4}}{10^{-4}} = 1$ weber/sq m

*Step III.* From Table I, for $B = 1$ weber/sq m in cast steel,

$$H = 800 \text{ AT/m}$$

*Step IV.* $\quad \mathcal{F} = Hl = 800 \times 0.157 = 125$ AT

*Step V.* $\quad\quad I = \dfrac{\mathcal{F}}{N} = \dfrac{125}{2000} = 62.5$ ma

In a simple magnetic circuit where all the magnetomotive force is devoted to producing flux in the uniform cross section of the iron core, it is not difficult to solve for the flux when we are given the magnetomotive force.

EXAMPLE 4: A current of 0.5 amp is passing through a coil consisting of 960 turns wound on a ring-type cast steel core whose cross-sectional area is 2 sq in. and whose average path length is 12 in. What is the total flux in the core?

*Solution:*

$$\mathcal{F} = NI = 960 \times 0.5 = 480 \text{ AT}$$

$$H = \frac{\mathcal{F}}{l} = \frac{480}{12} = 40 \text{ AT/in.}$$

From the $BH$ curve for cast steel (Fig. 7.15) when $H = 40$ AT/in.,

$$B = 83 \text{ kilolines/sq in.}$$

$$\therefore \quad \Phi = BA = 83 \times 10^3 \times 2 = 166 \text{ kilolines}$$

## 20. Leakage Flux

In the preceding section we wound the energizing coil along the full length of the magnetic circuit (toroid fashion) in an attempt to keep as much of the flux within the core as possible. This type of winding is expensive since it has to be wound by threading the wire through the center of the core. It is used only in cases where it is imperative that the number of lines of force traveling through the air outside the core be kept to a minimum. If a magnetic circuit is constructed as shown in Fig. 7.24, the coil can be wound on a bobbin and then the magnetic core can be assembled. From our investigation of parallel resistors, we learned that *all* the current does not flow through the path of least resistance. Actually the current splits up in proportion to the conductance of the parallel branches. When high permeability iron is used for the full length of the magnetic circuit, the majority of the lines of force will follow the path established by the iron. But since the air in the center of the core is not a magnetic insulator, and since magnetic lines of force have a tendency to try to become as short as possible, some of the flux will complete its circuit outside the core as shown in Fig. 7.24. These particular lines of force are called the **leakage flux.**

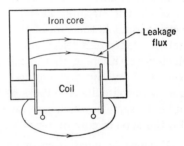

Fig. 7.24. Leakage flux in a magnetic circuit.

In designing a simple magnetic circuit similar to that of Fig. 7.24, there are several things we can do to keep the leakage flux to a minimum. By keeping the magnetic circuit compact, the length of a magnetic line of force taking the short cut through the air is not much shorter than the path length through the iron. The higher the permeance (the lower the reluctance) of the magnetic circuit, the greater will be the number of lines of force which stay within the magnetic circuit. High permeance is achieved by making sure that the cross-sectional area is great enough that the required flux density does not cause the core to saturate. As suggested by Fig. 7.21, many practical magnetic circuits contain air gaps. The presence of the air gap greatly increases the total reluctance of the magnetic circuit. Accordingly leakage flux will be more pronounced in such circuits.

In the magnetic circuit of Fig. 7.24, the total flux through the top section of circuit is less than that through the center of the coil due to the leakage flux bypassing the top section. The effect of the leakage flux then is that we must increase the current in the coil slightly in order to obtain as much flux in the top section of the core as there would be if there were no leakage flux. The ratio between the total developed flux and the useful flux is known as the **leakage factor.** Since the leakage flux is only a very small percentage of the total flux, we may quite safely neglect it in making our magnetic circuit calculations in this chapter if a specific value of leakage factor is not given.

## 21. Series Magnetic Circuits

Practical magnetic circuits are seldom as simple as the iron ring of Fig. 7.23. The magnetic circuit of Fig. 7.24 consists of two sections, a straight section and a U-shaped section in *series.* The two sections are in series since tracing around the complete loop of a line of force takes us first through one section and then through the other. As we have already noted, the equation for reluctance in magnetic circuits resembles Ohm's law of electric circuits. Therefore, just as the total resistance of a series electric circuit is the sum of the individual resistances, it follows that **the total reluctance of a series magnetic circuit is the sum of all the individual reluctances.** Keeping this in mind, we can solve the magnetic circuit of Example 5 by the first method that we used in solving Example 3. In many series circuits, the cross-sectional areas of the various sections may not be the same in which case we must find the flux density for each section. Also the type of core material may vary from section to section.

EXAMPLE 5: What magnetomotive force must be developed by a coil wound on the magnetic circuit of Fig. 7.25 to develop a total flux of 120 kilolines? (The varnish on the laminations accounts for 10% of the lamination's thickness.)

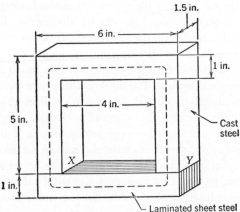

**Fig. 7.25.** Magnetic circuit for Example 5.

*Solution 1:*

*Step I.* Determine the reluctance of the U-shaped section: Examination of the specifications shows that all three arms of the U-shaped section have the same width (1 in.)

$$\therefore \quad A = 1 \times 1.5 = 1.5 \text{ sq in.}$$

The *average* path is marked out by the dotted lines in Fig. 7.25. Its length can be obtained by averaging the outside length of the U-shaped section (5 + 6 + 5 = 16 in.) and the inside length (4 + 4 + 4 = 12 in.).

$$\therefore \quad l = \frac{1}{2}(16 + 12) = 14 \text{ in.}$$

$$B = \frac{\Phi}{A} = \frac{120 \times 10^3}{1.5} = 80 \text{ kilolines/sq in.}$$

From the *BH* curves of Fig. 7.15, for *B* = 80 kilolines/sq in. in cast steel,
$$H = 36 \text{ AT/in.}$$

$$\therefore \quad \mu = \frac{B}{H} = \frac{80 \times 10^3}{36} = 2.22 \times 10^3 \text{ English units}$$

$$\mathcal{R} = \frac{l}{\mu A} = \frac{14}{2.22 \times 10^3 \times 1.5} = 4.2 \times 10^{-3} \text{ AT/line}$$

*Step II.* Determine the reluctance of the I-shaped stack of laminations:

$$A = 1 \times 1.5 \times 90\% = 1.35 \text{ sq in.}$$

$$l = \frac{1}{2}(8 + 4) = 6 \text{ in.}$$

$$B = \frac{\Phi}{A} = \frac{120 \times 10^3}{1.35} = 89 \text{ kilolines/sq in.}$$

From the *BH* curves of Fig. 7.15, for *B* = 89 kilolines/sq in. in sheet steel,
$$H = 26 \text{ AT/in.}$$

$$\therefore \quad \mu = \frac{B}{H} = \frac{89 \times 10^3}{26} = 3.42 \times 10^3 \text{ English units}$$

$$\mathcal{R} = \frac{l}{\mu A} = \frac{6}{3.42 \times 10^3 \times 1.35} = 1.3 \times 10^{-3} \text{ AT/line}$$

*Step III.* $\mathcal{R}_T = \mathcal{R}_1 + \mathcal{R}_2 = (4.2 \times 10^{-3}) + (1.3 \times 10^{-3})$

$$\therefore \quad \mathcal{R}_T = 5.5 \times 10^{-3} \text{ AT/line}$$

and $\qquad \mathcal{F} = \Phi \mathcal{R} = 120 \times 10^3 \times 5.5 \times 10^{-3} = 660 \text{ AT}$

Another characteristic of series electric circuits is that the total voltage is the sum of all the individual voltage drops. Similarly in magnetic circuits, **the total mmf is the sum of the mmf's required for each section of the circuit.** Applying this principle to Example 5, we may again completely by-pass the determination of permeability and reluctance in solving series magnetic circuits. Once we have determined the magnetizing force required for each section of the circuit, we can go right ahead and find the magnetomotive force required for that section.

*Solution 2:* For the U-shaped section,

$$H = 36 \text{ AT/in.} \quad \text{(from Solution 1).}$$

$$\therefore \quad \mathfrak{F} = Hl = 36 \times 14 = 504 \text{ AT}$$

For the I-shaped section,

$$H = 26 \text{ AT/in.} \quad \text{(from Solution 1).}$$

$$\therefore \quad \mathfrak{F} = Hl = 26 \times 6 = 156 \text{ AT}$$

$$\therefore \quad \mathfrak{F}_T = \mathfrak{F}_1 + \mathfrak{F}_2 = 504 + 156 = 660 \text{ AT}$$

## 22. Air Gaps

In all the magnetic circuits shown in Fig. 7.21, the complete loop of any line of force is not wholly within the high permeability path provided by the iron. Every line of force has to cross an air gap to complete its loop. This gap is necessary in order to provide space in which electric conductors can move in the case of motors, meters, and loudspeakers. Even in stationary equipment like the magnetic circuit of Fig. 7.25, an air gap may be inserted into the magnetic circuit at points $X$ and $Y$ between the U-shaped and the I-shaped sections. This is done to assist in preventing saturation of the iron portion of the magnetic circuit when a heavy current flows through the coil wound on the core, by increasing the total reluctance of the circuit. In such apparatus, the "air" gap is often a sheet of any nonmagnetic material such as fiberboard or brass so that the length of the air gap can be accurately and rigidly set.

Since all the magnetic lines of force must pass through the air gaps in these circuits, the gaps are in *series* with the remainder of the circuit. Therefore magnetic circuits with air gaps can be solved just like the series circuit of Example 5. Before we start to calculate the flux density in the air gap we must note how the magnetic lines of force try to spread out as they pass through the air gap as shown in Fig. 7.26. This effect follows from the characteristic of magnetic lines of force in that they tend to repel one another. Since the air outside of the gap is just as capable of passing magnetic lines of force as the air within the gap, the lines of force take advantage of this opportunity to get farther apart as they cross the gap. This spreading apart of the magnetic lines of force as they cross an air gap is called **fringing**. Fringing results in the flux density in the air gap being slightly less than that in the adjacent iron sections of the magnetic circuit.

If the length of the air gap is small, the fringing is small and correction for it can be made in magnetic circuit calculations by assuming that the cross-sectional dimensions of an air gap are greater than the cross-sectional

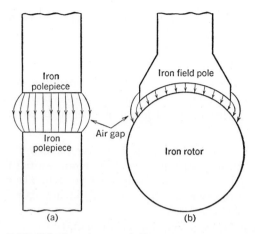

**Fig. 7.26.** Fringing of magnetic lines of force in an air gap.

dimensions of the adjacent iron by an amount equal to the length of the air gap.

EXAMPLE 6: What magnetomotive force must be developed by a coil wound on the magnetic circuit of Fig. 7.25 to develop a total flux of 120 kilolines if pieces of fiberboard 0.005 in. thick are inserted into the magnetic circuit at points $X$ and $Y$? (Allow 10% of the lamination thickness for varnish.)

*Solution 1:* Since the total flux is the same as in Example 5, the reluctances of the U-shaped and I-shaped steel sections will be the same as we have already calculated, $4.2 \times 10^{-3}$ and $1.3 \times 10^{-3}$ AT/line, respectively. Allowing for fringing, the cross-sectional area of the air gap is

$$A = 1.005 \times 1.505 = 1.5125 \text{ sq in.}$$

$$\mathcal{R} = \frac{l}{\mu A} = \frac{0.005}{3.2 \times 1.5125} = 1.03 \times 10^{-3} \text{ AT/line}$$

Since each line of force has to pass through *both* air gaps, they are in *series,* and since both air gaps are identical, each has a reluctance of $1.03 \times 10^{-3}$ AT/line.

$$\mathcal{R}_T = 4.2 \times 10^{-3} + 1.3 \times 10^{-3} + 1.03 \times 10^{-3} + 1.03 \times 10^{-3}$$

$$= 7.56 \times 10^{-3} \text{ AT/line}$$

$$\mathcal{F} = \Phi \mathcal{R}_T = 120 \times 10^3 \times 7.56 \times 10^{-3} = 907 \text{ AT}$$

*Solution 2:* The mmf required for the iron will be the same as in Example 5, 660 AT.

For each air gap, $B = \Phi/A = 120,000/1.5125 = 79.34$ kilolines/sq in.

$$H = \frac{B}{\mu} = \frac{79340}{3.2} = 24.8 \times 10^3 \text{ AT/in.}$$

$$\mathcal{F} = Hl = 24.8 \times 10^3 \times 0.005 = 124 \text{ AT}$$

$$\therefore \quad \mathcal{F}_T = 660 + 124 + 124 = 908 \text{ AT}$$

If we are given the magnetomotive force applied to a magnetic circuit made up of different sections in series, it is not quite so easy to solve for the total flux as it was in Example 4 since we do not know how much of the total mmf applies to each section. In this case we will have to make an educated guess at the answer and solve the magnetic circuit as we have done in Examples 5 and 6 to see if we arrive at the given value of magnetomotive force. If the first attempt is not close enough, we shall have to try again.

EXAMPLE 7: A current of 0.5 amp is passing through a coil consisting of 960 turns wound on a cast steel core whose cross-sectional dimensions are 2 in. $\times$ 1 in. and whose average path length is 12 in. The continuity of this core is broken by a single air gap which is 0.01 in. in length. What is the total flux in the core?

*Solution:* Area of air gap (allowing for fringing),

$$A = 2.01 \times 1.01 = 2.03 \text{ sq in.}$$

$$\mathcal{F} = NI = 960 \times 0.5 = 480 \text{ AT}$$

Let us assume that of this total mmf, 210 AT is required for the air gap.

Then $$H = \frac{\mathcal{F}}{l} = \frac{210}{0.01} = 21 \times 10^3 \text{ AT/in.}$$

$$B = \mu H = 3.2 \times 21 \times 10^3 = 67.2 \text{ kilolines/sq in.}$$

$$\therefore \quad \Phi = BA = 67.2 \times 2.03 = 136 \text{ kilolines}$$

If this is so, the flux density in the iron must be

$$B = \frac{\Phi}{A} = \frac{136}{2} = 68 \text{ kilolines/sq in.}$$

From the *BH* curve for cast steel (Fig. 7.15), if

$$B = 68 \text{ kilolines/sq in.}$$

$$H = 22 \text{ AT/in.}$$

then $$\mathcal{F} = Hl = 22 \times 12 = 264 \text{ AT}$$

$$\therefore \quad \mathcal{F}_T = 210 + 264 = 474 \text{ AT}$$

Since this is just slightly less than the given mmf, the total flux must be just slightly greater than 136 kilolines.

## 23. Parallel Magnetic Circuits

If we examine again the magnetic circuits of Figs. 7.21(c) and 7.21(d), we will note that although *all* the magnetic flux passes through some portions of the magnetic circuit, in other portions it splits with half going one way and half going the other. In electric circuits this is the condition that exists when two equal resistors are connected in *parallel*. Half the total current flows through each resistor and the *same* voltage drop appears across each branch. Designers have found that supplying more than one possible return path for magnetic lines of force appreciably reduces the leakage flux. Fortunately in most designs the parallel paths are limited to two symmetrical paths so that we can assume that the total flux splits half and half.

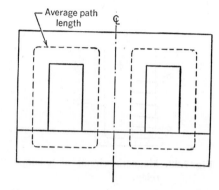

EXAMPLE 8: If a 1000 turn coil is placed on the center leg of the shell type core of Fig. 7.27 to form a filter choke, what is the maximum current it can pass without the total flux in the core exceeding 200 kilolines? The core is made of sheet steel laminations stacked to a total thickness of 1.5 in. (Allow 5% of the thickness for varnish.) The width of all outside legs of the core is 1 in. and that of the center leg is 2 in. The average path length (see Fig. 7.27) is 10 in.

**Fig. 7.27.** Magnetic circuit for Example 8.

*Solution:* We can divide the magnetic circuit down the center line of Fig. 7.27 and stack one section on top of the other without changing the total reluctance of the magnetic circuit. The cross-sectional area would then become

$$A = 2 \times 1 \times 1.5 \times 95\% = 2.85 \text{ sq in.}$$

$$B = \frac{\Phi}{A} = \frac{200{,}000}{2.85} = 70 \text{ kilolines/sq in.}$$

From the **BH** curve for sheet steel (Fig. 7.15), for

$$B = 70 \text{ kilolines/sq in.}$$

$$H = 14 \text{ AT/in.}$$

$$\mathfrak{F} = Hl = 14 \times 10 = 140 \text{ AT}$$

$$I = \frac{\mathfrak{F}}{N} = \frac{140}{1000} = 140 \text{ ma}$$

We would arrive at the same answer if we considered only *half* of the magnetic circuit carrying *half* of the total flux. The flux density in the iron would still be

$$B = \frac{\Phi}{A} = \frac{100{,}000}{1.425} = 70 \text{ kilolines/sq in.}$$

and again $\mathfrak{F} = 140$ AT. This *same* mmf would cause the other 100,000 lines to be set up in the other half of the magnetic circuit.

## 24. Tractive Force of an Electromagnet

One of the characteristics of magnetic lines of force is that they represent a tension along their length which tends to make them as short as possible. If we pass current through the solenoid of the relay shown in Fig. 7.28, a magnetic field will be set up in the iron. These magnetic lines of force must complete their loops via the air gap between the stationary polepiece and the moving arm of the relay. The tension along the length of the lines of force will therefore exert a force which attempts to close the air gap. In *any* magnetic circuit containing an air gap, a force will be exerted which tends to close the air gap. The force will depend on the number of lines of force crossing the air gap.

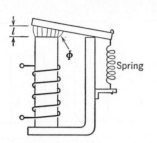

**Fig. 7.28.** Magnetic circuit of a simple relay.

To determine the extent of this **tractive force,** let us assume that current is flowing in the solenoid of Fig. 7.28 and that the air gap is closed. If we now apply a mechanical force $F$ to the moving arm to pull the air gap open to a distance $l$ we will be doing mechanical work.

$$W = Fl$$

Since increasing the length of the air gap increases the total reluctance of the magnetic circuit, we must pass more current through the coil if we wish to maintain the same total flux. In doing so we will be adding extra energy to the magnetic circuit. If the total flux is kept constant, this extra energy is added to the flux in the air gap and will be the product of the flux in the air gap and the *average* mmf maintaining that flux in the air gap. As the air gap is forced open, its length increases from zero to $l$ and consequently the magnetomotive force required to maintain flux in the air gap increases from zero to $\mathfrak{F}$. The average mmf will therefore have to be $\frac{1}{2}(0 + \mathfrak{F}) = \frac{1}{2}\mathfrak{F}$. The energy stored in the air gap will be

$$W = \tfrac{1}{2}\mathfrak{F}\Phi$$

But
$$\mathfrak{F} = Hl \quad \text{and} \quad \Phi = BA$$

$$\therefore \quad W = \tfrac{1}{2}HlBA$$

But
$$H = \frac{B}{\mu}$$

$$\therefore \quad W = l \times \frac{B^2 A}{2\mu}$$

This extra energy appearing in the air gap must equal the work done in pulling the moving arm away from the polepiece. Therefore,

$$Fl = l \times \frac{B^2 A}{2\mu}$$

and
$$F = \frac{B^2 A}{2\mu} \qquad (7.11)$$

where $F$ is the force acting to close the air gap in newtons, $B$ is the flux density in the air gap in webers/square m., $A$ is the cross-sectional area of the air gap in square meters, and $\mu$ is the permeability of air $(4\pi \times 10^{-7})$.

This equation will be more useful if we express it in terms of English units of measurement.

$$F = 1.4 \times 10^{-8} B^2 A \qquad (7.12)$$

where $F$ is the force acting to close the air gap in pounds, $B$ is the flux density in the air gap in lines/sq in. and $A$ is the cross-sectional area of the air gap in square inches.

EXAMPLE 9: Fig. 7.29 shows the cross section of an electromagnet used for lifting iron plates. The cross-sectional areas of both the center polepiece and the circular outside polepiece are 120 sq in. each. The energizing solenoid is producing a flux density of 80 kilolines per sq in. in each of the polepieces. What force is holding the sheet of boiler plate to the magnet?

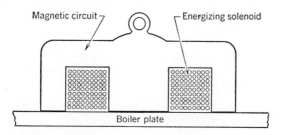

Fig. 7.29. Cross-section of an electromagnet.

*Solution:* There are two air gaps in the complete magnetic circuit of Fig. 7.29, one where the lines of force pass from the polepiece of the magnet into the boiler plate and one where the lines of force pass from the plate back into the magnet. The total tractive force will be the sum of both of these individual pulls. Therefore

$$F = 2 \times 1.4 \times 10^{-8} B^2 A = 2 \times 1.4 \times 10^{-8} \times (80 \times 10^3)^2 \times 120$$
$$= 21,500 \text{ pounds}$$

## Problems

1. Draw the magnetic lines of force around the conductor in Fig. 7.30(a) and indicate their direction.
2. Mark the conventional current direction on the conductor of Fig. 7.30(b).

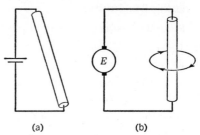

Fig. 7.30.

3. Draw the magnetic field around the coil in Fig. 7.31(a) and indicate its direction.

4. Mark the conventional current direction on the coil of Fig. 7.31(b).

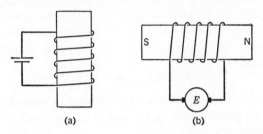

(a)                              (b)

**Fig. 7.31.**

5. What is the reluctance of a magnetic circuit in which a total flux of 2 webers is set up by a 5 amp current flowing in a solenoid consisting of 200 turns of wire?

6. State the answer to Problem 5 in English units.

7. What current must be passed through a 500 turn solenoid to produce a total flux of 1.2 webers in a magnetic circuit whose reluctance is 200 ampere-turns per weber?

8. How many turns of wire are there in a solenoid if a 500 ma current through it produces a total flux of 80 kilolines in a magnetic circuit whose reluctance is $5 \times 10^{-3}$ ampere-turn per line?

9. The core of a solenoid consists of a brass cylinder 10 cm in length and 2 cm in diameter. What is its reluctance?

10. The magnet in Fig. 7.4 has a rectangular cross section of $0.5 \times 1.0$ in. If the spacing between the two sections in Fig. 7.4(b) is 0.05 in., what is the reluctance of this air gap?

11. A piece of iron 10 cm in length and having a rectangular cross section of $1 \times 2$ cm has a reluctance of $1.25 \times 10^{6}$ ampere-turns per weber. What is the permeability of the iron?

12. State the answer to Problem 11 in English units.

13. A magnetizing force of 2000 ampere-turns per meter produces a flux density of 1.0 weber per square meter in a certain type of iron. What is its permeability at this flux density?

14. State the answer to Problem 13 in English units.

15. Determine the permeability of sheet steel when the flux density in it remains at 1.0 weber per square meter.

16. Determine the average permeability of sheet steel from the magnetization curve of Fig. 7.15.

17. Find the incremental permeability of cast iron between flux densities of 0.59 and 0.68 weber per square meter.

18. Determine the differential permeability of cast steel for a magnetizing force of 40 ampere-turns per in.

19. A coil of wire 8 cm in length is wound on a $\frac{1}{2}$ cm diameter hardwood dowel. If there are 500 turns on the coil, what current must it pass to develop a flux of $5.0 \times 10^{-7}$ weber at the center of the coil?

20. 800 turns of wire are wound on a 1 in. diameter fiber form. If the coil is 1 ft in length, what current must flow through it to develop a flux of 100 lines at the center of the coil?

21. What flux will be developed at the center of an air core coil passing a 600 ma current if its 750 turns occupy a length of 12 cm on a 1 cm form?

22. How many turns must be wound on a $\frac{3}{4}$ in. bakelite rod to produce 80 lines at the center of the coil from a 500 ma current through the coil? The length of the coil is 8 in.

23. The core for a low-loss inductor in a crossover filter is made from a piece of flat plastic stock $\frac{1}{4}$ in. thick by 1 in. wide by 6 in. long formed into a closed loop; 1200 turns of wire are wound toroid fashion on this form. What current must flow in the coil to develop a flux of 1000 lines in the core?

24. If the core in Problem 23 were a cast iron ring with the same dimensions, what must the current be to produce 10,000 lines?

25. The horseshoe shaped cast steel electromagnet of Fig. 7.32 is 1.2 in. in diameter and has an average length of 12 in. What current must flow through the windings of the electromagnet to develop a total flux of 100 kilolines in the sheet steel bar held by the magnet? The dimensions of the bar are $6 \times 1.5 \times 0.75$ in.

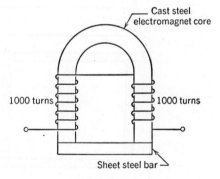

**Fig. 7.32.**

26. What is the total flux in the sheet steel bar if the current in the coils in the magnetic circuit of Fig. 7.32 is $\frac{1}{2}$ amp?

27. What force is required to pull the sheet steel bar away from the electromagnet in Problem 25?

28. If a $\frac{1}{16}$ in. sheet of aluminum is placed between the sheet steel bar and the electromagnet of Fig. 7.32, what current must flow in the coils to develop a total flux of 75 kilolines in the sheet steel bar if the leakage factor has now become 1.15?

29. If the sheet steel laminations of Fig. 7.33 are stacked to a total thickness of 1 in., how many turns of wire must be wound on the center leg in order for a 100 ma current to develop a total flux of 75 kilolines in the center leg. Allow 5% of each lamination thickness for varnish. Assume no air gap and negligible leakage flux.

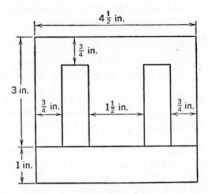

Fig. 7.33.

30. What is the total reluctance of the magnetic circuit of the dynamic loudspeaker shown in Fig. 7.34 if the total flux in the air gap is to be 50,000 lines?

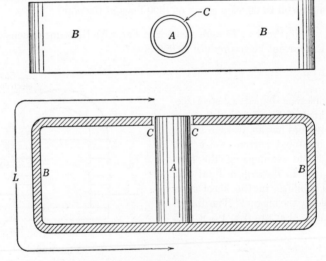

Fig. 7.34.

A — Cast steel polepiece, 1 in. diameter × 3 in. long

B — sheet steel saddle, 2 in. wide × ¼ in. thick × 8 in. long (average path length, L)

C — circular air gap, 20 mils across

## Review Questions

1. Draw a diagram of the magnetic field around a horseshoe shaped permanent magnet.

2. With reference to the characteristics of magnetic lines of force, show why a nail is attracted to either pole of a horseshoe shaped permanent magnet.

3. Show with sketches how it is possible to determine the direction of the current in an electric conductor with the aid of a compass needle.

4. Why is the flux density of a magnetic field greater in the center of a current-carrying solenoid than around a straight wire carrying the same current?

5. How is the magnitude of the **weber** established?

6. Define the term **reluctance.**

7. What is the distinction between **magnetomotive force** and **magnetizing force?**

8. Define the term **permeability.**

9. Given the permeability of air as $4\pi \times 10^{-7}$ mks units, prove that this is the same as 3.2 English units.

10. Account for the upper knee on the **BH** curve of ferromagnetic materials.

11. Draw a **BH** curve for aluminum.

12. What is the distinction between **differential** and **incremental** permeability?

13. Determine the conversion factor for converting webers per square meter to kilolines per square inch.

14. Compare permanent and temporary magnets in terms of coercive force.

15. Define the term **hysteresis.**

16. Some magnetic circuits consist of powdered iron pressed into form with a ceramic binder. Compare such a core with solid core of the same type of iron in terms of (a) permeability, (b) hysteresis, and (c) eddy current.

17. What causes **leakage flux** to occur in magnetic circuits? State two means of reducing leakage flux in magnetic circuit design.

18. What causes **fringing** of the magnetic lines of force in an air gap?

19. Why does the tractive force increase as an iron bar is placed closer to an electromagnet with a constant current through its exciting coils?

20. Mechanical work is required to pull a soft iron bar away from a U-shaped permanent magnet. Where does the energy go?

# Chapter 8

# ELECTRICAL MEASUREMENT

~~~~~~~~~~~~~~~~~~~~~~~~~~~~~~~~~~~~~~~~~~~~~~~~~~~~~~~~~~~~~~~~

In our study of electric circuits, we have been placing the emphasis on *understanding* the fundamental laws that govern their behavior. We have referred to actual apparatus only to the extent that it will help us to understand basic circuit theory and how basic circuit theory governs the performance of such equipment. In this chapter we shall examine electric measuring equipment only to the extent that it will add to our appreciation of what goes on in electric circuits. We shall not attempt to cover fully the construction and use of this equipment.

## 1. Mechanical Torque from Electric Current

In Chapter 7, we discovered that electric current flow in a conductor produces a magnetic field around the conductor. Figure 8.1(a) shows a cross section of a conductor in which the conventional current direction is away from us into the page (as indicated by the feathered end of an arrow). According to the right-hand rule for magnetic field around a straight wire, the lines of force will appear to us as concentric circles with a clockwise direction. If we now locate the current-carrying conductor between the poles of the U-shaped permanent magnet of Fig. 8.1(b), we cannot simply draw the magnetic field of the conductor superimposed on that of the permanent magnet. One of the characteristics of magnetic lines of force is that they cannot cross one another. Therefore the two component fields must combine to form one composite magnetic field. Below the conductor, the direction of its lines of force [Fig. 8.1(a)] is *opposing* that of the permanent magnet field [Fig. 8.1(b)]. This results in a canceling effect that will reduce the flux density below the conductor. Above the conductor, the direction of its lines of force is the *same* as that of the permanent magnet field, thus increasing the flux density. This produces the composite magnetic field shown in Fig. 8.1(c). We can think of the effect of current in the conductor as causing the lines of force of the permanent magnet in the vicinity of the current-carrying conductor to *detour* above the conductor.

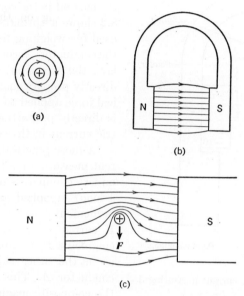

**Fig. 8.1.** Force acting on a current-carrying conductor in a magnetic field.

Another characteristic of magnetic lines of force is that they tend to become as short as possible and also tend to repel one another. Therefore the lines of force in the combined field of Fig. 8.1(c) will attempt to straighten out and to space themselves uniformly in order to regain the flux pattern of Fig. 8.1(b). To do so, the magnetic field will have to force the current-carrying conductor *downward*. The magnitude of this force will be directly dependent on the strength of the two component magnetic fields. The strength of the permanent magnet field can be represented by its flux density $B$. The strength of the magnetic field around the conductor will be proportional to the current $I$ in the conductor and also the length $l$ of the conductor within the magnetic field of the permanent magnet.

$$F = BIl \tag{8.1}$$

where $F$ is force acting on the conductor in **newtons**, $B$ is flux density of the permanent magnet in webers per square meter, $I$ is the current in the conductor in amperes, and $l$ is the length of the conductor perpendicular to the magnetic field in meters.

Since the flux density produced by a permanent magnet remains constant with a given magnetic circuit, both $B$ and $l$ in Equation (8.1) are constant. Therefore the mechanical force acting on the conductor is directly proportional to the current in it. If we can devise a means of indicating this mechanical force, we then have a device for measuring the current in the conductor. Figure 8.2 shows a spring scale like those used for weighing fish, attached to the conductor. According to Hooke's law, the extension of the spring is directly proportional to the mechanical force applied to it. This in turn is directly proportional to the electric current in the conductor.

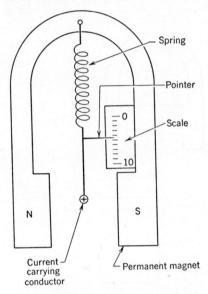

**Fig. 8.2.** A simple current measuring device.

A more practical form for a current measuring instrument is based on two conductors (the two sides of a loop) supported in the field of a permanent magnet by a pivot $X$. If current flows away from us in conductor $B$, it must flow toward us in the other side of the loop, conductor $A$. This current causes the composite magnetic field to be distorted as shown in Fig. 8.3. The mechanical force acting downward on conductor $B$ and upward on conductor $A$ results in a turning force or **torque** that attempts to rotate the loop in a clockwise direction about its pivot. This torque is counterbalanced by the countertorque produced by a flat spiral spring fastened from the pivot to some stationary point. Since the countertorque

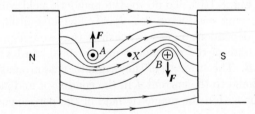

**Fig. 8.3.** Developing mechanical torque from electric current.

of the hairspring is directly proportional to the angle through which the pivot is rotated (Hooke's law), the angle through which the loop rotates is directly proportional to the current through it. Since torque is force times the length of the lever arm, the torque produced by each side of the loop will be

$$T = Fr$$

where $T$ is torque in newton-meters, $F$ is force acting on the conductor in newtons (Equation 8.1), and $r$ is the radius of the loop in meters. The total torque contributed by *both* sides of the loop will be

$$T = 2Fr = FD$$

where $D$ is the diameter of the loop in meters.

If the loop consists of more than one turn of wire, each side of the loop can be thought of as a stranded conductor with each strand carrying a current equal to the current in the coil. Therefore the effective current in the loop will be

$$I_{eff} = NI$$

where $N$ is the number of turns of wire in the pivoted coil. Therefore Equation (8.1) can be modified to apply to a loop in a magnetic field.

$$T = BIlND \qquad (8.2)$$

EXAMPLE 1: What torque is developed by a 1 ma current flowing in a 120 turn coil wound on a 1 cm × 1 cm square form? The flux density in the air gap is 0.1 weber/sq m.

*Solution:*

$T = BIlND = 0.1 \times 0.001 \times 0.01 \times 120 \times 0.01 = 1.2 \times 10^{-6}$ newton-meter

This principle has led to the development of the **moving coil** meter movement shown in Fig. 8.4. This movement is sometimes referred to as

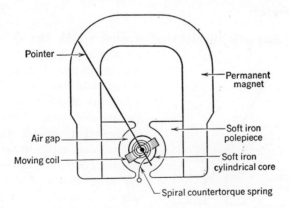

**Fig. 8.4.** The moving coil movement.

a D'Arsonval movement after the man who first patented a current measuring device based on the moving coil principle. Since Edward Weston developed the moving coil instrument from the delicate laboratory apparatus of D'Arsonval to the reasonably rugged panel type of meter in use today, the moving coil movement is also known as the Weston movement.

Since $B$, $l$, $N$, and $D$ are constant for a given meter movement, the torque is directly proportional to the current in the moving coil; and since the countertorque of the spiral spring is directly proportional to its angular extension, the angular displacement of the pointer is directly proportional to the current in the moving coil. If the spiral spring is adjusted so that the coil occupies the position shown in Fig. 8.3 when the current is zero, the movement is called a **galvanometer.** A galvanometer can indicate the flow of direct current in either direction since a clockwise torque will move the coil (and the pointer) in one direction from center; and a counterclockwise torque will move it in the other direction. In most circuit applications a current meter or **ammeter** is used in a circuit in which the current direction does not change. By readjusting the stationary end of the spiral spring, the moving coil and pointer can be set in the position shown in Fig. 8.4. Current through the coil in the proper direction will cause the pointer to be deflected across the scale; but reversed meter leads will cause the pointer to read off scale to the left, coming up against a mechanical stop.

The moving coil movement is the heart of most direct-current measuring instruments. In the following sections we shall adapt it to the measurement of electric circuit behavior. It is worth noting at this point that the same torque principle of Equation (8.2), which we have just developed into a current indicating meter movement, can be applied on a much larger scale as the basis of electric motors.

## 2. The Ammeter

By using magnetic circuits that produce a high flux density in the air gap and delicate countertorque springs, commercial movements can be built which will read full scale with a current of 20 $\mu a$ or less through the moving coil. The same spiral springs that provide the countertorque are used to connect the moving coil to the meter terminals. By using less turns of a larger wire size on the moving coil and a stronger spiral spring, moving coil movements can be built which require currents in the order of several milliamperes to obtain full-scale deflection. If the physical size of the meter is limited to about three inches in diameter, the maximum wire size which can be conveniently

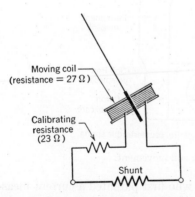

**Fig. 8.5.** Moving coil ammeter with shunt resistor.

inches in diameter, the maximum wire size which can be conveniently used for the moving coil limits the meter to about 30 ma for full-scale deflection. In order to use the moving coil instrument as an ammeter for larger currents, we must apply our knowledge of parallel electric circuits.

For the following example we shall use a moving coil movement which reads full scale when 1 ma flows through its moving coil. A 1 ma movement is a reasonable compromise between the more sensitive 50 $\mu$a movements used in electronic circuit measurements and the more rugged 5 ma movements used for measurements in electric power circuits. The moving coil of the 1 ma movement in question has a resistance of 27 ohms. It is usually customary to include a **calibrating resistor** in series with the moving coil to bring the total resistance of the movement up to some convenient round number. It is common practice to select this calibrating resistor so that the full-scale current through the movement and its calibrating resistor produces a 50 mv drop between the meter terminals. For the movement in question,

$$R_T = \frac{V}{I} = \frac{0.05}{0.001} = 50 \text{ ohms}$$

and therefore the resistance of the calibrating resistor will be

$$R_c = 50 - 27 = 23 \text{ ohms}$$

The calibrating or **swamping** resistor is included in the case of the meter and is made from precision resist-ance wire having a small negative temperature coefficient to offset the positive temperature coefficient of the moving coil.

In order to use the 1 ma move-ment to measure a current in the order of 0.6 amp as is the case in the circuit of Fig. 8.6, we must arrange the meter circuit so that the movement and its shunt resis-tor form two parallel branches with

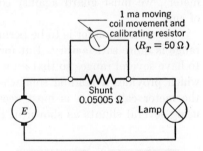

**Fig. 8.6.** Measuring electric current.

999 times as much current flowing through the shunt as through the meter movement. Since the shunt and the movement are in parallel, the *same* voltage drop appears across both and their current ratio is inversely proportional to their resistance ratio. Therefore

$$V_{sh} = V_M$$

$$\therefore \quad I_{sh} \times R_{sh} = I_M \times R_M$$

$$R_{sh} = \tfrac{1}{999} \times R_M = \tfrac{50}{999} = 0.05005 \text{ ohm}$$

If the current flowing through the lamp in Fig. 8.6 is sufficient to make the movement read full scale, the current in the moving coil branch will be 1 ma. Therefore the current through the shunt resistor will be 999 ma and the current through the lamp is $1 + 999 = 1$ amp. As long as this movement and shunt are used together, we can interpret the meter scale as being calibrated for 1 amp full scale.

If the lamp current happens to be 0.6 amp, this total current will split so that one part (0.6 ma) will flow through the moving coil and 999 parts (0.5994 amp) will flow through the shunt. Therefore we can again interpret the 0.6 scale marking of the basic 1 ma movement as indicating 0.6 amp. For currents up to about 25 amp, the shunt is physically small enough to be placed inside the meter case. For larger currents, external shunt resistors are required.

Connecting an ammeter into an electric circuit will have some slight effect on the circuit since we are adding a little extra resistance to the circuit. The total resistance of the meter and its shunt in Fig. 8.6 is 0.05 ohm. The hot resistance of the lamp is in the order of 200 ohms. Therefore the error in circuit current due to adding the ammeter to the circuit is only 0.05 parts in 200, or 0.025%. The main problem with making current measurements in practice is that the meter must be placed in *series* with the circuit whose current is to be measured. Unless the meter is to be left in the circuit permanently, this involves opening the circuit in order to include the meter and then reconnecting the circuit when the meter is removed. Because of its low resistance (0.05 ohm for the 1 amp meter), we must guard against connecting an ammeter *across* a source of emf.

When an ammeter is to be permanently connected in a circuit, a single range is quite satisfactory. But for a test ammeter, it would be desirable to have several ranges so that an unknown current can be read on a range which provides a reading somewhere around two-thirds full scale where the meter calibration is most accurate. This could be accomplished by using several shunts as shown in Fig. 8.7(a). The switch must be of the

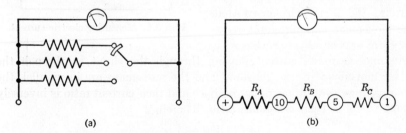

(a)                      (b)

**Fig. 8.7.** (a) Multirange shunt (b) Ayrton shunt.

*make before break* type so that the meter cannot be damaged by being in the circuit without a shunt as the range is changed.

The Ayrton shunt of Fig. 8.7(b) eliminates the possibility of the meter being in circuit without a shunt. This advantage is gained at the price of a slightly higher meter resistance. The Ayrton shunt also provides us with an excellent opportunity of applying our resistance network theory to a practical circuit.

EXAMPLE 2: Using a 1 ma movement with a total resistance of 50 ohms, determine $R_A$, $R_B$, and $R_C$ so that when the common + terminal and terminal 1 are used, the meter is a 1 amp meter; when the common + terminal and terminal 5 are used, the meter is a 5 amp meter; and when the common + terminal and terminal 10 are used, the meter is a 10 amp meter.

*Solution:* On the 1 amp range, $R_A + R_B + R_C$ forms the shunt and it must take 999 parts of the total current when the meter movement takes 1 part. Therefore, as in the example of the simple shunt,

$$R_A + R_B + R_C = \frac{1}{999} \times 50 = 0.05005 \text{ ohm} \tag{1}$$

On the 5 amp range, $R_A + R_B$ forms the shunt and $R_C$ is in series with the moving coil. For the 5 amp range, 4999 parts of the total current must flow through the shunt when the meter movement passes 1 part. Therefore

$$R_A + R_B = \frac{50 + R_C}{4999} \tag{2}$$

On the 10 amp range, $R_A$ is the shunt and $R_B$ and $R_C$ are in series with the meter. For the 10 amp range, $R_A$ takes 9999 parts of the total current, while 1 part flows through the meter and $R_B$ and $R_C$. Therefore

$$R_A = \frac{50 + R_B + R_C}{9999} \tag{3}$$

The solution now becomes an algebra problem involving solving the simultaneous equations (1), (2), and (3) for the values of $R_A$, $R_B$, and $R_C$

$$
\begin{array}{lll}
4999 \times (1) \text{ gives} & 4999R_A + 4999R_B + 4999R_C = 250.2 \\
(2) \text{ gives} & \underline{4999R_A + 4999R_B - \phantom{4999}R_C = \phantom{25}50} \\
\text{Subtracting:} & \phantom{4999R_A + 4999R_B - 499}5000R_C = 200.2
\end{array}
$$

$$R_C = \frac{200.2}{5000} = 0.04004 \text{ ohm}$$

$$
\begin{array}{lll}
9999 \times (1) \text{ gives} & 9999R_A + \phantom{99}9999R_B + \phantom{99}9999R_C = 500.45 \\
(3) \text{ gives} & \underline{9999R_A - \phantom{9999}R_B - \phantom{9999}R_C = \phantom{50}50} \\
\text{Subtracting:} & \phantom{9999R_A -}10{,}000R_B + 10{,}000R_C = 450.45
\end{array}
$$

Substituting for $R_C$: $10{,}000R_B + 400.4 = 450.45$,

$$\therefore \quad R_B = \frac{50.05}{10{,}000} = 0.005005 \text{ ohm}$$

And substituting for $R_B$ and $R_C$ in Equation (1):

$$R_A + 0.005005 + 0.04004 = 0.05005$$

$$\therefore \quad R_A = 0.05005 - 0.045045 = 0.005005 \text{ ohm}$$

## 3. The Voltmeter

The same moving coil movement forms the basis of a practical volt-meter. As we have already noted, if our 1 ma movement has a total resistance of 50 ohms, a voltage drop of $V = IR = 0.001 \times 50 = 0.05$ v will appear across it when it is reading full scale. If we now connect a 99,950 ohm resistor in series with the meter (as in Fig. 8.8) to bring the total resistance up to 100 kilohms, the voltage we must apply to produce a 1 ma current through the meter (and full-scale deflection) is $V = IR = 0.001 \times 100,000 = 100$ v. If we apply a 50 v potential difference to the voltmeter, the current through it will be $I = V/R = 50/100,000 = 0.5$ ma and the meter will read half scale. Therefore this particular voltmeter can be provided with a linear scale marked from 0 to 100 v. The series resistor which is required to convert the basic moving coil movement into a voltmeter is called a **multiplier resistor.**

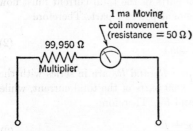
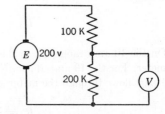

Fig. 8.8. A simple voltmeter.          Fig. 8.9. Effect of voltmeter sensitivity.

In order to measure open-circuit emf, a perfect voltmeter should draw no current. Since current must flow in a moving coil movement to obtain a reading, a 50 μa basic movement will make a much more accurate volt-meter for use in high-resistance circuits than the 1 ma movement. The resistance of a standard 50 μa movement and its calibrating resistor is 1000 ohms. Therefore, to obtain a 100 v full scale range, the total resist-ance must be $R_T = 100/0.00005 = 2$ megohms; and the multiplier re-sistance must be $2,000,000 - 1,000 = 1,999,000$ ohms. To obtain a 500 v scale, with a 50 μa movement, the total resistance must be 10 megohms; and to obtain a 1 v full-scale range, $R_T = 1/0.00005 = 20$ kilohms.

No matter what full-scale voltage we select for the 50 μa basic move-ment, the total resistance required is 20 kilohms for *each* volt of the full-scale reading. Therefore a 50 μa movement when used as a voltmeter is said to have a **sensitivity** of **twenty thousand ohms per volt.** Voltmeter sensitivity is determined by dividing the full-scale current into 1 v. The total resistance of a meter movement and the multiplier resistor for a given range is found by multiplying the full-scale voltage by the voltmeter sensitivity. Therefore when we use a 1 ma movement as a voltmeter, its sensitivity is $1/0.001 = 1000$ ohms per volt; and the total resistance required for a 500 v range will be $500 \times 1000 = 500$ kilohms.

When measuring voltage in electric power circuits where fairly large currents are flowing, an extra 5 ma does not alter the circuit conditions appreciably. Thus the more rugged and less sensitive voltmeters are quite satisfactory. However in electronic circuits where the normal circuit current is very small, an insensitive voltmeter can alter circuit conditions considerably.

EXAMPLE 3: (a) What is the actual voltage drop across the 200 kilohm resistor in Fig. 8.9 with no meter in the circuit? (b) What will a 20,000 ohm per volt meter with 150 v full scale read when connected across the 200 kilohm resistor? (c) What will a 1000 ohm per volt meter with 150 v full scale read when connected across the 200 kilohm resistor?

*Solution:* (a) From the characteristics of series circuits (voltage drops are directly proportional to the resistances),

$$V = \frac{200}{300} \times 200 = 133.3 \text{ v}$$

(b) A 20,000 ohm per volt meter with a 150 v range has a total resistance of $20,000 \times 150 = 3$ megohms. This 3 megohm resistance is in parallel with the 200 kilohm resistor, thus reducing the resistance of the parallel combination to

$$R = \frac{200 \times 3000}{200 + 3000} = 187.5 \text{ kilohms}$$

$$\therefore \quad V = \frac{187.5}{287.5} \times 200 = 130.4 \text{ v}$$

(c) A 1000 ohm per volt meter on a 150 v range has a total resistance of $1000 \times 150 = 150$ kilohms. Therefore the 200 kilohm resistor and the voltmeter in parallel have a total resistance of

$$R = \frac{200 \times 150}{200 + 150} = 85.7 \text{ kilohms}$$

$$\therefore \quad V = \frac{85.7}{185.7} \times 200 = 92.8 \text{ v}$$

Multirange voltmeter circuits are quite straightforward, as shown in Fig. 8.10.

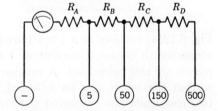

Fig. 8.10. A multirange voltmeter.

EXAMPLE 4: A 1 ma full-scale moving coil movement with a resistance of 50 ohms is to be made into a voltmeter with scales of 5 v, 50 v, 150 v, and 500 v. Calculate $R_A$, $R_B$, $R_C$, and $R_D$ in the circuit of Fig. 8.10.

*Solution:* Voltmeter sensitivity $= 1/0.001 = 1000$ ohms per volt. Therefore the total resistance for 5 v range $= 5$ kilohms, and $R_A = 5000 - 50 = 4950$ ohms.

The total resistance for 50 v range = 50 kilohms, and $R_B$ = 50,000 − 5000 = 45 kilohms.

The total resistance for 150 v range = 150 kilohms, and $R_C$ = 150 − 50 = 100 kilohms.

The total resistance of 500 v range = 500 kilohms, and $R_D$ = 500 − 150 = 350 kilohms.

The voltmeter is a very useful instrument for checking the operating conditions in electric circuits. With suitable test leads the voltmeter can be clipped *across* any part of an electric circuit without having to disconnect or disturb the circuit being checked as is the case when testing with an ammeter.

## 4. Resistance Measurement

We can determine the resistance of the unknown resistor in Fig. 8.11 by applying Ohm's law to the readings obtained from the voltmeter and ammeter. This system of resistance measurement has the disadvantage of having to connect the unknown resistance into a special circuit. However, it is used in the electric laboratory as a means of determining very small resistances such as the armature resistance of a motor, particularly if it is desired that the resistance be measured with its normal current flow through it.

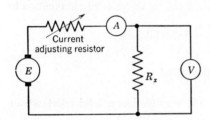

**Fig. 8.11.** Measuring resistance with a voltmeter and an ammeter.

For quick checks of circuit resistance we need a simpler apparatus than that of Fig. 8.11. We can again use the basic moving coil movement to construct an **ohmmeter.** The simple ohmmeter of Fig. 8.12(a) consists of a 1 ma movement, a $4\frac{1}{2}$ v battery and sufficient resistance to permit a current of 1 ma to flow when the ohmmeter terminals are short-circuited. A portion of the total resistance is adjustable so that the meter can be adjusted to read exactly full scale when the two test leads are connected together. In this example, the total resistance (including the meter movement) must be

$$R_T = \frac{E}{I} = \frac{4.5}{0.001} = 4.5 \text{ kilohms}$$

*Example 5:* In preparing the scale for the ohmmeter of Fig. 8.12, determine what resistance values must be marked at full scale, center scale, one-quarter of full scale, and 10% of full scale.

*Solution:* As we have already noted, the total internal resistance of the ohmmeter is adjusted so that the meter reads exactly full scale when the test leads

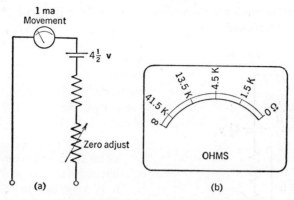

**Fig. 8.12.** A simple ohmmeter.

are short-circuited. This represents connecting the test leads to a zero ohm resistor. Therefore the full-scale point on the scale must be marked zero ohms.

For the meter to read half scale, we must connect the test leads to a resistor which has the same value as the total ohmmeter resistance so that the total resistance in the series loop is now doubled, thus reducing the current to 0.5 ma. Therefore the center scale point must be marked 4.5 kilohms.

$$I = \frac{E}{R_m + R_x} = \frac{4.5}{4500 + 4500} = 0.5 \text{ ma}$$

For one-quarter of full scale, the current must be 0.25 ma. Therefore the total resistance in the loop must be

$$R_T = \frac{4.5}{0.00025} = 18 \text{ kilohms}$$

$$\therefore \quad R_x = 18 - 4.5 = 13.5 \text{ kilohms}$$

Finally, the resistance value for the 10% of full-scale mark will be

$$R_x = \frac{4.5}{0.0001} - 4500 = 40.5 \text{ kilohms}$$

As shown in Fig. 8.12(b), the scale of an ohmmeter is nonlinear as far as the spacing of the ohms values is concerned. But since a few ohms one way or the other makes a greater *percentage* difference to a low resistance than to a high resistance, this nonlinear scale is not a disadvantage. The simple ohmmeter of Fig. 8.12 is limited in its usefulness in that it is not accurate for very low or very high resistances, since these appear at the ends of the scale. For use in electronic circuit testing where we need a high-range ohmmeter, we would start with a 50 μa movement rather than a 1 ma movement. If we use a 50 μa movement in Fig. 8.12(a), the total internal resistance of the ohmmeter will be

$$R_T = \frac{E}{I} = \frac{4.5}{0.00005} = 90 \text{ kilohms}$$

and therefore the center scale reading of the meter will also be 90 kilohms. From these examples we will note that the center scale resistance mark of the ohmmeter is inversely proportional to the full-scale current of the meter. Therefore we can convert the basic ohmmeter into a low-range ohmmeter by placing a shunt across the moving coil.

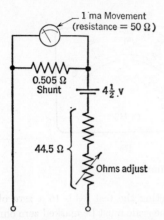

Fig. 8.13. Low range ohmmeter.

EXAMPLE 6: Design an ohmmeter using a 1 ma movement with an internal resistance of 50 ohms and a $4\frac{1}{2}$ v battery to read 45 ohms center scale rather than 4.5 kilohms.

*Solution:* The total internal resistance of the ohmmeter must be 45 ohms for the meter to read full scale with only the 45 ohms of the meter in circuit and half scale when the total loop resistance is

$$R_x + R_m = 45 + 45 \text{ ohms}$$

Therefore, full-scale current must be

$$I = \frac{E}{R} = \frac{4.5}{45} = 0.1 \text{ amp}$$

Since the meter movement passes 1 ma at full scale, the shunt current must be 99 ma and the shunt resistance

$$R_{sh} = \frac{1}{99} \times 50 = 0.505 \text{ ohm}$$

The total resistance of the meter movement and shunt in parallel is

$$R = \frac{50 \times 0.505}{50 + 0.505} = 0.500 \text{ ohm}$$

Therefore the total resistance of the series resistor and the ohms adjust rheostat will be

$$R_s = 45 - 0.5 = 44.5 \text{ ohms}$$

As a test instrument, the ohmmeter has the same advantage as the voltmeter in that it can be connected *across* a portion of a circuit without disconnecting any wiring. However since the ohmmeter is calibrated on the basis of its own source of emf (the $4\frac{1}{2}$ v battery) we must make sure that no other source of emf is acting in the circuit while its resistance is being measured.

When we wish to measure a very high resistance such as the leakage between the two conductors of a cable as in Fig. 8.14, we can apply our knowledge of electric circuit theory to make use of a voltmeter and a separate source of emf to form a high-resistance ohmmeter. This system has the additional advantage that we can measure resistance under actual applied voltage conditions and thus check for voltage breakdown of an insulator.

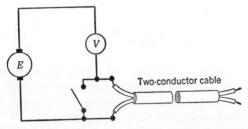

Two-conductor cable

**Fig. 8.14.** Using a voltmeter as a high resistance ohmmeter.

EXAMPLE 7: The voltmeter in Fig. 8.14 is a 20,000 ohm per volt meter with a 150 v scale. When the switch is closed, it reads 120 v and when the switch is open it reads 10 v. What is the leakage resistance of the cable insulation?

*Solution:* The resistance of the voltmeter is

$$R_m = 20,000 \times 150 = 3 \text{ megohms}$$

The voltage drop across the leakage resistance of the cable is $V = 120 - 10 = 110$ v. And since the resistance of the voltmeter and the leakage resistance of the cable form a simple series circuit,

$$\frac{R_x}{R_m} = \frac{V_x}{V_m}$$

$$\therefore \quad R_x = 3 \times \frac{110}{10} = 33 \text{ megohms}$$

For precision resistance measurements, various forms of the Wheatstone bridge which we met in Chapter 6 can be used. If we adjust the circuit of Fig. 8.15 so

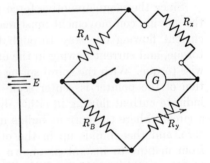

**Fig. 8.15.** Measuring resistance with a Wheatstone bridge.

that there is absolutely no deflection of the galvanometer when the switch is closed, the voltage drop across $R_x$ and $R_A$ must be exactly the same, so that no potential difference is applied to the galvanometer.

Since $\quad V_x = I_x R_x \quad$ and $\quad I_x = \dfrac{E}{R_x + R_y} \quad$ (switch open)

$$V_x = \frac{E R_x}{R_x + R_y}$$

Similarly $\qquad\qquad V_A = \dfrac{E R_A}{R_A + R_B}$

$$\therefore \quad \text{for perfect balance,} \quad \frac{ER_x}{R_x + R_y} = \frac{ER_A}{R_A + R_B}$$

Canceling out $E$ and cross-multiplying gives

$$R_x R_A + R_x R_B = R_x R_A + R_A R_y$$

And canceling out $R_x R_A$,

$$R_x = \frac{R_A R_y}{R_B} \tag{8.3}$$

An unknown resistance $R_x$ is connected into a Wheatstone bridge circuit and $R_y$ is adjusted until there is no galvanometer deflection when the switch is closed. With precision resistors for $R_A$, $R_B$, and $R_y$, the value of $R_x$ can be calculated accurately from Equation (8.3).

EXAMPLE 8: The Wheatstone bridge circuit of Fig. 8.15 is balanced when $R_A = 1.0$ ohm, $R_B = 50$ ohms, and $R_y = 17$ ohms. What is the resistance of $R_x$?

*Solution:*

$$R_x = \frac{R_A R_y}{R_B} = \frac{1.0 \times 17}{50} = 0.34 \text{ ohm}$$

## 5. The Moving Iron Movement

Since the magnetomotive force produced by the *permanent* magnet of the moving coil movement must maintain a fixed direction, it follows that current flowing one way through the moving coil develops a clockwise torque, and current flowing in the other direction develops a counterclockwise torque. With the spiral spring adjusted so that the zero current position of the pointer is center scale (a galvanometer), the movement can indicate current flowing in either direction. If we place the instrument in a circuit where the current builds up first in one direction, drops back to zero, and then builds up in the other direction, the torque will change from instant to instant as shown in Fig. 8.16(a). A negative value of torque on this graph simply indicates that the torque is attempting to rotate the pointer in the opposite direction to that produced by a positive value of torque. If this variation in current is quite slow (once a second),

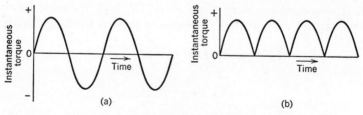

**Fig. 8.16.** Instantaneous torque developed by an alternating current: (a) moving coil movement; (b) moving iron movement.

the pointer will be able to follow the changing torque by swinging to the right and then to the left of zero. Since the pointer is never stationary, it is difficult to obtain a reading having any significance.

When the current in a circuit alternately flows in one direction around the circuit and then in the opposite direction, it is called an **alternating current.** If the current direction is reversed many times a second, the mechanical inertia of the moving coil assembly is too great for the pointer to follow the instantaneous variations in torque (and current through the moving coil). Therefore the pointer must take up a position dictated by the *average* value of the changing torque. In Fig. 8.16(a), the average torque is midway between the two maximum torque values. The pointer must then remain at the zero mark on the scale both for the center zero galvanometer movement and those whose spiral springs are adjusted to place the zero mark at the left-hand end of the scale. Because of the permanent magnets, moving coil instruments are therefore basically *direct-current* instruments.

We can use the moving coil instrument in some a-c circuit measurements by using a suitable **rectifier** to change the alternating current in the circuit into a proportional direct current through the meter movement. This adds to the cost of the instrument but it is used in **multimeters** in which the one meter movement is to be used for measurements in both d-c and a-c circuits. A **thermocouple** is a device which generates a direct emf when heat is applied to the junction between certain pairs of dissimilar metals. If we heat this junction with the heat developed by an alternating current flowing through a resistor, we can operate a moving coil movement with the emf produced and calibrate the meter scale in terms of the alternating current flowing through the heater resistor. This thermocouple instrument is used for measuring high (radio) frequency alternating currents.

The **moving iron** movement of Fig. 8.17 consists of a stationary solenoid with two soft iron vanes within the coil. One vane is stationary but the other is fastened to the pivot which carries the pointer and the countertorque spring. Since the soft iron vanes are located at the

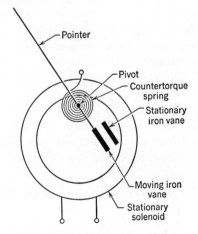

**Fig. 8.17.** The moving iron movement.

point where the flux density of the magnetic field created by the current through the solenoid is maximum, they become temporary magnets. And since the S pole of one vane is adjacent to the S pole of the other (the two N poles are also adjacent), the pivoted vane is *repelled* by the stationary vane. This repulsion is proportional to the current in the solenoid. Figure 8.17 shows only one of several possible shapes in which the soft iron vanes may appear. The scale of this moving iron instrument is not as linear as that of the moving coil instrument. The scale is cramped at the low-current end of the scale. Scale linearity can be improved by using specially shaped soft iron vanes.

The moving iron movement can be calibrated in terms of *direct* current through the solenoid and is sometimes used as an inexpensive direct current instrument where the greater accuracy of the moving coil instrument is not required. However, the moving iron instrument was developed primarily for measuring *alternating* currents at power line frequencies. When the direction of the current in the solenoid is reversed, the N and S poles of *both* vanes reverse and the moving vane is still *repelled* by the stationary vane. Therefore when alternating current flows in the solenoid, the torque developed by the moving iron vane is in the form of pulses which are always in the same direction as shown in Fig. 8.16(b). Since the mechanical inertia of the whole pointer and moving vane assembly is too great to allow it to follow the instantaneous variations in torque, the pointer will indicate the *average* value of the torque. When calibrating the scale of a moving iron instrument for alternating current, allowance must be made for hysteresis losses in the iron vanes. Therefore the calibration of an a-c moving iron instrument is accurate only for power line frequencies, not for direct current or high-frequency alternating currents.

Since the solenoid of the moving iron movement can be wound with a few turns of heavy wire or many turns of fine wire in order to produce the required ampere-turns of mmf for full-scale deflection, the range of full-scale current readings available is much greater than for moving coil instruments. The basic ammeter movement for a-c power circuits has a 5 amp full-scale reading. Shunts similar to those used with moving coil movements are used for larger currents. Although it is not possible to produce moving iron movements that are as sensitive as moving coil instruments, one with a solenoid consisting of many turns of fine wire is quite satisfactory for use with suitable series multiplier resistors to form a voltmeter for use in a-c circuits.

## 6. The Electro-Dynamometer Movement

As we noted in the preceding section, the fixed direction of the magnetomotive force of the permanent magnet is responsible for limiting the moving coil movement to d-c circuits. If we replace the two poles of the *permanent* magnet with an *electromagnet* consisting of two stationary coils as shown in Fig. 8.18, we have an **electro-dynamometer** movement in which we can reverse the direction of the stationary flux at will. Since it contains no iron, we can use the electro-dynamometer as the basic movement for either d-c or a-c instruments. We can use it to measure *alternating* current by connecting the stationary and moving coils in series. Whenever the current in the moving coil reverses its direction, the flux produced by the stationary coils also reverses. Therefore the resulting torque will tend to move the pointer in a clockwise direction regardless of the direction of the current in the coils. However, for voltmeter and ammeter applications, the electro-dynamometer movement cannot compete economically with either the moving coil movement for d-c measurement or the moving iron movement for a-c measurement.

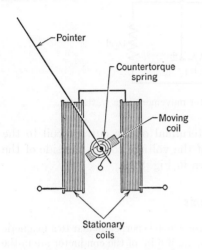

Fig. 8.18. The electro-dynamometer movement.

In developing the equation for the torque of a moving coil, we noted that the force acting on a conductor is proportional to the *product* of the stationary flux and the flux of the moving coil. Therefore the scale reading of an electro-dynamometer movement is proportional to the product of the stationary coil and moving coil currents. If the wire on the stationary coils is heavy enough to connect in series with a load as in Fig. 8.19, the stationary coil current is the same as the load current. And if the moving coil with a multiplier resistor in series with it is connected across the load, the moving coil current is directly proportional to the load voltage. Therefore the scale reading of the electro-dynamometer movement is proportional to the product of the load current and voltage. Since $P = IV$, we have a direct-reading **wattmeter.** If the load is in an a-c circuit, both load current and load voltage reverse their direction the same number of times per second. Therefore the electro-dynamometer movement as a wattmeter can be used in either d-c or a-c circuits. Although we can calculate the power in a load by taking separate ammeter and voltmeter readings, a direct-reading wattmeter is a very useful instrument, particularly in a-c circuits.

If we reverse the leads to *either* the current coil *or* the voltage coil when we are connecting a wattmeter into a circuit, a *negative* torque will be developed which moves the pointer *down scale*. To assist us in connecting a wattmeter properly, it is customary in practice to identify one end of each coil with ± marks as shown in Fig. 8.19. Standard connection re-

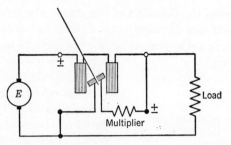

**Fig. 8.19.** The electro-dynamometer movement as a wattmeter.

quires that we connect the identified terminal of the current coil to the generator and the identified terminal of the voltage coil to the side of the line containing the current coil as shown in Fig. 8.19.

# Problems

1. What force in newtons acts on a conductor which is perpendicular to a magnetic field whose flux density is 50 kilolines/sq in. if 6 in. of the conductor are in the magnetic field and the current in the conductor is 5 amp?

2. The countertorque spring of a certain moving coil instrument develops a torque of $10^{-5}$ newton-meter when the pointer is at full scale. The flux density in the air gap is $5 \times 10^{-2}$ weber/sq m and there are 80 turns of wire wound on a form whose dimensions are 2 cm parallel to the pivot and 1.5 cm at right angles to the pivot. What current must flow through the coil for half-scale deflection?

3. The full-scale voltage drop across a 5 ma movement is 50 mv. Calculate the resistance of the shunt required if the movement is to be used as a 1 amp full-scale ammeter.

4. If the shunt calculated in Problem 3 is used with a 1 ma movement having a total resistance of 50 ohms, what current would its full-scale reading represent?

5. Calculate an Ayrton shunt to provide 100 ma, 1 amp, and 10 amp ranges with a 50 $\mu$a movement whose total resistance is 1000 ohms.

6. Calculate an Ayrton shunt for 30 ma, 100 ma, 300 ma, and 1 amp ranges with a 1 ma movement whose total resistance is 50 ohms.

7. Calculate the multiplier resistors required to form a voltmeter with 10 v, 50 v, 100 v, and 500 v ranges, using the meter movement of Problem 5.

8. The resistance of the movement for a 200 ohm per volt voltmeter is 10 ohms. Calculate the multiplier resistors required for 30 v, 150 v, and 1500 v ranges.

9. The terminal voltage of a 12 v source of emf whose internal resistance is 100 kilohms is checked by a 20,000 ohm per volt voltmeter on its 50 v range. What is the voltmeter reading?

10. The grid bias voltage of a vacuum tube is applied to the grid through a 470 kilohm resistor. If a 1000 ohm per volt meter on its 10 v range measures the

voltage at the grid as 0.8 v, what will it be when the voltmeter is removed if there is zero grid current?

11. What is the center scale reading of a basic ohmmeter constructed with a 50 $\mu$a movement and a $1\frac{1}{2}$ v battery?

12. What battery voltage would be required to use the same scale on a 1 ma movement?

13. What resistance must be connected to the terminals of the ohmmeter in Problem 11 for the pointer to read 20% of full-scale deflection?

14. Design an ohmmeter with 1000 ohms appearing at center scale, using a $1\frac{1}{2}$ v battery and a 50 $\mu$a movement having a resistance of 1000 ohms.

15. The insulation resistance of a solenoid is checked by connecting one terminal of a 1 kv source to the solenoid and the other terminal of the source through a 50,000 ohm per volt voltmeter having a 1500 v full-scale reading to the iron core of the solenoid. If the voltmeter reads 120 v, what is the insulation resistance?

16. What would the meter read in Problem 15 if the leakage resistance between the solenoid winding and the core dropped to 0.5 megohm?

17. In the Wheatstone bridge circuit of Fig. 8.15, balance is attained when $R_A$ = 5 kilohms, $R_B$ = 1000 ohms, and $R_y$ = 42 kilohms. What is the resistance of $R_x$?

18. What value must $R_y$ be set at to obtain a balance in the Wheatstone bridge of Fig. 8.15 if $R_A$ = 1000 ohms, $R_B$ = 1200 ohms, and $R_x$ = 600 ohms?

19. Fig. 8.20 is a variation of the Wheatstone bridge known as the **slide wire bridge.** The slide wire is a length of uniform resistance wire one meter long. The standard resistor $R_s$ = 24 ohms. What is the value of $R_x$ if the bridge is balanced when the slider is 37 cm from the end that is connected to the standard resistor?

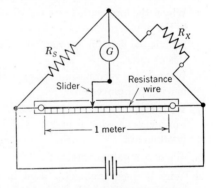

Fig. 8.20. The slide wire bridge.

20. Fig. 8.21 is a variation of the Wheatstone bridge known as the **Varley loop.** It is used for locating grounds on long transmission lines. To accomplish this, the far ends of two identical conductors are connected together. Assume negligible resistance between the ground on the switch and the fault ground on the transmission line. With the switch in the position shown, the bridge balances with $R_A$ = 100 ohms, $R_B$ = 1000 ohms, and $R_C$ = 200 ohms. When the switch is thrown to the ground position, $R_A$ and $R_B$ are unchanged but $R_C$ is changed to 150 ohms to obtain balance. How far is the ground from the end of the cable at which the apparatus is located?

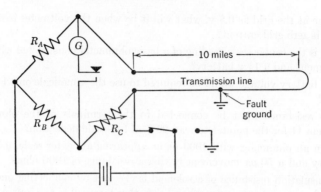

**Fig. 8.21.** The Varley loop.

## Review Questions

1. Draw a sketch showing the composite field when an electric conductor with a conventional current direction coming out of the page is placed in an air gap in a magnetic circuit in which the lines of force pass from left to right across the air gap.

2. Explain why the composite magnetic field in Question 1 has the shape you have shown.

3. Explain why the composite magnetic field in Fig. 8.3 has the pattern shown.

4. Why is the force acting on a coil of wire in a magnetic field directly proportional to the number of turns in the coil?

5. Why is the flat spiral spring essential in all the meter movements described in this chapter?

6. What is the relationship between Hooke's law and the scale markings on a moving coil movement?

7. What would be the effect on the operation of a moving coil movement if the soft iron cylinder (shown in Fig. 8.4) were left out during the assembly of the instrument?

8. What is a **galvanometer**?

9. Why is a galvanometer used in the circuit of Fig. 8.15 rather than a microammeter?

10. What is the purpose of the **calibrating resistor** used with moving coil movements?

11. Suggest an advantage in arranging that moving coil movements have a 50 mv drop across their terminals when full-scale current flows through them. (Refer to Problem 4.)

12. Show that $R_s = R_m \left( \dfrac{I_m}{I_T - I_m} \right)$ where $R_s$ is the resistance of an ammeter shunt, $R_m$ is the resistance of the moving coil movement and its calibrating resistor, $I_m$ is the current in the moving coil required for full-scale deflection, and $I_T$ is the desired full scale ammeter reading.

13. Figure 8.22 shows the right and wrong ways of connecting an ammeter with an external shunt into a circuit. What would be the effect of connecting the circuit incorrectly as in Fig. 8.22(a)?

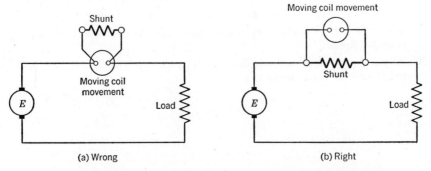

**Fig. 8.22.** Connecting an ammeter with an external shunt into a circuit.

14. Why is the insertion resistance of a multirange ammeter equipped with an Ayrton shunt greater than that of an ammeter using a separate shunt for each range?

15. The basic moving coil movement is a *current*-indicating device. How is it possible to calibrate it as a voltmeter?

16. What is the significance of **voltmeter sensitivity?**

17. Why is a 20,000 ohm per volt meter more suitable than a 1000 ohm per volt meter for checking electronic circuitry?

18. Why is a 200 ohm per volt meter satisfactory for use with electric machinery?

19. Discuss the possible errors that might occur when using the voltmeter, ammeter method of determining the resistance of a 50 kilohm resistor. (Draw a circuit diagram.)

20. What precaution must be observed when checking the resistance of an electric circuit with an ohmmeter?

21. Lay out a scale (see Fig. 8.12) for a simple ohmmeter using a 50 μa movement and a 1½ v battery.

22. Lay out a scale for the low-resistance ohmmeter shown in Fig. 8.23.

23. What would be the effect of connecting an ammeter *across* a load?

24. What would be the effect of connecting a voltmeter in *series* with a load?

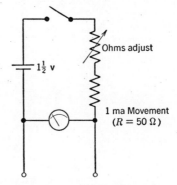

**Fig. 8.23.** A low resistance ohmmeter.

25. What circuit information could be obtained from the voltmeter reading in Question 24?

26. Which of the following movements would you select for the Wheatstone bridge

circuit of Fig. 8.15: a 50 $\mu$a movement or a 5 ma movement? Explain your selection.

27. What effect does the accuracy of the galvanometer scale calibration have on the accuracy of the resistance measurements made with a Wheatstone bridge?

28. Why does a moving coil movement read zero in an a-c circuit?

29. Why is the pointer of a moving iron movement able to indicate a steady reading in an a-c circuit?

30. Why is it possible to calibrate the scale of an electro-dynamometer movement to indicate the power input to an a-c load?

# Chapter 9

# INDUCTANCE

~~~~~~~~~~~~~~~~~~~~~~~~~~~~~~~~~~~~~~~~~~~~~~~~~~~~~~~~~~~~~~~~~~~~~~~~~~~~~~~~~~

So far we have considered only one property of an electric circuit: the ability of the circuit to oppose the flow of electric current through it. This property is called **resistance.** In this chapter we shall consider a second property of an electric circuit: the ability of the circuit to oppose any *change* in the current through it. This property is called **inductance.**

## 1. Electromagnetic Induction

In Chapter 7 we referred to Faraday's discovery of electromagnetic induction in order to define the mks unit of magnetic flux—the weber. Figure 9.1 shows another arrangement for demonstrating Faraday's discovery. As the conductor is moved downward through the magnetic lines of force, the galvanometer pointer swings one way from its center zero. As the conductor is moved upward, the galvanometer pointer swings in the opposite direction. But when there is no motion, there is no pointer deflection.

In order for current to flow through the galvanometer, there must be some source of emf in the loop consisting of the galvanometer and the conductor in the magnetic field. And, as experiment has shown, this emf appears only when the conductor is *cutting across* the magnetic lines of force. Moving the conductor parallel to the lines of force will produce no deflection of the galvanometer pointer. In Fig. 9.1 the conductor is being moved while the magnetic field remains stationary; whereas in the previous demonstration of Faraday's discovery the magnetic field was moved while the electric conductor remained stationary. In both cases there was a cutting across magnetic lines of force by an electric conductor and in both cases an emf appeared in the conductor.

The generation of an emf by the cutting of magnetic lines of force by

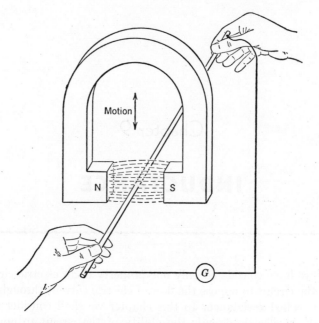

**Fig. 9.1.** Demonstrating electromagnetic induction.

an electric conductor is called **electromagnetic induction** and the resulting emf is called an **induced** emf.

Another method of demonstrating electromagnetic induction is shown in Fig. 9.2. In this example, *relative* motion between the magnetic lines of force and the electric conductor is achieved without mechanical motion of either the magnet or the electric conductor. As the resistance of the

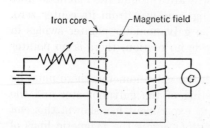

**Fig. 9.2.** Demonstrating mutual induction.

rheostat is reduced, the current flowing in the left-hand (**primary**) winding increases. This causes an increase in the number of magnetic lines of force appearing in the iron core. Since the right-hand (**secondary**) winding is wound on the same core, the number of lines of force passing through the winding is increasing and the deflection of the galvanometer pointer indicates that an emf is being induced into the secondary winding. Since most of the magnetic lines of force are confined to the iron core, it is more usual to think of the flux as **linking** the secondary winding rather than as cutting across the turns of the secondary winding. When the resistance of the rheostat is increased, the current becomes smaller and the number of lines of force linking the secondary is becoming less. While this is happening, the pointer of the galvanometer swings in the opposite direction, indicating that the induced emf has the opposite polarity. But as long as the current in the primary is steady, there is no deflection of the galvanometer pointer.

The generation of an emf in a secondary winding by a *changing* current in a primary winding is called **mutual induction.**

## 2. Faraday's Law

One apparent observation in the demonstration of mutual induction in Fig. 9.2 is that the faster the flux in the core builds up or collapses, the greater the deflection of the galvanometer pointer. When we consider the reason for this, we come to the conclusion which is referred to as

**Faraday's law:** The emf induced in a circuit is proportional to the time rate of change of the flux of magnetic induction linked with the circuit.

But
$$\Phi = \frac{\mathcal{F}}{\mathcal{R}} = \frac{NI}{\mathcal{R}}$$

The number of turns in the primary winding is fixed; and if we stay below the saturation point of the iron core, the reluctance of the magnetic circuit is reasonably constant. Therefore the *rate of change of flux* is directly proportional to the *rate of change of current.* Therefore when dealing with induction due to a changing current rather than mechanical motion, Faraday's law may be restated:

The **magnitude of the induced emf** is directly proportional to the rate of change of current.

## 3. Lenz's Law

We have already noted that the polarity of the induced emf depends on the direction in which the conductor is moved across the magnetic lines of force in Fig. 9.1; or whether the current in the primary is increasing or decreasing in Fig. 9.2. We can apply a law set forth by H. L. Lenz to determine the exact polarity of the induced emf. Lenz reasoned that the process of induction must conform to the well-known principle in physics that reaction is equal and opposite to action. Of several ways of stating Lenz's law, we shall use the following form:

**Lenz's law:** The direction of the induced emf must be such that any current resulting from it will develop a flux which tends to oppose any change in the original flux.

Applying Lenz's law to the mutual induction demonstration, when the switch is first closed in Fig. 9.3(a), the primary flux will increase from zero. Since a resistor is connected across the secondary winding to form a complete closed circuit, current will flow in the secondary winding when an emf is induced in it by the rising primary flux. According to Lenz's law, the flux produced by this secondary current must try to oppose the increase in primary flux. Applying our right-hand rule to the primary winding, the primary flux will have a clockwise direction around the core. To oppose an increase in this clockwise primary flux, the flux produced by the secondary current must have a *counterclockwise* direction. Again applying our right-hand rule, this time to the secondary winding, we can establish the direction in which the secondary current must flow through the resistor and from this we can determine the polarity of the emf in terms of the polarity of the voltage drop across the resistor.

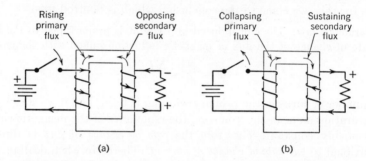

**Fig. 9.3.** Determining the direction of an induced emf by Lenz's law.

When the switch is opened as in Fig. 9.3(b) the primary current stops flowing and the primary flux collapses. According to Faraday's law, this reduction in flux will induce an emf into the secondary, and according to Lenz's law, the secondary current must try to oppose the collapse of the primary flux. To help sustain the primary flux which has a clockwise direction in the core, the secondary current must also produce a clockwise flux direction. Applying our right-hand rule, we obtain the polarity shown in Fig. 9.3(b). The polarity of the induced emf when the primary current is decreasing is therefore opposite to that induced when the primary current is increasing.

We can also use Lenz's law to determine the direction of the induced emf in the demonstration of Fig. 9.1. The galvanometer completes the circuit so that current will flow in the conductor as it is moved through the magnetic field. This results in the situation discussed in Chapter 8— a current-carrying conductor in a magnetic field. Therefore as the conductor is moved across the magnetic lines of force, an emf is induced which causes current to flow in the loop, which in turn results in a mechanical force being exerted on the conductor. According to the principle stated in Lenz's law, the direction of this mechanical force will *oppose* the motion of the conductor through the magnetic field. Therefore if we move the conductor downward in Fig. 9.4, the current flow must be in such a direction as to develop a mechanical force tending to move the conductor upward. Applying the procedure we used in determining the force acting on a current-carrying conductor in Chapter 8, the current resulting from the emf induced into the conductor in Fig. 9.4 must have a conventional direction coming out of the page. (Check this statement.)

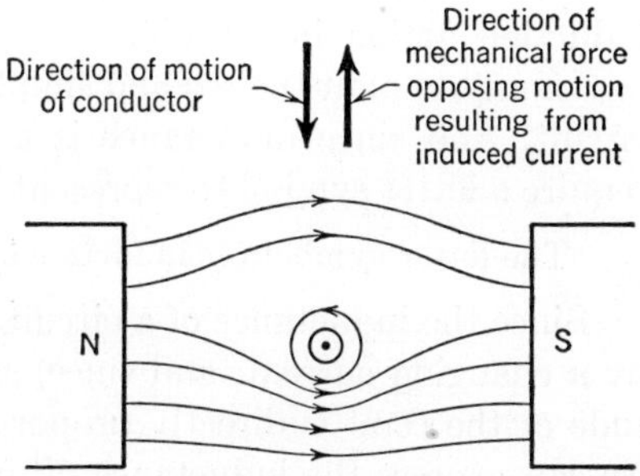

**Fig. 9.4.** Using Lenz's law to determine the direction of the current produced by an induced emf.

## 4. Self-Induction

The induction of an emf by a *changing* current is not restricted to mutual induction of an emf in a secondary winding by current changing in a primary winding. When the switch is first closed in the simple two-turn coil of Fig. 9.5, the increasing flux produced by the rising current in turn *A* will induce an emf into turn *B*. Similarly the rising current in turn *B* will induce an emf into turn *A*. These emf's are in series, and according to Lenz's law, both will have a direction such as to oppose the increasing flux. Since the increasing flux is due to the rising current, the induced emf will be in such a direction as to oppose the applied emf so that the current cannot rise instantly.

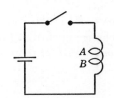

**Fig. 9.5.** Self induction.

This ability of an electric circuit to oppose a *change* in current in that circuit is called **self-induction.** And since the induced emf must *oppose* any change in current, it is called a **counter** emf, or cemf.

When the switch in Fig. 9.5 is opened, the magnetic field collapses and again induces an emf in turns *A* and *B*. In this case the polarity of the self-induced emf is reversed as the coil tries to maintain current flow by having the polarity of its cemf such that it adds to the source emf, thus raising the total emf in an attempt to maintain current flow in the circuit.

## 5. Self-Inductance

From the foregoing discussion we find that the simple electric circuit of Fig. 9.5 has the property of tending to oppose any *change* in current through it. This property is called **self-inductance.**

**Self-inductance** may be defined as that property of an electric circuit that opposes any change in current in that circuit.

Since it will be quite apparent from the circuit diagram whether the induction action in question is *self*-induction or *mutual* induction, it is customary to omit the *self* and simply speak of the **inductance** of an electric circuit. And since inductance is a property of electric circuits, we shall require a letter symbol to represent inductance and a unit of measurement.

The letter symbol for **inductance** is $L$.

Since the inductance of a circuit is responsible for a cemf being induced by a changing current, and since, according to Faraday's law, the magnitude of the cemf is directly proportional to the rate of change of current, we can express the inductance of an electric circuit in terms of these two quantities.

The **basic unit of inductance** is the henry.

A circuit has an inductance of **one henry** when current changing at the rate of **one ampere** per second induces a counter emf of **one volt** into that circuit.

This may be expressed in formula form thus:

$$L = \frac{E_L}{(dI/dt)} \tag{9.1}$$

where $L$ is the inductance of a circuit in henrys, $E_L$ is the counter emf induced into the circuit in volts, and $dI$ is the change in current (amperes) occurring during a small time interval $dt$. Therefore $dI/dt$ represents the rate of change of current.

## 6. Factors Governing Inductance

The inductance of an electric circuit is evidenced in the form of a counter emf which is generated whenever the current flowing in the circuit *changes*. Even a straight wire possesses inductance. As the current through a conductor increases, magnetic lines of force first appear as tiny loops at the center of the conductor and expand outward. As they expand, they cut across the copper of the conductor, thus inducing a cemf into the conductor. However, the inductance of a straight wire is so small that we can neglect it except at very high radio frequencies.

In establishing the mks unit of magnetic flux, we made use of the emf induced in a single-turn coil by a changing magnetic flux linking the coil in order to define the magnitude of the weber. From this, an emf of one volt will be induced into a single turn coil if the flux passing through the center of (linking) it changes at the rate of one weber per second. Therefore

$$\text{emf per turn} = \frac{d\Phi}{dt}$$

If we wish to construct a circuit component in which the inductance effect is very pronounced, we would wind the conductor into a coil of many turns since the same changing flux would induce an emf into each turn. Therefore,

$$E_L = N \frac{d\Phi}{dt} \qquad (9.2)$$

But

$$\Phi = \frac{\mathfrak{F}}{\mathfrak{R}} = \frac{NI}{\mathfrak{R}}$$

Dividing both sides of the equation by $t$,

$$\frac{\Phi}{t} = \frac{N}{\mathfrak{R}} \times \frac{I}{t}$$

from which

$$\frac{d\Phi}{dt} = \frac{N}{\mathfrak{R}} \times \frac{dI}{dt}$$

Substituting in Equation (9.2) gives

$$E_L = \frac{N^2}{\mathfrak{R}} \times \frac{dI}{dt}$$

Substituting this value for induced emf into Equation (9.1),

$$L = \frac{(N^2/\mathfrak{R})(dI/dt)}{dI/dt} = \frac{N^2}{\mathfrak{R}}$$

Hence the inductance of a coil of wire is dependent on the number of turns and the reluctance of the magnetic circuit on which the coil is wound. A circuit component that is constructed for the express purpose of displaying the property of inductance is called an **inductor**. An inductor is often referred to in an electric circuit as a **choke** or simply as a **coil**. As the above equation indicates, the use of iron cores to decrease the reluctance greatly increases the inductance of an inductor. Since doubling the number of turns of wire in the coil of Fig. 9.5 not only doubles the flux linking the coil (thus doubling the cemf per turn), but also doubles the number of turns that this flux links, the total cemf (and consequently the inductance) is proportional to the *square* of the number of turns. Therefore a change in the number of turns in the winding of an inductor has more effect on the inductance than an equivalent change in the reluctance of the magnetic circuit.

Finally, substituting for the reluctance of the magnetic circuit of the inductor from Equation (7.10),

$$L = \frac{N^2 \mu A}{l} \qquad (9.3)$$

where $L$ is the inductance of the inductor in henrys, $N$ is the number of turns in the coil, $\mu$ is the permeability of the magnetic circuit in mks units, $A$ is the cross-sectional area of the magnetic circuit in square meters, and

$l$ is the length of the magnetic circuit in meters (length of the coil for air-core coils).

In adapting Equation (9.3) to English units we must remember that the English unit of flux is the line of force and that it takes $10^8$ lines of force to equal one weber. Therefore

$$L = \frac{N^2 \mu A}{10^8 l} \tag{9.4}$$

where $L$ is the inductance of the inductor in henrys, $N$ is the number of turns in the coil, $\mu$ is the permeability of the magnetic circuit in English units, $A$ is the cross-sectional area of the magnetic circuit in square inches, and $l$ is the length of the magnetic circuit in inches (length of the coil for air-core coils).

In applying Equations (9.3) and (9.4) to practical inductors, we must realize that they are based on *all* the flux linking *all* the turns. In the case of iron core coils and toroids where the leakage flux is very small, these equations are reasonably accurate. But for long air-core coils where there is appreciable leakage flux, empirical formulas for inductance have been developed. These will be found in radio handbooks.

EXAMPLE 1: 2000 turns of wire are wound toroid fashion on a cast steel ring whose cross-sectional area is 1 sq cm, whose average path length is 15.7 cm, and whose permeability is $1.25 \times 10^{-3}$ mks unit. (See Example 3, Chapter 7.) What is the inductance of the toroid?

*Solution:*

$$L = \frac{N^2 \mu A}{l} = \frac{2000 \times 2000 \times 1.25 \times 10^{-3} \times 10^{-4}}{0.157} = 3.18 \text{ h}$$

If we connect two inductors in series as in Fig. 9.6(a), the same current flows through both and therefore both will be subject to the same rate of change of current. For the present we will assume that the two inductors are physically located so that the magnetic field of one cannot induce an emf into the other. A changing current in the circuit will induce a cemf $E_1$ in $L_1$ and $E_2$ in $L_2$. The total counter emf in the series circuit is

$$E_T = E_1 + E_2$$

From the definition of inductance,

$$L_T = \frac{E_T}{dI/dt} = \frac{E_1 + E_2}{dI/dt} = \frac{E_1}{dI/dt} + \frac{E_2}{dI/dt} = L_1 + L_2$$

Therefore, when there is no mutual coupling between inductors in series, the total inductance is the sum of the individual inductances.

$$L_T = L_1 + L_2 + L_3 + \text{etc.} \tag{9.5}$$

Note that the equation for inductances in series is similar to the equation for the total resistance of resistors in series.

If we now connect two inductances in parallel as in Fig. 9.6(b), each

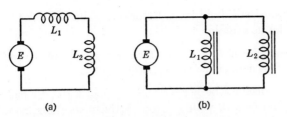

**Fig. 9.6.** (a) Air core inductances in series
(b) Iron core inductances in parallel.

must develop the same counter emf. In order to produce this counter emf, current in $L_1$ must change at the rate of $dI_1/dt$, and current in $L_2$ must change at the rate of $dI_2/dt$. Therefore, the total current must change at the rate of $(dI_1 + dI_2)/dt$.

$$\therefore \quad L_{eq} = \frac{E}{(dI_1 + dI_2)/dt}$$

To simplify this equation, we invert both sides.

$$\frac{1}{L_{eq}} = \frac{(dI_1 + dI_2)/dt}{E} = \frac{dI_1/dt + dI_2/dt}{E} = \frac{dI_1/dt}{E} + \frac{dI_2/dt}{E}$$

$$\therefore \quad 1/L_{eq} = 1/L_1 + 1/L_2$$

For only two inductances in parallel, this reduces to

$$L_{eq} = \frac{L_1 \times L_2}{L_1 + L_2}$$

Therefore the total inductance of inductors in parallel is

$$L_{eq} = \frac{1}{1/L_1 + 1/L_2 + 1/L_3 + \text{etc.}} \qquad (9.6)$$

## 7. Rise of Current in a Pure Inductance

To start our investigation of the behavior of inductance in d-c circuits, we shall assume that the inductor of Fig. 9.7 is a pure inductance with zero resistance. Such a situation is hypothetical, since in practice there is no conductor material that has absolutely no resistance at room temperature, with which to wind the coil. However, it will help us to determine what happens when the switch in Fig. 9.7 is closed if for the moment we do consider the resistance to be zero.

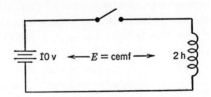

**Fig. 9.7.** A simple electric circuit containing pure inductance.

Even though there is no resistance in the circuit of Fig. 9.7, Kirchhoff's voltage law must still hold true. Before we write the voltage equation for this circuit, let us examine again the statement of Kirchhoff's voltage law:

> In any complete electric circuit, the algebraic sum of the emf's must equal the algebraic sum of the voltage drops.

We must now decide whether we will think of a *counter* emf in an inductance as an emf or as a voltage drop. Strictly speaking, as its name indicates, the voltage appearing between the terminals of an inductor is a form of emf induced in the inductance by a *changing* current through the inductance. If we are going to think of it as an emf, since there is no resistance in the circuit of Fig. 9.7, there is no voltage drop term to appear on the right hand side of the Kirchhoff's voltage law equation. Accordingly we would write the equation for the circuit of Fig. 9.7 thus:

$$E + E_L = 0$$

In order for the total emf to have an algebraic sum of zero, we must consider that when the applied emf is a positive quantity, *counter* emf is a *negative* quantity. Therefore when rearranging equation (9.1) to solve for counter emf, we would write it thus:

$$E_L = -L(dI/dt) \tag{9.1b}$$

The minus sign is the indication that the emf induced *in* the inductance must *oppose* the applied emf and is therefore called a *counter* emf. Many texts prefer to consider counter emf *in* an inductance as a source of emf with a negative sign.

However, we will be able to appreciate the behavior of inductance in a d-c circuit more readily if we can avoid having to think of the circuit of Fig. 9.7 as two equal and opposite sources of emf in series feeding a zero ohm resistance. Our interpretation of Kirchhoff's voltage law has been that, given a source of emf, the circuit connected *across* this source of emf must possess an identical voltage drop. The current in the circuit must then flow in such a manner as to develop the required voltage drop.

Comparing the circuit of Fig. 9.7, in which a pure inductance is connected across a source of emf, with Fig. 2.6, in which a pure resistance is connected across a source of emf, both circuits are similar in that before the switch is closed no voltage appears across either the resistance in Fig. 2.6 or the inductance in Fig. 9.7. Both circuits are similar in that after the switch is closed, the conventional current direction is from the + terminal of the source of emf, through the resistance (or inductance) *from the + terminal to the − terminal*, and then back through the source of emf *from the − terminal to the + terminal*.

Therefore we are quite justified in interpreting the term *counter* applied to the emf *in* an inductance as meaning that the voltage *across* the inductance acts like a voltage drop. We can then write the Kirchhoff's voltage law equation for the circuit of Fig. 9.7 in which there is only pure inductance as

$$E = V_L$$

By transposing the $E_L$ term to the right-hand side of the equation it has become a *positive* quantity. This then is a further reason why it is to our advantage to think of the effect of inductance in terms of the voltage drop *across* the inductor rather than in terms of the counter emf *in* the inductor although we must keep in mind that, in a pure inductance, this voltage drop can be developed only as a result of a *changing* current generating a counter emf *in* the inductor, in this text we shall discuss the behavior of inductance in electric circuits in terms of the voltage drop or simply *voltage across* the inductive elements of the circuit.

According to Kirchhoff's voltage law, all the time that the switch is closed in a simple electric circuit, a voltage drop exactly equal to the applied emf must appear across the load. If the load is a pure resistance, this voltage drop is produced by current flowing through the resistance. Therefore when the switch is closed, the current in a pure resistance circuit must *instantly* assume a magnitude of $I = V/R = E/R$. But if there is no resistance in the circuit, as is the case in Fig. 9.7, none of this voltage drop can be made up of $IR$ drop. Therefore the current in the coil (the dependent variable of most electric circuits) must flow in such a manner that a constant voltage equal to the applied emf will appear *across* the terminals of the pure inductance.

We can determine what this current must be by rearranging Equation (9.1) thus:

$$\frac{dI}{dt} = \frac{E}{L}$$

Since the applied emf is constant, the voltage across the inductor must also be constant. And since inductance depends on the number of turns and the reluctance of the core, the inductance of a given air-core coil is also constant. Therefore the ratio $E/L$ is a constant. As a result, the rate of change of current $dI/dt$ must also be constant, which allows us to drop the $d$ operator, giving

$$\frac{I}{t} = \frac{E}{L}$$

from which                            $$I = Et/L$$

For the numerical values given in Fig. 9.7,

$$I = 10t/2 = 5t \text{ amp}$$

Therefore $\frac{1}{2}$ sec after the switch is closed, the current will be 2.5 amp; 1 sec after the switch is closed, it will be 5 amp; and 2 sec after the switch is closed, the current must be 10 amp; etc., as shown by the graph of Fig. 9.8.

Since the cemf in this case must remain constant, the rate of change of current must be a constant and therefore the graph of Fig. 9.8 is a straight line. The *slope* of this graph of current plotted against time represents the *rate of change* of current. As the inductance of the circuit is reduced, the current must rise more rapidly in order to generate the required cemf. If the inductance is very small, the current must rise almost instantly to an infinitely high value. As the graph of Fig. 9.8 indicates, the presence of appreciable inductance in the circuit acts to oppose this sudden change in current from zero to a very high value by forcing the current to rise at a slower, steady rate governed by the ratio $E/L$.

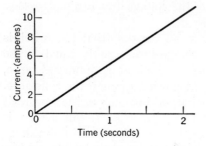

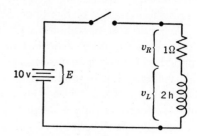

**Fig. 9.8.** The rise of current in a pure inductance.

**Fig. 9.9.** A simple electric circuit containing practical inductance.

## 8. Rise of Current in a Practical Inductance

Since we do not have at our disposal any wire which has zero ohms resistance at room temperature, all practical inductors possess some resistance as well as inductance. Since there is only the one path for current to flow through, we must consider the practical inductor as consisting of inductance and resistance in *series* as shown in Fig. 9.9.

At this point we must note an important convention regarding the letter symbols used to represent electrical properties in equations. Up to this point we have used upper case letters for everything except *time*. Since time never stands still, we indicate the fact that whatever numerical value we substitute for $t$ changes from instant to instant by the use of a lower case letter. Similarly then, any electrical quantity that changes from instant to instant will be represented in equations by lower case letter symbols to indicate that the numerical value that the symbol represents is dependent on some exact instant in time. Such a numerical value is called an **instantaneous** value.

The resistance of an electric circuit is dependent on such physical factors as length, cross section, and type of material. Inductance depends on number of turns and the length, cross section, and permeability of the magnetic circuit. Their numerical values are therefore essentially independent of time. Therefore resistance and inductance are represented by upper case letter symbols. In the circuits we have considered so far, the emf of the source has remained constant, hence the resulting current, voltage drop, and power have been independent of any exact instant in time. Accordingly we have represented all these properties with upper case letter symbols. But in dealing with the rise of current in an inductive circuit, the exact instantaneous values of current, $IR$ drop, and inductive voltage depend on how long the switch has been closed. These quantities then will be represented by lower case letters.

**Lower case letter symbols** represent instantaneous values which are dependent on the exact instant in time for their numerical value.

**Upper case letter symbols** represent steady state values which are not dependent on the exact instant in time for their numerical value.

Returning to the circuit of Fig. 9.9, when the switch is closed, the voltage drop across the resistance of the coil plus the voltage drop across the inductance of the coil (resulting from the cemf generated in it by the rising current) must equal the applied emf in order to satisfy Kirchhoff's voltage law. Therefore

$$E = v_R + v_L$$

From Ohm's law, $$v_R = iR$$

and from Equation (9.1), $$v_L = L\, di/dt$$

Note that we are using lower case letters for current and voltage since, as we shall discover shortly, they change with time immediately after the switch is closed. We are also using the lower case $i$ in the *rate of change of current* symbol which, strictly speaking, we should have been using in the preceding sections of this chapter.

Substituting for $v_R$ and $v_L$ in the Kirchhoff's law equation,

$$E = iR + L\, di/dt \tag{9.7}$$

If we can arrange this equation to solve for the instantaneous current in the circuit, we can then determine the voltage drop across the resistance from Ohm's law. Subtracting $v_R$ from $E$ then gives us the inductive voltage drop. However, solving Equation (9.7) for $i$ involves rather more than basic algebra. Therefore we shall set this equation aside for the moment and see if we can estimate the circuit behavior from our prior investigation of the rise of current in a pure inductance.

Since the inductance of the practical inductor and the applied emf in Fig. 9.9 are the same as for the theoretical inductor of Fig. 9.7, the current cannot rise at a more rapid rate than that shown in the graph of Fig. 9.8. Otherwise the counter emf of the inductance alone would be greater than the applied emf. Since there was no resistance in the circuit of Fig. 9.7, there was no limit to the value of the instantaneous current. But in the case of the practical inductor, it is not possible for the current to rise to a value such that the $IR$ drop across the resistance exceeds the applied emf, otherwise Kirchhoff's law again would not hold true. The greatest value that the instantaneous current can have is such that $v_R = E$. When this occurs, $v_L = 0$, and for the voltage across the inductance to be zero, $di/dt = 0$, and, therefore, the current must be a *steady* value (which allows us to use the upper case letter symbol);

$$\therefore \quad I_m = \frac{E}{R} \tag{9.8}$$

These two limits on the graph of the instantaneous current in a practical inductor are shown by the dashed lines in Fig. 9.10.

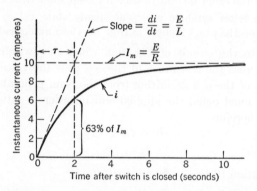

**Fig. 9.10.** Rise of current in a direct current circuit containing inductance and resistance.

As indicated by the graph of Fig. 9.8, inductance opposes any *change* in current; therefore current cannot instantly flow when the switch is closed. It must build up from zero. Therefore at the instant that the switch is closed in Fig. 9.9, the current through the resistance is zero and there will be no voltage drop across it. Therefore at the instant the switch is closed, an inductive voltage equal to the applied emf must appear across the inductance. Since $di/dt = v_L/L$,

$$\text{initial } \frac{di}{dt} = \frac{E}{L} \tag{9.9}$$

This is the same rate of change of current as for the pure inductance (since the resistance cannot make its presence known if there is no current flowing through it). Therefore the graph of the instantaneous current in Fig. 9.10 starts off with the same slope as in Fig. 9.8.

However, since the current is rising in order to induce a cemf in the inductance, the voltage drop across the resistance must be rising. Therefore the cemf required of the inductance for $v_R + v_L = E$ must decrease; and therefore the rate of change of current must become smaller. Therefore the slope of the instantaneous current curve in Fig. 9.10 becomes more gradual. Although the current is now rising less rapidly, nevertheless it is still rising and consequently the inductive voltage must be decreasing. As $v_L$ becomes smaller, the rate of change of current must become smaller. As a result, the instantaneous current curve in Fig. 9.10 continues to become still more gradual. After an appreciable period of time the current reaches its maximum value which produces a voltage drop across the resistance equal to the applied emf. Consequently the current is no longer changing but has settled to the steady value given by Equation (9.8).

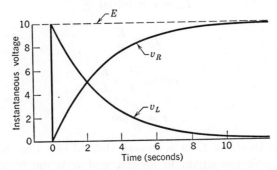

**Fig. 9.11.** Instantaneous voltages across the resistance and inductance.

Therefore, when we close the switch in a d-c circuit containing inductance and resistance in series, the current cannot instantly take on a value of $E/R$ as would be the case if there were no inductance in the circuit. The effect of the inductance is to force the current to rise to this steady state value along the solid curve of Fig. 9.10. Once the current reaches this steady value, the effect of the inductance in the circuit disappears. Since $v_R = iR$, and $R$ is a constant, the graph of the voltage drop across the resistance of the circuit must have the same shape as the instantaneous current graph (Fig. 9.11). The graph of the instantaneous voltage across the inductance is obtained by subtracting the instantaneous $IR$ drop from the constant applied emf.

$$v_L = E - v_R$$

## 9. Time Constant

When we close the switch in a d-c circuit containing inductance, it takes *time* for the current to rise to its steady state value. Later on we will calculate this time element directly from the equation of the solid curve for instantaneous current in Fig. 9.10. We can derive a simple and convenient method of indicating this time interval by assuming for the moment that the current can continue to rise at a *constant* rate equal to its initial rate of rise until it reaches the steady state value, as shown by the *dashed* lines in Fig. 9.10. This time interval is called the **time constant** of the *LR* circuit. On the basis of the above assumption, we can define time constant thus:

The **time constant of an *LR* circuit** is the time it would take the current to rise to its steady state value *if* it were to continue to rise at its initial rate of change for the whole time interval.

The letter symbol for **time constant** is the Greek letter $\tau$ (tau).

If the rate of change of current remains constant (as shown by the straight dashed line in Fig. 9.10), the steady state current would be simply

$$I_m = \tau \times \text{initial } \frac{di}{dt}$$

But
$$I_m = \frac{E}{R} \tag{9.8}$$

$$\text{initial } \frac{di}{dt} = \frac{E}{L} \tag{9.9}$$

From which
$$\tau = \frac{L}{R} \text{ sec} \tag{9.10}$$

where $\tau$ is the length of time in seconds defined as a time constant, $L$ is the inductance of the circuit in henrys, and $R$ is the resistance of the circuit in ohms.

Note that the time constant of an *LR* circuit is directly proportional to the inductance. If the inductance is doubled, the initial rate of rise of current will only be half as great and it will therefore take twice as long to reach the steady state value. Also the time constant is inversely proportional to the resistance. If we double the resistance, the steady state current will be only half as much. So, for a given inductance, the current (rising at the same rate) will only take half as long to reach the steady state value. Note also that the applied emf has no effect on the time constant. If we double the emf, we will double the initial rate of rise of current $E/L$, but we will also double the steady state current $E/R$. Therefore it will take exactly the same time to reach the steady state value.

However with resistance in the circuit, the instantaneous current does *not* continue to rise at its initial rate; it rises along an exponential curve as shown by the solid graph in Fig. 9.10. Nevertheless, this exponential curve must bear a fixed relationship to the two dashed straight lines in Fig. 9.10. It starts at the same point and with the same slope as the initial rate of change of current line and its slope gradually changes until it merges with the horizontal steady state current line. Therefore no matter what values of $L$ and $R$ are involved, in the time interval defined as a time constant, the instantaneous current actually rises to 63% of the steady state value. Therefore we may redefine time constant as the time it takes the instantaneous current in an *LR* circuit to reach 63% of its steady state value. Although we might argue that the instantaneous current theoretically never does quite reach the steady state value, we shall consider that, for practical purposes, the instantaneous current will reach the **steady state value** of $E/R$ after a time interval equal to five time constants has elapsed.

EXAMPLE 2: (a) What is the steady state current in the circuit of Fig. 9.9?
(b) How long does it take the current to reach this value after the switch is closed?

*Solution:*

(a) $$I_m = \frac{E}{R} = \frac{10}{1} = 10 \text{ amp}$$

(b) $$\tau = \frac{L}{R} = \frac{2}{1} = 2 \text{ sec}$$

$$\therefore \quad \text{total rise time} = \frac{5L}{R} = 5 \times 2 = 10 \text{ sec}$$

## 10. Graphical Solution for Instantaneous Current

There are some cases in which we will be asked what the instantaneous current is at a certain instant in time after the switch is closed or how long it takes the current to reach a certain percentage of its steady state value. If we draw the instantaneous current graph of Fig. 9.10 accurately enough,

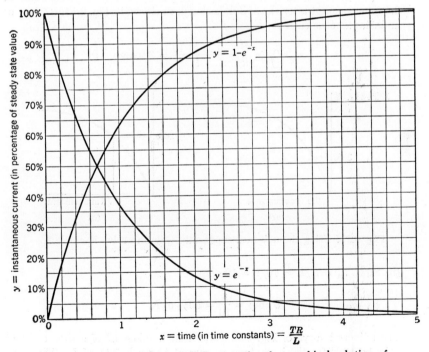

**Fig. 9.12.** Universal exponential curves for the graphical solution of the rise and fall of current in inductive direct current circuits.

we can solve such problems graphically from the exponential curve. We have already noted that, regardless of the numerical values of applied emf, inductance, and resistance, the initial rate of rise of current will always be $E/L$, the final steady state current will always be $E/R$, and it will take a time equal to $5L/R$ to reach that steady state value for all practical purposes. This allows us to prepare a **universal exponential graph** as in Fig. 9.12 which will apply to *all* numerical values of $E$, $L$, and $R$. This is accomplished by calibrating the vertical (instantaneous current) axis of the graph in percentage of the final current and calibrating the horizontal (time) axis in time constants rather than seconds.

EXAMPLE 3: (a) What is the instantaneous current in the circuit of Fig. 9.9 one second after the switch is closed?

(b) How long will it take the instantaneous current to rise from zero to 5 amp?

*Solution:* (a) We have already determined that the time constant of this circuit is

$$\tau = \frac{L}{R} = \frac{2}{1} = 2 \text{ sec}$$

Therefore, one second represents a time interval of 0.5 time constant on the universal graph of Fig. 9.12. Using this graph to find the instantaneous current 0.5 time constant after the switch is closed, as shown in Fig. 9.13(a), gives us an instantaneous current

$$i = 39\% \times \frac{E}{R} = \frac{0.39 \times 10}{1} = 3.9 \text{ amp}$$

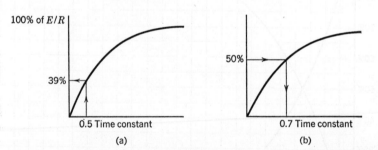

**Fig. 9.13.** Using the universal exponential graph to solve Example 3.

(b) Since $I_m = E/R = 10/1 = 10$ amp,

$$5 \text{ amp} = \frac{5}{10} = 50\% \text{ of } I_m$$

The universal curve of Fig. 9.12 shows that it takes 0.7 of a time constant [Fig. 9.13(b)] for the instantaneous current to reach 50% of $I_{\cdot m}$ Therefore,

$$t = 0.7\tau = 0.7 \times 2 = 1.4 \text{ sec}$$

EXAMPLE 4: In the circuit shown in
Fig. 9.14, switch $S_2$ is closed 1 sec
after switch $S_1$ is closed. What is the
instantaneous current 1 sec after
switch $S_2$ is closed?

*Solution:*

*Step I.* While $S_1$ is closed and $S_2$
is open, the total resistance in the circuit is

$$R_T = 4 + 1 = 5 \text{ ohms}$$

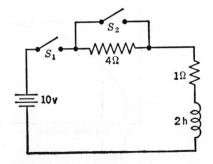

Fig. 9.14. Circuit diagram for Example 4.

Time constant $\qquad \tau = \dfrac{L}{R} = \dfrac{2}{5} = 0.4 \text{ sec}$

$$\therefore \quad 1 \text{ sec} = \frac{1}{0.4} = 2.5\tau$$

From the curve of Fig. 9.12, when $t = 2.5\tau$,

$$i = 92\% \text{ of } \frac{E}{R} = \frac{0.92 \times 10}{5} = 1.84 \text{ amp}$$

There are two lines of thought that we may use to solve the second step which
is the 1 sec interval after $S_2$ is closed.

*Step IIA.* The first method is to consider the instantaneous current curve
for the new circuit which has only 1 ohm of resistance in circuit. The final
steady state current now becomes

$$I_m = \frac{E}{R} = \frac{10}{1} = 10 \text{ amp}$$

But at the instant $S_2$ is closed, $i$ is already 1.84 amp. Therefore we must locate
this point on the graph and mark off the additional 1 sec from there
[Fig. 9.15(a)].

$$1.84 \text{ amp} = \frac{1.84}{10} = 18.4\% \text{ of } I_m$$

From the curve of Fig. 9.12, when $i = 18.4\%$ of $I_m$,

$$t = 0.2\tau = 0.2\frac{L}{R} = \frac{0.2 \times 2}{1} = 0.4 \text{ sec}$$

Therefore the instant in time we are concerned with will be 1 sec later, or the
1.4 sec mark on the curve of Fig. 9.15(a). In terms of time constants,

$$1.4 \text{ sec} = \frac{1.4}{2} = 0.7\tau$$

Again from Fig. 9.12, when $t = 0.7\tau$,

$$i = 50\% \text{ of } I_m = 0.5 \times 10 = \textbf{5 amp}$$

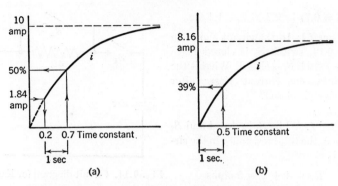

**Fig. 9.15.** Graphical solution of Step II of Example 4.

*Step IIB:* The alternate method requires only one reading from the universal exponential graph and is based on thinking in terms of the *additional* rise in current after $S_2$ is closed. Since we start Step II with 1.84 amp already flowing in the inductance and $I_m = E/R = 10/1 = 10$ amp, the maximum *additional* rise in current can be only $10 - 1.84 = 8.16$ amp.

Since the time constant $= L/R = 2/1 = 2$ sec, therefore a time interval of 1 sec after $S_2$ closes represents a time interval of $\frac{1}{2}\tau$. From Fig. 9.12, in $\frac{1}{2}$ time constant the instantaneous current will rise 39% of the maximum *additional* current [Fig. 9.15(b)].

$$\therefore \quad additional\ i = 39\% \text{ of } 8.16 = 3.16 \text{ amp}$$

The instantaneous current 1 sec after $S_2$ is closed will be 3.16 amp greater than when $S_2$ is first closed. Therefore

$$i = 1.84 + 3.16 = \textbf{5 amp}$$

## 11. Algebraic Solution for Instantaneous Current

The graphic solution for instantaneous current is sufficiently accurate for most purposes and has the advantage that it helps us to visualize the behavior of inductance in d-c circuits. If we are required to determine the instantaneous current with greater accuracy, we must return to an algebraic solution based on Equation (9.7).

$$E = iR + L\,(di/dt) \tag{9.7}$$

Solving for the instantaneous current involves the use of calculus which gives us the same equation in the form

$$i = \frac{E}{R}\,(1 - e^{-x}) \tag{9.11}$$

where $e = 2.718$ (the base of Naperian logarithms) and $x = tR/L$.

Since $$\tau = \frac{L}{R} \text{ sec,} \qquad x = \frac{t}{\tau}$$

Therefore $x$ can also be thought of as time measured in time constants. If we select values of $t$ which will make $x$ a whole number, we can solve Equation (9.11) by simple algebra.

EXAMPLE 5: What is the instantaneous current in the circuit of Fig. 9.9 4 sec after the switch is closed?

*Solution:*

$$x = \frac{tR}{L} = \frac{4 \times 1}{2} = 2$$

$$i = \frac{E}{R}(1 - e^{-x}) = \frac{E}{R}\left(1 - \frac{1}{e^x}\right)$$

$$\therefore \quad i = \frac{10}{1}\left(1 - \frac{1}{2.718^2}\right) = 10 \times 0.865 = 8.65 \text{ amp}$$

When $x$ is not a whole number we must resort to either tables or slide rule to solve the expression $e^{-x}$. Most engineering slide rules have scales for determining $e^{-x}$ and tables are included in the Appendix.

EXAMPLE 3A: (a) What is the instantaneous current in the circuit of Fig. 9.9 1 sec after the switch is closed?

(b) How long will it take the instantaneous current in this circuit to rise to 5 amp?

*Solution:*

(a)
$$x = \frac{tR}{L} = \frac{1 \times 1}{2} = 0.5$$

$$i = \frac{E}{R}(1 - e^{-x}) = \frac{10}{1}(1 - 2.718^{-0.5})$$

Actually we can solve this equation without referring to tables since

$$2.718^{-0.5} = \frac{1}{\sqrt{2.718}}$$

But from the table, when $x = 0.5$, $e^{-x} = 0.607$.

$$\therefore \quad i = 10(1 - 0.607) = 3.93 \text{ amp}$$

(b)
$$i = \frac{E}{R}(1 - e^{-x})$$

$$5 = \frac{10}{1}(1 - e^{-x})$$

from which $e^{-x} = 0.5$. From the table, when $e^{-x} = 0.5$, $x = 0.694$.

$$\therefore \quad t = \frac{xL}{R} = \frac{0.694 \times 2}{1} = 1.388 \text{ sec}$$

EXAMPLE 4A: In the circuit shown in Fig. 9.14, switch $S_2$ is closed 1 sec after switch $S_1$ is closed. What is the instantaneous current 1 sec after switch $S_2$ is closed?

*Solution:*

Step *I*. One second after $S_1$ is closed,

$$x = \frac{tR}{L} = \frac{1 \times 5}{2} = 2.5$$

$$\therefore \quad i = \frac{E}{R}(1 - e^{-x}) = \frac{10}{5}(1 - e^{-2.5}) = 2(1 - 0.0821) = 1.8358 \text{ amp}$$

Step *IIA*. Using the method illustrated by Fig. 9.15(a),

$$i = \frac{E}{R}(1 - e^{-x})$$

$$1.836 = \frac{10}{1}(1 - e^{-x})$$

$$\therefore \quad e^{-x} = 0.8164$$

from which $\qquad\qquad x = 0.204 = \frac{tR}{L}$

$$\therefore \quad t = \frac{0.204 \times 2}{1} = 0.408 \text{ sec}$$

One second later, $\qquad t = 1.408 \text{ sec}$

and now $\qquad\qquad x = \frac{1.408 \times 1}{2} = 0.704$

$$\therefore \quad i = \frac{E}{R}(1 - e^{-x}) = \frac{10}{1}(1 - e^{-0.704}) = 10(1 - 0.495) = \mathbf{5.05 \ amp}$$

Step *IIB*. Using the method illustrated by Fig. 9.15(b),

Maximum *additional* current $= 10 - 1.836 = 8.164 \text{ amp}$

Actual additional current 1 sec after $S_2$ is closed,

$$i = 8.164(1 - e^{-\frac{(1 \times 1)}{2}}) = 8.164(1 - 0.607) = 3.214 \text{ amp}$$

Therefore the total instantaneous current 1 sec after $S_2$ is closed is

$$i = 1.836 + 3.214 = \mathbf{5.05 \ amp}$$

## 12. Energy Stored by an Inductance

Returning for the moment to the theoretically pure inductance, if we connect it to a perfect source of emf, the cemf generated by the inductance must remain constant and equal to the applied emf; and therefore the current must rise at a constant rate as in Fig. 9.16. The source of emf is supplying electric energy to the inductance at the rate of $p = Ei$. But unlike resistance, pure inductance cannot convert this energy into heat or light. The energy that the source of emf supplies is stored in the magnetic field, since the rising current forces the magnetic lines of force to expand against their natural characteristic of trying to become as short as possible. We can think of the storing of energy in an inductance as being similar to winding up the rubber band motor of a model airplane. As we apply torque to the propeller with our finger, we twist the rubber band and build up a counter-torque in it. Since we are accomplishing motion against this counter-torque, we are doing work and thus storing energy in the rubber band. When we release the propeller, the energy stored in the rubber band is released and it drives the propeller until the stored energy is all used up.

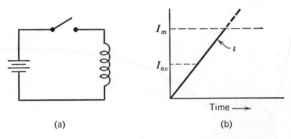

(a)                                              (b)

**Fig. 9.16.** Determining the energy stored by an inductance.

To determine the energy stored by an inductance, we must pick some final value of current [$I_m$ in Fig. 9.16(b)] and find out how much energy is stored as the current rises to this value. In pure resistance circuits where the current and voltage did not change with a change in time, we found that $W = Pt = EIt$. Although the cemf remains constant in the circuit of Fig. 9.16, the current steadily increases as time elapses. However, since the rate of change of current is constant, the *average* value of the instantaneous current as it rises from zero to $I_m$ in Fig. 9.16(b) will be $\frac{1}{2}I_m$. Therefore

$$W = E \times \tfrac{1}{2}I_m \times t$$

But
$$E = L \frac{di}{dt}$$

and, since the rate of change of current is constant,

$$E = L \times \frac{I_m}{t}$$

Substituting gives
$$W = \frac{LI_m}{t} \times \tfrac{1}{2}I_m \times t$$

$$\therefore \quad W = \tfrac{1}{2}LI_m^2 \tag{9.12}$$

In the case of the practical inductance, both the instantaneous cemf and current are changing and their rate of change is not constant. By plotting accurate graphs of the instantaneous voltage across and current through the inductance on a piece of graph paper, we can plot a graph of the instantaneous rate at which the inductance of the circuit stores energy from the relationship $p = vi$. By calculating instantaneous power for each division along the horizontal axis of the graph, we obtain the instantaneous power graph shown in Fig. 9.17. When the current in a practical inductance reaches its steady state value, the cemf generated by the inductance has dropped to zero and therefore the instantaneous power becomes zero. Therefore the inductance builds up stored energy only while the current is building up to its steady state value. As long as the current remains constant, a constant amount of energy is stored in the inductance.

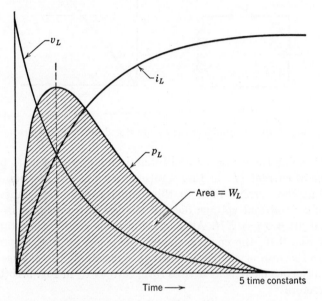

**Fig. 9.17.** Graphical representation of the energy stored by a practical inductance.

Since multiplying the length by the width of a rectangle gives us its area, the *area* contained by the instantaneous power graph of Fig. 9.17 represents the *product* of the *average power* and *time*, which in turn represents the *energy* stored by the inductance. Although calculation of this irregular area requires the use of calculus, we can make use of our definition of the time constant—the time it would take to reach the steady state current *if* the current were to continue to rise at its initial rate of change. We found that we obtained the same results from solving for instantaneous current by using the time constant approach as when we used the actual formula for instantaneous current. We will also find that we can obtain the same result for stored energy by assuming a constant rate of rise of current for a time interval of one time constant, as we would have by considering the actual exponential rise for a time interval of five time constants. Making this assumption provides us with the situation shown by

Fig. 9.16(b) if $I_m = E/R$. Therefore the energy stored by *any* inductance is

$$W = \tfrac{1}{2}LI^2 \tag{9.13}$$

where $W$ is the stored energy in joules, $L$ is the inductance in henrys, and $I$ is the steady current in amperes.

EXAMPLE 6: What energy is stored by the magnetic field of an inductor whose inductance is 5 h and whose resistance is 2 ohms when it is connected to a 24 v source of emf?

*Solution:*

$$I = \frac{E}{R} = \frac{24}{2} = 12 \text{ amp}$$

$$W = \frac{1}{2} LI^2 = \frac{1}{2} \times 5 \times 12 \times 12 = 360 \text{ joules}$$

## 13. Fall of Current in an Inductive Circuit

Interrupting the flow of current in an inductive circuit is like removing our finger after winding the rubber band motor of a model airplane; the stored energy is released. We have defined inductance as the property of a circuit which tends to oppose *any* change in current. If we examine the graphs of instantaneous current in this chapter we will note that it is not possible for the current to change instantly. It takes *time* for the current to change, even if only a few microseconds.

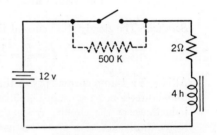

Fig. 9.18. Interrupting current flow in an inductance.

Therefore at the instant the switch is opened in the circuit of Fig. 9.18, the current in the inductance must be the same as it was just before the switch was opened. To assist us in determining the effect of interrupting current flow in an inductive direct current circuit, we shall give a specific value (500 kilohms) to the leakage resistance of the open switch. The steady state current before the switch is opened is

$$I = \frac{E}{R} = \frac{12}{2} = 6 \text{ amp}$$

At the instant the switch is opened the current in the inductance must still be 6 amp. Since this is a simple series circuit, this 6 amp current must flow through the leakage resistance of the switch creating a voltage drop between the switch contacts of

$$V = IR = 6 \times 500,000 = 3,000,000 \text{ v}$$

This extremely high voltage drop is matched by the cemf generated in the turns of the inductance by the rapidly collapsing magnetic field. If we allow such a high cemf to be induced in practice, not only will there be arcing of the switch contacts, but the insulation of the inductor will break down. Therefore we must design d-c circuits so that we never suddenly interrupt current flow in an inductance.

EXAMPLE 7: What is the voltage across the switch contacts in the circuit of Fig. 9.19 at the instant that the switch is opened?

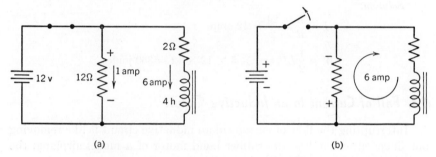

(a)                                                              (b)

**Fig. 9.19.** Circuit diagram for Example 7.

*Solution:* The steady state current through the inductance is

$$I = \frac{E}{R} = \frac{12}{2} = 6 \text{ amp}$$

Although a 1-amp current passes through the 12 ohm resistor with a conventional direction as shown in Fig. 9.19(a), this 1 amp does *not* flow through the inductance of the circuit. When the switch is opened, the inductance will momentarily act as a generator as its magnetic field collapses. Across this generator there is a total load of 12 ohms and 2 ohms in series. And since the current through the inductance cannot change instantly, a current of 6 amp with a conventional direction as shown in Fig. 9.19(b) will flow through the 12 ohm resistor. This will create a voltage drop across the 12 ohm resistor of

$$v = iR = 6 \times 12 = 72 \text{ v}$$

Between the switch contacts we have the 72 v drop across the 12 ohm resistor and the 12 v emf of the battery with their polarities such that they *add*. Therefore the total voltage across the switch contacts at the instant the switch is opened is

$$v = 72 + 12 = 84 \text{ v}$$

According to Kirchhoff's voltage law, the initial cemf must equal the voltage drop across the total resistance at the instant the switch is opened. Therefore

$$E_m = I_0 R_T \tag{9.14}$$

where $E_m$ is the peak cemf induced by the collapsing magnetic field, $I_0$ is the current through the inductance at the instant the switch is opened (which must be the same as the instant before the switch is opened, and $R_T$ is the total resistance of the loop containing the inductance. In Example 7, $E_m = 6 \times 14 = 84$ v.

According to Lenz's law, the direction of the induced emf will always be such as to oppose any change in current. When the current rises, the direction of the cemf tends to cancel out some of the applied emf. But when the source of emf is removed, the magnetic field of the inductor collapses. The polarity of the cemf induced by a collapsing field is opposite to that generated by a rising field. This reversed polarity tends to take the place of the original source of emf to maintain current flow in the original direction, through the inductance.

The 12 ohm resistor in the circuit of Fig. 9.19 is called a **discharge resistor**. As the numerical results of Example 7 have shown, the presence of this discharge resistor in the circuit protects both the switch contacts and the insulation of the inductor from an excessively high voltage surge. Some such provision must always be made with inductive direct current circuits which store appreciable energy, such as the field coils of d-c motors and generators. Thyrite resistors are excellent for this purpose.

Since the cemf in Example 7 is much smaller than when no discharge resistor is used, the magnetic field must be collapsing at a much slower rate and therefore it takes longer to discharge the stored energy when a discharge resistor is included in the circuit. Since the magnetic field *is* collapsing and since the magnetic field strength depends on the instantaneous current in the windings, the current must start to decrease as soon as the switch is opened. In determining the rise time for the current in an inductive circuit, we used the term **time constant** based on a constant rate of change of current. Using the same technique, we may define **discharge time constant** as the time it would take the current to drop to zero if it continued to drop at its initial rate for the whole time interval. If the current continues to drop at a constant rate equal to its initial rate, from Fig. 9.20,

$$\text{initial } \frac{di}{dt} = \frac{I_0}{\tau}$$

But                $\text{initial } \frac{di}{dt} = \frac{E_m}{L}$   and   $E_m = I_0 R_T$          (9.14)

from which                         $\tau = \frac{L}{R_T}$

**Therefore the time constant of an $LR$ circuit is determined in exactly the same manner for both rise and fall of current.**

However, the current cannot fall at a constant rate. If it were to do so, the cemf would remain constant. But since the current is decreasing, the voltage drop across the resistance must also decrease. And since Kirchhoff's voltage law requires the cemf to equal to voltage drop across the resistance

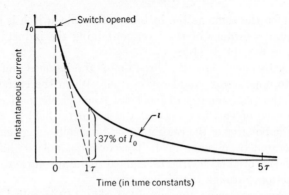

**Fig. 9.20.** Fall of current in an inductive direct current circuit.

at every instant in time, the cemf must also decrease. As the cemf decreases, the magnetic field must collapse more slowly. Thus the rate of change of current must become progressively smaller with the passing of time. Since this sequence of events is similar to the rise of current when the switch was first closed, the instantaneous discharge graph (Fig. 9.20) has the same basic exponential shape. An accurate graph of instantaneous discharge current is included in Fig. 9.12 for graphical solution of current decay in inductive d-c circuits.

Algebraic solution of the discharge of the energy stored in an inductance is based on the Kirchhoff's voltage law equation. In this case the original applied emf in the circuit is zero.

$$\therefore \quad 0 = iR_T + L\frac{di}{dt}$$

Solving for instantaneous current gives

$$i = I_0 \times e^{-x} \tag{9.15}$$

where $I_0$ is the initial current at the instant the switch is opened, $e = 2.718$, and $x = tR_T/L$.

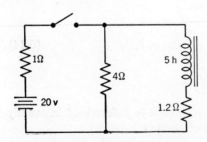

**Fig. 9.21.** Circuit diagram for Example 8.

EXAMPLE 8: The switch in the circuit of Fig. 9.21 is closed for 2 sec and then opened. What is the instantaneous current in the inductor 1 sec after the switch is opened?

*Solution:*

*Step I.* Since it is unlikely that the current will have reached a steady state value in 2 sec with the values shown for inductance and resistance, we can simplify the task of solving for the current 2 sec after the switch is closed by setting up a Thévenin equivalent circuit for the original circuit of Fig. 9.21 with the switch closed. We remove the 5 h inductance and its 1.2 ohm resistance from the original circuit and place it in the Thévenin equivalent circuit of Fig. 9.22. (Check the values of emf and internal resistance in the circuit of Fig. 9.22.)

Step II.

$$x = \frac{tR}{L} = \frac{2 \times 2}{5} = 0.8$$

$$\therefore \quad i = \frac{E}{R}(1 - e^{-x}) = \frac{16}{2}(1 - e^{-0.8})$$

$$= 8(1 - 0.449) = 4.41 \text{ amp}$$

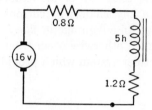  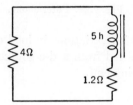

**Fig. 9.22.** Thévenin equivalent circuit of Fig. 9.21 with the switch closed.    **Fig. 9.23.** Discharge portion of Fig. 9.21.

Step III. When the switch is opened, the circuit becomes simply that of Fig. 9.23.

Now        $$x = \frac{tR_T}{L} = \frac{1 \times 5.2}{5} = 1.04$$

and        $$i = I_0 \times e^{-x} = 4.41 \times e^{-1.04} = 4.41 \times 0.352 = \textbf{1.55 amp}$$

## 14. Characteristics of Inductive d-c Circuits

In summarizing the behavior of inductance in d-c circuits, the most important characteristic is that the inductance develops a counter emf which always tends to oppose any *change* in current. As a result of his characteristic, the current in inductive circuits cannot change instantly. A definite time interval is required for current to either rise or fall between any two instantaneous values. This time interval depends on the inductance and resistance of the circuit.

When we close the switch in an inductive circuit, it takes time for the current to reach its steady state level. This delay is somewhat of an advantage in that it suppresses a sudden surge in the current drawn from the source of emf. But when current flow in an inductive circuit is interrupted, an extremely high counter emf is developed which can damage switch contacts and insulation unless we provide suitable circuit design so that current can decay gradually. Switches for d-c circuits are designed so that their contacts move far apart as rapidly as possible to prevent arcing. There are, however, some cases where we can use the very high cemf of a collapsing magnetic field to advantage. The ignition coil of an automobile engine is an example. Energy is stored gradually as current from the car battery builds up a magnetic field in the core of the coil.

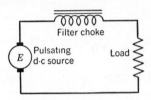

Fig. 9.24. Filter choke.

Then the current is suddenly interrupted by the breaker points and a 10 kv cemf generated by the rapidly collapsing magnetic field causes a spark between the points of the spark plug.

The tendency of inductance to oppose any change in current can be used to advantage in *filtering* or *smoothing* variations in load current that would otherwise occur when the load is fed from a d-c source such as a rectifier system which provides a pulsating emf.

## Problems

1. Current changing at the rate of 200 ma/sec in a coil induces in it a counter emf of 50 mv. What is its inductance?

2. What inductance must the plate load of a vacuum tube have if plate current rising at a uniform rate from 2 ma to 7 ma in 50 $\mu$sec induces in it a cemf of 20 mv?

3. What cemf will be induced into a 10 h inductor in which the current changes from 10 amp to 7 amp in 90 msec?

4. How long will it take the current in a 2 h inductor to rise from zero to 6 amp if the cemf across the inductor is constant at 3 v?

5. If we can assume no leakage flux, what is the approximate inductance of an air-core coil of 20 turns with an inside diameter of 2 cm and a length of 2 cm?

6. How many turns must we wind on an air core coil 1 in. long and 1 in. in diameter to obtain an inductance of 20 $\mu$h?

7. What is the inductance of the inductor in Example 7 of Chapter 7?

8. What is the inductance of the filter choke of Problem 29 of Chapter 7?

9. A 2 h inductor has 1200 turns. How many turns must we add to raise its inductance to 3 h?

10. A 500 mh inductance has 750 turns. Where must we place a tap to obtain an inductance of 250 mh between one end and the tap? What inductance is available if we use the other end and the tap?

11. A 120 mh inductance has a resistance of 6 ohms. The initial rate of rise of current is 1000 amp/sec.
    (a) What is the final current?
    (b) How long does it take the current to reach its steady state value?

12. A 20 h inductance whose resistance is 16 ohms is connected through a switch to a 24 v source of emf.
    (a) What is the initial current when the switch is closed?
    (b) What is the initial rate of change of current when the switch is closed?
    (c) What is the final steady state current?
    (d) How long does it take the current to reach 63% of its steady state value?
    (e) How long does it take the current to reach its maximum value?
    (f) What is the instantaneous current 2 sec after the switch is closed?
    (g) How long does it take the instantaneous current to reach a value of 1 amp?
    (h) How much energy is stored in the inductance once the current has reached its steady state value?

13. A 20 ohm resistor is connected in series with the circuit of Problem 12 and the resistor is short-circuited 1 sec after the switch is closed. What cemf is being developed by the inductance 1 sec after the 20 ohm resistor is short-circuited?

14. The field coils of a d-c motor have an inductance of 8 h, a resistance of 40 ohms, and are connected across a 120 v source of emf.
    (a) What value of discharge resistor must be connected across the field coils if the voltage between the terminals of the coils must never exceed 200 v?
    (b) How long will it take to discharge the energy stored in the field coils?
    (c) How much energy is dissipated by the discharge resistor after the source of emf is disconnected?

15. The field coil of an electro-dynamic loud speaker has an inductance of 20 h and a resistance of 500 ohms. In parallel with this coil is a 1000 ohm resistor. This combination is fed through a switch from a 120 d-c source of emf whose internal resistance is 250 ohms.
    (a) What is the initial current drawn from the source when the switch is closed?
    (b) What is the initial rate of change of current in the field coil?
    (c) What is the steady state current in the field coil?
    (d) What is the steady state current drawn from the source?
    (e) How long does it take the current to reach its steady state value?
    (f) What voltage appears across the switch contacts at the instant that the switch is opened?
    (g) How long does it take the field coil to discharge its stored energy?
    (h) If the switch is opened one second after it is closed, how long does it take the current in the field coil to drop to 25 ma?

## Review Questions

1. What is meant by **electromagnetic induction?**

2. What factors govern the magnitude of the emf induced into an electric conductor?

3. What factors govern the direction of the emf induced into an electric conductor?

4. Mark the conventional current direction in the sketches of Fig. 9.25. The arrows show the direction of motion.

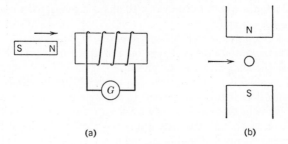

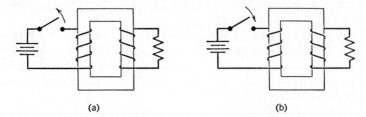

Fig. 9.25.

5. Mark the conventional current direction in both primary and secondary windings of Fig. 9.26; (a) as the switch is first closed; and (b) as the switch is opened.

Fig. 9.26.

6. What is meant by **self-induction?**

7. How is the unit of inductance derived from previously established units?

8. Why is the self-inductance of an inductor proportional to the *square* of the
   number of turns?

9. Why does the inductance of an iron core coil depend on the current through it?

10. What effect will the addition of an air gap to the magnetic circuit of a choke
    coil have on its inductance?

11. Why was it necessary to stipulate that there must be no magnetic coupling
    between the inductors in establishing the formula $L_T = L_1 + L_2 + L_3 +$ etc.
    for inductances in series?

12. Why is the total inductance of series inductances equal to the sum of the in-
    dividual inductances?

13. Why is the graph of Fig. 9.8 a straight line?

14. What is the significance of lower case letter symbols?

15. Why are lower case letter symbols used in representing the rise of current in
    inductive circuits?

16. Why must the rise of current follow the exponential curve of Fig. 9.10?

17. What effect does the resistance of an inductance have on:
    (a) The initial rate of change of current?
    (b) The final steady state current?
    (c) The time it takes the current to reach its steady state value?

18. What effect does the inductance of an inductor have on:
    (a) The initial rate of change of current?
    (b) The final steady state current?
    (c) The time it takes the current to reach its steady state value?

19. Justify the following description of a time constant: "A time constant is the time it takes the current in an inductive circuit to rise to 63% of its final steady state value."

20. Why does the value of the emf applied to an inductive circuit have no effect on the time it takes the instantaneous current to reach a steady state value?

21. Draw a detailed graph of the actual instantaneous current in Example 4.

22. Why is there no further increase in the energy stored in an inductance when the current has reached its steady state value? Where is the energy supplied by the source of emf going while a steady current flows in the circuit?

23. What is the effect of attempting to instantly interrupt current flow in an inductive d-c circuit?

24. How does a discharge resistor prevent insulation breakdown in an inductor?

25. Why can we say that the current through an inductance the instant after the switch is opened is the same as the instant before the switch is opened?

26. Why is a **thyrite** type of resistor particularly suitable for use as a discharge resistor?

27. Some designers use a rectifier which has a very high resistance to current flow in one direction and a very low resistance to current flow in the other direction in place of a discharge resistor as shown in Fig. 9.27. What are the advantages of such a circuit?

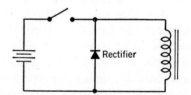

Fig. 9.27. Magnetic field discharge by a rectifier.

28. What effect does the resistance of the discharge loop of an inductive circuit have on
    (a) The initial current when the switch is opened?
    (b) The initial rate of fall of current?
    (c) The time it takes the current to fall to zero?

29. How are the characteristics of inductance used to advantage in the filter choke in a radio power supply?

30. Meter movements require some form of **damping** to keep the pointer from oscillating back and forth as the torque produced by the electric current and the countertorque of the spiral spring try to attain equilibrium. In moving iron and dynamometer movements, this is accomplished by attaching a paddle to the pointer shaft in such a manner that it has to move in a close-fitting chamber of trapped air. Moving coil movements do not require this air damping since the moving coil is wound on an aluminum coil form. Explain this statement in detail.

# Chapter 10

# CAPACITANCE

There are only three properties that an electric circuit can possess. Two of these, resistance and inductance, we have already considered. The third is **capacitance**. As we investigate capacitance we will find that for every characteristic displayed by inductance, there is an equivalent characteristic for capacitance. But we will also find that each of these characteristics is somewhat different from the equivalent inductive characteristic. For example, we define inductance as the property of an electric circuit which opposes any change in *current*. We will discover that capacitance is the property of an electric circuit which opposes any change in the *voltage* across it. Just as the inductance of an electric circuit is dependent on the magnetic field surrounding a current-carrying conductor, the capacitance of an electric circuit is dependent on an electric field which is associated with a difference in potential.

## 1. Static Electricity

In starting our investigation of capacitance, we must first review some of the basic ideas we developed in Chapter 2 about electric pressure. We will recall that the structure of the copper atom is such that it is fairly easy for the 29th electron to wander away from its orbit around the original nucleus and to take up an orbit around an adjacent nucleus. This leaves the original atom with a deficiency of one electron. The force of attraction which held the missing electron in an orbit around the nucleus now exerts an attraction on the 29th electron of a neighboring atom to fill the gap in its orbital pattern. As soon as an atom has its proper complement of electrons, the force of attraction disappears. Therefore, there is a mechanical force of attraction between electrons and atoms that are deficient in

206

electrons. In a piece of copper, as soon as a free electron leaves an atom, a free electron from an adjacent atom takes its place. Therefore although there is a random movement of free electrons, there is no definite tendency to separate electrons from atoms which are deficient electrons. And therefore no cumulative force of attraction is built up.

However due to the chemical action in a simple battery consisting of a copper rod and a zinc rod dipped into a weak acid solution, there is a unidirectional removal of electrons from the copper and adding of electrons to the zinc. As a result, a mechanical force is developed which tries to move the surplus electrons in the zinc rod back to fill the gaps in the atoms of the copper rod. Not only does the deficiency in the copper rod *attract* the electrons, but the zinc rod exerts a force which tries to *repel* the surplus electrons. The chemical action of the acid does not permit the electrons to flow from the zinc rod back to the copper rod through the electrolyte. But if we connect an *external* circuit consisting of a lamp between the two terminals of the battery, electrons will flow from the zinc rod to the copper rod through the lamp, thus creating an electric current. The forces of attraction and repulsion which cause the electrons to flow in a metallic conductor constitute electric pressure.

In circuit diagrams we represent a deficiency of electrons by a + sign and a surplus of electrons by a − sign. Rather than talk of deficiency of electrons and surplus of electrons, we call them positive and negative **charge,** respectively. (The + and − symbols in this case do not stand for the arithmetic operations of add and subtract. They indicate that the charges they represent are exactly opposite and attract one another.) We can summarize the forces which cause current to flow in a lamp connected to the battery by stating that **unlike charges attract and like charges repel.** We can summarize the chemical action within a battery by saying that it separates some electrons from their original atoms and then physically separates the positive charge from the negative charge by placing the positive charge on the copper rod and the negative charge on the zinc rod. If we do not connect a closed circuit to the battery terminals, no current will flow. Therefore we find it more convenient to speak of the electric pressure resulting from the chemical separation of the charges in terms of a **potential difference** rather than an electron-*moving* force.

The electrochemical action of a battery is only one method of separating unlike charges. Electric charges can be separated and a potential difference (PD) built up as a result of friction between two dissimilar materials. These materials do not have to be metallic conductors. They are more likely to be insulators. For example, if we rub a glass rod with a silk cloth (both excellent insulators), we will remove some electrons from the glass and transfer them to the silk thus leaving the glass with a + charge and the silk with a − charge.

Electric charges which are separated by friction between insulators are known as **static electricity** (since current cannot flow). The study of the behavior of these charges is known as **electrostatics.**

## 2. The Nature of an Electric Field

Back in the 18th century, Charles Coulomb was able to demonstrate the force that exists between two charged objects (meaning that these objects possess either a surplus or deficiency of electrons) by suspending a pair of light, charged balls by silk threads as in Fig. 10.1. If they were given unlike charges, there was a noticeable attraction between them, as shown.

In Chapter 7, we chose to explain the effect that a magnet had on a compass needle without physical contact between them by assuming that an invisible magnetic field surrounded the magnet. Similarly then, we can represent the force of attraction between the two unlike charges in Fig. 10.1 by assuming that an **electrostatic** (or simply **electric**) **field** exists between them. Therefore,

An **electric field** is that region in which a charged body is acted upon by a force.

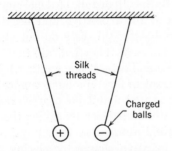

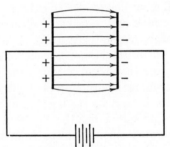

**Fig. 10.1.** Coulomb's demonstration of forces between charges.

**Fig. 10.2.** Electric field between parallel plates.

We can visualize an electric field as consisting of invisible lines of force. We can create such a field by connecting two parallel metallic plates to the two terminals of a battery as shown in Fig. 10.2. The left-hand plate becomes positively charged, since the + terminal of the battery removes some electrons from it; and the right-hand plate becomes negatively charged as the − terminal of the battery forces a surplus of electrons into it. If we suspend a very light positively charged particle between the plates by a silk thread, it will move toward the right-hand plate. If the particle has a negative charge, it will move toward the left-hand plate. Therefore, in drawing the electric lines of force which form the electric field in Fig. 10.2, the *electric lines of force represent the path along which a weightless charged particle will move from the one charged plate to the other.*

Since a positively charged particle can travel only toward the right-hand plate, and a negatively charged particle can travel only toward the left-hand plate, we can consider the electric lines of force as possessing *direction*. To fit the pattern set in establishing the conventional current direction, we assume that the **direction** *of an electric line of force is the direction in which a* **positively** *charged particle will travel between two charged plates.*

Electric lines of force are not complete loops like magnetic lines of force. *Electric lines of force always* **begin and end on charged bodies,** and, as shown in Figs. 10.2 and 10.3, *always meet a charged surface at* **right angles** *to that surface.*

Although we will be concerned mainly with the electric field between parallel plates, two other electric field patterns are of interest to us: the electric field between parallel conductors as shown in Fig. 10.3(a), and the electric field between concentric conductors as shown in Fig. 10.3(b).

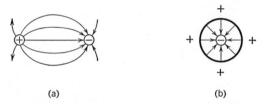

(a)                                                (b)

**Fig. 10.3.** Electric field between (a) parallel conductors, and (b) concentric conductors.

As we have noted, a positively charged particle between the two parallel plates will be repelled by the + plate and attracted by the − plate. Since we developed the concept of an electric field to show the force that will be exerted on charged particles, we must be able to express the **intensity** of the electric field numerically.

The letter symbol for **electric field intensity** is the Greek letter $E$ (*capital epsilon, boldface*).

No special unit is required for electric field intensity in the mks system of units since we can express it in terms of the charge on the particle and the force acting on the particle.

An **electric field** has an **intensity** of one mks unit at a certain point if a force of one newton is exerted on a charge of one coulomb located at that point.

This may be expressed in equation form:

$$E = \frac{F}{Q} \tag{10.1}$$

where $E$ is the electric field intensity in newtons per coulomb, $F$ is the force acting on the charge in newtons, and $Q$ is the magnitude of the charge in coulombs.

In the special case of the electric field between parallel plates, the electric field is quite uniform between the plates. Therefore a constant force is exerted on a charged particle as it moves from one plate to the other. (As the repulsion of one plate becomes weaker with an increase in distance, the attraction of the other plate increases as the distance decreases.) As the charge moves the complete distance from one plate to the other, the work done is

$$W = Fd$$

Since we established the magnitude of the volt in terms of the work done in moving a charge through a potential difference,

$$W = QV \qquad (2.2)$$

$$\therefore \quad Fd = QV$$

Substituting for $F$ from Equation (10.1),

$$EQd = QV$$

from which $\qquad E = \dfrac{V}{d}$ (parallel plates) $\qquad (10.2)$

where $E$ is the electric field intensity in newtons per coulomb *or* volts per meter, $V$ is the potential difference between the plates in volts, and $d$ is the distance between the plates in meters.

This expression for electric field intensity leads to an interesting characteristic of electric fields. According to Kirchhoff's voltage law, when we apply an emf of 400 v to the two parallel plates of Fig. 10.4, there must be a 400 v PD between them. Since the electric lines of force begin at the $+$ plate and end at the $-$ plate, this 400 v potential difference appears across each line of force. The voltmeter in the diagram draws no current. We connect one voltmeter lead to the bottom plate. The bottom plate is shown connected to ground so that we may refer all our voltage readings to ground without having to say "with respect to" for every point at which we locate the probe connected to the other voltmeter terminal.

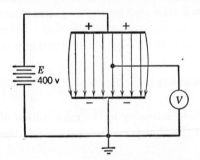

**Fig. 10.4.** Showing the voltage gradient along an electric line of force.

When we connect the voltmeter probe to the top plate, the meter will read 400 v. As we move the voltmeter probe one quarter of the way down from the top plate, the meter reads 300 v; when the probe is halfway between the plates, the meter reading is 200 v; etc. Therefore in the case of parallel plates, the total potential difference is distributed uniformly along the length of the electric line of force as if it were a resistance voltage divider. From this characteristic we can speak of the **voltage gradient** in volts per meter. Because of the uniform electric field between parallel plates, in this case the voltage gradient is numerically equal to the electric field intensity. Therefore, **E** can be expressed in volts per meter.

Since every electric line of force has the total PD distributed along its length, we can mark a point on each line of force having the same potential difference with respect to ground. Joining these points produces what is known as an **equipotential surface** for the electric field. Equipotential surface "maps" are very useful in applying the theory of electrostatics to the design of vacuum tubes. Equipotential surfaces for parallel plates and parallel conductors are shown by the dashed lines in Fig. 10.5.

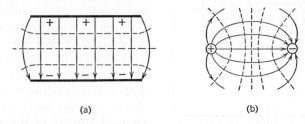

(a) (b)

**Fig. 10.5.** Equipotential surfaces in the electric fields between (a) parallel plates, and (b) parallel conductors.

If we think of an electric line of force joining every surplus electron in the negatively charged plate to every atom which is deficient an electron in the positively charged plate, the number of electric lines of force is directly proportional to the charge. In keeping with the designation for magnetic fields, the total number of electric lines of force is called the **electric flux.**

The letter symbol for **electric flux** is the Greek letter $\psi$ (psi).

Since the electric flux is directly proportional to the charge, we need no special unit for electric flux. We simply state that

$$\psi \equiv Q \qquad (10.3)$$

where $\psi$ is the electric flux in mks units, and $Q$ is the charge on each plate in coulombs.

The letter symbol for **electric flux density** is **D.**

Since the distribution of the electric lines of force is quite uniform for the special case of two parallel plates, the electric flux density is also uniform and becomes simply

$$D = \frac{\psi}{A} \qquad \text{(parallel plates)} \quad (10.4)$$

### 3. Electrostatic Induction

Fig. 10.6 shows an electric conductor in the electric field between two parallel plates. The conductor is shorter than the distance between the plates, so there is no electric connection between it and the plates. Since there are countless free electrons drifting around in a conducting material, some of these electrons will be attracted by the + plate and repelled by the − plate. As a result, a surplus of electrons (negative charge) will appear at the end of the conductor closest to the + plate and a deficiency of electrons (positive charge) at the end nearest the − plate. Since there is no electric connection between the conductor and the plates, these two equal and opposite charges that appear when the conductor is placed in the electric field are said to be **electrostatically induced** charges.

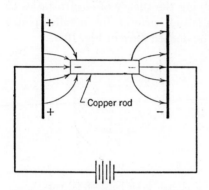

**Fig. 10.6.** Electrostatically induced charges.

Since a net movement of electrons in one direction constitutes an electric current, there was a slight surge of current in the conductor while the charges were taking up their positions. But since the conductor is insulated from the plates, there can be no continuous current flow. And since $V = IR$, when the **displacement** current ceases, there can be no voltage drop between the ends of the conductor. This means that there must be a redistribution of the electric field between the two parallel plates as shown in Fig. 10.6.

### 4. Dielectrics

As a final step in this brief study of electrostatics, we will place a piece of insulating material between the charged plates of Fig. 10.7. Insulating materials exposed to electric fields are known as **dielectrics.** Although the atomic structure of an insulator is such that it is very difficult for electrons to move from one atom to another, the electrons orbitting around each nucleus will be attracted by the + plate and repelled by the − plate. As a result, the orbits of the electrons in each atom of the dielectric will be displaced as shown for the single atom in Fig. 10.7. The net effect is that, although electrons cannot move from atom to atom in an insulator, each individual atom behaves like the conductor in Fig. 10.6. The center of the positive charge of each atom (the nucleus) no longer coincides with the center of the negative charge (the center of the electron orbit). The effect of the positive charge of the atom being closer to one side of the atom and the negative charge being closer to the other is called **polarization** of the atom.

The extent to which the orbits of the electrons in the atoms of the dielectric are distorted (and the extent to which the atoms become polarized) depends on the intensity of the electric field. As the intensity of the electric field is increased by increasing the PD between the two parallel plates, a value is reached at which so much force is exerted on the orbital electrons that they are torn free of their orbits, causing a breakdown of the dielectric. The dielectric then becomes a conductor and the two plates are short-circuited. Some dielectrics are able to withstand a much greater electric field intensity than others. The field intensity required to break down a

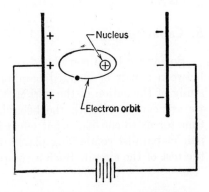

Fig. 10.7. Effect of an electric field on an atom of a dielectric.

dielectric is called its **dielectric strength.** The dielectric strength of some materials can vary considerably as a result of variations in manufacturing. The values of dielectric strength listed in Table I are typical average values for some of the common dielectric materials.

**Table I**

| Dielectric | Average Dielectric Strength volts per mil |
|---|---|
| Air | 75 |
| Barium-strontium titanate (ceramic) | 75 |
| Porcelain (ceramic) | 200 |
| Transformer oil (organic liquid) | 400 |
| Bakelite (plastic) | 400 |
| Paper | 500 |
| Rubber | 700 |
| Teflon (plastic) | 1500 |
| Glass | 3000 |
| Mica | 5000 |

After exposing a dielectric to a high electric field intensity in Fig. 10.7 we remove the source of emf and momentarily connect the parallel plates together to allow their charges to become neutralized. The stress on the electron orbits of the dielectric is removed and they can return to their normal positions. When the connection between the two plates is removed after the initial discharge, we will find that with some dielectrics a small potential difference still appears between the two plates. This indicates that the electron orbits in the dielectric did not instantly return to their original positions. Therefore, even though the plates were connected together, the residual electron orbit displacement in the dielectric held an induced charge in the plates in the same manner that charges were induced into the conductor in Fig. 10.6. This effect is called **dielectric absorption,** and is somewhat similar to the residual magnetism in ferromagnetic cores.

## 5. Capacitance

So far we have considered only what goes on in the insulated space between a pair of charged parallel plates. While this is important in a study of the action of the various types of electron tubes, at the moment we are concerned with the behavior of electric circuits. Therefore it is time for us to consider what effect including a component consisting of a pair of parallel conducting plates with a dielectric between them has on the rest of the circuit. Such a component is called a **capacitor.*** A capaci-

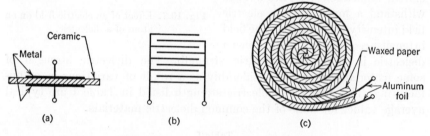

Fig. 10.8. Construction of capacitors.

tor may be constructed in the parallel plate form by supporting two insulated metal plates with air between them, or by coating the two sides of a ceramic disk with metal as in Fig. 10.8(a). Some capacitors consist

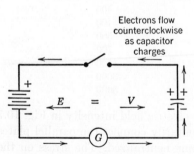

Fig. 10.9. Charging a capacitor.

of interleaved parallel plates with either air or mica dielectric as in Fig. 10.8(b), and still others consist of two long strips of aluminum foil rolled up with two strips of waxed paper dielectric as in Fig. 10.8(c).

Since we are not for the moment concerned with what goes on between the plates of a capacitor, we will use the standard graphic symbol to represent a capacitor as a circuit component in our schematic diagrams as in Fig. 10.9. Although the symbol somewhat resembles the parallel plates of a physical capacitor, one of the plates must be drawn

* Sometimes referred to by the now obsolete term **condenser.**

as a curved line to distinguish the capacitor symbol from the symbol for open-circuit relay contacts.

When we first connected a pair of parallel plates to a source of emf in Fig. 10.2, the charges could not appear on the plates *instantly*.* Electrons had to *flow* from the battery onto the right-hand plate to give it a negative charge, and a similar number of electrons had to flow into the battery from the left-hand plate to give it a positive charge. Since the current is the same in all parts of a series circuit, until the switch is closed in the circuit of Fig. 10.9, there can be no charging of either plate of the capacitor even though the bottom plate is permanently connected to the − terminal of the battery. If neither plate possesses any charge, there will be no electric field between them. And since $E = V/d$, there will be no potential difference between the plates.

When the switch is closed in Fig. 10.9, the galvanometer will register a sudden flow of electrons flowing counterclockwise around the circuit. Since electrons cannot flow right through the insulated area between the plates, a negative charge builds up on the bottom plate and a positive charge builds up on the top plate. As the charges build up, the intensity of the electric field increases and a potential difference builds up between the plates. According to Kirchhoff's voltage law, the potential difference between the two plates must stop building up when it is equal to the emf of the source. The galvanometer must therefore read zero after the initial charging surge is completed.

If, after the charging surge in Fig. 10.9 is over, we suddenly double the applied emf, there must be another similar surge as the capacitor plates charge sufficiently to raise the PD between them to equal the new emf. We will find that there is always a fixed ratio between the potential difference between any given pair of insulated conductors and the charge required to establish this PD. Therefore, for any given pair of insulated conductors,

$$\frac{Q}{V} = \text{a constant} \tag{10.5}$$

If we now open the switch in Fig. 10.9, there is no longer any electric circuit connection between the two plates. And therefore there is no way for the surplus electrons in the bottom plate to get to the atoms in the top plate which are deficient some electrons, thus neutralizing the charges. As a result, the pair of parallel plates (a capacitor) *stores* electric charge under pressure much as a cylinder of compressed air stores a charge of air under pressure. Since $Q/V$ is a constant, as long as charges remain on the plates, a potential difference exists between them. Therefore we can define **a**

---

* Because of the attraction between unlike charges, the charges are concentrated at the surface of each plate facing the other plate. Therefore we speak of the charge *on* the plate rather than the charge *in* the plate.

capacitor as a circuit component constructed for the purpose of storing an electric charge under pressure. In order to determine just how much charge a capacitor can store when we connect it to a given source of emf, we must determine what factors govern the numerical value of the constant in Equation (10.5). This numerical constant which represents the ability of a capacitor to store an electric charge is called its **capacitance.*\***

The letter symbol for **capacitance** is $C$.

The basic unit of capacitance is the **farad.**

A circuit has a **capacitance of one farad** when a charge of one coulomb is required to raise the potential difference by one volt.

$$\therefore \quad C = \frac{Q}{V} \tag{10.6}$$

where $C$ is the capacitance in farads, $Q$ is the charge in coulombs, and $V$ is the potential difference in volts.

In order to satisfy the specifications for the mks system of units, the basic unit of capacitance had to be defined in terms of *one* coulomb and *one* volt. But the farad represents a much greater capacitance than appears in practical circuits. In practice the largest unit size used to express capacitance is the **microfarad** (1 $\mu$f $= 10^{-6}$ farad). In many cases even the microfarad is too large and the **micromicrofarad** (1 $\mu\mu$f $= 10^{-12}$ farad) is used. However we must remember, when substituting for $C$ in any equation, that these equations were set up in terms of the *basic* unit of capacitance, the *farad.*

You will note that in defining the farad we spoke in general terms of the capacitance of a *circuit*. This was done purposely so that we would not be suggesting that capacitance appears in a circuit only when we con-

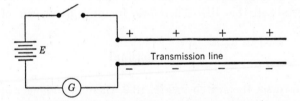

**Fig. 10.10.** Capacitance between parallel conductors.

nect a capacitor into the circuit. We will find exactly the same conditions existing in the circuit of Fig. 10.10 when we connect a source of emf to a pair of conductors which form an open-circuit transmission line. Capacitance therefore is an electric circuit property possessed by *any* pair of

---

* The ability of a capacitor to store a charge at a certain potential difference is sometimes referred to as its **capacity.** However in present-day usage, the term capacitance (which rhymes with resistance and inductance) is gradually replacing the older form—capacity.

conductors that are insulated from each other. A capacitor is merely a device for *lumping* this property into a small physical space. (All conductors possess inductance but when we desire a large value of inductance we wind the conductor into a coil.)

We have noted that one of the characteristics of capacitance is the ability of the capacitance of a circuit to store electric charge. But in defining capacitance we would like to have a definition which is in keeping with definitions for resistance and inductance. We have already noted that a capacitance cannot charge instantly. It takes time, even if only a fraction of a second, for the charge to be built up. Therefore the PD across a capacitor cannot appear at the instant the switch is closed. It takes *time* for the potential difference across a capacitor to rise, and when the switch is opened, the PD across the capacitor does not disappear. It remains until we supply a conducting path for electrons to flow from the negatively charged plate to the positive plate. Therefore, since the time element is involved in any change in the potential difference between the plates of a capacitance, we may think of the capacitance of a circuit as opposing any change in the potential difference across it. (Such is not the case for resistance and inductance.) Therefore

**Capacitance** may be defined as that property of an electric circuit that **opposes any change in the voltage** across that circuit.

*Inductance* may be defined as that property of an electric circuit that *opposes any change in the current* through that circuit.

*Resistance* may be defined as that property of an electric circuit that *opposes the flow of current* through that circuit.

## 6. Factors Governing Capacitance

In setting up equations for electric field intensity and flux, we considered only the case of the uniform field between two parallel plates. Therefore we shall develop only those factors governing the capacitance of parallel plates.* All the capacitors shown in Fig. 10.8 can be considered parallel plate capacitors. The equation, $C = Q/V$ is an *electrical* expression defining the magnitude of the farad. In order to determine the *physical* factors governing the capacitance of a circuit, we can solve for those factors governing the magnitude of the electric field, since the electric flux is directly proportional to the charges on the plates, and the electric field intensity is directly proportional to the potential difference between the plates.

If we double the area of the plates, we have room for twice as many electric lines of force with the same PD across them. Therefore the charge

---

* Formulas for the capacitance of parallel conductors, concentric conductors, etc. are found in electrical and radio handbooks.

that a capacitor can hold at a given potential difference is doubled, and since $C = Q/V$, the capacitance is doubled. Therefore, **the capacitance of parallel plates is directly proportional to their area.**

To assist us in visualizing the effect of the spacing between the plates on their capacitance, we can refer back to Fig. 10.6. When we placed an insulated conductor between the two plates, the positively charged plate attracted the electrons in the conductor toward the end closest to the positively charged plate and the negatively charged plate repelled some electrons from the end of the conductor closest to the negatively charged plate. The two parallel plates of a capacitor have a similar effect on each other. The positively charged plate helps to attract a greater number of surplus electrons from the − terminal of a source of emf onto the negatively charged plate of the capacitor. The negatively charged plate in turn helps to drive a greater number of electrons out of the positively charged plate into the + terminal of the source. As the plates are brought closer together, these forces of attraction and repulsion are increased and the capacitor is able to store a greater charge when connected to a given source of emf. Therefore **the capacitance of the parallel plates is inversely proportional to their spacing.**

In an electric conductor, resistance is the opposition to the flow of electric current, and

$$R \propto \frac{l}{A}$$

In a magnetic circuit, reluctance is the opposition to the setting up of magnetic lines of force, and

$$\Re \propto \frac{l}{A}$$

In an electric insulator or dielectric, **elastance** is the opposition to the setting up of electric lines of force.

The letter symbol for **elastance** is $S$.

Similarly then,

$$S \propto \frac{l}{A} \quad \text{or} \quad S \propto \frac{d}{A} \tag{10.7}$$

where $S$ is the elastance of the dielectric in darafs, $l$ is the length of the dielectric, or $d$ is the spacing between the plates $(\therefore \quad d = l)$, and $A$ is the cross-sectional area of the dielectric or each parallel plate.

In solving for the reluctance of a magnetic circuit, we found that the ratio of the flux density to the magnetic field intensity for a given non-ferrous material is constant. This constant is called the permeability of that material, $\mu = B/H$. Similarly we will find that the ratio between electric flux density and electric field intensity is a constant for a given dielectric material. This constant is called the **permittivity** of that material.

The letter symbol for **permittivity** is the Greek letter $\epsilon$ (epsilon).

$$\therefore \quad \epsilon = \frac{D}{E} \tag{10.8}$$

where $\epsilon$ is the absolute permittivity of a given dielectric in mks units, $D$ is the electric flux density in coulombs per square meter, and $E$ is the electric field intensity in volts per meter.

From Equations (10.4) and (10.3),

$$D = \frac{\psi}{A} = \frac{Q}{A}$$

and from Equation (10.2),

$$E = \frac{V}{d}$$

$$\therefore \quad \epsilon = \frac{Qd}{VA}$$

But

$$\frac{Q}{V} = C$$

$$\therefore \quad \epsilon = \frac{Cd}{A}$$

and

$$C = \epsilon \frac{A}{d} \qquad \text{(parallel plates)} \quad (10.9)$$

where $C$ is the capacitance in farads, $\epsilon$ is the absolute permittivity of the dielectric in mks units, $A$ is the area of each plate in square meters, and $d$ is the spacing between plates in meters.

Since the charge stored by a capacitor is proportional to the electric field, capacitance represents the ability of a dielectric to set up electric lines of force; whereas elastance represents the opposition to the setting up of electric lines of force. Therefore,

$$C = \frac{1}{S} \tag{10.10}$$

It is not absolutely essential to have a dielectric material between the plates of a capacitor in order to set up an electric field. If we place two parallel plates in a vacuum, an electric field will be set up between them when an emf is applied to the plates. The ratio of electric flux density to electric field intensity will be

$$\frac{D}{E} = 8.85 \times 10^{-12} = \epsilon_v \tag{10.11}$$

where $\epsilon_v$ is called the permittivity of free space.

When we do place a dielectric between the plates of a capacitor, the electron orbits of the atoms are forced off center as shown in Fig. 10.7. This has the effect of placing the negative charge of each atom of the dielectric a little closer to the positive plate and the positive charge of each atom of the dielectric a little closer to the negative plate. This has the same effect on the capacitance as moving the parallel plates a little closer together. Therefore the absolute permittivity of most solid and liquid dielectrics is considerably greater than that of free space. Because of their low density, the absolute permittivity of air and other gases is very close to that of free space. Substituting Equation (10.11) in Equation (10.9), the capacitance of a parallel plate air dielectric capacitor becomes:

$$C = \frac{8.85A}{10^{12}d} \qquad (10.12)$$

Rather than state the absolute permittivity of liquid and solid dielectrics, it has become the custom to prepare tables stating the ratio between the absolute permittivity of a given dielectric and the absolute permittivity of free space. This ratio is called the **relative permittivity** or the **dielectric constant** of that material.

$$k = \frac{\epsilon_r}{\epsilon_v} \qquad (10.13)$$

where $k$ is the dielectric constant, $\epsilon_r$ is the absolute permittivity of a given dielectric, and $\epsilon_v$ is the absolute permittivity of free space.

Therefore the equation for the capacitance of any parallel plate capacitor becomes

$$C = \frac{8.85kA}{10^{12}d} \qquad \text{(parallel plates)} \quad (10.14)$$

where $C$ is the capacitance in farads, $k$ is the dielectric constant, $A$ is the area of each plate in square meters, and $d$ is the distance between plates in meters.

Making the necessary conversions to allow us to state area in square inches, distance between plates in inches, and capacitance in microfarads:

$$C = \frac{2.25kA}{10^7d} \qquad \text{(parallel plates)} \quad (10.15)$$

where $C$ is the capacitance in microfarads, $k$ is the dielectric constant, $A$ is the area of each plate in square inches, and $d$ is the distance between plates in inches.

The dielectric constant of a given type of material can vary considerably as a result of variation in manufacturing. Table II gives typical average values of dielectric constant for those dielectric materials listed in Table I. On comparing Tables I and II we will note that there is no correlation between dielectric strength and dielectric constant. In manufacturing a capacitor for use in high-voltage circuits, often we are not able to choose a dielectric with a high dielectric constant because its dielectric strength is too low. Distilled water has a dielectric constant of 80 but its dielectric strength is so low that it is not practical to build water dielectric capacitors.

**Table II**

| Dielectric | Average Dielectric Constant |
|---|---|
| Air | 1.0006 |
| Barium-strontium titanate (ceramic) | 7500 |
| Porcelain (ceramic) | 6 |
| Transformer oil | 4 |
| Bakelite (plastic) | 7 |
| Paper | 2.5 |
| Rubber | 3 |
| Teflon (plastic) | 2 |
| Glass | 6 |
| Mica | 5 |

Some ceramics such as barium-strontium titanate have dielectric constants which are extremely high in comparison with the average dielectric materials. Such materials are called **ferroelectric** since their dielectric constant in relation to other dielectrics is similar to the relationship that exists between the permeabilities of ferromagnetic materials and non-magnetic materials. And just as the permeability of ferromagnetic materials is dependent on the magnetizing force applied to them, the dielectric constant of ferroelectric materials is somewhat dependent on the electric field intensity.

EXAMPLE 1: A capacitor consists of a disk of barium-strontium titanate $\frac{1}{4}$ in. in diameter and 5 mils thick, silver plated on each side. Using the average values of dielectric strength and dielectric constant given in Tables I and II, (a) what is its capacitance; and (b) what is the maximum voltage that should be applied to it?

*Solution:*

(a) $\quad C = \dfrac{2.25kA}{10^7 d} = \dfrac{2.25 \times 7500 \times 3.14 \times 0.125^2}{10^7 \times 0.005} = 0.0165 \ \mu f$

(b) $\qquad\qquad\qquad V_m = 75 \times 5 = 375 \ v$

As even the graphic symbols in Fig. 10.11(a) suggest, connecting capacitors in parallel is like increasing the area of the plates of a single capacitor. Therefore the total capacitance is greater than that of either one. Since both capacitors have to charge from the same battery, the total charge drawn from the battery is

$$Q_T = Q_1 + Q_2 \qquad\qquad (10.16)$$

And, since Fig. 10.11(a) is a simple parallel circuit,

$$E = V_1 = V_2$$

$$\therefore \quad \frac{Q_T}{E} = \frac{Q_1}{V_1} + \frac{Q_2}{V_2}$$

and $\qquad\qquad\qquad C_T = C_1 + C_2$

Therefore, when capacitors are connected in parallel, the total capacitance is the sum of all the individual capacitances.

$$C_T = C_1 + C_2 + C_3 + \text{etc.} \qquad (10.17)$$

When capacitors are connected in series, the charging action will be similar to that shown in Fig. 10.6. The bottom plate of $C_1$ in Fig. 10.11(b) and the top plate of $C_2$ will be charged by electrostatic induction. And,

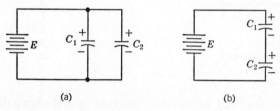

(a)                              (b)

**Fig. 10.11.** Capacitors (a) in parallel; and (b) in series.

as the graphic symbols suggest, the effect is much the same as increasing the spacing between the plates of a single capacitor. The total capacitance is less than that of either one, but the combination is capable of withstanding a higher total potential difference than either one by itself.

Since Fig. 10.11(b) is a simple series circuit,

$$E = V_1 + V_2$$

And, since the current is the same in all parts of a simple series circuit,

$$Q_T = Q_1 = Q_2$$

$$\therefore \quad \frac{E}{Q_T} = \frac{V_1}{Q_1} + \frac{V_2}{Q_2}$$

or

$$\frac{1}{C_{eq}} = \frac{1}{C_1} + \frac{1}{C_2}$$

Therefore, the equivalent capacitance of series capacitors is

$$C_{eq} = \frac{1}{1/C_1 + 1/C_2 + 1/C_3 + \text{etc.}} \qquad (10.18)$$

or, if we prefer, for series capacitors,

$$S_T = S_1 + S_2 + S_3 + \text{etc.} \qquad (10.19)$$

Since

$$Q_1 = C_1 V_1 \quad \text{and} \quad Q_2 = C_2 V_2,$$

and, since $Q_1 = Q_2$ in a series circuit,

$$C_1 V_1 = C_2 V_2$$

from which

$$\frac{V_1}{V_2} = \frac{C_2}{C_1} \qquad (10.20)$$

When capacitors are connected in series, the ratio between any two potential differences is the *inverse* ratio of their capacitances.

EXAMPLE 2: A 0.01 μf capacitor and a 0.04 μf capacitor are connected first in parallel and then in series to a 500 v source of emf.

(a) What is the total capacitance in each case?

(b) What is the total charge in each case?

(c) What is the charge on each capacitor and the potential difference across each capacitor in each case?

*Solution:*

(a) Parallel: $C_T = C_1 + C_2 = 0.01 + 0.04 = 0.05 \ \mu f$

     Series    $C_{eq} = \dfrac{C_1 C_2}{C_1 + C_2} = \dfrac{0.01 \times 0.04}{0.01 + 0.04} = 0.008 \ \mu f$

(b) Parallel: $Q_T = C_T V_T = 0.05 \times 500 = 25 \ \mu$ coulomb

     Series:    $Q_T = C_{eq} V_T = 0.008 \times 500 = 4 \ \mu$ coulomb

(c) Parallel: $V_1 = V_2 = E = 500 \ v$

               $Q_1 = C_1 V_1 = 0.01 \times 500 = 5 \ \mu$ coulomb

               $Q_2 = C_2 V_2 = 0.04 \times 500 = 20 \ \mu$ coulomb

     Series:    $Q_1 = Q_2 = Q_T = 4 \ \mu$ coulomb

               $V_1 = \dfrac{Q_1}{C_1} = \dfrac{4}{0.01} = 400 \ v$

               $V_2 = \dfrac{Q_2}{C_2} = \dfrac{4}{0.04} = 100 \ v$

## 7. Charging a Capacitor

In the remainder of this chapter we will notice the similarities between the procedures we use for determining the charge and discharge of a capacitor and those we used in Chapter 9 for dealing with the rise and fall of current in an inductance. Strictly speaking, when we speak of *charging* a capacitor, we should think in terms of the *charge* stored by it in *coulombs*. But $Q = CV$, and for a given capacitor, $C$ is a constant based on such physical factors as the area of the plates, the distance between plates and the type of dielectric. Therefore the charge is directly proportional to the potential difference between the plates. Since we have voltmeters for reading potential difference directly, it is more convenient to speak of the charging of a capacitor in terms of the potential difference built up between its plates. This point of view is consistent with our definition of capacitance.

At the instant the switch is closed in the circuit of Fig. 10.12, there can be no potential difference across the capacitor, since it takes *time* for electrons to flow into the bottom plate and out of the top plate in order to build up a PD between the plates. But Kirchhoff's voltage law states that there must be a voltage drop in the circuit equal to the applied emf when the switch is closed. Although no resistance is shown, we will assume that the resistance of the wiring and the internal resistance of the battery adds up to 0.5 ohm. Therefore at the instant the switch closes, since there is no PD across the capacitor, there will have to be an $IR$ drop in the circuit equal to the applied emf. To produce this voltage drop the current which must flow the instant the switch is closed is

$$\text{initial } I = \frac{E}{R} = \frac{100}{0.5} = 200 \text{ amp}$$

Since current is the rate of flow of electrons past a certain point in a circuit, a 200 amp current will charge the plates of the capacitor very

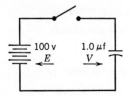

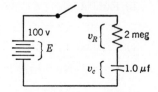

**Fig. 10.12.** Charging a capacitor without a current limiting resistor.     **Fig. 10.13.** Charging a capacitor through a current limiting resistor.

rapidly and the potential difference of the capacitor will take only a few microseconds to rise to 100 volts. When the PD across the capacitor equals the applied emf, current must cease flowing. Therefore if we charge a capacitor by connecting it directly across a source of emf, there is a very short duration pulse of very high current. Since this is rather rough on the source of emf, in practice we prefer to charge capacitors through a resistance which limits the peak value of the initial current surge.

All the time the switch is closed in the circuit of Fig. 10.13, the sum of the PD across the capacitor and the IR drop across the resistor must equal the applied emf.

$$\therefore \quad E = v_c + iR \tag{10.21}$$

Again at the instant the switch is closed there will be no PD across the capacitor and therefore the initial current must be such that the $IR$ drop in the circuit is equal to the applied emf.

$$\therefore \quad \text{initial } I = \frac{E}{R} \tag{10.22}$$

The initial current in the circuit of Fig. 10.13 is only 50 $\mu$a. This current immediately starts to charge the capacitor and a potential difference starts to build up across the capacitor. To satisfy Kirchhoff's voltage law, the $IR$ drop across the resistor must decrease. Therefore the instantaneous current (the dependent variable of our electric circuits) must become smaller. As a result the potential difference across the capacitor must rise more slowly. Therefore the rate of rise of the instantaneous PD across the capacitor depends on the instantaneous current, which depends on how

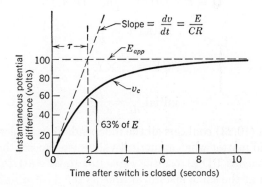

**Fig. 10.14.** Rise of potential difference across a capacitor charging through a resistance.

much $IR$ drop must appear across the resistance of the circuit which in turn depends on the instantaneous PD across the capacitor which depends on how long the switch has been closed. This interdependence produces the same exponential rise of voltage across a capacitor (as shown in Fig. 10.14) that we found for the rise of current through an inductance.

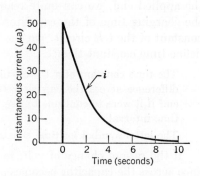

**Fig. 10.15.** Instantaneous charging current.

When the switch is closed, the instantaneous current must instantly flow at its initial value and then becomes progressively smaller as the PD across the capacitor rises, as shown by the graph of Fig. 10.15. Since resistance is a physical constant, the instantaneous voltage drop across it must always be proportional to the instantaneous current through it (Ohm's law) and the graph of the $IR$ drop across the resistor will have the same shape as the instantaneous current graph of Fig. 10.15.

## 8. Time Constant

Since the initial current in the circuit of Fig. 10.13 is only 50 $\mu$a, it will take appreciable time for the capacitor to charge, i.e., for the PD across the capacitor to rise to the same value as the applied emf. Since we know the magnitude of the initial current, we can determine the initial *rate of rise* of voltage across the capacitor.

Since $\qquad\qquad Q = CV$ (10.6), and $\quad Q = It$ $\qquad\qquad$ (2.1)

and $\qquad\qquad\qquad$ initial $I = \dfrac{E}{R}$ $\qquad\qquad\qquad\qquad$ (10.22)

$$CV = \frac{E}{R} \times t$$

from which $\qquad\qquad$ initial $\dfrac{dv}{dt} = \dfrac{E}{CR}$ $\qquad\qquad\qquad$ (10.23)

Since Equation (10.23) contains all the independent variables in the circuit of Fig. 10.13, no matter what numerical values we choose, the graph of the actual instantaneous PD across the capacitor must start to rise with the same slope and at the same instant in time as the dashed line in Fig. 10.14 representing the initial rate of change of capacitor voltage. The slope of the actual potential difference must then become progressively more gradual until it finally ends up tangent to the dashed line representing the applied emf.

If we assume for the moment that the potential difference across the capacitor can rise at a steady rate equal to its initial rate until it equals the applied emf, we can quite readily derive a convenient expression for the charging time of the capacitor. This time interval is called the **time constant** of the $CR$ circuit. On the basis of the above assumption, we can define time constant thus:

> The **time constant of a CR circuit** is the time it would take the potential difference across the capacitor to rise to the same value as the applied emf if it were to continue to rise at its initial rate of change for the whole time interval.
>
> The letter symbol for **time constant** is $\tau$ (tau).

If the rate of change of voltage remains constant, the potential difference across the capacitor becomes simply

$$V = \tau \times \text{initial } \frac{dv}{dt}$$

But $\qquad\qquad V = E \qquad$ and $\qquad$ initial $\dfrac{dv}{dt} = \dfrac{E}{CR}$ $\qquad\qquad$ (10.23)

From which $\qquad\qquad\qquad \tau = CR$ sec $\qquad\qquad\qquad\qquad$ (10.24)

where $\tau$ is the length of time in seconds defined as a time constant, $C$ is the capacitance of the capacitor in farads, and $R$ is the resistance through which the capacitor charges in ohms. Since the farad is not a practical unit, we can still make Equation (10.24) balance if we express capacitance in microfarads and resistance in megohms.

Note that the time constant of a $CR$ circuit is directly proportional to the capacitance. If the capacitance is doubled, twice the charge must flow in order to raise the PD across the capacitor to the applied emf. But if the resistance is not changed, the initial current remains unchanged and therefore it will take twice as long for the capacitor to charge. If the resistance is doubled, the initial current is cut in half and it will therefore take twice as long for the PD of a given capacitor to rise until it equals the applied emf. Note also that the magnitude of the applied emf has no effect on the time constant. If we double the emf, the capacitor must store twice the charge but the initial current will be twice as great. Therefore it will take exactly the same time for the PD of the capacitor to reach the applied emf.

Because of the fixed relationship between the solid exponential graph of Fig. 10.14 representing the actual rise in potential difference across the capacitor, and the dashed lines from which we solved for the time constant, the actual charging time of a $CR$ circuit bears a fixed relationship to the time constant. The instantaneous potential difference across a capacitor will always be 63% of the applied emf one time constant after the switch is closed. For all practical purposes, the potential difference across the capacitor will have reached a value equal to the applied emf after a time interval equal to *five* time constants has elapsed.

EXAMPLE 3: (a) What is the initial rate of change of potential difference across the capacitor in Fig. 10.13?
(b) How long will it take the capacitor in Fig. 10.13 to charge to a PD of 100 v?
*Solution:*

(a) $\quad\quad\quad$ Initial $\dfrac{dv}{dt} = \dfrac{E}{CR} = \dfrac{100}{10^{-6} \times 2 \times 10^6} = 50$ v/sec

(b) $\quad\quad\quad\quad\quad \tau = CR = 10^{-6} \times 2 \times 10^6 = 2$ sec

Since $\quad\quad\quad\quad 100$ v $= E =$ full charge

$\quad\quad\quad\quad\quad\quad \therefore \quad t = 5\tau = 5 \times 2 = 10$ sec

## 9. Graphical Solution for Instantaneous Potential Difference

Because of the fixed relationship between the time constant and the time it actually takes the potential difference of a capacitor to rise to the same value as the applied emf, if we carefully replot the exponential curve of Fig. 10.14 with a horizontal (time) axis in terms of time constants rather than seconds, and a vertical (instantaneous PD) axis in percentage of the applied emf, we can solve graphically for the instantaneous potential difference of any $CR$ circuit at any instant in time from the universal exponential graph of Fig. 10.16.

EXAMPLE 4: (a) What is the instantaneous PD across the capacitor in the circuit of Fig. 10.13 3 sec after the switch is closed? (b) How long will it take the potential difference across the capacitor to rise from zero to 55 v?

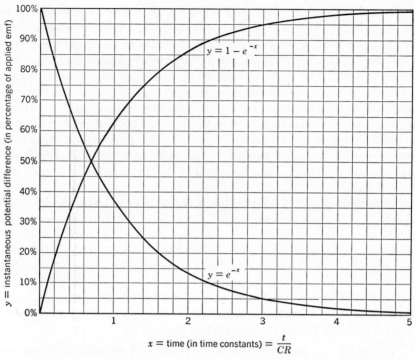

**Fig. 10.16.** Universal exponential curves for the graphical solution of the charge and discharge of capacitors in direct current circuits.

*Solution:*

(a) $$\tau = CR = 1 \ \mu\text{f} \times 2 \ \text{meg} = 2 \ \text{sec}$$

$$\therefore \quad 3 \ \text{sec represents} \ \frac{3}{2} = 1.5\tau$$

From Fig. 10.16, when $t = 1.5\tau$,

$$v_c = 77\% \ \text{of} \ E = 0.77 \times 100 = 77 \ \text{v}$$

(b) $$55 \ \text{v represents} \ \frac{55}{100} \times 100\% = 55\% \ \text{of} \ E$$

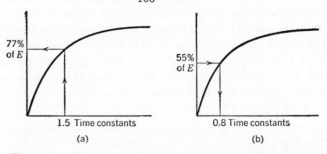

**Fig. 10.17.** Using the graph of Fig. 10.16 to solve Example 4.

From Fig. 10.16, when $v_c = 55\%$ of $E$,

$$t = 0.8 \text{ time constants} = 0.8 \times 2 = 1.6 \text{ sec}$$

## 10. Discharging a Capacitor

If the switch in the circuit of Fig. 10.18(a) has been in Position 1 for a length of time equal to at least five time constants, the PD across the capacitor will be equal to the applied emf, 200 v. If the switch is now placed in the open circuit Position 2, the PD across the capacitor will remain at 200 v for some considerable time since there is no conducting path between the plates except a bit of leakage through the dielectric. At the instant the switch is thrown to Position 3, the potential difference across the capacitor will still be 200 v since it takes *time* for the surplus electrons to flow from the bottom plate to the top plate of the capacitor. To satisfy Kirchhoff's voltage law, the initial current will have to be such that a 200 v $IR$ drop will be developed across the resistance of the conductor connecting the two plates together. Therefore the initial current is very high and the capacitor discharges very rapidly.

If we wish to reduce the magnitude of the initial discharge current, we can change the circuit to that shown in Fig. 10.18(b) so that in switch

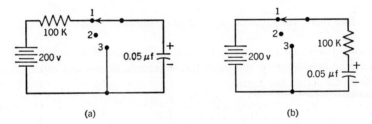

(a)                                   (b)

**Fig. 10.18.** Discharging a capacitor.

Position 3 a resistance of 100 kilohms is connected across the charged capacitor. The initial current is now limited to

$$\text{initial } I = \frac{V_{init}}{R} = \frac{200}{100,000} = 2 \text{ ma} \tag{10.25}$$

Since the charge stored in the capacitor is being released at a slower rate $i = dq/dt$, it will take much longer for the capacitor to discharge fully.

The potential difference across the capacitor will have its maximum value just as the switch is thrown to Position 3. Therefore the initial current is the maximum value that the instantaneous discharge current can have and as a result, the PD across the capacitor starts to fall fairly rapidly. But as the charge diminishes, the PD across the capacitor must also decrease and, according to Kirchhoff's voltage law, the $IR$ drop must have the same value as the PD of the capacitor. Therefore the current must decrease, and as a result the capacitor will discharge more slowly. This interdependence among the potential difference, the $IR$ drop, the current and the rate of decrease of the potential difference results in the exponential discharge of Fig. 10.19(a). The current in the 100 kilohm resistor flows in the opposite direction when the capacitor of Fig. 10.18(b) is discharging with the switch in Position 3 to that when the capacitor is charging in switch Position 1. This means a reversal in the polarity of the $IR$ drop across the resistance when the capacitor discharges. This is indicated in the graph of the instantaneous current and $IR$ drop in Fig. 10.19(b) by using the negative vertical axis to plot instantaneous current or instantaneous voltage drop across the resistance.

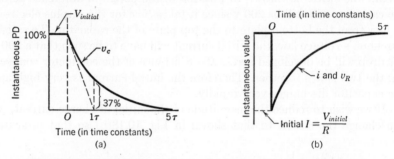

**Fig. 10.19.** Instantaneous voltage and current as a capacitor discharges.

Using the same procedure we used in deriving Equation (10.23), the initial rate of change of the potential difference across the capacitor as it starts to discharge becomes

$$\frac{dv}{dt} = -\frac{V_{init}}{CR} \tag{10.26}$$

The $-$ sign is a result of the discharge current flowing in the opposite direction through the resistance to that during the charging of the capacitor. Therefore the rate of change of voltage is a *negative* quantity, which indicates that the voltage across the capacitor is decreasing rather than increasing. If we define the discharge time constant as the time it would take for the capacitor to discharge completely *if* it were to continue to discharge at the initial rate of fall of potential difference for the whole time interval, Equation (10.26) reduces to

$$\tau = CR$$

Therefore discharge time constant is found in exactly the same manner as charge time constant. Again the exponential discharge curve bears a fixed relationship to the time constant. In a time interval equal to one time constant, the potential difference of the capacitor will have dropped to 37% of its initial value. Or if we wish we can say that the capacitor loses 63% of its initial potential difference in a time interval of one time constant. The time required for the capacitor to fully discharge will again be five time constants for practical purposes. In Fig. 10.18(b),

$$\tau = CR = 0.05 \times 10^{-6} \times 10^5 = 5 \text{ msec}$$

and total discharge time $= 5 \times 5 = 25$ msec.

The following example illustrates several important points that can arise in solving $CR$ circuit problems.

EXAMPLE 5: After being open for a considerable period of time, the switch is closed for 1 sec, opened for 1 sec, closed for 1 sec, and then opened again. What is the potential difference across the capacitor at the instant that the switch is opened the second time?

*Solution:*

*Step I.* To simplify the solution of the *charging* portions of the problem, we can convert the given circuit into the Thévenin equivalent circuit of Fig. 10.21. (Check the Thévenin transformation.)

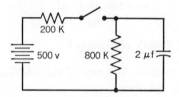
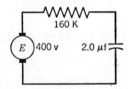

**Fig. 10.20.** Circuit diagram for Example 5.        **Fig. 10.21.** Thévenin equivalent circuit for Fig. 10.20.

*Step II.* Charging time constant $= CR = 2 \mu f \times 0.16 \text{ meg} = 0.32 \text{ sec}.$

$$\therefore \quad 1 \text{ sec} = \frac{1.0}{0.32} = 3.1 \text{ time constants}$$

Since the switch was originally open, the capacitor starts to charge with zero PD between its plates. Therefore from the graph of Fig. 10.16, when $t = 3.1$ time constants,

$$v_c = 95\% \text{ of } E = 0.95 \times 400 = 380 \text{ v}$$

*Step III.* Discharge time constant $= CR = 2 \times 0.8 = 1.6$ sec. Therefore one second $= 1.0/1.6 = 0.625$ time constants.

From the discharge graph of Fig. 10.16, when $t = 0.63$ time constant,

$$v_c = 54\% \text{ of } V_{init} = 0.54 \times 380 = 205 \text{ v}$$

As we enter the third second, we return to the Thévenin equivalent circuit of Fig. 10.21 and we have a choice of two lines of thought in handling the rise in PD across a partially charged capacitor.

*Step IVA.* 205 v represents $(205/400) \times 100\% = 51.25\%$ of $E$. On the charge curve of Fig. 10.16, if the capacitor had had to charge from zero, a time interval of 0.72 time constant would have elapsed [Fig. 10.22(a)] for the PD across the capacitor to reach 205 v.

Since one second = 3.1 charging time constants, one second after the switch is returned to the *charge* position, the potential difference across the capacitor will be the same as if it had charged from zero for a period of

$$0.72 + 3.1 = 3.82 \text{ time constants}$$

From Fig. 10.16, when $t$ = 3.8 time constants,

$$v_c = 98\% \text{ of } E = 0.98 \times 400 = 392 \text{ v}$$

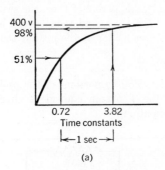 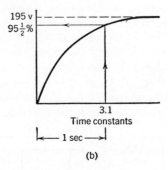

(a)                                             (b)

**Fig. 10.22.** Graphical solution of Step IV of Example 5.

*Step IVB.* The alternate method is to think in terms of the *additional* potential difference to which the capacitor can charge.

Since $E$ = 400 v and the PD across the capacitor is already 205 v, the maximum *additional* emf is only 400 − 205 = 195 v.

From Fig. 10.16, in a time interval of 3.1 time constants, the PD can rise by $95\frac{1}{2}\%$ of this additional $E$.

$$\therefore \quad \text{additional } v_c = 95.5\% \times 195 \text{ v} = 187 \text{ v} \quad [\text{Fig. 10.22(b)}]$$

Therefore the final PD across the capacitor is its *initial* PD + its *additional* potential rise.

$$\therefore \quad v_c = 205 + 187 = 392 \text{ v}$$

## 11. Algebraic Solution of Instantaneous Potential Difference

When we require greater accuracy than the universal exponential graph of Fig. 10.16 provides, we may solve for instantaneous voltage across a capacitor using the equations from which the curves of Fig. 10.16 were plotted. Since a purely algebraic solution does not provide an opportunity to visualize what is going on in the circuit, it is well worth while accompanying any algebraic solution with a freehand graphic solution to check any serious error in the more accurate algebraic solution. The equation for the instantaneous potential difference across the capacitor while it is charging is derived from the Kirchhoff's voltage law equation for the basic circuit of Fig. 10.13.

$$E = iR + v_c \tag{10.21}$$

Since the instantaneous current is the instantaneous rate of charging,

$$i = \frac{dq}{dt}$$

And since the instantaneous charge is the product of the capacitance and the instantaneous PD across it, $q = Cv_c$.

$$\therefore \quad i = C\frac{dv}{dt}$$

and

$$E = CR\frac{dv}{dt} + v_c$$

Solving for $v_c$ with the aid of calculus gives

$$v_c = E(1 - e^{-x}) \tag{10.27}$$

where $e = 2.718$ (the base of Naperian logarithms) and $x = t/CR$.

When the capacitor is discharging in the circuit of Fig. 10.18(b), the emf in the loop consisting of the capacitor and the resistor is zero and therefore the $IR$ drop across the resistance and the PD across the capacitor must at all times be numerically equal in order to satisfy Kirchhoff's voltage law.

$$\therefore \quad 0 = iR + v_c = CR\frac{dv}{dt} + v_c$$

This can be reduced to

$$v_c = V_{init}\, e^{-x} \tag{10.28}$$

where $e = 2.718$ and $x = t/CR$.

EXAMPLE 6: In the circuit of Fig. 10.23, the switch is initially in the closed position.

(a) What is the PD across the capacitor 1 msec after the switch is opened?

(b) After being open for 1 msec, the switch is closed again. What is the PD across the capacitor 1 msec after the switch is closed?

*Solution:* When the switch is open, the 10 kilohm resistor can be neglected and the circuit of Fig. 10.23 becomes a simple series circuit in which the capacitor will eventually charge to a potential difference between its plates of 300 v.

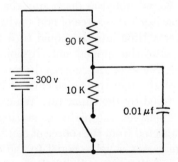

Fig. 10.23. Circuit diagram for Example 6.

To solve the circuit with the switch closed, it will be to our advantage to place the capacitor in the Thévenin equivalent circuit of Fig. 10.24. Therefore if the capacitor's PD is more than 30 v, it can discharge only to a 30 v potential difference.

(a) When the switch first opens, the capacitor already has a PD of 30 v between its plates. We can then solve for instantaneous potential difference by either of the methods described in Example 5 and illustrated in Fig. 10.22.

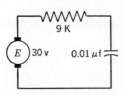

**Fig. 10.24.** Thévenin equivalent discharge circuit of the circuit of Fig. 10.23.

Using the *additional* voltage method,

additional $v_c$ = additional $E(1 - e^{-x})$

$$x = \frac{t}{CR} = \frac{10^{-3}}{10^{-8} \times 9 \times 10^4} = 1.11$$

$\therefore$  additional $v_c = 270(1 - e^{-1.11})$

From tables or a slide rule, $e^{-1.11} = 0.33$.

$\therefore$  additional $v_c = 270 \times 0.67 = 181$ v

And the total $v_c = 30 + 181 = 211$ v

(b) Since the PD of the capacitor with the switch in this position cannot go below 30 v, we would consider the initial PD to be $211 - 30 = 181$ v.

Of this 181 v, the instantaneous PD after 1 msec will be

$$v_c = V_{init}\, e^{-x}$$

$$x = \frac{t}{CR} = \frac{10^{-3}}{10^{-8} \times 9 \times 10^3} = 11.1$$

When $x = 11.1$, $e^{-x} \approx 0$. Therefore all the additional 181 v will be discharged, and the actual instantaneous PD still across the capacitor will be 30 v.

## 12. Energy Stored by a Capacitor

As we noted in discussing the circuit of Fig. 10.18, when we connect a capacitor to a source of emf (switch position 1), the capacitor charges until after a time interval equal to 5 time constants its potential difference is equal to the applied emf. In doing so, energy is drawn from the source of emf. Some of this energy is converted into heat as the charging current flows through the series current limiting resistor. But some of the energy is stored by the capacitor. We can consider the electric field in the dielectric between the plates as storing the energy. When the capacitor is disconnected from the source of emf (switch position 2), its potential difference remains at a value equal to the original emf for a considerable period of time if there is negligible leakage between the plates of the capacitor.

Since no current flow is required to maintain the potential difference and the electric field associated with it (as is the case in an inductance), we can consider the capacitor as storing energy in a **static** form. We can plot a graph of the *rate* at which a capacitor is storing energy since instantaneous power represents this rate and $p = vi$. By calculating the product of the instantaneous potential difference across a capacitor and the instantaneous charging current for each division along the horizontal (time) axis of the graph of Fig. 10.25, we can plot a graph of the rate at which energy is being stored by the capacitor from instant to instant. After a period of time equal to 5 time constants, the charging current has ceased to flow and the instantaneous power has therefore decreased to zero. The capacitor has now stored all the energy it is capable of storing when connected to that particular source of emf. Since the total energy is the product of the average power and the time involved, we can represent the energy stored by the capacitor by the *area* contained by the instantaneous power curve in Fig. 10.25. (Note the similarity between Fig. 10.25 and Fig. 9.17.)

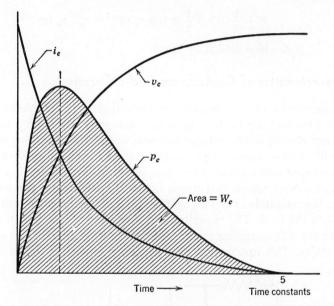

**Fig. 10.25.** Graphical representation of the energy stored by a capacitor.

Since the instantaneous power graph of Fig. 10.25 is not a straight line, the solution for the actual energy stored by a capacitor involves calculus. However, in determining the equation for the stored energy, we may use the fixed relationship between the actual exponential rise of PD across a capacitor and the theoretical straight line rise of PD which we used to define a time constant. If the potential difference rises at a constant rate equal to its initial rate of rise, the current must remain constant at its initial value of $I = E/R$. If the PD across the capacitor rises at a steady rate from zero to its final value of $V = E$, the *average* PD during this time must be $\frac{1}{2}V$. Under these hypothetical conditions of linear charging, $W = Pt$ becomes

$$W = \tfrac{1}{2}V \times I \times \tau$$

But
$$I = \frac{E}{R} = \frac{V}{R} \quad \text{and} \quad \tau = CR$$

$$\therefore \quad W = \tfrac{1}{2}CV^2 \tag{10.29}$$

This expression which we derived from the hypothetical linear charging of a capacitor is the same as we would obtain by calculus from the actual instantaneous power graph of Fig. 10.25.

EXAMPLE 7: How much energy is stored in the 500 $\mu\mu f$ high-voltage filter capacitor of a television receiver when it is charged to 15 kv?

*Solution:*

$$W = \frac{1}{2}CV^2 = \frac{1}{2} \times 500 \times 10^{-12} \times 225 \times 10^6$$

$$\therefore \quad W = 5.63 \times 10^{-2} \text{ joule}$$

## 13. Characteristics of Capacitance in d-c Circuits

The properties of capacitance are such that it is considerably more useful in practical d-c circuits than is inductance. Its ability to oppose any instant change in the voltage across it makes the capacitor very suitable for filtering or smoothing any fluctuations in the output from a pulsating source of emf such as a rectifier, as shown in Fig. 10.26(a). When the instantaneous source emf drops below the PD across the capacitor, the capacitor maintains the load voltage by discharging some of its stored energy into the load. The capacitor will then recover this charge the next time that the instantaneous source emf rises to its peak value, as shown in Fig. 10.26(b). This application of a capacitor is similar to the use of a

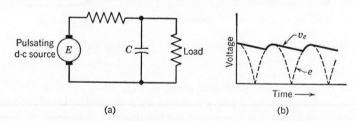

**Fig. 10.26.** Filtering voltage fluctuations with a capacitor.

reservoir tank with an air compressor used with a paint spray. Since the pressure of the air in the tank cannot change without the flow of the stored air, the tank maintains a fairly constant pressure at the paint spray in spite of the fluctuations in the pressure developed by the piston action of the compressor. (The compressed air tank analogy provides a fairly accurate means of visualizing the charge and discharge action of capacitance, with the friction of the air hose representing resistance.)

We recall that in Chapter 9 we ran into the problem of sparking at switch or breaker contacts when we opened inductive circuits. By placing a capacitor across the switch contacts as in Fig. 10.27, the potential difference across the capacitor is zero while the switch is closed. Since the PD cannot rise instantly when the switch is opened, there is sufficient time to move the switch contacts far enough apart that they do not spark.

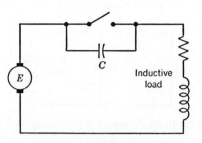

Fig. 10.27. Suppressing a voltage surge with a capacitor.

The energy storage ability of a capacitor is very useful in cases where we wish to obtain a very high current for a short period of time without subjecting the source of emf to a severe current surge. With a circuit patterned after the basic circuit of Fig. 10.28, the capacitor charges slowly from the source and then discharges rapidly when the low-resistance load is connected across it. The peak current drawn from the source is limited by the series resistor. This system is used to obtain a 1 μsec pulse for radar transmitter oscillator tubes with a peak power during the pulse of over a million watts. This system is also used in electric spot welding of aluminum where a short duration surge of very high current is required to make the weld. The same system is used on a smaller scale in making the delicate welds which hold vacuum tube elements in place. In this case the circuit of Fig. 10.28 is used not because of its ability to limit the peak current drawn from the source of emf, but because we are able to control very precisely the amount of energy in each discharge pulse by setting the potential difference to which the capacitor is allowed to charge.

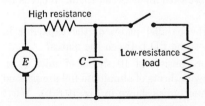

Fig. 10.28. Obtaining short duration, high current pulses from a reservoir capacitor.

The instantaneous potential difference across the capacitor of a given $CR$ combination is an exponential function of elapsed time and will always rise along exactly the same curve. Therefore we can use a series $CR$ circuit as the basis for a very accurate timing device for time intervals of from a small fraction of a second to several seconds. In the simple circuit of Fig. 10.29, the neon lamp "strikes" (glows) when the potential difference across it is 100 v and extinguishes when the PD drops below 20 v. When a neon lamp is not struck, the gas is an insulator and we may consider the lamp to be an open circuit. When the lamp strikes, the gas becomes ionized and becomes an excellent electric conductor with the free electrons knocked out of the gas molecules flowing in one direction and the positively charged gas ions moving in the other direction. The resistance of the neon lamp under these conditions is only around 100 ohms. If the time constant of

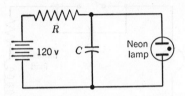

**Fig. 10.29.** Using a $CR$ time constant for timing purposes.

the series $CR$ circuit in Fig. 10.29 is several seconds, it will take several seconds for the potential difference across the capacitor to rise to the striking voltage of the neon lamp. The low resistance of the ionized neon will then quickly discharge the capacitor down to the extinguishing voltage of the lamp, whereupon the resistance of the neon lamp again becomes extremely high and the capacitor starts to recharge. The time interval between the short flashes from the neon lamp is therefore dependent on the time constant of $C$ and $R$.

## Problems

1. Two parallel plates 1 cm apart are connected to a 500 v source of emf. What force will be exerted on a free electron between the plates?

2. If $2 \times 10^{10}$ electrons are removed from one parallel plate and added to the other, what is the total electric flux between the plates?

3. If the potential difference between the plates in Problem 2 is 180 v, what is the capacitance of the plates?

4. How many electrons must be removed from one plate of a 270 $\mu\mu f$ capacitor and added to the other to raise the PD between the plates to 420 v?

5. A neutralizing capacitor in a radio transmitter consists of two aluminum disks each 10 cm in diameter and 0.5 cm apart with air between them. What is its capacitance?

6. If the electric flux density between the parallel plates of the capacitor in Problem 5 is 1.0 $\mu$coulomb/sq m, what is the PD between the plates?

7. An interleaved parallel plate capacitor consists of 10 sheets of mica $\frac{1}{2}$ in. long $\times \frac{1}{4}$ in. wide and 1.0 mil thick. Eleven sheets of aluminum foil are pressed firmly between the mica sheets and connected as shown in Fig. 10.8(b). What is the capacitance of this capacitor?

8. Two sheets of aluminum foil 1 in. wide and 3 ft long and two sheets of 3 mil thick waxed paper $1\frac{1}{4}$ in. wide and 3 ft long are rolled as shown in Fig. 10.8(c) to form a tubular capacitor. The waxed paper has a dielectric strength of 150 v/mil and a dielectric constant of 3. What is the capacitance and voltage rating of this capacitor?

9. A 10 $\mu f$ and a 40 $\mu f$ capacitor are connected in parallel to a 400 v source of emf.
   (a) What is the total capacitance?
   (b) What is the magnitude of the charge stored by each capacitor?
   (c) What is the total static energy stored by the two capacitors?

10. The 10 $\mu$f capacitor in the circuit of Fig. 10.30 is completely discharged. Draw a graph showing how the PD across the 10 $\mu$f capacitor changes with time as the switch is operated for 5 complete cycles. Label the exact instantaneous value of this PD after each cycle of switch operation. (Assume no leakage.)

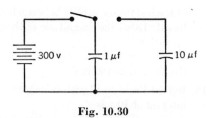

**Fig. 10.30**

11. A 10 $\mu$f, a 20 $\mu$f, and a 40 $\mu$f capacitor are connected in series to a 400 v source of emf.
    (a) What is the total capacitance?
    (b) What is the magnitude of the charge stored by each capacitor?
    (c) What is the PD across each capacitor?

12. After charging, the three capacitors in Problem 11 are disconnected from the source and each other. They are then connected in parallel (with + plate connected to + plate). What is the PD across each capacitor?

13. A sheet of glass 0.3 cm thick is placed between the plates of the neutralizing capacitor of Problem 5. What is its capacitance? (*Hint:* Capacitors in series.)

14. If the potential difference between the plates of the capacitor in Problem 13 is 1 kv, what is the voltage gradient in the air and in the glass?

15. A 20 $\mu$f capacitor is to be charged through a 200 kilohm resistor from a 250 v d-c source of emf.
    (a) What is the initial current?
    (b) What is the initial PD across the capacitor?
    (c) What is the initial rate of rise of PD across the capacitor?
    (d) What is the charging time constant?
    (e) How long will it take the capacitor to charge?
    (f) What is the PD across the capacitor 5 sec after the switch is closed?
    (g) What is the instantaneous charging current 2 sec after the switch is closed?
    (h) How long will it take the PD across the capacitor to rise from 50 v to 150 v?

16. If the resistor in the circuit of Fig. 10.29 is 5 megohms and the capacitor has a capacitance of 8 $\mu$f, calculate the time interval between the flashes of the neon lamp. The lamp strikes at 100 v and its resistance then becomes 100 ohms. It extinguishes when the voltage across it drops to 20 v and its resistance then becomes infinitely high. How much energy is transferred to the neon lamp with each flash?

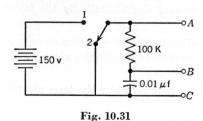

**Fig. 10.31**

17. The switch in the circuit of Fig. 10.31 is alternately thrown to position 1 for 1 msec and then to position 2 for 9 msec.
    (a) Draw an accurate graph of the voltage between terminals $A$ and $C$ for an interval of 30 msec.
    (b) Superimpose (in another color) on the graph of part (a), a graph

of the instantaneous PD between terminals $B$ and $C$ during the same time interval. Label the magnitude of the instantaneous PD at each instant of switch operation.

(c) Draw a separate graph of the voltage drop between terminals $A$ and $B$ for the same time interval.

18. Repeat Problem 17 with switch remaining 1 msec in each position. Show a time interval of 10 msec.

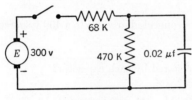

**Fig. 10.32.**

19. Commencing from the open position, the switch in the circuit of Fig. 10.32 alternately closes for 1 msec and opens for 1 msec. Draw an accurate graph of the PD across the capacitor for the first 6 msec of switch operation, labeling the instantaneous PD each time the switch operates.

20. Repeat the procedure of Problem 19 for the circuit shown in Fig. 10.33.

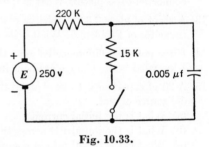

**Fig. 10.33.**

## Review Questions

1. How does a positively charged object differ from a similar object which has no electric charge?

2. How can a neutral electric conductor be given a positive charge?

3. In Chapter 2, we defined a coulomb as a quantity of $6.24 \times 10^{18}$ electrons. Why then can we express a positive charge in terms of coulombs?

4. Why does a potential difference exist between two conductors possessing unlike charges?

5. What is the conventional manner of showing diagrammatically the forces existing between charged objects?

6. Why are we more concerned with the attraction between unlike charges in electric circuits than we are in the repulsion between like charges which we can demonstrate in electrostatics?

7. What characteristic of an electric field is referred to by the term **electric field intensity**?

8. What is meant by the **potential gradient** of an electric field?

9. How are electric field intensity and potential gradient related in the case of charged parallel plates?

10. What factors govern the flux density of the electric field between charged parallel plates?

11. Draw a sketch showing the equipotential surfaces in the electric field between two charged concentric conductors.

12. Draw a sketch showing the equipotential surfaces in the electric field of Fig. 10.6.

13. Why must the + and − charges at the two ends of the insulated conductor in Fig. 10.6 be equal?

14. Define a **displacement current.**

15. What is meant by a **polarized** atom?

16. What type of atoms can become polarized?

17. Why is the strength of a dielectric dependent on the voltage gradient of an electric field rather than the total potential difference?

18. Define **dielectric absorption.**

19. Why must the ratio between the charge on a given pair of insulated conductors and the PD between them be a constant?

20. Define the term **capacitance** in terms of $Q$ and $V$.

21. Define the term **capacitor** in terms of $Q$ and $V$.

22. Why can we define capacitance as that property of an electric circuit that opposes any change in voltage across that circuit?

23. Why does the spacing between two parallel plates have an effect on their capacitance?

24. Why does the emf applied to two parallel plates not have an effect on their capacitance?

25. Why is it possible to have capacitance between two parallel plates when the space between them is evacuated?

26. Why does the presence of an insulating material between the parallel plates increase their capacitance as compared with that of the same plates in a vacuum?

27. Since we are concerned with electric circuits, we defined the farad in terms of the charge on the conducting *plates* and the PD between the *plates*. Define the farad in terms of flux density and intensity of the electric *field* in the dielectric between the plates.

28. Distinguish between the absolute permittivity and the relative permittivity of a given dielectric.

29. Why is it possible to define the dielectric constant of a given insulating material as the ratio between the capacitance of a pair of parallel plates with that material as a dielectric and the same parallel plates with air as a dielectric?

30. Derive Equation (10.15) from Equation (10.14).

31. When two capacitors are connected in series, one plate of each has no electric connection to any source of emf. How is it possible for these capacitors to become charged?

32. Why must capacitors in series all take the same charge?

33. A 0.1 $\mu f$, 400 v capacitor and a 0.05 $\mu f$, 200 v capacitor are connected in series. What is the maximum emf that can be safely applied to this combination?

34. When a discharged capacitor is connected to a source of emf, the current changes instantly from zero to a value of $E/R$. Why then can the PD across the capacitor not change instantly?

35. Why must the rate of change of voltage across a capacitor diminish as the charge on its plates increases?

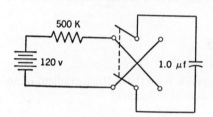

**Fg. 10.34.**

36. Draw an accurately labeled graph of the instantaneous PD across the capacitor in the circuit of Fig. 10.34 plotted against time as the double-pole-double-throw switch is thrown to the opposite position.

37. Using the techniques employed in producing Fig. 10.25, plot a graph of the instantaneous power in a resistor when a charged capacitor is connected across it.

38. An air dielectric capacitor is charged from a source of emf and then disconnected. The plates are then moved twice as far apart. Assuming no leakage of the charge, account for the difference in the energy stored by the capacitor before and after moving the plates.

39. Instead of changing the spacing between the plates in Question 38, a dielectric with a dielectric constant of 2.0 is placed between the plates after the capacitor is disconnected from the source of emf. Account for any change in the energy stored by the capacitor.

40. Fig. 10.35 shows the circuit diagram of a BC (battery-capacitor) type of photoflash unit. Explain its operation and advantages.

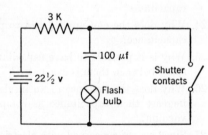

**Fig. 10.35.** Circuit diagram of a BC type photoflash unit.

# Chapter 11

# ALTERNATING CURRENT

~~~~~~~~~~~~~~~~~~~~~~~~~~~~~~~~~~~~~~~~~~~~~~~~~~~~~~~~~~~~~~~~~~~~

## 1. A Simple Rotating Generator

The only practical source of emf we have considered so far is the battery. Because of the nature of the chemical action within it, the battery is able to maintain a constant emf for a considerable period of time. Although the battery is a convenient source of emf for flashlights and portable radios, it does not offer a suitable means of developing the large amounts of electric energy which we require for both home and industry.

In Chapter 9 we discussed a second method of developing an emf based on Faraday's discovery of electromagnetic induction. As an electric conductor is moved in such a manner that it cuts across magnetic lines of force, an emf is induced in it. In order to maintain an emf by this method, the conductor must be kept in motion within a stationary magnetic field. This can be achieved by the arrangement shown in Fig. 11.1. The electric conductor is in the form of a loop which can be rotated continuously within the magnetic field in the air gap between a North and a South pole. Electric connection to the rotating loop is maintained through a pair of **sliprings** and **brushes.**

As the loop rotates, the two sides of the loop must always cut across the magnetic lines of force in opposite directions. This results in the two induced emf's being connected so that they aid each other as far as supplying emf to the brushes is concerned, just as two flashlight cells may be connected in series to double the emf. If a load resistor is connected to the brushes of this simple generator, the induced emf will cause current to flow in the closed circuit consisting of the loop and the load. This load current flowing in the rotating loop produces a magnetic field which, according to Lenz's law, reacts with the stationary magnetic field in such a manner as to *oppose* the rotation of the loop. Therefore in order to

243

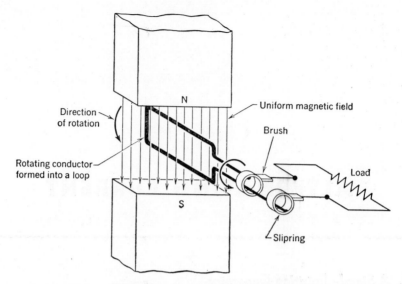

**Fig. 11.1.** A simple AC generator.

maintain rotation, the loop must be rotated against this mechanical force opposing its rotation. Whenever motion is accomplished against an opposing force, mechanical energy is expended. Therefore the electric energy that is converted into heat energy in the load resistance is generated directly at the expense of the mechanical energy maintaining the rotation of the loop.

## 2. The Nature of the Induced emf

If we consider the sequence of events as the conductor forming either side of the loop in Fig. 11.1 rotates through a complete revolution (360°), it first of all must cut across the magnetic lines of force in one direction and then move back across the same magnetic lines of force in the opposite direction. Since the emf appearing at the brushes of this simple generator must reverse its polarity with each half revolution, the basic rotating machine generator for converting mechanical energy into electric energy develops an **alternating** emf.

Since most of our electric energy is generated by rotating machines, it is necessary for us to be able to cope with an *alternating* emf in electric circuits just as readily as we have been able to do with the *direct* emf from a battery which we have been using up to this point. Figure 11.2(a) is a cross-sectional drawing of the simple generator of Fig. 11.1. Only one side of the loop is shown in this sketch. This one conductor is shown in twelve positions during one rotation. In order to be able to relate the rotation of the conductor to numerical calculations, it is conventional to consider the

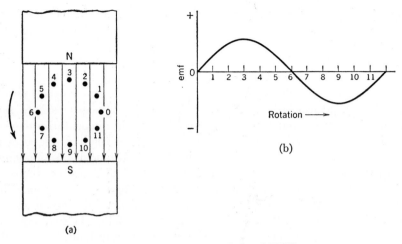

**Fig. 11.2.** Nature of the induced EMF.

normal or *positive* direction of rotation as being counterclockwise starting from an angular position representing three o'clock.

At position 0, the motion of the conductor is parallel to the magnetic lines of force. Therefore at that moment, no lines of force are being cut by the conductor. Therefore the induced emf at the instant the conductor passes through point 0 is zero volts. At position 1, the conductor has started to cut across the lines of force. Thus appreciable emf is induced into the conductor as it passes through point 1. At position 2, the conductor is cutting across the magnetic lines of force at an even steeper angle. Thus the *rate* of cutting and therefore the emf induced into the conductor as it passes through point 2 is even greater. At position 3, the conductor is cutting across the magnetic lines of force at right angles, which results in the greatest possible rate of cutting. Therefore maximum emf is induced into the conductor as it passes through point 3.

The manner in which the rate of cutting increases as the conductor rotates through the first 90° can be compared to four men walking along a sidewalk at the same velocity. As they reach a certain point, the first man continues to walk parallel to the street and therefore never reaches the other side. So his *rate of crossing the street* is zero. The second man makes a 30° turn and crosses the street at an angle. The third man makes a 60° turn and crosses the street at a steeper angle, while the fourth man makes a 90° turn and goes straight across the street. With all four men turning at the same instant and walking at the same speed, the fourth man has the shortest distance to go and therefore gets to the other side first. His rate of crossing the street is maximum even though his absolute velocity is the same as that of the other three. Number three man is the next to reach the other side and number two man is the third to reach the opposite sidewalk. Their rates of crossing are proportionately less than that of number four man. Since the magnetic lines of force are parallel like the opposite sidewalks on a street, the same situation exists if we consider the actual direction in which the conductor is moving at each position.

Returning to Fig. 11.2(a), from positions 3 to 6, the *rate of cutting* across magnetic lines of force becomes progressively less, so the induced emf at each position of the conductor gradually decreases back to zero volts as it passes through point 6, where it is again momentarily moving parallel to the lines of force. From positions 6 to 12, the same sequence of events occurs, with the induced emf rising to a maximum at position 9 and then dropping back to zero at position 12 except that the conductor is cutting across the magnetic lines of force in the opposite direction. This results in the polarity of the induced emf being reversed during the second half of the revolution. The $+$ sign on the graph of Fig. 11.2(b) indicates the reference polarity of the emf. The $-$ sign simply indicates that the polarity of the emf is reversed with respect to the reference polarity. One complete rotation of the loop constitutes one **cycle**. The time taken to complete one cycle is called the **period** of the waveform.

## 3. The Sine Wave

In the preceding section we observed the manner in which the alternating emf induced into a conductor rotating in a uniform magnetic field varies continually as the angular position of the conductor changes. We can show the nature of this continual change best by plotting a graph showing the magnitude and polarity of the induced emf at any position of the loop as shown in Fig. 11.2(b). In order to appreciate fully the manner in which electric circuits behave when the emf applied to the system is of the alternating type, we must be able to determine exactly what the induced emf is at any instant during the rotation of the conductor.

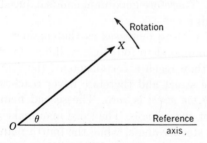

**Fig. 11.3.** Vector representation of the rotating conductor.

For such an analysis, we shall replace the cross-sectional sketch of Fig. 11.2(a) with a much simpler diagram as shown in Fig. 11.3. The straight line $OX$ represents the rotating conductor pivoted at point $O$ (for origin). The end that is free to rotate is indicated by an arrowhead. This symbolic representation of the rotating conductor is termed a **vector**. As we have already noted, mathematical convention requires this vector to rotate in a counterclockwise direction starting from a position representing three o'clock and referred to as the **reference axis.** Instead of showing its position at twelve particular points as in Fig. 11.2(a), the position of the rotating vector at a certain instant in time is located by stating the angle $\theta$ through which it has rotated from the reference axis. Also to keep the sketch as simple as possible, in Fig. 11.3 we have not shown the magnetic lines of force, which are assumed to be uniformly spaced and in a vertical plane as they were in Fig. 11.2(a).

Faraday's law tells us that the emf induced in a rotating conductor is directly proportional to the *rate* at which it cuts across the magnetic lines of force. If we assume a uniform flux density and a constant angular velocity, the rate of cutting will depend only on the angular position of the loop. At 0° (with respect to the reference axis), the loop moves parallel to the magnetic lines of force, hence no emf is induced into the loop at that instant. As the loop swings around toward 90°, the rate of cutting increases, becoming maximum at 90°. In order to determine the exact value of the induced alternating emf at any instant, we must be able to determine the exact rate of cutting of magnetic lines of force by the conductor at that instant with respect to the maximum rate of cutting of lines of force.

In Fig. 11.4, $OX$ represents the rotating conductor after it has traveled through an angular distance $\theta$ from the reference axis. Since $OX$ is pivoted at $O$, the line $XY$ drawn perpendicular to $OX$ represents the direction of motion of the tip of the vector (or conductor) at that particular moment. If the angular velocity of the conductor is constant,

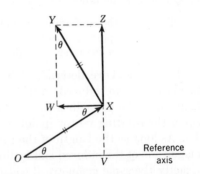

**Fig. 11.4.** Geometric representation of the rate of cutting of magnetic lines of force.

the linear velocity of the tip of the vector must also be constant. This can be represented by drawing $XY = OX =$ a constant for any value of $\theta$. We can resolve the motion represented by $XY$ into a vertical component of motion $XZ$ which is parallel to the lines of force and therefore is ineffective in inducing any emf; and a horizontal component $XW$ which cuts across the lines of force at right angles. The induced emf will be directly proportional to the length of the line $XW$ since this represents the component of the motion of the conductor which is effective in inducing an emf. When $\theta$ become 90°, $XW = XY$. Therefore the ratio $XW/XY$ in Fig. 11.4 represents the ratio between the rate of cutting of magnetic lines of force at angle $\theta$ and the maximum rate of cutting.

From geometry:

Since $\quad\quad\quad WX \;//\; OV, \quad\quad \therefore \quad \angle WXO = \angle XOV = \theta$

Since $\quad \angle YXO = 90°, \quad\quad \therefore \quad \angle WXY = 90° - \theta = \angle OXV$

Since $\quad \angle XWY = 90°, \quad\quad \therefore \quad \angle XYW = \theta$

Since $\quad\quad\quad XY = OX, \quad\quad \therefore \quad \triangle XOV \equiv \triangle XYW$

$$\therefore \quad \frac{XW}{XY} = \frac{XV}{OX}$$

Therefore as the loop rotates, the rate of cutting of magnetic lines of force at any instant is directly proportional to $XV/OX$. If $OX$ remains constant, this ratio depends only on the magnitude of the angle $\theta$. Since $XV$ is the side of a right-angled triangle opposite the angle $\theta$ and $OX$ is the hypotenuse, in trigonometry the ratio $XV/OX$ is called the **sine** of the angle $\theta$. Since the value of the sine of any angle is recorded in table form (see Appendix), we can determine accurately the ratio of $XV/OX$ for any magnitude of the angle $\theta$ from these tables.

Therefore the **emf induced into the rotating conductor** at any point is directly proportional to the *sine* of the angle through which the loop has rotated from the reference axis.

In Fig. 11.4 we determined by geometrical construction the relative magnitude of an induced emf for an angle $\theta$ which is less than 90°. In its final form, the procedure amounted to drawing a perpendicular from the tip of the rotating vector (point $X$) to the horizontal reference axis (point $V$). As long as the length of the rotating vector $OX$ remains constant, the magnitude of the induced emf is directly proportional to the length of $XV$. Exactly the same geometrical construction applies to angular distances of more than 90° from the reference axis. In Fig. 11.5(a), the vector $OX$ has rotated through an angle of 120°. When we draw a perpendicular from

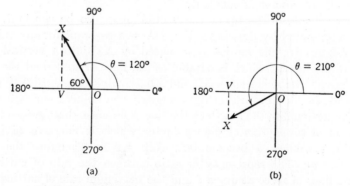

(a)                                  (b)

**Fig. 11.5.** Determining the sine of angles greater than 90°.

point $X$ to the reference axis, we form a right-angled triangle in which the side $XV$ is opposite an angle which is equal to $180° - \theta$ or $60°$.

$$\therefore \quad \sin 120° = \sin (180° - 120°) = \sin 60°$$

Similarly in Fig. 11.5(b), when $\theta = 210°$, the right-angled triangle has an angle opposite $XV$ of $210° - 180° = 30°$. But in this case $XV$ is *below* the reference axis. Relating this diagram to the rotating loop of Fig. 11.2, $XV$ now represents a *negative* value of induced emf, since the loop is moving in the opposite direction across the magnetic lines of force. Therefore whenever $XV$ is below the reference axis, it represents a negative quantity. So we must say then that $\sin 210° = -\sin 30°$.

There are two conclusions we can draw from the geometrical construction of Fig. 11.5: First, it is not necessary for sine tables to state values for angles greater than $90°$; and second, it is not necessary to memorize any rules for the sine of angles greater than $90°$, since a simple geometrical construction as in Fig. 11.5 will show us exactly what angle to look up in the table and will also show us whether it will be a positive or a negative quantity.

Since the emf induced into a conductor rotating at a constant angular velocity in a uniform magnetic field is constantly varying, it

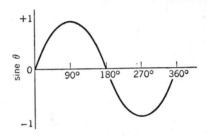

Fig. 11.6. The sine curve

is difficult for us to visualize its nature by a simple statement in words. Hence it is customary to plot a linear graph of the variation in the induced emf over a complete cycle by expressing angular distance $\theta$ as a linear distance along the horizontal axis of the graph and the induced emf for each value of $\theta$ along the vertical axis of the graph as in Fig. 11.6. Since the emf at any point during the rotation of the loop is directly proportional to the *sine* of the angle through which it has rotated from the reference axis, we can plot an accurate graph of the variations in an alternating emf by plotting the readings from a sine table (at approx $5°$ intervals) on a sheet of graph paper and then joining the plots to form a smooth curve. The resulting graph is termed a **sine curve.**

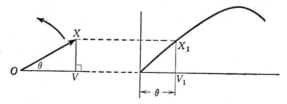

Fig. 11.7. Preparing a sine curve by geometric projection.

Another method of producing a sine curve, without the use of sine tables, is shown in Fig. 11.7. This is a projection of the geometric construction we used in Figs. 11.4 and 11.5. Since the length of the rotating vector $OX$ is constant, the altitude $VX$ of the tip of the rotating vector is proportional to the sine of the angle $\theta$, and therefore $VX$ is directly proportional to the induced emf. By projecting $VX$ to a position $V_1X_1$ on the linear graph at a distance along the horizontal axis representing the angular distance $\theta$, the point $X_1$ will be a proper plot as required to draw a sine curve. If we repeat this geometric projection at 5° intervals, we will have sufficient plots to draw a complete sine curve.

## 4. The Peak Value of a Sine Wave

As we discovered in determining the nature of an alternating emf, the greatest value that the induced emf can attain occurs when $\theta = 90°$. At this point the rate of cutting of magnetic lines of force is maximum. When $\theta = 270°$ the same maximum value is attained but the polarity of the induced emf is reversed. The numerical value that the alternating emf attains at these two angles is termed the **peak** value of the a-c waveform.

The letter symbol for the **peak value of an emf** is $E_m$ ($m$ for maximum).

This peak value is a numerical quantity in volts and does not have any polarity, since the same peak value in volts occurs at both 90° and 270°. The peak value is also independent of time since no matter where the rotating conductor may be at a certain instant, the peak value will appear as it passes the 90° and 270° points in its rotation. Therefore the peak value is a constant for a given generator and does not have the sine wave shape of the emf induced from instant to instant.

In the simple a-c generator, the peak voltage will depend on just what the maximum rate of cutting of magnetic lines of force by the rotating loop happens to be. This in turn depends on (1) the total number of lines of force in the magnetic field, (2) the angular velocity of the loop, and (3) the number of turns of wire in the loop. When a conductor cuts across magnetic lines of force at the *rate* of $10^8$ lines per second or 1 weber per second, an emf of 1 volt is induced in that conductor.

## 5. The Instantaneous Value of a Sine Wave

The graphs of Figs. 11.2, 11.6, and 11.7 show the manner in which the induced emf changes from instant to instant as the loop rotates. As we noted in Chapter 9, any value that is continually changing and therefore is dependent on the exact instant in time for its numerical value is called an instantaneous value. Therefore in representing the instantaneous value of the emf induced in the rotating loop of the simple a-c generator of Fig. 11.1, we must use the lower case letter symbol $e$.

In the simple a-c generator of Fig. 11.1, during the first 180° of rotation of the loop the emf rose to a peak value in one direction and dropped back to zero; then during the second 180° of rotation it rose to a similar peak value but in the opposite direction and again dropped back to zero. Therefore it took one complete revolution for the emf to vary through the whole possible range of values. As the loop rotates past 360° the same series of events recurs. We define this complete excursion of the instantaneous value of the induced emf as one **cycle** of a **sine wave**. The time it takes for the instantaneous value to complete one cycle is called the **period** of the sine wave. The number of cycles completed in one second is called the **frequency** of the sine wave. Therefore frequency is expressed in **cycles per second.**\*

The letter symbol for **frequency** is $f$ (lower case).

Although the instantaneous emf is never constant, its exact magnitude at any instant is directly proportional to sin $\theta$. Since the instantaneous emf reaches its peak value at 90° and since sin 90° = 1, the instantaneous emf for any particular instant in time as the loop rotates can be determined from

$$e = E_m \sin \theta \qquad (11.1)$$

In order to use equation (11.1) one complete cycle must equal 360°. In the simple **two-pole** generator of Fig. 11.1, it required one complete mechanical revolution of the loop in order to generate one complete cycle of an electrical sine wave of emf. But in practical generators like the four-pole generator of Fig. 11.8, one complete cycle of emf will be generated as the loop moves through the magnetic flux under a N pole and then through the flux under a S pole. In order to use Equation (11.1), this cycle must be subdivided into 360 *electrical* degrees but the loop has only rotated through 180 *mechanical* degrees. The relationship between *electrical* degrees and *mechanical* degrees will depend on the number of *pairs* of magnetic poles in the piece of rotating machinery. Sine waves of emf can also be generated in **oscillator** circuits where there is no mechanical rotation. Again in order to solve sin $\theta$, a complete cycle must be subdivided into 360 *electrical* degrees.

EXAMPLE 1: At what speed must the shaft of a 6-pole, 60 c alternator be turned?

*Solution:* With 3 pairs of poles, 1 mechanical revolution generates 3 electrical cycles. Therefore the shaft speed is

$$\frac{60}{3} = 20 \text{ rev/sec} = 1200 \text{ rpm}$$

* To be strictly correct, frequency should be expressed in cycles *per second* (or kilocycles *per second* and megacycles *per second*). But the popular (lazy) trend is to neglect to state *per second* when speaking of a frequency of 60 cycles or 800 kilocycles, etc. It would be worth our while to develop the habit of automatically reading in the *per second* when referring to frequency, whether it actually appears in print or not.

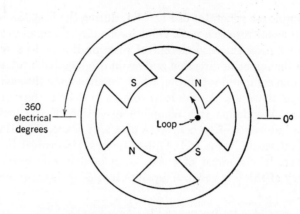

**Fig. 11.8.** Relationship between electrical and mechanical degrees in a four-pole generator.

Our next problem is how to determine the angle $\theta$ in electrical degrees. We are usually given the frequency of the sine wave. Since frequency is expressed in cycles *per second*, if we multiply frequency by the time elapsed since the instantaneous value passed through zero, we will have the angular position expressed in cycles and fractions of complete cycles. Multiplying this product by 360 will then give us an angle representing the instantaneous position of the induced emf in its cycle in electrical degrees. Therefore we can express Equation (11.1) in a more useful form as

$$e = E_m \sin (360 \, ft)° \tag{11.2}$$

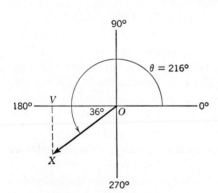

**Fig. 11.9.** Determining sin 216°.

where $e$ is the instantaneous emf at a given instant in time, $E_m$ is the peak value of the sine wave in question, sin is the sine of the angle expressed in electrical degrees, $f$ is the frequency of the sine wave in cycles per second and $t$ is the elapsed time in seconds.

EXAMPLE 2: What is the instantaneous emf of a 60 cycle sine wave whose peak voltage is 150 v, 10 msec after the instantaneous emf passes through zero volts?

*Solution:*

$$e = E_m \sin (360 \, ft)° = 150 \sin (360 \times 60 \times 0.01) = 150 \sin 216°$$

Since the sine table does not include 216°, we must construct a vector diagram as we did in Fig. 11.5 to help us determine the angle to look up in the sine table. From Fig. 11.9, sin 216° = −sin 36° and

$$e = 150 \times (-\sin 36°) = 150 \times (-0.588)$$
$$\therefore \quad e = -88.2 \text{ v}$$

EXAMPLE 3: A radio transmitter generates a sine wave carrier with a frequency of 600 kc. If the peak voltage fed to the antenna is 1 kv, what is the instantaneous voltage 2.0 μsec after the instantaneous value passes through zero volts?

*Solution:*

$$e = E_m \sin (360 \, ft)° = 1000 \sin (360 \times 600{,}000 \times 0.000{,}002)°$$
$$= 1000 \sin 432°$$

But $432° = 360° + 72°$. After any whole number of complete cycles. the sine wave starts through exactly the same cycle as the first cycle.

$$\therefore \quad \sin 432° = \sin 72°$$
$$e = 1000 \sin 72° = 1000 \times 0.951 = 951 \text{ v}$$

EXAMPLE 4: The instantaneous emf from a 400 c aircraft generator is 95 **v** when $t = 1$ msec. What is the instantaneous voltage when $t = 2$ msec?

*Solution:* Since $e = E_m \sin (360 \, ft)°$,

$$\therefore \quad E_m = \frac{e}{\sin (360 \, ft)°}$$

$$\therefore \quad E_m = \frac{95}{\sin (360 \times 400 \times 0.001)°} = \frac{95}{\sin 144°}$$

Referring to Fig. 11.10(a), $\sin 144° = \sin 36°$.

$$\therefore \quad E_m = \frac{95}{\sin 36°} = \frac{95}{0.588} = 161.5 \text{ v}$$

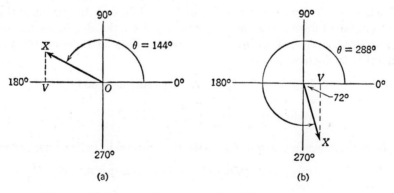

Fig. 11.10. Determining sin 144° and sin 288°.

The new value of instantaneous emf is

$$e = E_m \sin (360 \, ft)° = 161.5 \sin (360 \times 400 \times 0.002)° = 161.5 \sin 288°$$

From Fig. 11.10(b), $\sin 288° = -\sin 72°$.

$$\therefore \quad e = 161.5 \times (-\sin 72°) = 161.5 \times (-0.951) = -153.6 \text{ v}$$

*Note:* Although sine tables are included in the Appendix, the student is advised to practice using the sine scale on his slide rule.

## 6. The Radian

In dealing with the rotating conductor of Fig. 11.1, we have been talking about angular *distance* and angular *velocity*. Although the Babylonian 360° system of angular measurement is very convenient for purposes of geometry and trigonometry, it is not suited to showing the relationship between the linear velocity of the conductor in Fig. 11.1 as it moves around the circumference of a circle and its angular velocity. The linear velocity of the conductor governs the actual rate of cutting across magnetic lines of force. Therefore for electrical purposes it would be very useful to have a unit of angular distance which is related to the distance traveled by the free end of a rotating vector. The **radian** is just such a unit. By definition,

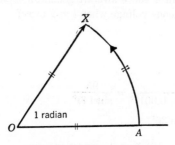

**Fig. 11.11.** The radian.

**one radian is the angular distance through which the rotating vector travels when its free end ($X$ in Fig. 11.11) travels through a linear distance equal to the length of the vector ($OX$).** Since the rotating vector is the radius of a circle, and the circumference of a circle $= 2\pi r$, there are $2\pi$ radians in one complete cycle. The significance of radian measure will become apparent when we deal with a-c circuits in later chapters. In the meantime, since our sine tables and slide rules are based on the degree as the unit of angular distance, if we are given angular data in radians, we must convert it to degrees. Since

$$1 \text{ cycle} = 360°, \qquad \therefore \quad 2\pi \text{ radians} = 360°$$

$$1 \text{ radian} = \frac{360}{2\pi} = \frac{360}{2 \times 3.14} = 57.3°$$

In radian measure, angular velocity is measured in **radians per second.**

The letter symbol for **angular velocity** in radians per second is the Greek letter $\omega$ (omega).

Therefore, expressed in radian measure, Equation (11.2) becomes

$$e = E_m \sin \omega t \tag{11.3}$$

Since there are $2\pi$ radians in a cycle,

$$\omega = 2\pi f \tag{11.4}$$

Therefore Equation (11.3) may be written

$$e = E_m \sin 2\pi f t \qquad\qquad (11.5)$$

*In both Equation (11.3) and Equation (11.5), the angle is numerically expressed in radians.*

Although Equation (11.3) using radian measure is considered to be the general form for the instantaneous emf, at the present stage of our study of electric circuits, we have no occasion to apply it. Except for problems similar to Example 5, Equation (11.2) is a more suitable form for use in solving the following problems.

EXAMPLE 5: Write the general equation for the instantaneous emf of a 60 c generator whose peak voltage is 170 v.

*Solution:*

$$e = E_m \sin 2\pi f t$$

But $\qquad\qquad 2\pi f = 2 \times 3.14 \times 60 = 377$ radians/sec

$$\therefore \quad e = 170 \sin 377t$$

*Since 60 c is the standard power line frequency, it is worth memorizing:*

$$60 \text{ c} \doteq 377 \text{ radians/sec}$$

## 7. Instantaneous Current in a Resistance

Now that we are acquainted with the sinusoidal nature of the instantaneous emf of a basic a-c generator, we can determine the nature of the current that will flow when a resistance is connected to the generator terminals in the simple a-c circuit of Fig. 11.12. Just as in d-c circuits, in order to satisfy Kirchhoff's voltage law, the voltage drop across the resistance at every instant in time must be exactly equal to the instantaneous emf appearing at the generator terminals. We have also noted that the only way a voltage drop can be developed across a resistance is for current to flow through it so that $V = IR$.

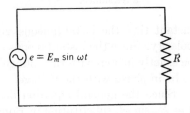

$e = E_m \sin \omega t$

**Fig. 11.12.** A simple alternating current circuit.

If we consider one particular instant in time, there is no difference between the simple a-c circuit of Fig. 11.12 and the equivalent d-c circuit. The difference between them is that at the *next* instant in time the magnitude of the instantaneous alternating emf will have changed, but the emf in the d-c circuit will continue on at a fixed magnitude. Therefore if we consider any particular *instant* in time, all the formulas summarized at the end of Chapter 4 will apply to the a-c circuit of Fig. 11.12.

Therefore we can state that the instantaneous current through the resistance in Fig. 11.12 will be

$$i = \frac{e}{R} \tag{11.6}$$

where $i$ is the instantaneous current through the resistance, $e$ is the instantaneous emf applied to the resistance, and $R$ is the resistance of the circuit.

Since resistance is determined by such physical factors as type of material, length, and cross section, it is a constant for a given circuit at a given temperature [indicated by an upper case $R$ in Equation (11.6)]. Therefore since $R$ is a constant in Equation (11.6), whatever the variation in instantaneous voltage, the instantaneous current must stay right in step in order to make Ohm's law hold true. If the instantaneous emf is a sine wave, the instantaneous current must also be a sine wave, as shown in Fig. 11.13. The instantaneous current must reach its peak value at the same instant that the instantaneous emf becomes maximum. It will become zero at the same instant that the instantaneous emf becomes zero and it will reverse its direction of flow at the same instant that the instantaneous voltage across the resistance reverses its polarity. Since the instantaneous current through a resistance must always be exactly in step with the voltage across the resistance, the current is said to be **in phase** with the voltage.

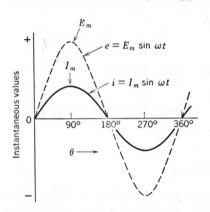

**Fig. 11.13.** Instantaneous current through a resistance.

Since the general equation describing a sine wave alternating emf is $e = E_m \sin \omega t$, substituting in Equation (11.6) gives

$$i = \frac{E_m}{R} \sin \omega t$$

And since the peak value of the instantaneous current depends on the peak value of the applied emf,

$$I_m = \frac{E_m}{R}$$

$$\therefore \quad i = I_m \sin \omega t \tag{11.7}$$

where $i$ is the instantaneous current through a resistance when a sine wave of emf is applied, and $I_m$ is the peak current as determined by the relationship $I_m = E_m/R$.

## 8. Instantaneous Power in a Resistance

If we again think in terms of instantaneous values, we may apply Equations (4.2), (4.3), and (4.4) from Chapter 4 to an a-c circuit. Therefore

$$p = ei = i^2R = \frac{e^2}{R} \tag{11.8}$$

where $p$ is the instantaneous power in a resistance, $e$ is the instantaneous emf applied to the resistance, $i$ is the instantaneous current through the resistance, and $R$ is the resistance of the circuit.

Since $R$ is a constant for a given circuit, and since the instantaneous voltage and current in the basic a-c circuit are *both* sine waves, the instantaneous power must be a sine *squared* wave. To determine the nature of a sine squared wave, we can plot a graph of instantaneous power in the same manner that we plotted the sine curve of Fig. 11.6. If we take values from a sine table at 5° intervals and plot the *squares* of these values on a linear graph, the instantaneous power curve takes on the shape shown in Fig. 11.14. Note that the instantaneous power in a resistance is always positive since squaring a negative quantity results in a positive quantity. In an electric system, *positive* power can be interpreted as electric energy being converted into some other form of energy (heat in the case of a resistor). On this basis, *nega-tive* power would consist of some other form of energy being converted into electric energy. A resistor is not capable of doing this; therefore the waveform of instantaneous power in a resistance has no negative component.

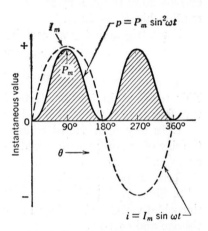

**Fig. 11.14.** Instantaneous power in a resistance.

As Fig. 11.14 indicates, the instantaneous power in the basic a-c system is pulsating in nature, swinging from zero to maximum and back *twice* each cycle. If we consider an electric lamp as the resistance in Fig. 11.12, as far as heating the filament is concerned, it does not matter which way the current flows through it. There will be one pulse of energy converted into heat and light on the one *half* cycle of current and another similar pulse on the second half cycle. Therefore if the lamp is operated from a 60 c source, it will increase in brilliance 120 times a second. Therefore the instantaneous power pulsations are at *twice* the frequency of the voltage and current. This pulsating characteristic of instantaneous power is responsible for the flicker in 25 c lighting as used in some localities and vibration of small a-c motors.

We can also show the pulsating nature of the power in an a-c system by deriving an equation for instantaneous power.

By substituting $i = I_m \sin \omega t$ in Equation (11.8),

$$p = (I_m \sin \omega t)^2 \times R = I_m{}^2 R \times \sin^2 \omega t$$

And since peak values are maximum instantaneous values, from Equation (11.8)

$$P_m = I_m{}^2 R$$

$$\therefore \quad p = P_m \sin^2 \omega t \tag{11.9}$$

where $p$ is the instantaneous power in a resistance when a sine wave of current flows through it, and $P_m$ is the peak power as determined by the relationship $P_m = I_m{}^2 R$.

From trigonometry we can show that

$$\sin^2 \omega t = \tfrac{1}{2}(1 - \cos 2\omega t)^*$$

$$\therefore \quad p = \tfrac{1}{2}P_m - \tfrac{1}{2}P_m \cos 2\omega t \tag{11.10}$$

This relationship tells us three things about the instantaneous power waveform which we can check by referring to Fig. 11.14.

1. In any right-angled triangle, the cosine of one acute angle is also the sine of the other acute angle. Therefore the general shape of the cosine curve and the sine curve are the same. Therefore the fluctuations in instantaneous power are sinusoidal in nature.

2. Since $2\omega$ is twice the angular velocity of $\omega$, the frequency of the sinusoidal variation is twice as great as the frequency of the instantaneous voltage and current.

3. Since the limits of the value of a cosine are $+1$ when $\theta = 0°$ and $-1$ when $\theta = 180°$, the value of the expression $\tfrac{1}{2}(1 - \cos 2\,\omega t)$ can vary between zero and $+1$. Therefore the instantaneous power waveform for a resistance is always positive.

## 9. The Effective Value of a Sine Wave

As far as electric circuit theory is concerned, instantaneous values merely serve to call our attention to the manner in which voltage, current, and power are continually varying in a sinusoidal manner. Instantaneous

---

$$\cos (A - B) = \cos A \cos B + \sin A \sin B$$
$$\cos (A + B) = \cos A \cos B - \sin A \sin B$$

If $A = B$, then $\cos 0° = \cos^2 A + \sin^2 A$ and $\cos 2A = \cos^2 A - \sin^2 A$. Since $\cos 0° = 1$, subtracting gives $1 - \cos 2A = 2 \sin^2 A$, from which $\sin^2 A = \tfrac{1}{2}(1 - \cos 2A)$.

values are not satisfactory for measurement purposes, since the pointers of meters cannot follow the rapid changes in direction. Instantaneous values are not suitable for calculation purposes, since by the time we complete the computation, the instant to which the calculation applied has long since passed.

This problem does not arise in d-c circuits since the voltage, current, and power in a resistive circuit remain constant for a considerable period of time. As far as the end result of converting electric energy into light is concerned, it makes no difference whether the lamp is lighted by a direct current or an alternating current flowing through it. Perhaps then we can establish effective *steady state* values for alternating current and emf to which meters can be calibrated and which allow us to use the same inter-relationships among voltage, current, resistance, power, work, etc. that are used in d-c circuits. The **effective** value of an alternating current can be determined experimentally by finding out what direct current must flow through a given resistance to produce the same amount of heat energy in a certain time interval as when the resistance in connected to a source of alternating emf. From this experiment, the **effective** value of an alternating current is sometimes referred to as the **equivalent d-c** value.

In order to determine the effective value of a sine wave, we can conduct the same experiment algebraically with pencil and paper. The basis of comparison in the experiment is *the same amount of heat energy in a certain time interval*. This can be translated to *average work per unit time* or simply **average power.** From Fig. 11.14, we note that the instantaneous power is swinging alternately and uniformly between zero and peak power. It appears quite reasonable to state therefore that *the average power in a resistance through which a sine wave current is flowing is one half the peak power.*

We can also determine this relationship from the general Equation (11.9) for instantaneous power: $p = P_m \sin^2 \omega t$. As we have already shown, $\sin^2 \omega t = \frac{1}{2}(1 - \cos 2\omega t)$. If we average a sine or cosine function over a *complete* cycle, the average must be zero, since for every positive value during the first half cycle, there is an equivalent negative value during the second half cycle. This is quite apparent when we consider the simple a-c generator of Fig. 11.1. Therefore, when averaged over a complete cycle, $\cos 2\omega t$ becomes zero and Equation (11.9) becomes

$$\text{average power} = \tfrac{1}{2} \text{ peak power}$$

Since the effective values of a sine wave are to represent d-c equivalent values, the same letter symbols can be used for both, i.e., upper case letters without subscripts. Therefore when a sine wave of current flows through a resistance,

$$P = \tfrac{1}{2}P_m \qquad\qquad (11.11)$$

In a d-c circuit, $P = I^2R$. Since **effective** a-c values are d-c equivalent values, in an a-c circuit the **average** power must equal the square of the **effective** current times the resistance through which the current flows. Therefore in an a-c circuit,

$$P = I^2R \quad \text{and} \quad P_m = I_m{}^2R$$

But
$$P = \tfrac{1}{2}P_m = \tfrac{1}{2}I_m{}^2R$$

$$\therefore \quad I^2R = \tfrac{1}{2}I_m{}^2R, \quad \text{from which} \quad I^2 = \tfrac{1}{2}I_m{}^2$$

and
$$I = I_m/\sqrt{2} = 0.707\,I_m \tag{11.12}$$

Therefore **the effective value of a sine wave of current is $1/\sqrt{2}$ or 0.707 of the peak value.***

The effective value of the sine wave voltage should be such that the average power is the product of the effective voltage across and effective current through a pure resistance, just as in the equivalent d-c circuit.

$$\therefore \quad P = EI$$

But when a sine wave current flows through a resistor,

$$P = \tfrac{1}{2}P_m$$

Since peak instantaneous power occurs at the instant when both the instantaneous voltage across and instantaneous current through a pure resistance simultaneously reach their peak values,

$$P_m = E_mI_m$$

And, as we have already determined,

$$I = I_m/\sqrt{2}$$

Making these substitutions gives us

$$\frac{E_mI_m}{2} = \frac{EI_m}{\sqrt{2}}$$

from which
$$E = E_m/\sqrt{2} = 0.707E_m \tag{11.13}$$

Note also that
$$E_m = \sqrt{2}E = 1.414E$$

Since effective values are used for the majority of a-c circuit measurements and computations, we will assume that *all voltages and currents are stated as effective values unless it is specifically stated otherwise.*

EXAMPLE 6: What is the peak voltage of the customary 120 v, 60 c electric service?

---

*Since we determined the effective value of a sine wave of current by taking the square *root* of the average or *mean* value of the instantaneous power, which in turn was plotted (Fig. 11.14) by taking the *squares* of the instantaneous values of current over a complete cycle, the **effective** value of a sine wave of current (or voltage) is often referred to as the rms (*root-mean-square*) value.

*Solution:*

$$E_m = 1.414E = 1.414 \times 120 = 170 \text{ v}$$

## 10. Average Voltage and Current

In deriving the effective values of alternating voltage and current, we started by determining the average power over a *complete* cycle. This was possible since the instantaneous power in a resistance is always positive. But if we attempt to average either voltage or current over a complete cycle, we get a numerical value of *zero*, since for every positive value of voltage or current during the one half cycle, there is a similar negative value during the next half cycle. But if we average *one-half cycle only*, we will obtain a numerical constant. One method of determining the average value of a *half* cycle of a sine wave is to prepare a column of figures by writing down the sine of 5°, 10°, 15°, and so on to 180°. To find the average value of any column of numbers (e.g., examination marks) we add the column of figures and divide by the number of figures in the column. From the column of figures prepared as above from the sine table, we find that the average value of sin $\omega t$ over a period of one half cycle is $22.93 \div 36 = 0.637$. If we had averaged the half cycle of a sine wave by integration, we would have arrived at the same result, expressing it in the form $2/\pi$.

Since          $i = I_m \sin \omega t,$      $\therefore$   $I_{av} = I_m \times 0.637$

$$\therefore \quad I_{av} = 0.637 I_m = 2I_m/\pi \tag{11.14}$$

and                 $E_{av} = 0.637 E_m = 2E_m/\pi \tag{11.15}$

Since this value is obtained by averaging only *half* a cycle, it is useful only in those applications where we have to deal with a half cycle rather than a full cycle. One such case is in determining the average emf induced in a rotating loop as it passes one way through the magnetic field under a pole face in a generator. Another example is in the use of rectifiers to allow current to flow during one-half cycle but not in the reverse direction during the next half cycle. However, in the electric circuits discussed in this text, we are usually dealing with *complete* cycles of voltage and current and therefore have little occasion to use their average values.

## Problems

1. If the peak emf of a 60 c a-c generator is 150 v, what is the instantaneous emf after the loop has rotated through 135°?

2. If the peak voltage of a 1 kc audio oscillator is 20 v, what is the instantaneous emf when $\theta = 210°$?

3. What is the instantaneous emf after the loop of the generator in Problem 1 has rotated through 1 radian?

4. What is the instantaneous emf from the audio oscillator of Problem 2 when $\theta = 5^r$?

5. What is the instantaneous emf after the loop of the generator in Problem 1 has rotated for 15 msec?

6. What is the instantaneous emf from the audio oscillator of Problem 2 when $t = 600\ \mu\text{sec}$?

7. The instantaneous emf of an 800 c sine wave is 5 v when $t = \frac{1}{2}$ msec. What is the peak voltage?

8. If the instantaneous emf from a 50 c source is $-263$ v when $t = 0.013$ sec, what is the instantaneous emf when $t = 0.017$ sec?

9. Write the general voltage equation for a 400 c generator whose peak emf is 200 v.

10. A certain alternating voltage is described by the equation

$$e = 120 \sin 1570t$$

(a) What is the frequency of the sine wave?

(b) What is the instantaneous emf when $t = 5$ msec?

11. What is the peak voltage in the European 230 v, 50 c system?

12. What is the peak value of a 60 $\mu$v radio frequency signal appearing at the input terminals of a receiver?

13. The equation of an alternating emf is $e = 100 \sin 377t$. What effective current will flow through a 15 ohm resistor connected to this source?

14. Write the equation for the instantaneous emf of a 117 v, 400 c alternator.

15. The average power of an 80 ohm soldering iron is 160 w. What is the peak voltage across the iron?

16. What current will an a-c ammeter show when connected in series with a 16 ohm load whose peak power is 288 w?

17. How long will it take a 10 ohm heater connected to a 120 v, 60 c source to convert 1 kwhr of electric energy into heat?

18. What is the wattage rating of a lamp whose hot resistance is 150 ohms when connected to a 117 v, 25 c source?

19. The conductor in the simple generator of Fig. 11.1 cuts across a total of 4 million magnetic lines of force during the first 180° of rotation. If the frequency of the a-c output is 60 c, what is the average induced emf?

20. What is the effective value of the alternating emf induced into the loop in Problem 19?

## Review Questions

1. What conditions govern the generation of an emf by electromagnetic induction?

2. Why does the angular velocity of the rotating loop in Fig. 11.1 tend to decrease when a load resistor is connected to the brushes?

3. Why is it not possible to maintain a constant polarity of induced emf in the loop in Fig. 11.1?

4. Why do we describe the instantaneous emf waveform from the simple generator of Fig. 11.1 as a **sine wave?**

5. Show that sin 135° = sin 45°.

6. What effect has the angular velocity of the loop in Fig. 11.1 on (a) the frequency of the emf waveform? (b) the peak value of the induced emf?

7. Why does doubling the number of turns in the loop double the peak voltage?

8. Why is the peak value of the induced emf never a negative quantity?

9. Why is the answer to Example 2 a negative quantity?

10. What is the significance of a negative value of instantaneous current?

11. What is the significance of a negative value of instantaneous power?

12. What is meant by angular *distance?*

13. What is the significance of radian measure?

14. Why can we use instantaneous a-c values in the various equations we derived for use in d-c resistive circuits?

15. Why must the instantaneous current through a resistance have the same waveform as the instantaneous voltage drop across the resistor?

16. What is meant by the statement that the current through a resistor is in phase with the voltage across it?

17. What is the significance of the sine wave in studying electric circuit theory?

18. What is the significance of peak values of a-c quantities as far as a-c circuit theory is concerned?

19. What is the significance of instantaneous values of a-c quantities as far as a-c circuit theory is concerned?

20. Why is the instantaneous power fed to a resistance never negative?

21. Why does the instantaneous power into a resistance have a sine wave shape at twice the frequency of the applied emf?

22. Why is the average power input to a resistor operating from a sine wave source of emf one-half the peak power input?

23. Why is it necessary to consider average *power* when deriving an effective value for alternating current and voltage sine waves?

24. The equation for instantaneous emf in an a-c system is sometimes written in the form $e = \sqrt{2}\, E \sin \omega t$. Suggest a reason for using this form.

25. We obtain the average value of the alternating power input to a resistive load by averaging the instantaneous power input over a complete cycle. Why can we not determine the average value of an alternating current in the same manner?

# Chapter 12

# REACTANCE

~~~~~~~~~~~~~~~~~~~~~~~~~~~~~~~~~~~~~~~~~~~~~~~~~~~~~~~~~~~~~~~~~

As we discovered in Chapter 11, when we apply a sine wave of emf to a resistance, the instantaneous current in the circuit must be an a-c sine wave exactly in phase with the applied emf. We established this relationship on the basis that current is the dependent variable in the circuit and that even in an alternating current circuit it must automatically take on a magnitude such that Ohm's law will hold true. As long as we keep in mind the continuously varying nature of a sine wave alternating emf, all the laws and theorems we have studied in dealing with d-c circuits must also hold true for a-c circuits. Any statement that would apply only for a special case and not for the general situation would not pass as a basic law of electric circuit theory.

Therefore we were able to state Ohm's law in the form

$$i = \frac{e}{R} \tag{11.6}$$

where both $e$ and $i$ are instantaneous values. Although resistance is an electrical property of conductors, it is dependent on such physical factors as length, cross section, and type of material. Therefore resistance cannot change in the short period of one cycle of a sine wave; and therefore as far as Equation (11.6) is concerned, resistance is a constant. Therefore the instantaneous current must always be directly proportional to the instantaneous voltage.

Since the instantaneous current in a resistance reaches its peak value at the same instant as the instantaneous voltage across the resistance, we are also able to state Ohm's law in the form $I_m = E_m/R$, and since the effective value of a sine wave is the d-c equivalent value which we will use for most of our a-c circuit calculations, the most useful form of Ohm's law is simply $I = E/R$, where $I$ is the effective (rms) value of the sine wave current through a resistor, and $E$ is the effective (rms) value of the sine wave voltage across the resistor.

## 1. Nature of the Instantaneous Current in an Inductance

In setting out to determine the nature of the instantaneous current that must flow in the circuit of Fig. 12.1, we will assume that the resistance is so small that we can neglect it. In Chapter 9 we decided that we would think of the inductor as a load connected across a source of emf. Therefore, in order to satisfy Kirchhoff's voltage law, at every instant in time the inductive voltage drop across the coil in Fig. 12.1 must exactly equal the applied emf.

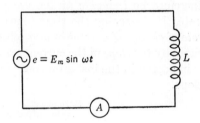

$$\therefore \quad v_L = e = E_m \sin \omega t$$

If there is no resistance in the circuit, any voltage drop that appears across the terminals of an inductor must be due to the counter emf induced in the coil by a *changing*

**Fig. 12.1.** Inductance in an alternating current circuit.

current through it. Note that the inductive voltage drop *across* an inductor depends on the counter emf induced *in* the coil which in turn depends on the *rate of change* of current *through* the coil. However, in determining the behavior of inductance in a-c circuits, we can avoid much mathematical confusion if we skip the in between reference to cemf and think in terms of, "How must the instantaneous current through an inductor adjust itself in order to have a voltage drop across the inductance which, at every instant in time, is exactly equal to the applied emf?" *

From Equation (9.1) which established the unit of inductance, we can express the instantaneous voltage that must appear across the inductor in Fig. 12.1 as

$$v_L = L \frac{di}{dt}$$

$$\therefore \quad L \frac{di}{dt} = E_m \sin \omega t$$

from which

$$\frac{di}{dt} = \frac{E_m}{L} \sin \omega t \tag{12.1}$$

By integrating Equation (12.1), we can establish a mathematical expression for the instantaneous current through a pure inductance in an a-c circuit in one fell swoop. However, in order to develop an *understanding* of the behavior of inductance in a-c circuits, we can determine the nature

* Refer to page 182 for a discussion on the strict mathematical relationship between the counter emf *in* and the inductive voltage drop *across* an inductor.

of the instantaneous current through the inductor in Fig. 12.1 by applying principles we have already learned. Since Kirchhoff's voltage law requires the voltage across the inductor in Fig. 12.1 to be exactly equal to the applied emf at every instant in time, we can represent the instantaneous voltage $v_L$ across the inductance by the dashed sine curve of Fig. 12.2. According to Faraday's law of electromagnetic induction, the magnitude of this inductive voltage at any instant is directly proportional to the *rate of change* of current through the coil at that instant. At the instant when we require maximum *positive* voltage across the inductor, the current must therefore be *changing* at the greatest *rate* in a *positive* direction. As we noted in discussing the rise of current through an inductor in Chapter 9, *rate of change of current* in a graph of current plotted against time is indicated by the *slope* of the current graph. Therefore maximum rate of change is indicated in the instantaneous current graph of Fig. 12.2 by the steepest slope.

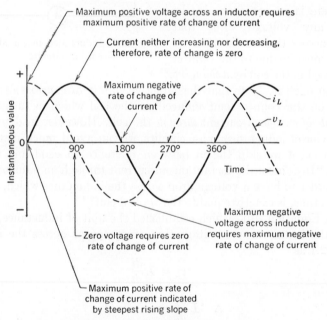

**Fig. 12.2.** Instantaneous current in an inductance.

One-quarter cycle later in time when the instantaneous voltage across the inductor must momentarily drop to zero, the current must stop changing. It does not matter how great the current may be, as long as it is neither rising nor falling, there will be no change in the number of magnetic lines of force linking the turns of the coil in order to induce an emf in them. Therefore at the 90° point on the graph of Fig. 12.2, the *slope* of the instantaneous current curve must become horizontal. Between 0° and 90°

the voltage across the inductor had to decrease along a sine curve, and therefore the *rate of change* of current had to decrease in the same manner.

One-quarter cycle still later in time, the instantaneous inductive voltage must become maximum negative, and therefore the instantaneous current must again change at a maximum rate but this time in the opposite direction. If we draw an instantaneous current graph that fulfills the conditions of having a maximum positive rate of change when the instantaneous voltage across the inductor is maximum positive, neither rising nor falling when the inductive voltage is zero, having a maximum negative rate of change when the voltage across the inductor is maximum negative, etc., we will find that the instantaneous current through the inductor in Fig. 12.1 must have the *sine wave* shape shown by the solid curve in Fig. 12.2. But the instantaneous current sine wave reaches its positive peak 90° later in time than the instantaneous voltage drop across the inductor and it passes through zero going in a negative direction 90° later in time than the inductive voltage drop.

> Therefore **for a sine wave voltage drop to appear across an inductance,** the current through it must be a sine wave which lags the inductive voltage drop (and also the applied emf) by 90°.

## 2. Inductive Reactance

When we connected a pure inductance across a d-c source of emf in Chapter 9, it was necessary for the current to keep rising at a constant rate in order to maintain a constant voltage across the inductor. But when we connect an inductance across a sine wave source of emf, the instantaneous current must take on a sine wave form lagging the applied emf sine wave by 90° in order to produce a sine wave voltage drop across the inductance. If the current in the inductance is a sine wave, it must have some definite effective value and we would discover a constant reading on the a-c ammeter in Fig. 12.1. Therefore, for a given source of alternating emf and a given inductance, the ratio $E/I$ is constant.

In discussing Ohm's law of constant proportionality, we decided that a constant $E/I$ ratio represented the opposition of the circuit to the flow of current and we called this opposition the **resistance** of the circuit. We can therefore say that the constant $E/I_L$ ratio in Fig. 12.1 represents the opposition of the inductance to the flow of *alternating* current. However, we cannot call this opposition resistance, since the alternating current in a resistance is in phase with the voltage across it whereas the current in an inductance lags the voltage across it by 90°. Furthermore, an inductor does not convert electric energy into heat as does a resistor. Therefore we must use a different term which suggests *opposition* to the flow of alternating current.

Therefore **inductive reactance** is the opposition created by an inductance to the flow of alternating current.

The letter symbol for **inductive reactance** is $X_L$, and

$$X_L = \frac{E_L}{I_L} \tag{12.2}$$

Since inductive reactance is an $E/I$ ratio just as is resistance, we can use the **ohm** as the unit of inductive reactance.

Therefore **an a-c circuit has an inductive reactance** of one ohm when an alternating current having an effective value of one ampere flowing through the inductance creates an inductive voltage drop with an effective value of one volt across the inductance.

## 3. Factors Governing Inductive Reactance

Assuming that the shape of the applied emf in the circuit of Fig. 12.1 is to remain sinusoidal, there are only three factors which we can vary independently: the peak voltage or **amplitude** of the sine wave of applied emf (hence also its effective value), the frequency of the emf, and the inductance. Let us consider the effect of each independent variable in turn on the current of the circuit.

If we double the peak value of the applied emf leaving the frequency constant, the maximum rate of change of current must be doubled in order to develop the required inductive voltage drop. Since the frequency is unchanged, the current will reach its maximum value in the same length of time, yet at each instant in time its slope is twice as steep as its original values. Therefore the peak value of the current must also be twice as great as originally. Consequently doubling the amplitude of the applied emf also doubles the current. As we would expect, since $X_L = E/I_L$, there is no change in inductive reactance.

Therefore the **magnitude of the applied alternating emf** has no effect on the inductive reactance of an a-c circuit.

If we double the frequency leaving the peak value of the emf the same, the instantaneous current in the inductance must have the *same* maximum rate of change. But since the frequency is doubled, the instantaneous current must cease rising in half the original time. Therefore, since the current rises with the same maximum slope for half as long, the amplitude of the current sine wave is now only half as great as originally, even though the amplitude of the voltage waveform is unchanged. Therefore, since $X_L = E_L/I_L$, the inductive reactance has been doubled.

Therefore **inductive reactance** is directly proportional to frequency.

If we double the inductance leaving the source of emf unchanged, according to Equation (9.1) the maximum rate of change of current will have to be cut in half to develop the same voltage. Therefore the amplitude of the current is again only half as great for the same amplitude of voltage.

Therefore **inductive reactance** is directly proportional to the inductance.

We can avoid calculus in solving Equation (12.1) by substituting the *average* rate of change of current for $(di/dt)$ and the *average* value for $\sin \omega t$. This is the technique we used in determining the energy stored by inductors in Chapter 9. Since the current must rise from zero to $I_m$ in one-quarter cycle, and since the **period** of one cycle is $1/f$ seconds,

$$\text{average} \left( \frac{di}{dt} \right) = \frac{I_m}{\frac{1}{4} \times (1/f)} = 4fI_m$$

Therefore Equation (12.1) becomes

$$4fI_m = \frac{E_m \times 2/\pi}{L}$$

from which

$$\frac{E_m}{I_m} = 2\pi fL$$

$$\therefore \quad X_L = 2\pi fL \tag{12.3}$$

where $X_L$ is inductive reactance in ohms, $f$ is frequency in cycles per second, and $L$ is inductance in henrys.

Since

$$\omega = 2\pi f \tag{11.4}$$

$$X_L = \omega L \tag{12.4}$$

where $\omega$ is angular velocity in radians per second.

## 4. Nature of the Instantaneous Current in a Capacitance

We can follow a similar procedure in order to determine the behavior of capacitance in a-c circuits. If we connect a capacitor across a sine wave source of emf as in Fig. 12.3, Kirchhoff's voltage law requires the PD across the capacitor at every instant in time to be exactly the same as the applied emf at that instant. But the only way that a PD across a capacitor can change is for the capacitor to charge or discharge. Therefore the capacitor in Fig. 12.3 must charge and discharge in such a manner that the PD across it is a sine wave equal to the applied emf at every instant in time.

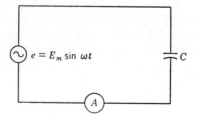

**Fig. 12.3.** Capacitance in an alternating current circuit.

Since $$q = Cv \qquad (10.7)$$

$$\frac{dq}{dt} = C\frac{dv}{dt}$$

But by definition, $i = dq/dt$.

$$\therefore \quad i = C\frac{dv}{dt} = C\frac{de}{dt} \qquad (12.5)$$

Since capacitance depends on such physical factors as the area and spacing of the plates and the dielectric constant, it cannot change in the short period of one cycle. Therefore, as far as Equation (12.5) is concerned, capacitance is a constant. Therefore, in determining the nature of the instantaneous current in Fig. 12.3, we can state that it is always directly proportional to the *rate* at which the PD across the capacitor is changing.

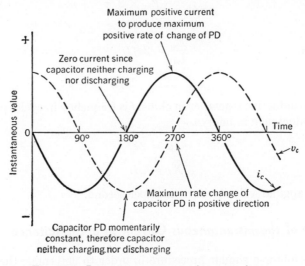

**Fig. 12.4.** Instantaneous current in a capacitance.

Upon examining the dashed sine curve of Fig. 12.4 representing the instantaneous PD across the capacitor, we will note that the maximum potential difference across the capacitor and the maximum *rate of change* of PD occur 90° apart in time. When the PD across the capacitor is maximum, momentarily it is neither rising nor falling. Therefore at this particular instant, the instantaneous current must be zero. Maximum rate of change of voltage occurs when the dashed sine curve of Fig. 12.4 is steepest. The steepest slope of the instantaneous voltage sine wave occurs at the instant that the capacitor switches over from discharging its stored charge to charging up with the opposite polarity. Therefore the instantaneous current must be maximum at the instant that the PD across the capacitor reverses its polarity.* The current will be maximum in the positive direction when the PD across the capacitor is changing from a negative polarity to a positive polarity. It will be maximum negative when the PD changes from a positive polarity to a negative polarity as shown in Fig. 12.4.

When we plot an instantaneous current graph to fulfill the conditions of being zero when the PD across the capacitance of the circuit is maximum and having a maximum positive value when the PD is changing from a negative to a positive polarity, etc., we will find that the instantaneous current in the circuit of Fig. 12.3 must follow a sine curve as shown by the solid graph of Fig. 12.4. But the instantaneous current must be maximum positive at the instant that the PD across the capacitance is just starting to build up in the positive direction. Then 90° later in time when the PD across the capacitance has reached its positive peak, the instantaneous current has passed its positive peak and has dropped back to zero.

Therefore for a **sine wave potential difference** to be developed across a capacitance, the current through it must be a sine wave which leads the instantaneous PD by 90°.

## 5. Capacitive Reactance

When we connect a capacitor across a sine wave source of emf, the instantaneous current must take on a sine wave form leading the voltage sine wave by 90° in order to produce a sine wave of potential difference across the capacitance. If the current in the capacitance is a sine wave, it must have some definite effective value and we would discover a steady reading on the a-c ammeter of Fig. 12.3.† Therefore, for a given source of alternating emf and a given capacitance, the ratio $E/I$ is constant. Just as in the case of resistance and inductive reactance, the constant $E/I$ ratio represents the opposition of the capacitor to the flow of alternating current.

* If we consider the manner in which a capacitor is discharged by electrons flowing into the plate which has a deficiency of electrons and flowing out of the plate which has a surplus of electrons, we will realize that if this flow continues in the same direction after the original charges have been neutralized, the plate which was originally positively charged due to a deficiency of electrons will start to accumulate a surplus of electrons, thus becoming negatively charged. Similarly the plate which was originally negatively charged will lose more electrons than are required to neutralize the original charge, thus starting to build up a positive charge. Therefore there would be no change in the direction of the current flow as the polarity of the PD across the capacitor reverses.

† A steady reading on the ammeter does not mean that current is flowing *through* the insulating dielectric of the capacitor. In an a-c circuit, instantaneous current flows in one direction for one-half cycle and then in the opposite direction for the next half cycle. (The average of one complete cycle of a sine wave of current is zero.) Therefore the capacitor can alternately charge, discharge, recharge with the opposite polarity, etc., with the required *displacement* current for the charging and discharging process forming a sine wave alternating current in the circuit.

Therefore **capacitive reactance** is the opposition created by a capacitance to the flow of alternating current.

The letter symbol for **capacitive reactance** is $X_C$, and

$$X_C = \frac{E_C}{I_C} \tag{12.6}$$

An a-c circuit has a **capacitive reactance** of one ohm when alternating current with an effective value of one ampere creates an alternating PD across the capacitance with an effective value of one volt.

## 6. Factors Governing Capacitive Reactance

Now that we have established that the displacement current charging and discharging a capacitor in an a-c circuit is a sine wave, we can restate Equation (12.5) as follows:

$$\frac{de}{dt} = \frac{I_m \sin \omega t}{C} \tag{12.7}$$

Although integration of Equation (12.7) will give us a mathematical expression which will indicate the factors governing capacitive reactance, we will again follow the procedure of independently varying the amplitude and frequency of the applied emf in Fig. 12.3 and the value of the capacitance.

If we double the amplitude of the applied emf, leaving the frequency constant, the capacitor will have to store twice as much charge in the same time interval. Therefore the peak charging current must be twice as great. Since $X_C = E_C/I_C$, if both $E_C$ and $I_C$ are doubled, the capacitive reactance remains unchanged.

Therefore the **magnitude of the applied alternating emf** has no effect on the capacitive reactance of an a-c circuit.

If we double the frequency, leaving the peak value of the applied emf the same, the capacitor must store the same charge, but in half the time. Therefore the peak charging current must be twice as great. Therefore, although $E_C$ is unchanged, $I_C$ is doubled; and since $X_C = E_C/I_C$, the magnitude of the capacitive reactance has been cut in half.

Therefore **capacitive reactance** is *inversely* proportional to frequency.

Finally, if we double the capacitance, leaving the source of emf unchanged, according to Equation (10.7), at the peak of the voltage sine wave the capacitor must have stored twice as much charge. Since the frequency is unchanged, the capacitor must acquire this greater charge in the same length of time. Therefore the peak charging current must be twice as great. Again $E_C$ is unchanged and $I_C$ is doubled.

Therefore **capacitive reactance** is *inversely* proportional to the capacitance.

We can solve Equation (12.7) by substituting the *average* rate of voltage rise for $de/dt$ and the *average* value for sin $\omega t$. Since the PD across the capacitor must rise from zero to $E_m$ in one-quarter cycle,

$$\text{average } \frac{de}{dt} = 4fE_m$$

Therefore Equation (12.7) becomes

$$4fE_m = \frac{I_m \times 2/\pi}{C}$$

from which

$$\frac{E_m}{I_m} = \frac{1}{2\pi fC}$$

$$\therefore \quad X_C = \frac{1}{2\pi fC} \tag{12.8}$$

where $X_C$ is capacitive reactance in ohms, $f$ is frequency in cycles per second, and $C$ is capacitance in farads.

Since

$$\omega = 2\pi f \tag{11.4}$$

$$X_C = \frac{1}{\omega C} \tag{12.9}$$

where $\omega$ is angular velocity in radians per second.

## 7. Resistance, Inductive Reactance, and Capacitive Reactance

These represent the opposition of the respective circuit properties or components to the flow of alternating current through them. All three properties are expressed in ohms. But each property requires a different phase relationship between the voltage across and the current through that part of the circuit. The current through a resistance is in phase with the voltage drop across it, the current through an inductance lags the voltage across it by 90°, and the current through a capacitance leads the PD across it by 90°. Therefore, when we state a numerical value in ohms in an a-c circuit, we must indicate in some manner which of the three types of opposition to a-c flow it represents.

As we shall discover in Chapter 14, we can make this distinction by writing the **operator** $+j$ in front of the numerical value in ohms for *inductive* reactance and $-j$ in front of the numerical value in ohms for *capacitive* reactance. As long as we clearly indicate reactance in this manner, we need no symbol in front of the numerical value of resistance. If we observe this distinction in all our a-c circuit solutions, there is no danger of mistaking an inductive reactance or a capacitive reactance for a resistance at some step in the solution.

EXAMPLE 1: What is the resistance of a 660 w toaster operated from a 110 v, 60 c source of emf?

*Solution:*

$$R = \frac{E^2}{P} = \frac{110 \times 110}{660} = 16.7 \text{ ohms}$$

EXAMPLE 2: What inductive reactance develops a 40 v cemf when the current through it has an rms value of 80 ma?

*Solution:*

$$X_L = \frac{E_L}{I_L} = \frac{40}{0.08} = +j500 \text{ ohms}$$

EXAMPLE 3: What is the reactance of a 4 $\mu$f capacitor when it is used in a 60 c circuit?

*Solution:*

$$X_C = \frac{1}{\omega C} = \frac{1}{377 \times 4 \times 10^{-6}} = -j663 \text{ ohms}$$

## Problems

1. What is the inductive reactance of a pure inductance which allows a 4 amp current to flow when it is connected across a 117 v a-c source?

2. What value of inductive reactance is required to limit the current through it to 24 ma when the cemf across it is 35 v rms?

3. What value of capacitive reactance will allow a 3 ma alternating current to flow when it is connected to a 50 v, 400 c source?

4. What is the reactance of a capacitor which allows a 7 $\mu$amp current to flow when the PD across it is 22 mv rms?

5. What is the 60 c reactance of a 4 h choke?

6. What is the reactance of a 250 mh radio frequency choke at a frequency of 4.5 megacycles per second?

7. What is the reactance of a 0.05 $\mu$f coupling capacitor at 400 c?

8. What is the reactance of a 27 $\mu\mu$f capacitor at a frequency of 88 megacycles per second?

9. At what frequency will a $\frac{1}{2}$ h inductor have a reactance of 2000 ohms?

10. At what frequency will a 48 $\mu$h inductor have a reactance of 250 ohms?

11. What value of inductance will have a reactance of 1400 ohms at 475 kc?

12. What value of inductance will draw a 160 ma rms current when connected to a 110 v, 25 c source of emf?

13. At what frequency will an 8 $\mu$f capacitor have a reactance of 160 ohms?

14. At what frequency will a 0.002 $\mu$f capacitor have a reactance of 80 ohms?

15. What value of capacitance is required if its 400 c reactance is to be 50 ohms?

16. A resistance coupled audio amplifier has a 470 kilohm grid resistor. What value of coupling capacitor should be used if its reactance is to equal the grid resistance at 20 c?

17. What value of inductance is required in order that its reactance at 580 kc be equal to the reactance of a 350 $\mu\mu$f capacitor at that frequency?

18. At what frequency will the reactance of a 640 $\mu$h coil equal that of a 400 $\mu\mu$f capacitor?

## Review Questions

1. Why must the instantaneous current sine wave be *exactly* 90° out of phase with the applied voltage waveform across a pure inductance?

2. Referring to the definition of inductance in Chapter 9, why must the current *lag* the voltage by 90° rather than lead it?

3. Why is it possible for us to label the *time* axis of the graph of Fig. 12.2 in terms of *degrees*?

4. What condition is imposed in expressing the elapse of time in degrees?

5. Why does the meter in Fig. 12.1 show a constant reading?

6. The term *resistance* is used in both d-c and a-c circuits. Why does the term *inductive reactance* not apply to d-c circuits?

7. Why is it possible to express inductive reactance in *ohms*?

8. What is the significance of the symbol $\omega$ in the equation which states the factors governing inductive reactance?

9. Referring to the definition of capacitance in Chapter 10, why does the current *lead* the PD across the capacitor by 90° rather than lag it?

10. When we connect the terminals of a capacitor to an ohmmeter, we obtain an infinitely high resistance reading. Nevertheless the ammeter in Fig. 12.3 can indicate a current of many amperes flowing in the circuit. Explain.

11. The reactance of an inductor increases with an increase in frequency but the reactance of a capacitor decreases with an increase in frequency. Explain.

12. In an a-c circuit, two components labeled 30 ohms and $-j40$ ohms are connected in series across a 120 v, 60 c source. Draw a schematic diagram for the circuit. What would be the effect on the diagram you draw if someone had neglected to include the $-j$ symbol in the data? Discuss the significance of $j$ notation in expressing resistance, inductive reactance, and capacitive reactance in a-c circuits.

# Chapter 13

# VECTOR ALGEBRA

~~~~~~~~~~~~~~~~~~~~~~~~~~~~~~~~~~~~~~~~~~~~~~~~~~~~~~~~

## 1. Addition of Sine Waves

Ever since we were first introduced to it in Chapter 5, we have made constant reference to Kirchhoff's voltage law. In Chapter 5 we used it in solving d-c circuits containing only resistance and therefore we did not find it necessary to include any mention of *time* in stating the law. In *algebraically* adding the various voltage drops around a loop, we had to note carefully the polarity of each. But having done this, simple arithmetical addition and subtraction gave us the total voltage. In dealing with the rise of current in an inductance in Chapter 9 and the charging of a capacitor in Chapter 10, we first encountered circuits in which the various voltages changed with the passage of time. We then restated Kirchhoff's voltage law: *At every instant in time*, the algebraic sum of the voltage drops in any complete electric circuit must equal the algebraic sum of the emf's. Again we were able to determine the required sum by simple arithmetical addition.

In this chapter, we must determine how this *algebraic sum* applies to the sine wave voltages appearing in an a-c circuit. The circuit of Fig. 13.1 is a typical example of the problem confronting us. The sine wave source of emf will cause a sine wave of current to flow in the circuit. Since this is a simple series circuit, the current must be the same in all parts of the circuit. The current in the inductance must have the same magnitude as the current in the resistance, must reach its peak magnitude at the same instant, and become zero at the same instant. In fact, the sine wave currents in the inductance and the resistance are one and the same thing and the letter symbol for current in a series circuit requires no subscript.

The sine wave of current through the resistance will cause a sine wave voltage drop to occur across it. This sine wave of voltage is exactly in

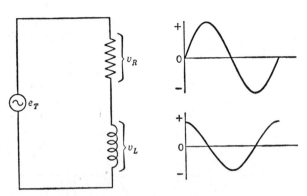

**Fig. 13.1.** A simple series AC circuit.

phase with the current. The instantaneous voltage across the resistance becomes maximum when the instantaneous current is maximum, etc. In Chapter 12 we found that the current through a pure inductance had to lag the voltage applied to it by 90°. Conversely then, the voltage across the pure inductance portion of the circuit of Fig. 13.1 must *lead* the current through it by 90°. Therefore the sine wave voltage across the inductance and the sine wave voltage across the resistance are 90° *out of phase*, with the instantaneous voltage across the inductance reaching its positive peak 90° earlier in time than the instantaneous voltage across the resistance.

Our problem now is to determine the algebraic sum of these two out of phase sine wave voltages. Fortunately, all the sine waves in the circuit of Fig. 13.1 have the same frequency. Indeed, all the procedures we shall describe in this chapter are based on the addition of sine waves of the *same frequency*.

## 2. Addition of Instantaneous Values on a Linear Graph

Since Kirchhoff's voltage law states that at *every instant in time* the algebraic sum of the various voltage drops must equal the algebraic sum of the emf's, we can then state that

$$e_T = v_R + v_L \qquad (13.1)$$

at each instant in time. Therefore we can add the *instantaneous* values of sine waves by simple algebraic addition. Although such an addition for only one instant in time does not give us the over-all picture of the addition of complete sine waves, we can use this procedure at approximately 5° intervals over a complete cycle to determine the nature of the resultant sum. To assist us in this chore, we can draw the sine curves for the two sets of instantaneous values we wish to add on a common time axis as in Fig. 13.2. Since the voltage across the pure inductance leads the voltage across the resistance in the circuit of Fig. 13.1 by 90°, it must reach its positive peak 90° earlier in time than the voltage across the resistance. The passage of time is indicated by distance to the right along the horizontal axis of the graph in Fig. 13.2.

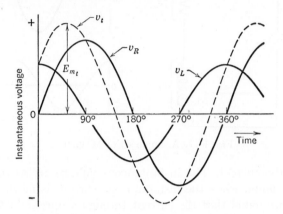

**Fig. 13.2.** Addition of instantaneous values of two out of phase sine waves on a linear graph.

At 0° in time, the instantaneous voltage across the resistance is zero; therefore the instantaneous value of the total voltage is the same as the voltage across the inductance at that instant. As time elapses, the instantaneous voltage across the inductance is decreasing and the instantaneous voltage across the resistance is increasing. At approximately 55° their sum is a maximum and the resultant waveform reaches its peak value at this point. At 90° the instantaneous voltage across the inductance is zero and the instantaneous value of the total voltage becomes the same as the instantaneous voltage across the resistance. At approximately 145° the instantaneous values of the voltages across the resistance and the inductance are equal but opposite in polarity. Therefore at this point the instantaneous value of the sum must become zero.

As we draw the dashed curve of Fig. 13.2 through the plots we obtained by finding the simple algebraic sum of the instantaneous values at regular time intervals, we will note that **the resultant sum of sine waves of the same frequency is also a sine wave of the same frequency.** But we will also note that, since the two sine waves we are adding do not reach their peak values at the *same* instant in time, the peak value of the resultant occurs at a time when the instantaneous values of the two component voltages are less than their peak values.*

* In Chapter 2 we resolved to maintain a distinction between the letter symbol $E$ for emf and $V$ for voltage drop. In dealing with d-c circuits and in developing the behavior of inductance and capacitance in a-c circuits we did retain this distinction even though the modern trend is to dispense with the letter symbol $V$. However, in expressing peak and effective values in simple single-phase a-c circuits, we will find it

$$\therefore \quad E_{mT} \neq E_{mR} + E_{mL}$$

and since the effective value of any sine wave is 0.707 of the peak value,

$$\therefore \quad E_T \neq E_R + E_L$$

Therefore, although simple algebraic addition applies to the instantaneous values of sine waves, it does *not* apply to the peak and effective values if the sine waves being added are out of phase. But since we want to use effective values in a-c circuit calculations, we must find a method that does allow us to determine the sum of the effective values of sine waves. The procedure we require is called **vector addition.**

Although $E_T \neq E_R + E_L$, since such a form implies simple algebraic addition of quantities possessing magnitude only, we can indicate that each of the terms in the equation possesses *angular* as well as magnitude information by printing the letter symbols in **boldface** type.

$$\therefore \quad \mathbf{E}_T = \mathbf{E}_R + \mathbf{E}_L \tag{13.2a}$$

*where* $\mathbf{E} = E\underline{/\theta}$, *the italic symbol representing magnitude only.* The use of this type face in a textbook reminds us that the addition indicated by Equation (13.2a) must be carried out by one of the *vector* addition methods. Another method of indicating vector quantities, which is more suitable for longhand notes, is to place a dot over the letter symbols for those quantities which possess angular as well as magnitude information.

$$\therefore \quad \dot{E}_T = \dot{E}_R + \dot{E}_L \tag{13.2b}$$

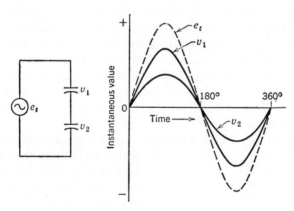

**Fig. 13.3.** Addition of instantaneous values of two in phase sine waves on a linear graph.

less confusing if we do follow the popular trend and settle for the single letter symbol $E$ to represent all voltages, relying on our knowledge of the circuit to distinguish emf from voltage drop. Later when we have to deal with three-phase systems, we will find that returning to the use of the symbol $V$ for voltage drop will help us in keeping track of which voltages are which.

In the special case of sine waves which are exactly in phase as in Fig. 13.3, the resultant and all component sine waves do reach their peak values at the same instant in time. For *in-phase* sine waves,

$$E_{m_T} = E_{m_1} + E_{m_2} \quad \text{and} \quad E_T = E_1 + E_2$$

Therefore we may add by simple arithmetic the effective values of sine waves that are exactly in phase.

If we are asked to write the general equation for the instantaneous value of the resultant voltage in Equation (13.1) showing the fixed 90° phase angle between the component voltages, we must make sure that the expression for the angle of the voltage across the inductance is always 90° larger than the angle of the voltage across the resistance since $v_L$ leads $v_R$ by 90°. Since it is customary to use radian measure in writing the general equation for the instantaneous values of a sine wave, we must first convert the fixed phase angle into radians. Since 360° = $2\pi$ radians, 90° = $\pi/2$ radians. Therefore with respect to the circuit of Fig. 13.1, Equation (13.1) becomes

$$e_T = E_{m_R} \sin \omega t + E_{m_L} \sin (\omega t + \pi/2) \tag{13.3}$$

## 3. Representing a Sine Wave by a Vector

Although we can determine the effective value of the resultant sine wave and its phase angle with respect to the component sine waves by means of the graphical addition of instantaneous values as in Figs. 13.2 and 13.3, the main feature of these graphs, which is apparent at a glance, is the sine wave shape of the resultant. Once we accept that the resultant of the addition of sine waves of the same frequency is also a sine wave of the same frequency, the tedious procedure required to produce Figs. 13.2 and 13.3 is not warranted. The original information from which we constructed the graphs of Figs. 13.2 and 13.3 was simply their effective values and the phase angle between them. Effective value and phase angle will also serve to identify the resultant.

In Chapter 11 we used a rotating vector as a means of drawing a simple sketch to indicate the position of a loop of wire as it cut across magnetic lines of force. The length of this vector represented the maximum rate of cutting or $E_m$ which was a constant, and its position indicated the angular distance the loop had traveled in its cycle at that particular instant in time. If we draw vectors for the two sine wave voltages in the circuit of Fig. 13.1, the rotating vector for the voltage across the inductance will always stay exactly

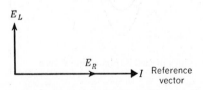

**Fig. 13.4.** Vector diagram for the circuit of Fig. 13.1.

90° ahead of the rotating vector for the voltage across the resistance. Since the conventional direction for indicating this motion on a vector diagram is counterclockwise, the vector for $v_L$ will then be 90° further counterclockwise than the vector for $v_R$ at every instant of time.

Since the rotating vectors representing the voltages across the inductance and resistance are always 90° apart, there is no motion of the one with respect to the other. Therefore **we can represent sine waves of the same frequency by stationary vectors with the angle between the vectors representing the phase angle between the sine waves.** And since the effective value of a sine wave is always 0.707 of its peak value, we can make the length of the vectors proportional to the effective values of the sine waves they represent.

In the simple series circuit of Fig. 13.1, current is common to all components. Therefore in constructing the vector diagram of a series circuit (Fig. 13.4), we draw a vector representing the effective value of this current as the **reference vector** (due east position). The voltage across the resistance being in phase with the current through it, $E_R$ is marked in the same direction as the reference vector. Since the voltage across a pure inductance leads the current through it by 90°, the vector for $E_L$ is drawn 90° counterclockwise from the reference vector.

The **vector diagram** of Fig. 13.4 was prepared much more quickly than the instantaneous voltage graphs of Fig. 13.2. Nevertheless the pertinent data regarding effective values and phase angles can be seen at a glance in Fig. 13.4, whereas they had to be derived from the data shown in Fig. 13.2. If we can now locate the vector for the resultant voltage on the vector diagram of Fig. 13.4 without excessive calculations, we will have a very powerful aid to the solution of a-c circuits.

## 4. Vector Addition by Geometrical Construction

The resultant of two vector quantities in an electrical vector diagram (as in the vector diagram of forces in mechanics), is the diagonal from the origin to the opposite corner of a parallelogram with the two vectors as sides. If we draw the vectors representing two vector quantities as accurately as possible on *polar* graph paper, we can draw the resultant with ruler and compass as shown in Fig. 13.5. Adjusting the compass to a radius equal to the length of $E_1$, we trace an arc using

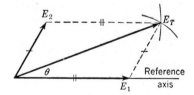

**Fig. 13.5.** Geometrical construction of the resultant vector.

the tip of the $E_2$ vector as the center. Then adjusting the compass to a radius equal to the length of $E_2$, we draw an arc using the tip of $E_1$ as the center. The resultant is drawn by joining the intersection of the two arcs to the origin with a straight line.

If we perform the geometrical construction carefully, we can measure the phase angle $\theta$ between the total applied emf and the current, and the effective value of the total voltage to two-figure accuracy directly from the vector diagram. Although geometrical solutions are not considered accurate enough for the a-c circuit problems in later chapters, the vector diagram is a valuable guide in performing the more accurate vector algebra solutions. If we draw the vectors in their proper proportions and mark off reasonably accurate phase angles, we can construct a freehand vector diagram very quickly that will give us an approximate answer to the problem. The vector diagram also assists us in determining sine, cosine, and tangent functions of angles larger than 90°. The vector diagram also shows us whether we have the correct sign for the numerical quantities used in the algebraic solution. Therefore we *always* construct a vector diagram in solving a-c circuits to show us what we have to do and to provide a quick check for the more accurate vector algebra procedures.

EXAMPLE 1: Three generators producing sine wave voltages of the same frequency have effective values and phase relationships as listed. $E_1 = 80V\underline{/0°}$, $E_2 = 100V\underline{/150°}$, and $E_3 = 40V\underline{/45°}$. Solve for the total emf by geometrical construction on a vector diagram.

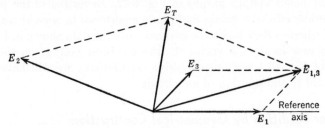

**Fig. 13.6.** Solving Example 1 by geometrical construction on a vector diagram.

*Solution:*

   *Step I.* Construct a vector for each given voltage.

   *Step II.* Construct a resultant vector for any pair of vectors ($E_1$ and $E_3$ in Fig. 13.6).

   *Step III.* Construct a resultant vector for the resultant of Step II and the remaining vector.

   *Step IV.* Measure the length and phase angle of the final resultant (approx. 79 v$\underline{/80°}$ in Fig. 13.6).

## 5. Addition of Vectors Which Are at Right Angles

We have already noted that, for the specific case of vector quantities having a zero degree angle between them, vector addition can be accomplished by simple arithmetical addition (Fig. 13.3). Similarly when the angle between a pair of vector quantities is exactly 180°, the vector sum can be determined by simple arithmetical subtraction. In the specific case of two vector quantities with an angle of exactly 90° between them, we can determine the vector sum very accurately by making use of the relationships among the various sides and angles of a right-angled triangle as defined in trigonometry. Geometry also supplies a very useful relationship which applies to this specific case of two vector quantities with a 90° angle between them. Pythagoras' theorem states that the square of the hypotenuse of a right-angled triangle is equal to the sum of the squares of the other two sides.

Returning to the simple series circuit of Fig. 13.1, since the voltage drop across the resistance must be exactly in phase with the current and the voltage across the inductance must lead the current by exactly 90°, the two voltage vectors we wish to add are exactly 90° out of phase. If we solve for the resultant sum by geometrical construction as in Fig. 13.7(a), the parallelogram becomes a rectangle with side $AC$ exactly equal to the vector $OB$ which represents the voltage across the inductance. Since the triangle of Fig. 13.7(b) contains exactly the same data as the conventional vector diagram of Fig. 13.7(a) which has all vectors starting from the same point of origin, we are allowed to use triangular diagrams in solving problems in vector addition if we find that data can be shown more clearly in this form.

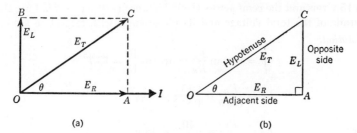

(a)                            (b)

Fig. 13.7. Addition of vectors at right angles.

Since $E_T$ is a vector quantity, it must possess angle information as well as magnitude information. Solving first for the angle between the total voltage and the current, from trigonometry,

$$\tan \theta = \frac{\text{opposite side}}{\text{adjacent side}} = \frac{AC}{OA} = \frac{E_L}{E_R}$$

Therefore if we know the magnitude of the cemf across the inductance and the voltage drop across the resistance, we can determine the phase angle $\theta$ from trigonometric tangent tables.

$$\therefore \quad \theta = \arctan (E_L/E_R) \tag{13.4}$$

where **arctan** means "the angle whose tangent is."

We now have a choice of two methods of solving for the magnitude of the total voltage vector **OC**. From trigonometry,

$$\sin \theta = \frac{\text{opposite side}}{\text{hypotenuse}} = \frac{AC}{OC}$$

from which $\qquad E_T = E_L/\sin \theta \qquad\qquad$ (13.5)

or $\qquad\qquad \cos \theta = \frac{\text{adjacent side}}{\text{hypotenuse}} = \frac{OA}{OC}$

from which $\qquad E_T = E_R/\cos \theta \qquad\qquad$ (13.6)

The second method for determining the magnitude of the resultant is based on Pythagoras' theorem.

In Fig. 13.7(b),

$$OC^2 = OA^2 + AC^2$$

$$\therefore \quad E_T = \sqrt{E_R^2 + E_L^2} \qquad\qquad (13.7)$$

Note that it is conventional to state the resistive component before the reactive component in Equation (13.7). Since both magnitude and angle information are required to identify the exact nature of the total voltage, we may combine Equations (13.7) and (13.4) in the form

$$E_T = \sqrt{E_R^2 + E_L^2}/\underline{\arctan\ (E_L/E_R)} \qquad\qquad (13.8)$$

EXAMPLE 2: If the voltage drop across the resistance in the circuit of Fig. 13.1 is 15 v rms and the cemf across the inductance is 10 v rms, what are the magnitude of the total voltage and its phase angle with respect to the current?

*Solution:*

$$\theta = \arctan \frac{E_L}{E_R} = \arctan \frac{10}{15} = 33.7°$$

$$E_T = \frac{E_R}{\cos \theta} = \frac{15}{0.832} = 18\ \text{v}$$

or $\qquad\qquad E_T = \frac{E_L}{\sin \theta} = \frac{10}{0.555} = 18\ \text{v}$

or $\qquad\qquad E_T = \sqrt{E_R^2 + E_L^2} = \sqrt{225 + 100} = 18\ \text{v}$

$$\therefore \quad E_T = 18\ \text{v}\underline{/+33.7°}$$

The positive angle shows that the voltage *leads* the current.

## 6. Expressing a Vector Quantity in Rectangular Coordinates

When we describe a vector quantity by stating its magnitude and phase angle with respect to the reference axis as we did in Example 2, we are stating the vector quantity in **polar coordinates**; i.e., the coordinates that identify the vector quantity are its length along a radius from the origin and its angular distance from the reference axis. Polar coordinates are desirable for expressing the final answer to electric circuit calculations since the numerical quantities involved in this method of representation are those which we obtain in the laboratory with measuring instruments such as voltmeters, ammeters, and wattmeters.

By applying the basic trigonometric relationships to the vector diagram of Fig. 13.7, we were able to determine the polar coordinates of the total voltage from two components, one of which lies along the reference axis and one of which is perpendicular to the reference axis. Therefore if we are given a vector quantity in polar form $(E\underline{/\theta})$ in Fig. 13.8, we can use the same basic trigonometric functions to express it in terms of one component along the reference axis and one component at right angles to the reference axis. The reference axis component (called the **real** component in mathematics) is found by multiplying the magnitude of the vector quantity by the cosine of its phase angle. The **quadrature** (perpendicular) component (called the **imaginary** component in mathematics) is found by multiplying the magnitude of the vector quantity by the sine of its phase angle.

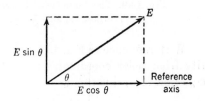

Fig. 13.8. Determining the rectangular co-ordinates of a vector quantity.

We can therefore identify a vector quantity by two coordinates, one of which is the magnitude of the reference axis component and one of which is the magnitude of the quadrature component. These two components are called the **rectangular coordinates** of the vector quantity. We now require some means of simply and distinctly identifying which numerical value is the reference axis component and which is the quadrature component. If we were to identify them in terms of their actual angle with respect to the reference axis, there is a chance that we would mistake the rectangular coordinates for polar values. In polar coordinate representation we identify the boundaries between the four quadrants in terms of Babylonian degrees as shown in Fig. 13.9(a). These boundaries represent the four possible positions of the rectangular coordinates of a vector quantity. As shown in Fig. 13.9(b), a component along the reference axis is identified by a $+operator$. A quadrature component at a $+90°$ angle with respect to the reference axis is identified by a $+j$ operator. A component which is displaced $180°$ from the reference axis is identified by a $-$ operator and a quadrature component at a $-90°$ angle with respect to the reference axis is identified by the operator $-j$. In writing the rectangular coordinates of a vector quantity, it is conventional to write the reference axis component before the $j$ component.

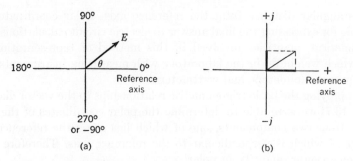

Fig. 13.9. The boundaries between the quadrants in (a) polar co-ordinates, and (b) rectangular co-ordinates.

With reference to Fig. 13.8, the procedure for converting a vector quantity from polar coordinates to rectangular coordinates can be stated in equation form thus:

$$E\underline{/\theta} = +E \cos \theta + jE \sin \theta \qquad (13.9)$$

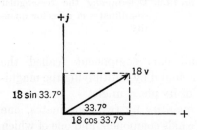

Fig. 13.10. Vector diagram for Example 3.

Since one of the rectangular coordinates has the operator $j$ in front of it and the other has not, we are reminded that the vector addition must be carried out by the Pythagorean (root of the sum of the squares) method.

EXAMPLE 3: Express 18 v$\underline{/33.7°}$ in rectangular coordinates.

*Solution:*

*Step I.* Always draw a freehand vector diagram as a quick means of identifying the correct operators to use with the rectangular coordinates.

*Step II.*

$$E = +E \cos \theta + jE \sin \theta = +18 \cos 33.7° + j18 \sin 33.7°$$

$$= +(18 \times 0.832) + j(18 \times 0.555) = +15 + j10 \text{ v}$$

EXAMPLE 4: State 4 amp$\underline{/240°}$ in rectangular coordinates.

*Solution:*

*Step I.* Again a reasonably accurate freehand vector diagram shows us exactly what angle to look up in the sine and cosine tables and what operators to use with the two rectangular coordinates without having to memorize any rules for angles greater than 90°.

*Step II.* Therefore from Fig. 13.11,

$$I = -4 \cos 60° - j4 \sin 60° = -2 - j3.46 \text{ amp}$$

EXAMPLE 5: State 48$\underline{/-45°}$ in rectangular coordinates.

*Solution:* A *negative* angle is simply one measured *clockwise* from the reference axis. Therefore from Fig. 13.12,

$$48\underline{/-45°} = +48 \cos 45° - j48 \sin 45° = +33.9 - j33.9$$

The procedure for converting from rectangular coordinates into polar coordinates is similar to that indicated by Equation (13.8). The magnitude of the polar quantity is simply the root of the sum of the squares of the reference axis rectangular coordinate and the $j$ or quadrature rectangular coordinate. The proper phase angle for the resultant is found by drawing a vector diagram of the rectangular coordinates. The angle contained within the triangle constructed on the horizontal axis is numerically equal to

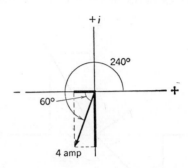

**Fig. 13.11.** Vector diagram for Example 4.

$$\arctan \frac{\text{quadrature coordinate}}{\text{reference axis coordinate}}$$

From the position of the resultant in the vector diagram, the actual phase angle with respect to the reference axis can then be determined.

EXAMPLE 6: State $-60 + j30$ volts in polar form.

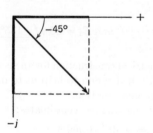

**Fig. 13.12.** Vector diagram for Example 5.

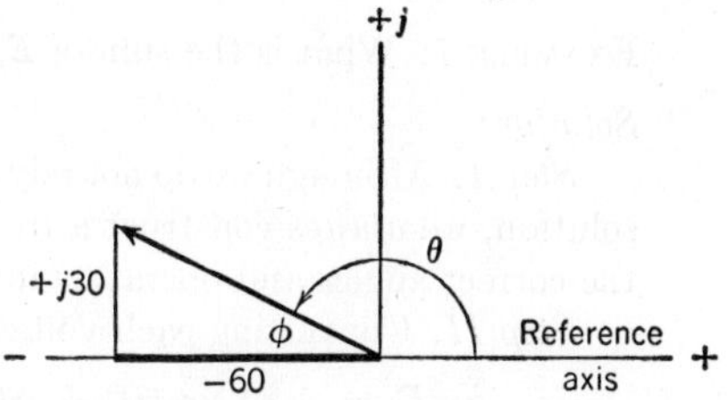

**Fig. 13.13.** Vector diagram for Example 6.

*Solution:*

$$\phi = \arctan \frac{30}{60} = 26.6°$$

From Fig. 13.13,     $\theta = 180° - 26.6° = +153.4°$

$$E = \frac{60}{\cos 26.6°} = 67 \text{ v}$$

or             $E = \sqrt{60^2 + 30^2} = 67 \text{ v}$

$$\therefore \quad E = 67 \text{ v}\underline{/+153.4°}$$

## 7. Vector Addition by Rectangular Coordinates

Although there are trigonometric procedures for adding vectors having angles between them of other than 0° or 90°, now that we can express vector quantities in rectangular coordinates, we have no need for such procedures. When we are required to add several vector quantities with various phase angles, we first convert each one to its rectangular coordinates. We can now add all components in a horizontal (+ and −) direction by simple algebraic addition. Similarly we can add all components falling in the vertical (+$j$ and −$j$) direction by simple algebraic addition. This leaves us with one + or − coordinate and one +$j$ or −$j$ coordinate. These then are the rectangular coordinates of the sum of the individual vectors. All that remains is to convert these final rectangular coordinates into polar form. This procedure as set forth in Example 7 is the conventional method of vector addition for alternating current circuit problems.

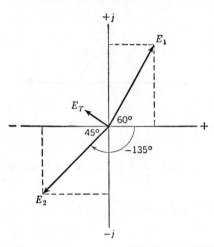

**Fig. 13.14.** Vector diagram for Example 7.

EXAMPLE 7: What is the sum of $E_1 = 80 \text{ v}\underline{/+60°}$ and $E_2 = 80 \text{ v}\underline{/-135°}$?

*Solution:*

*Step I.* Although we do not rely on geometrical construction for an accurate solution, we *always* construct a freehand vector diagram to help us to obtain the correct angles and operators for our algebraic solution.

*Step II.* Converting each voltage into its rectangular coordinates:

$$E_1 = +80 \cos 60° + j80 \sin 60° = +40 \quad + j69.3$$
$$E_2 = -80 \cos 45° - j80 \sin 45° = \underline{-56.6 - j56.6}$$

*Step III.* Adding gives $\quad E_T = -16.6 + j12.7$

*Step IV.* Converting the resultant into polar coordinates:

$$\phi = \arctan \frac{12.7}{16.6} = 37.4°$$

Therefore, from Fig. 13.14,

$$\theta = 180 - 37.4 = +142.6°$$

$$E_T = \frac{16.6}{\cos 37.4°} = 20.9 \text{ v} \quad \text{or} \quad E_T = \sqrt{16.6^2 + 12.7^2} = 20.9 \text{ v}$$

$$\therefore \quad E_T = 20.9 \text{ v}\underline{/+142.6°}$$

## 8. Subtraction of Vector Quantities

When expressed in rectangular coordinates, subtraction of two vector quantities requires only simple algebraic subtraction of the reference axis and the quadrature components. The resultant rectangular coordinates may then be converted into polar form.

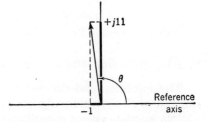

EXAMPLE 8: Subtract $4 - j5$ from $3 + j6$.

*Solution:*

$$3 + j6$$
$$\underline{4 - j5}$$
Subtracting:   $-1 + j11$

**Fig. 13.15.** Vector diagram for Example 8.

Drawing a simple vector diagram of $-1 + j11$ to help us determine the phase angle of the polar form:

$$\therefore \quad -1 + j11 = \sqrt{1^2 + 11^2}/180 - \arctan 11/1 = 11.05/\underline{+95.2°}$$

We can also subtract by reversing the $+$ and $-$ signs in the subtrahend and then carry out an algebraic *addition.*

$$3 + j6$$
$$\underline{-4 + j5}$$
Adding gives   $-1 + j11$

This latter procedure gives us a clue as to how to go about subtracting vectors on a vector diagram. If we locate $+4 - j5$ and $-4 + j5$ on a vector diagram as in Fig. 13.16, we will note that they represent vectors which are exactly equal in length but 180° apart in angular location. There-

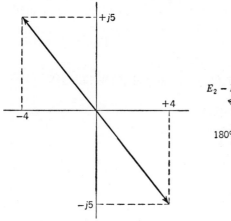

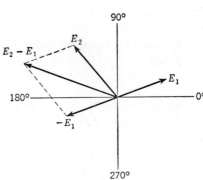

**Fig. 13.16.** Reversing the signs of rectangular co-ordinates.

**Fig. 13.17.** Subtraction of vectors by geometrical construction.

fore we can subtract two vector quantities by geometrical construction by simply reversing the direction of the subtrahend vector and then carrying out the customary geometric construction for the addition of vectors on a vector diagram.

EXAMPLE 9: Subtract $E_1 = 40\underline{/30°}$ from $E_2 = 50\underline{/135°}$ by geometrical construction on a vector diagram.

*Solution:* See Fig. 13.17.

## 9. Multiplication and Division of Vector Quantities

Multiplication and division of vector quantities in polar form is the simplest of all the vector algebra processes.

**To multiply vector quantities expressed in polar form, multiply their magnitudes and algebraically add their phase angles.**

$$\therefore \quad E_1\underline{/\theta_1} \times E_2\underline{/\theta_2} = E_1E_2\underline{/\theta_1 + \theta_2} \tag{13.10}$$

**To divide vector quantities expressed in polar form, divide their magnitudes and algebraically subtract their phase angles.**

$$\therefore \quad E_1\underline{/\theta_1} \div E_2\underline{/\theta_2} = \frac{E_1}{E_2}\underline{/\theta_1 - \theta_2} \tag{13.11}$$

EXAMPLE 10: Solve $80\underline{/40°} \times 11\underline{/-15°}$ and $80\underline{/40°} \div 11\underline{/-15°}$

*Solution:*

$$80\underline{/40°} \times 11\underline{/-15°} = 80 \times 11\underline{/40 + (-15)} = 880\underline{/25°}$$

$$80\underline{/40°} \div 11\underline{/-15°} = \tfrac{80}{11}\underline{/40 - (-15)} = 7.27\underline{/55°}$$

Although the procedure for multiplying and dividing vector quantities expressed in rectangular coordinates is quite straightforward, it does require skill in manipulating algebraic terms. Therefore it is often safer to carry out vector multiplication and division by the simple polar method even though this often requires conversion from rectangular to polar coordinates. To illustrate the procedure for multiplication and division in rectangular form, we can refer to Example 11.

EXAMPLE 11: Solve $(8 + j6) \times (2 - j4)$ and $(8 + j6) \div (2 - j4)$.

*Solution:*

$$8 + j6$$
$$\underline{2 - j4}$$

Multiplying by 2: $\qquad 16 + j12$

Multiplying by $-j4$: $\qquad \underline{\quad - j32 - j^2 24}$

Adding: $\qquad 16 - j20 - j^2 24$

The next step is to take care of the term $j^2$. Since the operator $j$ represents a rotation of 90° from the reference axis, $j^2$ represents a rotation of 180° from the reference axis. Therefore the operator $j^2$ is the same as the operator $-$. If we wish, we can say $j^2 = -1$.

$$\therefore \quad 16 - j20 - j^2 24 \quad \text{becomes} \quad 16 - j20 + 24$$

and                   the product becomes   $40 - j20$

The procedure for division is more involved. The vector quantities involved are first set up in fraction form. If we multiply both numerator and denominator of a fraction by the same quantity, we do not change the value of the fraction. In choosing this extra factor, we wish to get rid of any $j$ term in the denominator. To do this, the extra factor must have the same reference axis coordinate as the denominator and the same magnitude of quadrature coordinate as the denominator *but with the opposite sign.*

$$\therefore \quad (8 + j6) \div (2 - j4) = \frac{8 + j6}{2 - j4} = \frac{(8 + j6) \times (2 + j4)}{(2 - j4) \times (2 + j4)}$$

Completing the multiplication gives

$$(8 + j6) \div (2 - j4) = \frac{-8 + j44}{20}$$

Now that there is no $j$ term in the denominator, the division can be done quite readily.

$$\therefore \quad (8 + j6) \div (2 - j4) = -0.4 + j2.2$$

## Problems

Solve problems 1, 2, and 3 by drawing reasonably accurate freehand sine curves on a sheet of graph paper and determining the resultant by the addition of instantaneous values.

1. A 200 v sine wave lags a 100 v sine wave by 45°. Find the rms value of the resultant.

2. A 2 amp sine wave current flows through a capacitor and a pure inductance in series. The reactance of the capacitor is 200 ohms and the reactance of the inductor is 150 ohms. Find the effective value of the total voltage.

3. The currents in the two branches of a parallel circuit are given as $i_1 = 80 \sin 377t$ and $i_2 = 50 \sin (377t - \pi/3)$. Solve graphically for the total current.

4. Draw vector diagrams for Problems 1 and 2 and solve by geometrical construction.

5. Three sources of alternating emf each generate 120 v rms, but $E_2$ leads $E_1$ by 120°, and $E_3$ lags $E_1$ by 120°. Draw a vector diagram and determine the resultant emf when all three sources are connected in series.

6. Draw a vector diagram and determine the resultant emf if the leads to source $E_1$ in Problem 5 are reversed.

7. Find the resultant of the following vectors by geometrical construction: $80\underline{/+45°}$, $60\underline{/-135°}$, $40\underline{/-\pi/3^r}$, $20\underline{/2^r}$.

8. An induction motor draws a 10 amp current from a 120 v, 60 c source. This current lags the applied emf by 30°. A pure capacitance in parallel with the motor draws a 5 amp current from the source. Draw a schematic diagram, a

vector diagram, and solve for the total current drawn from the source by geometrical construction.

9. Convert the following vector quantities into rectangular coordinates.
   (a) $25\underline{/36.9°}$.  (b) $36\underline{/140°}$.  (c) $178\underline{/300°}$.
   (d) $60\underline{/-120°}$.  (e) $14.2\underline{/2^r}$.  (f) $6.8\underline{/\pi/5^r}$.

10. Convert the following to polar coordinates.
    (a) $3 + j4$.  (b) $-14 - j10$.  (c) $12.7 + j0$.
    (d) $-0.8 + j1.2$.  (e) $0 - j18$.  (f) $0.67 - j0.43$.

    Express all answers in polar coordinates.

11. Add $13 - j7$ and $11 + j18$.

12. Add $1.4 + j0.8$, $-0.9 + j2.1$, and $0 - j3.9$.

13. Add $170\underline{/200°}$ and $88\underline{/-75°}$.

14. Add $1.8\underline{/125°}$, $2.7\underline{/-157°}$, and $1.3\underline{/-66°}$.

15. Add $40 + j72$ and $60\underline{/100°}$.

16. Add $120 + j0$, $120\underline{/-120°}$, and $-60 + j104$.

17. Subtract $2.8\underline{/60°}$ from $3.1\underline{/45°}$.
    (a) By geometrical construction.
    (b) By vector algebra.

18. Add $120 + j0$, $-120\underline{/-120°}$, and $-60 + j104$.

19. Solve $4.1\underline{/-64°} \times 13\underline{/13°}$ and $4.1\underline{/-64°} \div 13\underline{/13°}$.

20. Solve $(3 + j4) \times (5 - j6)$ and $(3 + j4) \div (5 - j6)$.

21. Solve $Z_{eq} = \dfrac{Z_1 Z_2}{Z_1 + Z_2}$ if $Z_1 = 40$ ohms$\underline{/30°}$ and $Z_2 = 12$ ohms$\underline{/-45°}$.

22. Solve $\dfrac{(47 + j13)(-21 - j32)}{51\underline{/-111°} + 19\underline{/+70°}}$.

## Review Questions

1. Effective values in an a-c circuit are defined as d-c equivalent values. Why then can we not add effective values by simple algebra as we can in a d-c circuit?

2. Why is it possible to add instantaneous values in an a-c circuit by simple algebra?

3. When writing an equation for the instantaneous value of the sum of two sine waves, how is the phase difference between them indicated?

4. What advantage does the vector diagram have over the linear graph of instantaneous values plotted against time?

5. What information does a linear graph show that is not shown by a vector diagram?

6. Why is a knowledge of vector algebra required in solving a-c circuit problems?

7. What condition is required to be able to add effective values in an a-c circuit either by vector construction or by vector algebra?

8. Is it possible to add the instantaneous values of two sine waves if their frequencies are different? Explain.

9. What is the significance of an equation such as $\dot{I}_T = \dot{I}_1 + \dot{I}_2$?

10. Show with a vector diagram that sin 210° = −sin 30°.

11. Show with a vector diagram that cos 135° = −cos 45°.

12. What is meant by algebraic addition?

13. What is meant by Pythagorean addition?

14. What is meant by polar coordinates?

15. What is meant by rectangular coordinates?

16. Why is it possible to convert vector quantities from one set of coordinates to the other?

17. What is the significance of the operator $j$ in dealing with vector quantities?

18. What is the advantage of expressing vector quantities in rectangular coordinates?

19. Explain the procedure for subtracting vector quantities by geometrical construction on a vector diagram.

20. Is it possible to determine the product of two vector quantities by geometrical construction on a vector diagram? Explain.

# Chapter 14

# IMPEDANCE

## 1. Resistance and Inductance in Series

In Chapter 13 we noted that all rules and laws which apply to d-c circuits must also apply to a-c circuits provided that we keep in mind the sinusoidally varying nature of the source emf in an a-c system. The most important of the rules of series circuits is the one by which we define a series circuit. **The same current must flow in all components in a series circuit.** Therefore the starting point in determining the behavior of all series a-c circuits is to represent this common current by the reference vector of a vector diagram as in Fig. 14.1.

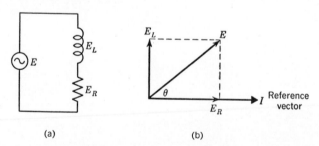

(a)                      (b)

**Fig. 14.1.** Vector diagram of voltage and current relationships in a series circuit containing resistance and inductance.

A second characteristic of series circuits is that the sum of the various voltage drops must equal the applied emf. If we use instantaneous values, this becomes a simple algebraic sum. However, using instantaneous values is a tedious means of solving an a-c circuit. In order to use the more practical *effective* values of voltage and current, we can restate this second characteristic of series circuits thus:

In a series a-c circuit, the *vector* sum of the various voltage drops must equal the applied emf.

Since the voltage drop across the resistance must be in phase with the current, its vector falls along the + rectangular coordinate axis in Fig. 14.1. Similarly since the voltage across a pure inductance must lead the current by 90°, its vector falls along the +$j$ rectangular coordinate axis. Therefore we may express the relationship among the voltages in a simple a-c series circuit quite readily in rectangular coordinates as

$$E = E_R + jE_L \tag{14.1}$$

Drawing in the resultant vector on the vector diagram of Fig. 14.1, we can also express this relationship in polar form.

$$E = \sqrt{E_R{}^2 + E_L{}^2} \; \Big/ \arctan\left(\frac{E_L}{E_R}\right) \tag{14.2}$$

Since current is the only parameter common to all components in a series circuit, in constructing the vector diagram of Fig. 14.1 we started with current as the reference vector and solved by geometrical construction for the location of the vector representing the total voltage or applied emf. In the actual circuit, when an inductance and resistance are connected in series to a given source of emf, the current (the dependent variable) must automatically take on a sine wave shape and a magnitude and phase which will develop a voltage drop across the resistance and a voltage across the inductance such that their vector sum will equal the applied emf. Nevertheless, we always think of current as the reference vector for series circuits, and the angle in Equation (14.2) is the phase angle of the applied emf *with respect to* the common current.*

* American Institute of Electrical Engineers standards for letter symbols designate the Greek letter $\theta$ as the symbol for the phase angle of a voltage *with respect to* the current. In *series* circuits, current is common to all components and is therefore considered to be the reference vector. For series circuits, phase angle (the angle between the voltage and current vectors) will therefore be designated by the symbol $\theta$. The AIEE standards designate the Greek letter $\phi$ as the letter symbol for the phase angle of a current *with respect to* the voltage. In *parallel* circuits, voltage is common to all branches and is therefore considered to be the reference vector. For parallel circuits, phase angle will therefore be designated by the symbol $\phi$.

As far as the source of emf is concerned, for a given circuit $\theta$ and $\phi$ are the same thing. In many cases all that matters is the magnitude of the phase angle. Accordingly many texts do not maintain a distinction between $\theta$ and $\phi$. Institute of Radio Engineers standards for letter symbols do not distinguish between $\theta$ and $\phi$. American texts show a preference for $\theta$ as the general symbol for phase angle *between* current and voltage in a circuit. European texts insist on $\phi$ for angular difference between voltage and current in both series and parallel circuits.

## 2. Impedance

Since the current in the series circuit of Fig. 14.1 must automatically take on a sine wave form of certain magnitude and phase with respect to the applied emf, for a given circuit the ratio between the applied emf and the current is a constant. Just as $E_R/I$ represents the opposition of a resistor to the flow of alternating current and $E_L/I$ represents the opposition of an inductance to the flow of alternating current, the ratio $E/I$ represents the *total* opposition of the circuit to the flow of alternating current. In a resistance the voltage and current are in phase, and in a reactance the voltage and current are exactly 90° out of phase. But as we can see from the vector diagram of Fig. 14.1, the angle $\theta$ between the applied emf and the current is between 0° and +90°. Therefore this total opposition cannot be called either resistance or reactance.

The **total opposition to the flow of current** in an a-c circuit is called **impedance.**

The letter symbol for **impedance** is $Z$.

$$\therefore \quad Z = \frac{E}{I} \tag{14.3}$$

where $Z$ is the impedance of an a-c circuit in ohms, $E$ is the applied emf in volts, and $I$ is the current drawn from the source in amperes.

Since current is the dependent variable in the circuit, we must have some means of determining the impedance before we can solve for the current. Once impedance is known, we can use Equation (14.3) to determine the current in the circuit. Since the current is common to all components in a series circuit, we can divide every term in Equation (14.1) by $I$. Therefore

$$\frac{E}{I} = \frac{E_R}{I} + j\frac{E_L}{I}$$

from which
$$\mathbf{Z} = R + jX_L \tag{14.4}$$

Also by dividing each term in Equation (14.2) by $I$,

$$\mathbf{Z} = \sqrt{R^2 + X_L^2} \Big/ \arctan\frac{X_L}{R} \tag{14.5}$$

Therefore the impedance of a series circuit is the *vector* sum of the resistance and reactance. Resistance, reactance, and impedance are *not* sinusoidally varying quantities like voltage and current. We might refer to them as the *ohmage* of the circuit, which is a *scalar* quantity having only magnitude. But with current as a common denominator, the relationship among impedance, resistance, and reactance is *numerically* the same as the relationship among the applied emf and the voltage drops across the resistance and inductance. Therefore, although we should *not* refer to impedance, resistance, and reactance as *vector* quantities, we can represent their relationship diagrammatically by constructing the customary right-angled triangle relationship shown in the **impedance diagram** of Fig. 14.2. To remind us that impedance, resistance, and reactance are not vector quantities, **impedance diagrams** should always be drawn in triangular form without arrows, to distinguish them from the common origin **vector diagrams** used to represent voltage and current relationships.

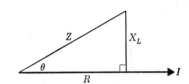

**Fig. 14.2.** Impedance diagram for a series circuit containing resistance and inductance.

The voltage drop across a resistance is always in phase with the current and the voltage across an inductance always leads the current by 90°. But the phase angle between the applied emf and the current in the series $RL$ circuit may be any angle between 0° and 90° depending on the ratio between the magnitudes of the inductive reactance and resistance. Therefore stating only the magnitude of an impedance does not give any indication of the phase angle between the current through and the voltage across this impedance. If the impedance is stated in rectangular coordinates as in Equation (14.4), we can solve for the phase angle between voltage and current from the relationship $\theta = \arctan X/R$ (with reference to Fig. 14.2). However if we express impedance in polar form, even though impedance is not strictly speaking a vector quantity, we must also include an angle with it as indicated by Equation (14.5). Otherwise there is nothing to indicate whether the impedance is largely resistive or largely inductive. Note also that we use **boldface** type for the symbol $Z$ whenever we wish to draw attention to requirement that phase angle must be stated as well as the magnitude of the impedance. If the reactance portion of a given impedance is inductive, the angle associated with the impedance must be between 0° and +90° as shown in Fig. 14.2. This results from considering the current as the reference vector when we carry out the vector division represented by

$$Z = \frac{E\underline{/\theta}}{I\underline{/0°}} \tag{14.3}$$

EXAMPLE 1: A solenoid having an inductance of 0.5 h and a resistance of 100 ohms is connected to a 120 v, 60 c source. What is the magnitude and phase of the current with respect to the applied emf?

*Solution:*

*Step I.* In an a-c circuit we are more concerned with the *reactance* of the solenoid than its inductance. Therefore the first step is to express its reactance at 60 c.

$$X_L = \omega L = 377 \times 0.5 = +j188.5 \text{ ohms}$$

*Step II.* Always draw a circuit diagram, labeling it with all pertinent data and draw either a voltage vector diagram or an impedance diagram to show the relationships that exist in the given circuit.

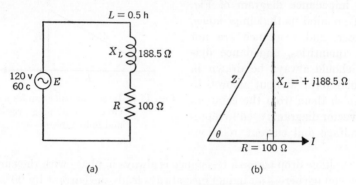

(a)                                                                              (b)

**Fig. 14.3.** Impedance diagram for Example 1.

*Step III.* From the impedance diagram the rectangular coordinates of the impedance are

$$Z = R + jX_L = 100 + j188.5 \text{ ohms}$$

*Step IV.* Solve for the impedance in polar form.

$$\theta = \arctan\frac{X_L}{R} = \arctan\frac{188.5}{100} = 62°$$

$$Z = \sqrt{R^2 + X_L^2} = \sqrt{100^2 + 188.5^2} = 213 \text{ ohms}$$

$$\therefore \quad Z = 213 \text{ ohms}\underline{/+62°}$$

*Step VA.* Solving for the magnitude of the current,

$$I = \frac{E}{Z} = \frac{120}{213} = 0.563 \text{ amp}$$

And from Fig. 14.3, this current *lags* the applied emf by 62°.

*Step VB.* Treating the terms of Equation (14.3) as *vector* quantities with the angle of the applied emf as 0°, we can solve for both magnitude and angle of the current with respect to the applied emf by *vector* division. Therefore

$$I = \frac{E}{Z} = \frac{120\underline{/0°}}{213\underline{/62°}} = 0.563 \text{ amp}\underline{/-62°}$$

## 3. Practical Inductors

In practical circuits we are not able to obtain pure inductance since the wire used in the winding possesses some resistance. Therefore the practical inductor is not a pure reactance with a +90° angle. With only two leads from the choke in Fig. 14.4, we cannot connect a voltmeter to read only the inductive voltage drop across its inductance or the $IR$ drop across its resistance. We can read only the total voltage drop between the two leads. This voltage leads the current through the choke by something *less* than 90°. If we are given the *impedance* of the choke in polar form with its proper angle, we can determine what the resistance and inductance components of the practical inductor are by conversion to rectangular coordinates.

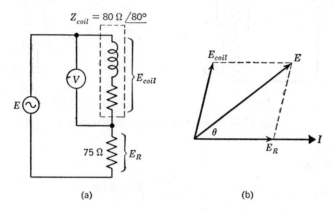

Fig. 14.4. A practical inductor and resistor in series.

EXAMPLE 2: The choke in the circuit of Fig. 14.4 has an impedance of 80 ohms$\underline{/80°}$. What is the total impedance when it is connected in series with a 75 ohm resistor?

*Solution:* Since we do not directly tackle the addition of two vectors with an 80° angle between them as in the vector diagram of Fig. 14.4, we must first express the impedance of the choke in rectangular coordinates.

$$\therefore \quad Z_{coil} = 80 \cos 80° + j80 \sin 80° = 14 + j79 \text{ ohms}$$

The total impedance of the circuit in Fig. 14.4 now becomes

$$Z_T = 75 + 14 + j79 \text{ ohms}$$

Since the two resistance components are both along the + axis of an impedance diagram, they may be added by simple arithmetic.

$$\therefore \quad Z_T = 89 + j79 \text{ ohms}$$

Changing back to polar form,

$$\theta = \arctan \frac{79}{89} = 41.6°$$

$$Z_T = \sqrt{89^2 + 79^2} = 119 \text{ ohms}$$

$$\therefore \quad Z_T = 119 \text{ ohms}\underline{/+41.6°}$$

EXAMPLE 3: A coil and a resistor each have an 80 v drop across them when connected in series to a 120 v, 60 c source. If they draw a 0.5 amp current from the source, what is the resistance of the coil?

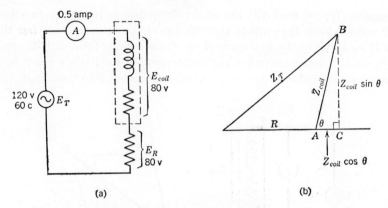

**Fig. 14.5.** Impedance diagram for Example 3.

*Solution:*
   *Step I.*

$$Z_T = \frac{E_T}{I} = \frac{120}{0.5} = 240 \text{ ohms}$$

$$Z_{coil} = \frac{E_{coil}}{I} = \frac{80}{0.5} = 160 \text{ ohms}$$

$$R = \frac{E_R}{I} = \frac{80}{0.5} = 160 \text{ ohms}$$

*Step II.* Since the coil possesses both resistance and inductance, the angle of the impedance $\theta$ must be something less than $+90°$ as shown in Fig. 14.5.

$$\therefore \quad Z_{coil} = 160 \text{ ohms}\underline{/\theta}$$

This can be expressed in rectangular coordinates as

$$Z_{coil} = 160 \cos \theta + j160 \sin \theta$$

   *Step III.*

$$\therefore \quad Z_T = 160 + 160 \cos \theta + j160 \sin \theta = 240 \text{ ohms}$$

In polar form this becomes

$$240 = \sqrt{(160 + 160 \cos \theta)^2 + (160 \sin \theta)^2}$$

Squaring both sides of the equation,

$$57,600 = 25,600 + 51,200 \cos \theta + 25,600 \cos^2 \theta + 25,600 \sin^2 \theta$$

$$\therefore \quad \cos \theta = \frac{32,000 - 25,600(\cos^2 \theta + \sin^2 \theta)}{51,200} = \frac{5 - 4(\cos^2 \theta + \sin^2 \theta)}{8}$$

*Step IV.* But from triangle $ABC$ in Fig. 14.5,

$$\cos^2 \theta = \frac{AC^2}{AB^2} \quad \text{and} \quad \sin^2 \theta = \frac{BC^2}{AB^2}$$

$$\therefore \quad \cos^2 \theta + \sin^2 \theta = \frac{AC^2}{AB^2} + \frac{BC^2}{AB^2} = \frac{AC^2 + BC^2}{AB^2}$$

But from Pythagoras' theorem, $AC^2 + BC^2 = AB^2$

$$\cos^2 \theta + \sin^2 \theta = 1$$

$$\therefore \quad \cos \theta = \frac{5-4}{8} = 0.125$$

*Step V.* The resistance of the coil then becomes

$$R_{coil} = Z_{coil} \cos \theta = 160 \times 0.125 = 20 \text{ ohms}$$

## 4. Resistance and Capacitance in Series

In the circuit of Fig. 14.6, the current again is common to all components. Since the potential difference across the capacitor *lags* the current through it by 90°, the vector diagram shows the total emf vector located in quadrant IV. From this vector diagram we can state that

$$E = E_R - jE_C \tag{14.6}$$

or $$E = \sqrt{E_R{}^2 + E_C{}^2} \left/ -\arctan \frac{E_C}{E_R} \right. \tag{14.7}$$

and $$Z = R - jX_C \tag{14.8}$$

or $$Z = \sqrt{R^2 + X_C{}^2} \left/ -\arctan \frac{X_C}{R} \right. \tag{14.9}$$

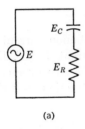 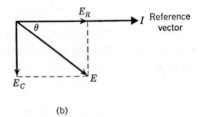

       (a)                          (b)

**Fig. 14.6.** Vector diagram of voltage and current relationships in a series circuit containing resistance and capacitance.

Note that in rectangular coordinates, *inductive* reactance is always a $+j$ quantity and *capacitive* reactance is always a $-j$ quantity. As a result, in polar form an inductive impedance always has a $+$ angle between 0° and 90° and a capacitive impedance always has a $-$ angle between 0° and $-90°$.

EXAMPLE 4: What capacitance when connected in series with a 50 ohm resistor will limit the current drawn from a 120 v, 60 c source to 0.5 amp?

*Solution:*

$$Z = \frac{E}{I} = \frac{120}{0.5} = 240 \text{ ohms}$$

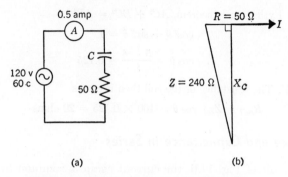

Fig. 14.7. Impedance diagram for Example 4.

From Pythagoras' theorem with respect to Fig. 14.7,

$$X_C = \sqrt{Z^2 - R^2} = \sqrt{240^2 - 50^2} = 235 \text{ ohms}$$

Since $X_C = 1/\omega C$,

$$C = \frac{1}{\omega X_C} = \frac{10^6}{377 \times 235} = 11.4 \ \mu\text{f}$$

## 5. Resistance, Inductance, and Capacitance in Series

The sum of the various voltages in the series circuit of Fig. 14.8 can be expressed in rectangular form thus:

$$E = E_R + jE_L - jE_C \tag{14.10}$$

The voltage across the inductance *leads* the common current by 90°, and the voltage across the capacitance *lags* the current by 90°. Therefore these two voltages are exactly 180° out of phase. These two vector quantities can then be added by simple arithmetical subtraction, and Equation (14.10) becomes

$$E = E_R + j(E_L - E_C) \tag{14.10}$$

Unless the two reactive voltages are exactly equal, this leaves the circuit with an **equivalent reactive voltage** ($E_X$ in Fig. 14.8), which will be either inductive or capacitive depending on which of the original reactive voltages is the larger. Note that as far as a fixed frequency generator is concerned in the circuit of Fig. 14.8, the circuit appears to contain only inductance since $E_L$ is greater than $E_C$. The over-all circuit cannot be both inductive and capacitive at the same time. The current must *either* lead *or* lag the applied emf; it cannot do both.

Therefore converting Equation (14.10) into polar coordinates gives

$$E = \sqrt{E_R^2 + E_X^2} \ \bigg/ \arctan \frac{E_X}{E_R} \tag{14.11}$$

where $E_X = E_L - E_C$ (the net reactive voltage).

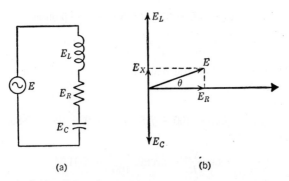

**Fig. 14.8.** Vector diagram of voltage and current relationships in a series circuit containing resistance, inductance and capacitance.

By dividing every term in Equations (14.10) and (14.11) by the common current, the impedance of series circuits containing $R$, $L$, and $C$ becomes

$$\mathbf{Z} = R + jX_L - jX_C = R + j(X_L - X_C) \qquad (14.12)$$

or

$$\mathbf{Z} = \sqrt{R^2 + X_{eq}^2}\;\Big/\!\arctan \frac{X_{eq}}{R} \qquad (14.13)$$

where $X_{eq} = X_L - X_C$ (the net equivalent reactance).

EXAMPLE 5: What is the total impedance at 60 c of a series circuit consisting of a 0.5 h choke with a 100 ohm resistance and a 26.5 $\mu$f capacitor?

*Solution:*

*Step I.* Again we are interested only in the *reactance* of the inductor and capacitor in a-c circuits.

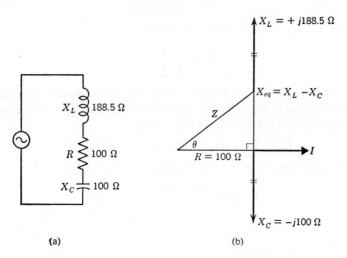

**Fig. 14.9.** Impedance diagram for Example 5.

$$X_L = \omega L = 377 \times 0.5 = +j188.5 \text{ ohms}$$

$$\therefore \quad X_c = \frac{1}{\omega C} = \frac{10^6}{377 \times 26.5} = -j100 \text{ ohms}$$

*Step II.* Draw a schematic diagram and either a vector diagram or impedance diagram.

*Step III.*

$$Z = R + jX_L - jX_C = 100 + j188.5 - j100 = 100 + j88.5 \text{ ohms}$$

*Step IV.*

$$\theta = \arctan \frac{X_{eq}}{R} = \arctan \frac{88.5}{100} = +41.5°$$

$$Z = \sqrt{R^2 + X_{eq}^2} = \sqrt{100^2 + 88.5^2} = 133.5 \text{ ohms}$$

$$\therefore \quad Z = 133.5 \text{ ohms} \underline{/+41.5°}$$

## 6. Resistance, Inductance, and Capacitance in Parallel

The characteristic of a parallel circuit by which it is defined is that **the same voltage appears across all parallel branches.** Therefore in preparing a vector diagram for any parallel circuit, we always use this common voltage as the reference vector. If we are given the numerical value of this voltage, we can solve for the individual branch currents by Ohm's law:

$$I_R = \frac{E\underline{/0°}}{R\underline{/0°}}$$

Therefore $I_R$ is in phase with the reference vector.

$$I_L = \frac{E\underline{/0°}}{X_L\underline{/+90°}}$$

Therefore $I_L$ lags the reference voltage by 90°.

$$I_C = \frac{E\underline{/0°}}{X_C\underline{/-90°}}$$

Therefore $I_C$ leads the reference voltage by 90° as shown in Fig. 14.10. The total current in the parallel circuit then becomes the *vector* sum of the branch currents. Therefore from Fig. 14.10,

$$I_T = I_R - jI_L + jI_C = I_R - j(I_L - I_C) \qquad (14.14)$$

Converting Equation (14.14) to polar coordinates gives

$$I_T = \sqrt{I_R^2 + I_x^2} \underline{\Big/ \arctan \frac{I_x}{I_R}} \qquad (14.15)$$

where $I_x = I_C - I_L$ (the net reactive current). The equivalent impedance of a parallel circuit can now be determined by using Equation (14.3).

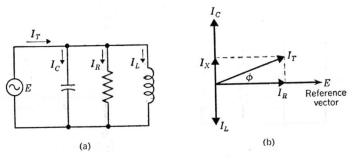

**Fig. 14.10.** Vector diagram of voltage and current relationships in a parallel circuit containing resistance, inductance and capacitance.

$$\mathbf{Z}_{eq} = \frac{E}{I_T} \qquad (14.3)$$

This method of solving for the equivalent impedance of a parallel circuit is called the *total current method.* Even if the exact value of the applied emf is not known, we may assume any convenient value in order to solve for the equivalent impedance.

EXAMPLE 6: What is the equivalent impedance at 60 c of a circuit consisting of a pure inductance of 0.5 h, a 100 ohm resistance and a 26.5 $\mu$f capacitance all connected in parallel?

*Solution:*

Step I.

$$X_L = \omega L = 377 \times 0.5 = +j188.5 \text{ ohms}$$

$$X_C = \frac{1}{\omega C} = \frac{10^6}{377 \times 26.5} = -j100 \text{ ohms}$$

*Step II.* Assume a convenient value of applied emf. e.g., Let $E = 200$ v$\underline{/0°}$.

$$\therefore \quad I_R = \frac{E}{R} = \frac{200\underline{/0°}}{100\underline{/0°}} = 2 \text{ amp}\underline{/0°}$$

$$I_L = \frac{E}{X_L} = \frac{200\underline{/0°}}{188.5\underline{/+90°}} = 1.06 \text{ amp}\underline{/-90°}$$

$$I_C = \frac{E}{X_C} = \frac{200\underline{/0°}}{100\underline{/-90°}} = 2 \text{ amp}\underline{/90°}$$

Note that $R$, $X_L$, and $X_C$ were expressed in polar form with an angle rather than their rectangular coordinate operators in order to facilitate the division of vector quantities. Note also that dividing a quantity with the same angle as the reference vector by a $+j$ quantity creates a $-j$ quantity and vice versa.

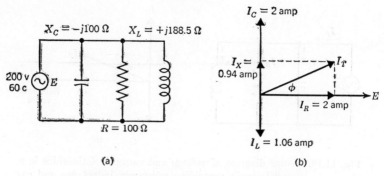

**Fig. 14.11.** Vector diagram for Example 6.

*Step III.* Prepare a circuit diagram and vector diagram.
*Step IV.*

$$I_T = I_R - jI_L + jI_C = 2 - j1.06 + j2 = 2 + j0.94 \text{ amp}$$

*Step V.*

$$\phi = \arctan \frac{I_X}{I_R} = \arctan \frac{0.94}{2} = +25.2°$$

$$I_T = \sqrt{I_R^2 + I_X^2} = \sqrt{2^2 + 0.94^2} = 2.21 \text{ amp}$$

$$\therefore \quad I_T = 2.21 \text{ amp} \underline{/+25.2°}$$

*Step VI.*

$$Z_{eq} = \frac{E}{I_T} = \frac{200 \underline{/0°}}{2.21 \underline{/+25.2°}} = 90.5 \text{ ohms} \underline{/-25.2°}$$

Note that the equivalent impedance is capacitive, since the capacitive branch draws a greater current from the source than the inductive branch.

## 7. Conductance, Susceptance, and Admittance

Although we listed the total current method in solving for the equivalent resistance of parallel d-c circuits, we preferred to use a method that did not require the in-between step of solving for total current. To do this we found it necessary to change our point of view in dealing with parallel circuits. Rather than thinking in terms of the ability of a circuit to *oppose* the flow of current, we found that in dealing with parallel circuits we could obtain a better picture of the circuit behavior if we thought in terms of the ability of the various branches to *pass* current. This reciprocal property of resistance is called **conductance**.

**Conductance** is a measure of the ability of a resistance to pass electric current.

The letter symbol for **conductance** is $G$.

The unit of conductance is the **mho** as defined by the equation $G = 1/R$.

Since the *same* voltage appears across all components in a simple parallel circuit, we can divide each term in Equation (14.14) by $E$.

$$\therefore \quad \frac{I_T}{E} = \frac{I_R}{E} - j\frac{I_L}{E} + j\frac{I_C}{E}$$

From which
$$\frac{1}{Z} = \frac{1}{R} - j\frac{1}{X_L} + j\frac{1}{X_C} \tag{14.16}$$

But as we have already noted, the reciprocal of resistance is called conductance. Similarly then, the reciprocal of impedance is called **admittance**.

Therefore, **admittance** is the over-all ability of an electric circuit to pass alternating current.

The letter symbol for **admittance** is $Y$, and $Y = 1/Z$ mhos.

Also the reciprocal of reactance is called **susceptance**.

Therefore, **susceptance** is the ability of an inductance or capacitance to *pass* alternating current.

The letter symbol for **susceptance** is $B$, and $B = 1/X$ mhos.

Therefore, Equation (14.16) becomes
$$Y = G - jB_L + jB_C \tag{14.17}$$

Note that when we divide a vector quantity with a $+90°$ angle into $1/\underline{0°}$, the quotient has a $-90°$ angle and vice versa. Therefore, although inductive reactance is a $+j$ quantity, inductive susceptance is a $-j$ quantity. Similarly, capacitive susceptance is a $+j$ quantity. Using the now familiar relationship, we can express the polar coordinates of admittance as

$$Y = \sqrt{G^2 + B^2_{eq}} \Big/ \arctan \frac{B_{eq}}{G} \tag{14.17}$$

where $B_{eq} = B_C - B_L$ (the net equivalent susceptance).

EXAMPLE 6A: What is the equivalent impedance at 60 c of a circuit consisting of a pure inductance of 0.5 h, a 100 ohms resistance, and a 26.5 $\mu$f capacitance all connected in parallel?

*Solution:*

Step I.
$$X_L = \omega L = +j188.5 \text{ ohms}, \qquad X_C = \frac{1}{\omega C} = -j100 \text{ ohms}$$

Step II.
$$G = \frac{1}{R} = \frac{1}{100/\underline{0°}} = 0.01 \text{ mho}/\underline{0°}$$

$$B_L = \frac{1}{X_L} = \frac{1}{188.5/\underline{+90°}} = 0.0052 \text{ mho}/\underline{-90°}$$

$$B_C = \frac{1}{X_C} = \frac{1}{100/\underline{-90°}} = 0.01 \text{ mho}/\underline{+90°}$$

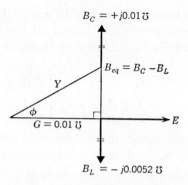

**Fig. 14.12.** Admittance diagram for Example 6A.

*Step III.* Prepare a current vector diagram or preferably an admittance diagram for the circuit of Fig. 14.11(a).

Note that it is impossible to draw an *impedance* diagram using the actual values given in the circuit of Fig. 14.11(a) since the equivalent impedance of a parallel circuit must be *less* than the resistance and it is impossible for the hypotenuse of a right-angled triangle to be smaller than either of the other two sides.

*Step IV.*

$$Y = G - jB_L + jB_C = 0.01 - j0.0052 + j0.01 = 0.01 + j0.0048 \text{ mho}$$

*Step V.*

$$\phi = \arctan \frac{B_{eq}}{G} = \arctan \frac{0.0048}{0.01} = +25.2°$$

$$Y = \sqrt{G^2 + B^2_{eq}} = \sqrt{0.01^2 + 0.0048^2} = 0.01105 \text{ mho}$$

$$\therefore \quad Y = 0.01105 \text{ mho}\underline{/+25.2°}$$

*Step VI.*

$$Z_{eq} = \frac{1}{Y} = \frac{1}{0.01105\underline{/+25.2°}} = 90.5 \text{ ohms}\underline{/-25.2°}$$

## Problems

Draw a schematic diagram and either a vector diagram or impedance diagram for each problem.

1. The voltages across a capacitor and a resistor connected in series in an a-c circuit are measured as 60 v and 80 v rms, respectively. What is the magnitude and phase angle of the total voltage with respect to the common current?

2. A choke coil connected to a 120 v, 60 c source has an *IR* drop of 72 v across the resistance of its winding. What is the magnitude and angle of the cemf across its inductance with respect to the applied emf?

3. When the operating coil of a contactor is connected to a 120 v, 60 c source, it draws a 0.9 amp current which lags the applied emf by 72°. What is its impedance?
   (a) In polar coordinates?
   (b) In rectangular coordinates?

4. What are the magnitude and phase angle of the current that a $80 - j95$ ohm impedance will draw from a 117 v a-c source?

5. Find the total impedance (polar coordinates) at 60 c of a 1.8 h inductance in series with a 500 ohm resistance.

6. Find the total impedance (polar coordinates) at 60 c of a 10 $\mu$f capacitor and a 500 ohm resistor in series.

7. What is the resistance of a 4 h choke whose impedance at 25 c has a magnitude of 750 ohms? What is the angle of the impedance?

8. At what frequency will a 0.02 $\mu$f capacitor and a 120 kilohm resistor in series have an impedance of 200 kilohms?

9. What is the total 60 c impedance (polar form) of a 1 h choke whose resistance is 100 ohms in series with a 10 $\mu$f capacitor?

10. At a frequency of 400 c, what value of capacitor must be connected in series with an impedance of 75 ohms$/+60°$ to form a total impedance of 75 ohms$/-60°$?

11. The cathode bias circuit of an audio amplifier consists of a 2200 ohm resistor and 0.2 $\mu$f capacitor in parallel. At a frequency of 1000 c,
    (a) What is the admittance of the cathode circuit in polar form?
    (b) What is the equivalent impedance of the cathode circuit in rectangular coordinates?

12. What value of resistance must be connected in parallel with a pure inductance of 1.5 h to produce a 60 c impedance of 400 ohms?

13. When connected to a 12 v battery, a certain choke draws a current of 0.25 amp. When connected to a 120 v, 60 c source, it draws a current of 1.0 amp. Determine the resistance and inductance of the choke.

14. When connected to a 117 v, 25 c source, a certain choke draws a 5.0 amp current. When connected to a 120 v, 60 c source, the same choke draws a 3.0 amp current. Determine the resistance and inductance of the choke.

15. A relay coil requires a 100 ma current through it in order to close its contacts. If operated from a d-c source, the required voltage is 24 v. If operated from a 60 c source, the required voltage is 160 v. What value of capacitance in series with the relay will allow its operation from a 120 v, 60 c supply?

16. At a frequency of 400 c, what value of capacitance must be connected in series with an impedance of 75 ohms$/+60°$ to form
    (a) An inductive impedance of 50 ohms?
    (b) A capacitive impedance of 50 ohms?

17. What value of capacitor must be connected in series with a 560 ohm resistor to limit its dissipation to 5 w when connected to a 120 v, 60 c source?

18. A projector using a special 120 v, 300 w lamp is operated on the European 230 v, 50 c system by connecting a choke in series with it. If the resistance of the choke is 10 ohms, what must its inductance be in order to provide the correct voltage drop across the lamp?

19. A 15 w fluorescent lamp operates with a ballast inductance in series with it. The voltage across the lamp is measured as 56 v rms and the voltage across the ballast inductor is measured as 100 v rms when the total applied emf is 120 v,

60 c. What are the resistance and inductance of the ballast? (The lamp itself represents pure resistance.)

20. A coil and capacitor are connected in series across a 400 c source. The voltage across the coil is measured as 48 v, across the capacitor as 52 v and across the whole circuit as 6 v. The current in the circuit is 100 ma. Determine
    (a) The resistance of the coil.
    (b) The inductance of the coil.
    (c) The capacitance of the capacitor.
    (d) The total impedance in polar form.

## Review Questions

1. Why is the additional term **impedance** required in dealing with the opposition of a circuit to the flow of alternating current?
2. Why must we add the resistance and reactance of a series circuit by the Pythagoras method in order to find the total impedance?
3. Why is it necessary to state an angle as well as a magnitude when an impedance is given in polar form?
4. Why does a + angle with an impedance always represent a circuit possessing some inductive reactance?
5. How is the angle of an impedance related to the voltage across and the current through the impedance?
6. Why is it not necessary to state an angle when an impedance is stated in rectangular coordinates?
7. What is the significance of a total impedance having a 0° angle?
8. Why must the angle of the impedance of a practical inductor be something less than +90°?
9. Expressing the impedance of a practical inductor in rectangular coordinates gives us the actual resistance and reactance components which form the practical inductor. Explain.
10. How do we go about determining the total impedance of a practical inductor and a resistor in series when the angle between them is less than 90°?
11. Under what circumstances is it possible for the total impedance to decrease when a capacitor is added in series with a given impedance?
12. Under what circumstances is it possible for the rms current drawn from a certain source of emf to have the same magnitude when an inductance is connected in series with a given impedance?
13. Explain the statement that an a-c circuit containing both inductance and capacitance appears to the source only as either an inductive circuit or a capacitive circuit.
14. What is meant by **equivalent reactance?**
15. Why is quadrant I the capacitive quadrant of a parallel circuit vector diagram, whereas quadrant IV is the capacitive quadrant of a series circuit vector diagram?

16. Why can we not prepare a vector diagram for a parallel circuit with the length of each vector representing the resistance or reactance of each branch in ohms?

17. What is the advantage of thinking in terms of admittance, conductance, and susceptance in dealing with parallel a-c circuits?

18. Show that $B_C = \omega C$.

19. Why is $B_L$ a $-j$ quantity, whereas $X_L$ is a $+j$ quantity?

20. What is meant by the **equivalent impedance** of a parallel a-c circuit?

# Chapter 15

# POWER IN ALTERNATING CURRENT CIRCUITS

## 1. Power in a Pure Resistance

In Chapter 11 we investigated the nature of the instantaneous power in a resistance in order to establish effective values for voltage and current in an a-c circuit. We can set a pattern for dealing with power in a-c circuits in general by reviewing the procedure we used to determine the power (or rate of conversion of electric energy) in a pure resistance.

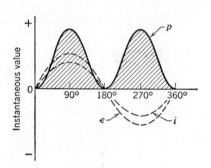

If we consider only one particular instant in time, all the power equations we used in direct current circuits must apply to a-c circuits. Therefore

$$p = ei \qquad (15.1)$$

**Fig. 15.1.** Instantaneous power in a pure resistance.

Therefore if we plot the sine wave applied voltage and current through a pure resistance as shown by the dashed curves of the graph of Fig. 15.1, we can place a series of plots on the graph at approximately 5° intervals representing the product of $e$ and $i$ at those particular instants. Joining these plots gives us the solid curve of Fig. 15.1 representing the instantaneous power in a pure resistance.

Since the voltage drop across a pure resistance must be exactly in phase with the current through it, the instantaneous voltage and current reach their peak values simultaneously and pass through zero simultaneously.

Therefore whenever $i$ is a positive quantity, $e$ is also a positive quantity, and whenever $i$ is a negative quantity, $e$ is also a negative quantity. Since the product of two negative quantities is a positive quantity, the instantaneous power graph for a pure resistance is always positive. This indicates that the resistor must always convert electric energy into heat, never vice versa. We also noted that the instantaneous power in a resistance in an a-c circuit is pulsating in nature, fluctuating sinusoidally between zero and a peak value of $P_m = E_m I_m$ twice during each complete cycle of voltage and current. Because of this smooth, sinusoidal variation between zero and $P_m$, we concluded that, as far as effectiveness in doing work is concerned, we can consider the power in a pure resistance in an a-c circuit as having an average, or d-c equivalent value equal to $\frac{1}{2}P_m$.

In Chapter 11 we used this average value of power in a resistance to establish the effective value of a sine wave of voltage or current as 0.707 of its peak value. Therefore it follows that the average power input to a pure resistance in an a-c circuit is simply the product of the effective value of the voltage drop across and the effective value of the current through the resistance. Therefore,

$$P = E_R I_R \qquad (15.2)$$

Since a resistor can convert energy only from an electric form into heat or light but never vice versa, the power in watts determined by Equation (15.2) is the **true power** that the resistor draws from the source. Note that the letter symbol for **true power** in an a-c circuit is the same as that for power in a d-c circuit.

Since $R = E_R/I_R$, just as in direct current circuits,

$$P = E_R I_R = I^2_R R = \frac{E^2_R}{R} \qquad (15.3)$$

where $E_R$ is the rms voltage across only the resistance portion of the circuit, and $I_R$ is the rms current through only the resistance portion of the circuit.

EXAMPLE 1: A wattmeter shows a true power of 144 w in an a-c circuit in which the effective current is 2 amp. What is the resistance of this circuit?

*Solution:*

$$R = \frac{P}{I^2} = \frac{144}{2 \times 2} = 36 \text{ ohms}$$

## 2. Power in a Pure Inductance

We can determine the nature of the instantaneous power in a pure inductance by the same technique of plotting the product of the instantaneous voltage and current on a linear graph. But in preparing the dashed sine curves of Fig. 15.2, we must note that the current in a pure inductance *lags* the applied voltage by exactly 90°.

At the 0° point on the graph of Fig. 15.2, the instantaneous current is zero and therefore the product $e \times i$ must also be zero. Between 0° and 90°, both $e$ and $i$ are positive quantities. Therefore the product $e \times i$, and consequently the instantaneous power, is a positive quantity reaching its

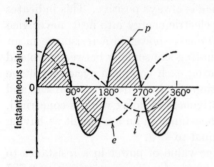

peak value at 45° and dropping to zero at 90° when the instantaneous voltage becomes zero. Between 90° and 180°, the voltage has reversed its polarity, but since the current lags the voltage, the current still maintains its original direction. Therefore although $e$ is now a negative quantity, $i$ is still a positive quantity. Therefore between 90°

**Fig. 15.2.** Instantaneous power in a pure inductance.

and 180°, the product $ei$, hence the instantaneous power, is a negative quantity becoming maximum at 135° and returning to zero at 180° when the instantaneous current becomes zero.

Between 180° and 270°, both the instantaneous voltage and instantaneous current are negative quantities. Therefore the instantaneous power again becomes a positive quantity rising to a peak at 225° and dropping back to zero at 270° when the instantaneous voltage becomes zero. Between 270° and 360°, the instantaneous voltage has become a positive quantity again, while the instantaneous current still remains negative. Again the instantaneous power must be a negative quantity rising to its peak value at 315° and dropping to zero at 360° when the instantaneous current becomes zero.

We will note from the solid instantaneous power curve of Fig. 15.2 that the instantaneous power in a pure inductance is sinusoidal in shape at twice the frequency of the voltage and current, just as it is in a pure resistance. But in the case of the pure inductance, the instantaneous power is *negative* between 90° and 180° to the same extent that it was positive between 0° and 90°. If we examine Fig. 15.2 closely, we will notice that between 0° and 90° the instantaneous current is *increasing*, thus building up a magnetic field around the inductor. During this time interval the inductor is taking energy from the source and storing it in its magnetic field, hence the instantaneous power is a positive quantity. Between 90° and 180° the current is *decreasing*. Therefore the magnetic field is collapsing and returning its stored energy back into the system. Therefore the negative value of instantaneous power between 90° and 180° represents this return of energy from the inductance to the source. Similarly from 180° to 270°, the current is rising in the reverse direction, a magnetic field is being built up and the instantaneous power is a positive quantity; and from 270° to

360°, as the current decreases, the stored energy is again returned to the source and the instantaneous power is a negative quantity.

Since a pure inductance in an a-c circuit alternately takes from and returns to the source equal amounts of energy, **the average or true power in a pure inductance is zero.** In the case of a pure resistance, we are able to determine the true power by simply multiplying the effective values of voltage and current. In the circuit of Fig. 15.3, the meters will show us the effective values of voltage and current for the pure inductance. But since the true power in a pure inductance is zero, $E_L I_L$ does *not* represent true power.

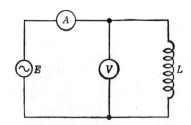

Fig. 15.3. Reactive power in a pure inductance.

However this product is directly proportional to the amount of energy stored and returned by the inductor each time the current changes direction. Therefore

the product of the effective voltage and current in a pure inductance is called the **reactive power** of the inductor.

The letter symbol for **reactive power** is $P_q$.

$$\therefore \quad P_q = E_L I_L \tag{15.4}$$

Since the true power in the pure inductance is zero, in order to avoid the possibility of mistaking reactive power for true power, in a-c circuits we reserve the **watt** exclusively for **true** power. Reactive power is simply the product of the voltage across and the current through a pure reactance.

Therefore the unit of **reactive power** is the **voltampere** (reactive), which is abbreviated to **var.**

Since
$$X_L = \frac{E_L}{I_L}, \tag{12.2}$$

$$P_q = E_L I_L = I_L^2 X_L = \frac{E_L^2}{X_L} \text{ vars} \tag{15.5}$$

EXAMPLE 2: What is the reactive power of a pure inductance of 0.5 h drawing 0.5 amp from a 60 c source?

*Solution:*
$$X_L = \omega L = 377 \times 0.5 = +j188.5 \text{ ohms}$$
$$P_q = I_L^2 X_L = 0.5 \times 0.5 \times 188.5 = 47.1 \text{ vars}$$

## 3. Power in a Pure Capacitance

Since the current in a pure capacitance leads the PD across the capacitor by exactly 90°, we again find that the instantaneous power graph of Fig.

15.4, although a sine wave at twice the frequency of the voltage and current, goes alternately positive and negative for equal time intervals. As we would expect, on examining Fig. 15.4 we find that the instantaneous power is positive while the PD across the capacitor is rising and the capacitor is taking energy from the source to store up a charge on its plates. While the PD across the capacitor is decreasing, the capacitor is discharging the stored energy back into the system. During this 90° interval, the instantaneous power is a negative quantity.

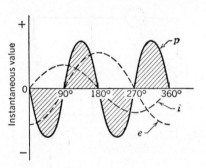

**Fig. 15.4.** Instantaneous power in a pure capacitance.

Since a pure capacitance must discharge as much energy between 180° and 270° as it stored between 90° and 180°, **the average or true power in a pure capacitance is zero.** Therefore again we find that the product of the effective voltage across and current in a pure capacitance does *not* represent true power. Like a pure inductance, a pure capacitance represents reactance in an alternating current circuit. Therefore $E_cI_c$ represents the reactive power of a capacitor which must be expressed in **vars.**

$$\therefore \quad P_q = E_cI_c = I_c{}^2X_c = \frac{E_c{}^2}{X_c} \text{ vars} \qquad (15.6)$$

EXAMPLE 3: What value of capacitance will have a reactive power of 50 vars when connected to a 120 v, 60 c source of emf?

*Solution:* Since $P_q = E_c{}^2/X_c$,

$$X_c = \frac{E_c{}^2}{P_q} = \frac{120 \times 120}{50} = -j288 \text{ ohms}$$

Since $X_c = 1/\omega C$,

$$C = \frac{1}{\omega X_c} = \frac{10^6}{377 \times 288} = 9.2 \ \mu\text{f}$$

## 4. Power in a Circuit Containing Resistance and Reactance

If a circuit consists of equal resistance and inductive reactance in series as in Fig. 15.5, the current lags the applied emf by 45°. Therefore when we plot the instantaneous power on the graph of Fig. 15.6, it is a positive quantity between 0° and 135° and becomes a negative quantity only for the short period of time between 135° and 180°.

The instantaneous power graph for an a-c circuit containing both resistance and reactance is again a sine wave at twice the frequency of the voltage and current. But for the circuit of Fig. 15.5, the instantaneous

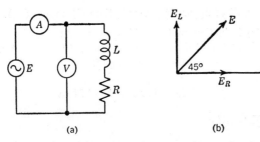

**Fig. 15.5.** An AC circuit containing resistance and inductive reactance in series.

power graph is neither all positive as in the case of a pure resistance nor equally positive and negative as in the case of a pure inductance. Since the instantaneous power graph is more positive than negative, there is an average or true power component which represents the true power of the resistance of the circuit. And since the portion of the instantaneous power which is a negative quantity is offset by a similar positive portion, there is a reactive power component in the reactance of the circuit.

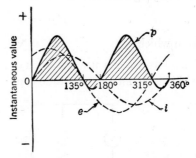

**Fig. 15.6.** Instantaneous power in an AC circuit containing both resistance and inductive reactance.

Therefore the product of the total voltage and total current represents neither the true power of the circuit in **watts** nor the reactive power in **vars**. If we have only the voltmeter and ammeter readings to go by in the circuit of Fig. 15.5, we have no means of determining the true power and the reactive power of the circuit. Therefore

the product of the total voltage and the total current in an a-c circuit is called the **apparent power** of the circuit.

The letter symbol for **apparent power** is $P_s$.

$$\therefore \quad P_s = E_T I_T \tag{15.7}$$

Since
$$\frac{E_T}{I_T} = Z, \tag{14.3}$$

$$P_s = E_T I_T = I_T^2 Z = \frac{E_T^2}{Z} \tag{15.8}$$

Since the apparent power is neither all true power in **watts** nor reactive power in **vars,** it must always be expressed simply as the product of volts and amps.

Therefore the unit of **apparent power** is the voltampere (va).

EXAMPLE 4: An induction motor (which represents a load possessing both resistance and inductance) draws a 3.4 amp current from a 110 v, 60 c source. What apparent power must the source supply?

*Solution:*

$$P_s = E_T I_T = 110 \times 3.4 = 374 \text{ va}$$

## 5. The Power Triangle

Although total voltage times total current does not give us any indication of the true power and reactive power in the circuit of Fig. 15.5, we can find the true power from the product of $E_R$ and $I$ and the reactive power from the product of $E_L$ and $I$. Since $E_L$ leads $E_R$ by 90° (Fig. 15.5), we can state that

$$E_T = \sqrt{E_R^2 + E_L^2} \tag{14.2}$$

Multiplying each side of the equation by the common current,

$$E_T I = \sqrt{(E_R I)^2 + (E_L I)^2}$$

from which          $$P_s = \sqrt{P^2 + P_q^2} \text{ va} \tag{15.9}$$

Therefore we can use the sides of a right-angled triangle to represent the relationship among the three types of power in an a-c circuit.

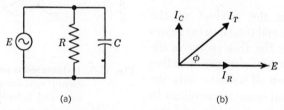

(a)                                              (b)

**Fig. 15.7.** An AC circuit containing resistance and capacitive reactance in parallel.

Similarly in the parallel circuit of Fig. 15.7, since the current in the capacitor branch must lead the current in the resistor branch by exactly 90°,

$$I_T = \sqrt{I_R^2 + I_C^2} \tag{14.15}$$

Multiplying each side of the equation by the common voltage,

$$E I_T = \sqrt{(E I_R)^2 + (E I_C)^2}$$

and again          $$P_s = \sqrt{P^2 + P_q^2} \text{ va} \tag{15.9}$$

One of the interesting features about any equations for power is that the *same* equations apply to both series, parallel, and series-parallel circuits.

Although instantaneous power does vary sinusoidally, it does so at *twice* the frequency of the voltage and current. Therefore we prefer not to represent the relationship among true power, reactive power, and apparent power by the conventional vector diagram of the type shown in Fig. 15.5(b) and 15.7(b). It is customary to represent this Pythagorean relationship by means of right-angled triangles as shown in Fig. 15.8.

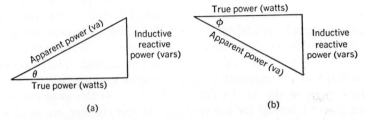

(a)                                    (b)

**Fig. 15.8.** The power triangle; (a) based on common current as reference axis; and (b) based on common voltage as reference axis.

As we would expect, the side of the triangle representing true power is drawn horizontally. The side representing reactive power is drawn in a vertical plane with the right angle at the *right*-hand end of the side representing true power. Since Equation (15.9) applies to either a series or a parallel circuit, we must decide on some convention for determining whether inductive reactive power will be shown in a positive or a negative direction when preparing power triangles. If we start with an impedance triangle based on $Z = R + jX$, multiplying each side of the triangle by a constant (the common current), does not change the relationship among the sides of the triangle.

$$\therefore \; IZ = IR + jIX$$

from which $E = E_R + jE_X$, which gives us the voltage vector diagram of Fig. 15.5(b). Multiplying all terms by the common current again gives us

$$EI = E_R I + jE_X I$$

from which $P_s = P + jP_q$. This produces the power triangle of Fig. 15.8(a).

However, if we start with the admittance triangle for an inductance and resistance in parallel and multiply all sides by the common voltage, we will obtain the current vector diagram for the circuit. Multiplying again by the common voltage produces the power triangle of Fig. 15.8(b).

If all electric circuits were either simple series or simple parallel circuits, we would simply select the appropriate power triangle. But practical electric circuits combine both series and parallel components as shown in Fig. 15.9(a). We must then decide on *either* current *or* voltage as the reference axis and construct all power triangles accordingly. Electric power distribution is based on sources of constant emf across which we connect various loads in parallel. Therefore in 1935 the International Electrotechnical Commission decided that inductive reactive power should be shown in a *negative* direction as in Fig. 15.8(b). According to the standards for letter symbols, if we use voltage as the common reference, the **power factor angle** between the true power and the apparent power in the power triangle of Fig. 15.8(b), which is the same as the phase angle of the total current *with respect to* the total voltage, should be represented by the symbol $\phi$.

When the American Institute of Electrical Engineers was revising its standards for graphical and letter symbols in 1948, common current was chosen as the preferred reference for power triangles. This places inductive reactive power in the *positive* direction as in Fig. 15.8(a). The power factor angle would now be represented by the symbol $\theta$, since it is the same as the phase angle of the total voltage *with respect to* the total current. In drawing power triangles for the examples in this chapter, we shall follow the AIEE preference.

Since the voltage across the inductance in a series circuit is 180° out of phase with the voltage across the capacitance, the net reactive voltage is the *difference* between the two reactive voltages. Similarly in a simple parallel circuit the net reactive current is the *difference* between the inductive and capacitive branch currents. Therefore, since $P_q = E_X I_X$, the net reactive power in any alternating current circuit (either series or parallel) is the *difference* between the inductive reactive power and the capacitive reactive power.

If we examine Fig. 15.2 closely, we will note that the instantaneous power in an inductance is positive when the current is rising and building up a magnetic field around the inductor. But Fig. 15.4 shows that, when the current is rising, the capacitance is discharging its stored energy back into the system. Therefore in an a-c circuit containing both inductance and capacitance, the capacitance always returns energy to the circuit when the inductance takes energy from the circuit, and vice versa. Therefore a certain amount of energy can be traded back and forth between the inductance and the capacitance of the circuit and as far as the source is concerned, the only reactive power required by the circuit is the *difference* between the inductive reactive power and the capacitive reactive power.

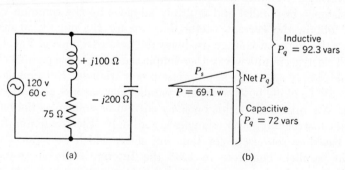

**Fig. 15.9.** Diagram for Example 5.

EXAMPLE 5: A circuit consists of two branches connected in parallel to a 120 v, 60 c source. Branch I consists of a 75 ohm resistance and a 100 ohm inductive reactance in series. Branch II consists of a 200 ohm capacitive reactance. Determine the apparent power of the circuit.

*Solution I:*

   *Step I.*

$$Z_1 = R + jX_L = 75 + j100 = 125 \text{ ohms}\underline{/+53.1°}$$

$$\therefore \quad I_1 = \frac{E}{Z_1} = \frac{120}{125} = 0.96 \text{ amp}$$

   *Step II.* True power of the circuit is

$$P = I_1^2 R = 0.96^2 \times 75 = 69.1 \text{ w}$$

Reactive power of the inductance is

$$P_q = I_1^2 X_L = 0.96^2 \times 100 = 92.3 \text{ vars}$$

Reactive power of the capacitance is

$$P_q = \frac{E^2}{X_C} = \frac{120^2}{200} = 72 \text{ vars}$$

Net reactive power of the circuit is

$$P_q = 92.3 - 72 = 20.3 \text{ vars} \quad \text{(inductive)}$$

   *Step III.*

$$P_s = \sqrt{P^2 + P_q^2} = \sqrt{69.1^2 + 20.3^2} = 72 \text{ va}$$

*Solution II:* A somewhat similar procedure involves solving Steps **II** and **III** in terms of current rather than power.

   *Step I.*

$$Z_1 = R + jX_L = 75 + j100 = 125 \text{ ohms}\underline{/+53.1°}$$

$$\therefore \quad I_1 = \frac{E}{Z_1} = \frac{120\underline{/0°}}{125\underline{/+53.1°}} = 0.96 \text{ amp}\underline{/-53.1°}$$

$$\therefore \quad I_1 = 0.58 - j0.77 \text{ amp}$$

   *Step II.*

$$I_C = \frac{E}{X_C} = \frac{120\underline{/0°}}{200\underline{/-90°}} = 0.6 \text{ amp}\underline{/+90°}$$

$$\therefore \quad I_C = 0 + j0.6 \text{ amp}$$

$$I_T = I_1 + I_C = (0.58 - j0.77) + (0 + j0.6)$$

$$\therefore \quad I_T = 0.58 - j0.17 = \sqrt{0.58^2 + 0.17^2} = 0.6 \text{ amp}$$

   *Step III.*

$$\therefore \quad P_s = E_T I_T = 120 \times 0.6 = 72 \text{ va}$$

## 6. Power Factor

Since the hypotenuse of a right-angled triangle must be greater than either of the other two sides, the apparent power that a generator must supply to a reactive load is always greater than the true power that the load can convert into some other form of energy. Since most industrial loads possess appreciable inductive reactance, this relationship between the true power that the load can use and the apparent power that the source must supply is of considerable importance.

The **ratio between the true power and the apparent power** of a load in an a-c circuit is called the **power factor** of the load.

The letter symbol for **power factor** is $F_p$.

$$\therefore \quad F_p = \frac{P}{P_s} \tag{15.10}$$

To distinguish between inductive loads and capacitive loads, we say that *inductive* loads always have a lagging power factor and that *capacitive* loads always have a leading power factor.* Since the true power cannot be greater than the apparent power, the power factor cannot have a numerical value greater than unity. Since it is a simple ratio, power factor is always a positive quantity. We may express power factor as either a decimal fraction or a percentage.

EXAMPLE 6: What are the true power and power factor of a load whose impedance is 60 ohms$/+60°$ when connected to a 120 v, 60 c source of emf?

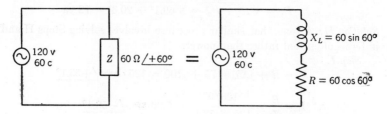

**Fig. 15.10.** Schematic diagram for Example 6.

*Solution:*

*Step I.* Expressing the impedance in rectangular coordinates produces the equivalent of a series circuit consisting of pure resistance and reactance in series.

$$\therefore \quad Z = 60 \cos 60° + j60 \sin 60°$$

from which $R = 30$ ohms.

*Step II.*

$$I = \frac{E}{Z} = \frac{120}{60} = 2.0 \text{ amp}$$

$$\therefore \quad P = I^2R = 4 \times 30 = 120 \text{ w}$$

$$P_s = I^2Z = 4 \times 60 = 240 \text{ va}$$

* Obviously this terminology is based on the phase angle of the current *with respect to* the voltage, which is no longer the preferred method in North America for drawing power triangles.

*Step III.*

$$\therefore \quad F_p = \frac{P}{P_s} = \frac{120}{240} = 0.5 \text{ lagging}$$

Although our solution to Example 6 follows the definition of power factor, it is a roundabout way of tackling the problem. We have already noted that the angle between the true power and apparent power in a power triangle (Fig. 15.8) is the same as the phase angle between the total voltage and total current in the circuit. Since apparent power is the hypotenuse of the power triangle, $P/P_s = \cos \theta$.

$$\therefore \quad F_p = \cos \theta \quad (15.11)$$

We can also arrive at Equation (15.11) from our solution to Example 6.

$$P = I^2R = I^2Z \cos \theta$$

$$P_s = I^2Z$$

$$\therefore \quad F_p = \frac{P}{P_s} = \frac{I^2Z \cos \theta}{I^2Z} = \cos \theta$$

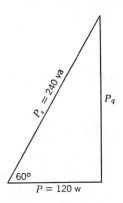

**Fig. 15.11.** Power triangle for Example 6A.

EXAMPLE 6A: What are the power factor and true power of a load whose impedance is 60 ohms$\underline{/+60°}$ when connected to a 120 v, 60 c source of emf?
*Solution:*
    *Step I.*

$$F_p = \cos \theta = \cos 60° = 0.5 \text{ lagging}$$

    *Step II.*

$$P_s = \frac{E^2}{Z} = \frac{120^2}{60} = 240 \text{ va}$$

Since $F_p = P/P_s$,

$$P = F_pP_s = 0.5 \times 240 = 120 \text{ w}$$

From this solution we will note that we can express true power in terms of power factor and apparent power. This leads to the following useful expression for true power in a-c circuits.

$$P = EI \cos \theta \quad (15.12)$$

Once we know the true power and apparent power of an a-c load, we can determine the reactive power by Pythagoras' theorem.

$$P_q = \sqrt{P_s^2 - P^2}$$

Since $P = F_pP_s$, this becomes

$$P_q = P_s\sqrt{1 - F_p^2} \quad (15.13)$$

Although our main concern in dealing with a-c loads is the ratio between true power and apparent power, there are some instances when we wish to solve directly for the reactive power of the load. In these cases it is useful to be able to express the ratio between reactive power and apparent power.

**Reactive factor** is the ratio between the reactive power and apparent power of an a-c load.

The letter symbol for **reactive factor** is $F_q$.

$$\therefore \quad F_q = \frac{P_q}{P_s} \tag{15.14}$$

and from the position of $P_q$ and $P_s$ in the power triangle,

$$F_q = \sin \theta \tag{15.15}$$

## 7. Power Factor Correction

We can appreciate the consequences of a low power factor in an industrial load by considering the state of affairs illustrated by Fig. 15.12. Since the motor in Fig. 15.12(a) has a 70% lagging power factor, the apparent power as far as the source is concerned is

$$P_s = \frac{P}{F_p} = \frac{840}{0.7} = 1200 \text{ va}$$

and therefore the current drain on the source is

$$I = \frac{P_s}{E} = \frac{1200}{120} = 10 \text{ amp}$$

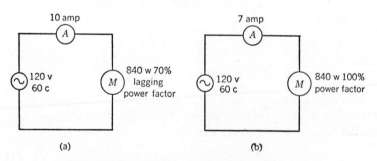

Fig. **15.12.** Effect of load power factor.

If we now replace the original motor by one capable of developing a true power of 840 w at 100% power factor as in Fig. 15.12(b), the power apparently drawn from the source will now be 840 va. The current drawn by the second motor is only 7 amp. Therefore the 70% power factor motor requires a current of 10 amp to do the same work that the unity power factor motor can do by drawing only 7 amp from the source.

The wire size used in the windings of the generator and the conductors connecting the load to the generator depends on the *current* they have to pass, and the copper losses in the system depend on the square of the *current*. Therefore it is more economical for an electrical utility company to feed an 840 w, 100% power factor load than to feed an 840 w, 70% lagging power factor load. Since a great many industrial loads possess considerable inductive reactance, these electrical utility companies are very much concerned with maintaining a high over-all power factor in their systems.

As we have noted, an 840 w, 70% lagging power factor motor draws 3 amp more from the source than an equivalent 840 w, 100% power factor motor. As a power triangle shows, this additional current is involved in supplying the reactive power required by the inductive reactance of the motor. But as shown in Fig. 15.2, this portion of the current alternately transfers energy from the system into the magnetic field of the inductance and then returns the stored energy back to the system. Although the average power used by the inductance during this process is zero, this charge and discharge current has to flow through the generator windings and connecting conductors, thus forcing us to use a larger wire size for a given load power.

We can illustrate this charge and discharge or *reactive* current component by expressing the current of each of the motors in Fig. 15.12 in rectangular coordinates. In the case of the 70% lagging power factor motor, the current lags the applied emf by arccos $0.7 = 45.6°$.

$$\therefore \quad I = 10 \cos 45.6° - j10 \sin 45.6° = 7 - j7.14 \text{ amp}$$

In the case of the 100% power factor motor, the current is in phase with the applied emf.

$$\therefore \quad I = 7 - j0 \text{ amp}$$

When we express the load current in this manner, we note that both have the same *reference axis* component. It is this component that contributes to the true power of the load. The 70% lagging power factor load requires the additional *quadrature* component to take care of the inductance of the load.

We will recall that in an a-c circuit containing both inductance and capacitance, the capacitance returns energy to the system, while the inductance takes energy from

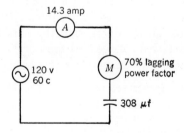

Fig. 15.13. Effect of series capacitance on a lagging power factor load.

the system and vice versa. If we then place a capacitor in the circuit containing the 70% lagging power factor motor, it should be possible for the capacitor and the inductance of the load to trade their reactive power back and forth without the reactive component of the current having to travel all the way from the source to the load and back. This would allow us to use low power factor loads in practice yet obtain the advantages of a high system power factor.

For the moment we will connect a 308 μf capacitor in *series* with the 70% lagging power factor motor as in Fig. 15.13. The impedance of the motor is $Z_M = E/I = 120/10 = 12$ ohms.

$$\theta = \arccos 0.7 = 45.6°$$

$$\therefore \quad Z_M = 12 \text{ ohms} \underline{/+45.6°}$$

$$= 12 \cos 45.6° + j12 \sin 45.6° = 8.4 + j8.6 \text{ ohms}$$

$$X_C = \frac{1}{\omega C} = \frac{10^6}{377 \times 308} = -j8.6 \text{ ohms}$$

Since the motor and capacitor are in series,

$$Z_T = 8.4 + j8.6 - j8.6 = 8.4 + j0 \text{ ohms}$$

$$\therefore \quad Z_T = 8.4 \text{ ohms} \underline{/0°}$$

Since the phase angle of the total impedance is now 0°, the current drawn from the generator is in phase with the source emf. But

$$I = \frac{E}{Z_T} = \frac{120}{8.4} = 14.3 \text{ amp}$$

Therefore connecting a capacitor in *series* with an inductive load to reduce the net reactive power does not *reduce* the current drain on the source. It *increases* it. Moreover, since the impedance of the motor itself is still 12 ohms, the voltage across the motor in the circuit of Fig. 15.13 becomes

$$E_M = IZ_M = 14.3 \times 12 = 172 \text{ v}$$

Although connecting a capacitor in *series* with the motor has raised the system power factor to 100%, it has served only to aggravate the original problem by increasing the current drawn from the source by applying excessive voltage to the motor. Therefore we *cannot* correct for a low power factor by connecting a capacitor in *series* with an inductive load.

> **Power factor correction or improvement** consists of adding a capacitive reactive power to an a-c circuit in such a manner that the apparent power drawn from the source is reduced without altering the current through or the voltage across the load itself.

One of the characteristics of a parallel circuit is that, although a change in one branch will affect the *total* current, it will *not* affect the current in the other branches. Therefore in the circuit of Fig. 15.14 we have connected a capacitor in parallel with the 840 w, 70% lagging power factor motor. Since the motor is still connected directly across the 120 v source, its current is still 10 amp lagging the applied emf by 45.6°. Because of its lagging power factor, the motor has a reactive power of $P_q = EI \sin \theta = 120 \times 10 \times 0.714 = 860$ vars. If the capacitor in parallel with the motor also has a reactive power of 860 vars, they will be able to trade this reac-

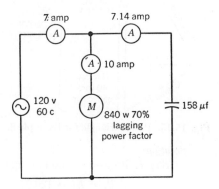

Fig. 15.14. Power factor correction.

tive power back and forth between them, and as far as the generator is concerned, the net reactive power in the circuit is zero. Since the voltage across and current through the motor are unchanged, the true power is still 840 w. Therefore the over-all apparent power that the generator must supply is 840 va and the current drawn from the genera-tor becomes 7 amp. Note that adding the capacitor to the circuit has decreased the generator current to 7 amp while the motor current still remains at 10 amp. As far as the generator is concerned, the 70% lagging power factor motor and capacitor in parallel are the equivalent of a unity power factor motor.

Although we can solve for the required capacitance by noting that the capacitor current must equal the reactive component of the load current or that the susceptance of the capacitor must equal the susceptance com-ponent of the load admittance, the simplest procedure is to work in terms of reactive power since power equations are independent of series or parallel connection of the circuit components.

**To obtain an over-all unity power factor** with a lagging power factor in a load, a capacitor having a reactive power equal to the reactive power of the load is connected in parallel with the load.

EXAMPLE 7: What value of capacitor must be connected in parallel with a motor drawing 10 amp at 70% lagging power factor from a 120 v, 60 c source in order for the generator current to be minimum?

*Solution:*

*Step I.* The reactive power of the load is

$$P_q = EI\sqrt{1 - F_p{}^2} = 120 \times 10\sqrt{1 - 0.7^2} = 860 \text{ vars}$$

Therefore the reactive power of the capacitor must be 860 vars.

*Step II.* But $P_q = E^2/X_C$.

$$\therefore \quad X_C = \frac{E^2}{P_q} = \frac{120^2}{860} = 16.7 \text{ ohms}$$

$$C = \frac{1}{\omega X_C} = \frac{10^6}{377 \times 16.7} = 158 \ \mu f$$

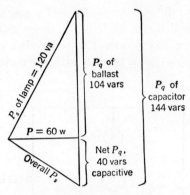

**Fig. 15.15.** Power triangle for Example 8.

*Note:* As a check that *adding* an extra branch current does reduce the total current drawn from the source without affecting the load current, draw an accurate vector diagram for the circuit of Fig. 15.14.

EXAMPLE 8: A fluorescent lamp and its ballast inductance draw a 1.0 amp current at a 50% lagging power factor from a 120 v, 60 c source. What is the over-all power factor when a 26.5 μf capacitor is connected across the fixture?

*Solution:*

Step I. Prepare a power triangle for the lamp and its ballast inductance.

$$P_s = EI = 120 \times 1.0 = 120 \text{ va}$$

$$P = F_p P_s = 0.5 \times 120 = 60 \text{ w}$$

$$P_q = \sqrt{P_s^2 - P^2} = \sqrt{120^2 - 60^2} = 104 \text{ vars}$$

Step II.

$$X_C = \frac{1}{\omega C} = \frac{10^6}{377 \times 26.5} = 100 \text{ ohms}$$

$$P_q = \frac{E^2}{X_C} = \frac{120^2}{100} = 144 \text{ vars}$$

Step III. Net $P_q = 144 - 104 = 40$ capacitive vars, and over-all

$$P_s = \sqrt{P^2 + P_q^2} = \sqrt{60^2 + 40^2} = 72 \text{ va.}$$

Step IV.

$$\therefore \quad \text{Over-all } F_p = \frac{P}{P_s} = \frac{60}{72} = 83.3\% \text{ leading.}$$

EXAMPLE 9: What value of capacitor must be connected in parallel with a load drawing 1 kw at 70.7% lagging power factor from a 208 v, 60 c source in order to raise the over-all power factor to 91% lagging?

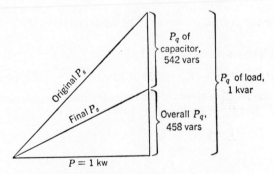

**Fig. 15.16.** Power triangle for Example 9.

*Solution:*

    *Step I.* Original $P_s = P/F_p = 1000/0.707 = 1.41$ kva.

        Reactive power of load,

$$P_q = \sqrt{P_s{}^2 - P^2} = \sqrt{1.41^2 - 1^2} = 1 \text{ kvar}$$

    *Step II.*

        Final     $P_s = \dfrac{P}{F_p} = \dfrac{1000}{0.91} = 1.1$ kva

        Over-all $P_q = \sqrt{P_s{}^2 - P^2} = \sqrt{1.1^2 - 1^2} = 458$ vars.

    *Step III.* Therefore from the power triangle, the reactive power of the capacitor must be

$$P_q = 1000 - 458 = 542 \text{ vars}$$

$$\therefore \quad X_c = \frac{E^2}{P_q} = \frac{208^2}{542} = 80 \text{ ohms}$$

$$C = \frac{1}{\omega X_c} = \frac{10^6}{377 \times 80} = 33 \ \mu\text{f}$$

## 8. Measuring Power in an a-c Circuit

In a d-c system we seldom require wattmeters to indicate power input to a load since we can obtain this data simply by multiplying the voltmeter reading by the ammeter reading. However in an a-c system, the product of the voltmeter and ammeter readings gives us only the *apparent* power input to a load. Unless we have further information as to the power factor of the load or the phase angle between load voltage and load current, we cannot determine the true power input to the load in this manner.

In Chapter 8 we discussed briefly the use of the electro-dynamometer movement to provide a direct indication of the power into a load. We noted that the torque which moved the pointer was proportional to the product of the current in the stationary current coil and the current through the moving coil, which in turn was proportional to the voltage across which the voltage coil and its series multiplier resistor were connected. We can now consider the effect of the load power factor on the electro-dynamometer reading by referring first to the voltage and current relationships in a pure resistance as shown in Fig. 15.1.

The current through the current coil is represented by the dashed current curve and the current through the voltage coil is represented by the dashed voltage curve. The instantaneous power curve in Fig. 15.1 represents the product $e \times i$ and also represents the instantaneous torque developed by the electro-dynamometer movement. Since the current in both coils reverses at the same instant, the instantaneous torque (like the instantaneous power) is always positive. However the inertia of the pointer and voltage coil assembly will not allow the pointer to follow the variations in instantaneous torque due to the alternating current in the coils. There-

fore the pointer will take up a position which represents the average between zero and maximum instantaneous torque. The position of the pointer
then represents the average power into the resistor.

If we now connect the electro-dynamometer to a pure inductance, the
currents in the two coils will be 90° out of phase as indicated by the dashed
curves in Fig. 15.2. Therefore the product of the two instantaneous fluxes
will produce a clockwise torque for one quarter cycle and a counterclockwise torque for the next quarter cycle. As a result the net meter deflection
is zero, just as the average of the instantaneous power (the true power) in a
pure inductance is zero. If we connect the electro-dynamometer to the
circuit of Fig. 15.5(a), the instantaneous torque can be represented by the
instantaneous power curve in Fig. 15.6. Now the clockwise torque is
greater than the counterclockwise torque and the meter will give a reading.
We can consider that the instantaneous torques due to the inductance
average to zero, leaving a net positive torque representing the true power
into the resistance of the circuit.

Therefore when an electro-dynamometer movement is connected with
its current coil in series with a load and its voltage terminals across the
load in an a-c circuit, it will indicate the *true power* input to the load.
The instrument can therefore be called a **wattmeter.** We should also note
that the wattmeter reading can be represented by

$$P = EI \cos \theta \qquad (15.16)$$

where $E$ is the voltage applied to the voltage terminals, $I$ is the current
flowing through the current terminals, and $\theta$ is the phase angle between the
voltage and current applied to the wattmeter.

In the wattmeter movement, the required current through the moving
voltage coil is determined by a *multiplier resistor* in series with the coil.
If we replace this resistor with a *capacitor* having the required capacitive
reactance at the power line frequency, the current through the voltage coil
will have the same magnitude but now will be 90° out of phase with the
voltage applied to the voltage terminals of the meter (since the capacitor
current leads the applied voltage by 90°). If we connect this meter to a
pure resistance circuit, the net torque is zero since the voltage coil current
is now 90° out of phase with the current through the current coil. Similarly
the meter will now show a reading when connected to a pure inductance
or capacitance load. This modification to the electro-dynamometer has
produced a meter which indicates *reactive power*. The meter can therefore
be called a **varmeter.**

## 9. Effective Resistance

In Chapter 8 we found that we can determine the resistance of a practical resistor by measuring the voltage across and the current through it.

However, for the results to be accurate, we must be sure that the voltage across the resistor is due only to $IR$ drop. We will recall that, as the current through an electric conductor increases, closed loop magnetic lines of force expand outward from the center of the conductor. As a result, in addition to the $IR$ drop, a small counter emf is induced in the copper being linked by the expanding magnetic lines of force. In a d-c circuit where the current is not changing, these induced voltages do not appear. Therefore when we make *direct* current measurements of the voltage across and current through a practical resistor, we are reasonably sure that the value of resistance determined from $R = V/I$ is the actual **ohmic** resistance of the resistor.

In an a-c circuit, the ratio between the voltage across and the current through a circuit component is, by definition, the **impedance** of that component rather than just its resistance. It is impossible for us to connect a voltmeter in such a manner as to read only the $IR$ drop across the resistance of the component. However, as we noted in Chapter 14, the *same* current flows through both the resistance and the reactance of practical imped- ances. We can then accurately measure $I_R$ in an a-c circuit even though we cannot accurately measure $E_R$. As we have noted earlier in this chapter, the *true* power in an a-c circuit represents the power input to the *resistance* of the circuit, and the operation of the wattmeter is such that it indicates only the true power input to the circuit. Therefore we are able to deter- mine the **effective** resistance of an a-c circuit from wattmeter and ammeter readings using the relationship

$$R = \frac{P}{I^2} \tag{15.17}$$

After going to this trouble to obtain a true resistance value in a practical a-c circuit, we would find that the **effective** resistance of the circuit with an alternating current flowing through it is not the same as the plain **ohmic** resistance when direct current flows through the circuit. One reason for this is apparent if we again consider the expanding and collapsing mag- netic lines of force around an electric conductor in an a-c circuit. There will be more changes in flux linkage at the center of the conductor than at the surface of the conductor. Therefore there is more opposition to the flow of alternating current in the center of the conductor than there is at the surface. As the frequency of the alternating current is increased, the rate of change of flux increases, which in turn increases the counter emf at the center of the conductor. This effect is so pronounced that, at radio frequencies, almost all the current flows along the surface of the conductor. This is called **skin effect.** Since practically no current flows in the center of the conductor at radio frequencies, its effective cross-sectional area is greatly reduced and therefore the effective resistance of the conductor is much greater than its d-c ohmic resistance.

Suppose that we now connect an ammeter and a wattmeter so that we can determine the effective resistance of a coil of wire in an a-c circuit. Having made the necessary calculations, we now insert an iron core into the coil. Due to the increase in inductive reactance, both meter readings decrease. But when we now calculate the effective resistance we find that it is greater than before. We can blame this on the hysteresis of the iron core and also eddy current in the core. Both hysteresis and eddy current cause energy taken from the electric source of emf to be converted into heat. This requires an increase in the true power input to the coil for a certain coil current. Since this increase in true power will be registered by the wattmeter, the effect of hysteresis and eddy current show up in our calculation of the effective resistance of the iron core coil. Again, the higher the frequency, the greater the discrepancy between ohmic resistance and effective resistance.

Similarly a capacitor which, when measured in a d-c circuit has an infinitely high resistance, can cause an appreciable wattmeter reading in an a-c circuit. This produces the effect of a resistance in parallel with the capacitor. The wattmeter in this case is indicating the transfer of energy into heat as the dielectric of the capacitor is stressed first in one direction and then in the other many times a second.

## Problems

1. A toaster draws a 6 amp current from a 110 v, 60 c source.
   (a) What is the true power of the toaster?
   (b) What is the peak value of the instantaneous power input to the toaster?
2. The voltage drop across the heater of a certain vacuum tube is 6.3 v rms when the current through it is 0.3 amp. What is the average rate of conversion of electric energy into heat?
3. What is the true power dissipation of a 75 ohm resistor in which the sine wave current reaches a peak value of 2.0 amp?
4. What wattage rating must a 300 ohm dummy antenna resistor possess if the rms voltage drop across it is 96 v?
5. A pure inductance of 3.0 h passes a current of 20 ma when connected into a 60 c circuit.
   (a) What is the true power input?
   (b) What is its reactive power?
   (c) What is the peak rate at which it can store energy?
6. A $26\frac{1}{2}$ μf capacitor is connected across a 120 v, 60 c source of emf.
   (a) What is its reactive power?
   (b) What is the apparent power input?
   (c) What is the peak rate at which it can discharge its stored energy back into the circuit?
7. A solenoid having an inductance of 0.5 h and a resistance of 24 ohms is connected to a 120 v, 60 c source of emf.

(a) What is the apparent power input to the solenoid?

(b) What is the true power of the solenoid?

(c) What is the power factor of the solenoid?

8. The operating coil of a relay draws 100 ma from a 24 v, 25 c source at a 10% lagging power factor.

(a) What is the resistance of the coil?

(b) What is the inductance of the coil?

9. What value of resistance and inductance in series will draw the same current from a 120 v, 60 c source as a 500 w, 60% lagging power factor load?

10. What value of resistance and inductance in parallel will draw the same current from a 120 v, 60 c source as a 500 w, 60% lagging power factor load?

11. (a) What current must a 110 v alternator supply to operate a 2 kw, 75% lagging power factor load?

(b) What true power could the alternator supply for the same magnitude of current in its windings to a unity power factor load?

12. An industrial capacitor used in power factor correction is rated at 7.5 kvar when connected to a 208 v, 60 c circuit. What is its capacitance?

13. An impedance coil having an 0.2 lagging power factor is connected in series with a 300 w lamp to supply the lamp with 120 v from a 208 v, 60 c source. What is the voltage across the terminals of the impedance coil?

14. An induction motor which draws 2.0 amp from a 120 v, 60 c source at 0.8 lagging power factor and a 100 w lamp are connected in parallel. What is their over-all power factor?

15. An induction motor draws 6.0 amp at 0.8 lagging power factor from a 208 v, 60c source.

(a) What value of capacitance must be placed in parallel with the motor to raise the over-all power factor to unity?

(b) What are the magnitudes of the final motor current, capacitor current, and line current?

16. What value of capacitance is required to produce an over-all power factor of 0.96 lagging with the motor of Problem 15?

17. What is the over-all power factor when a 50 $\mu f$ capacitor is connected in parallel with the motor of Problem 15?

18. A synchronous motor capable of operating with a leading power factor draws 15 kw from a distribution transformer while driving an air compressor. The remainder of the load on the transformer is 80 kw at 0.85 lagging power factor.

(a) How many kilovars of capacitive reactive power must the synchronous motor produce to raise the over-all power factor to 0.96 lagging?

(b) What is the reactive factor of the synchronous motor?

19. The power factor of a load on a 120 v, 60 c source is raised from 0.707 lagging to 0.866 lagging by connecting a 53 $\mu f$ capacitor across the load. What is the true power of the load?

20. A 10 $\mu f$ capacitor is connected in parallel with a coil having an inductance of 1 h and a resistance of 100 ohms. At what frequency will this combination have unity power factor?

## Review Questions

1. Why can we state that $p = ei$ in any a-c circuit?

2. Why is the instantaneous power in a pure resistance always a positive quantity?

3. Why can we state that the average power in a pure resistance in a sine wave a-c system is one-half the peak power?

4. Why is the product $E_R$ time $I_R$ called the true power?

5. Given an a-c voltmeter and an a-c ammeter how would you determine the peak value of the instantaneous power as a pure inductance builds up its magnetic field in an a-c circuit?

6. Why is the average power of a pure inductance zero?

7. What is the significance of the term reactive power?

8. What is the significance of the term apparent power?

9. What is the apparent power of a pure resistance?

10. What is the apparent power of a pure capacitance?

11. Why can we not express apparent power in watts?

12. Why can we say that the net reactive power of an a-c circuit is the difference between the inductive reactive power and the capacitive reactive power?

13. Why is the total true power of a network always the sum of the individual true powers regardless of series or parallel connection of the components?

14. Why is the apparent power of an a-c circuit the root of the sum of the squares of the true and reactive powers rather than the simple sum?

15. Why is the angle between the true power and apparent power in a power triangle the same as the angle between the total current and total voltage of a load?

16. What is the significance of the term power factor in dealing with industrial loads?

17. What is meant by a leading power factor?

18. Why are a-c generators and transformers rated in terms of kilovolt-amperes rather than kilowatts?

19. Of what practical use is the term reactive factor?

20. Derive an expression for reactive factor in terms of power factor.

21. Although placing capacitance in series with an inductive load raises the over-all power factor, why can we not consider this to be power factor correction?

22. What is the purpose of power factor correction?

23. Why does adding capacitance in parallel with an inductive load achieve this purpose?

24. Review the operation of the electro-dynamometer movement in Chapter 8 and then explain why an a-c wattmeter indicates **true** power.

25. In determining the effective value of a sine wave by laboratory experiment, we determine the equivalent direct current that will produce the same lamp brilliance. Why do we work with current rather than voltage?

# Chapter 16

# IMPEDANCE NETWORKS

## 1. Impedances in Series

Resistance and impedance both represent opposition to the flow of alternating current. Both are measured in terms of the same unit, the **ohm.** But impedance is the *vector* sum of the resistance and reactance of a circuit. However, **as long as we carry out all the necessary arithmetical processes by vector algebra, all the relationships developed in Chapters 5 and 6 for resistance networks may be applied to impedance networks.**

Therefore it follows that *the total impedance of several impedances in series is their* **vector** *sum.*

$$Z_T = Z_1 + Z_2 + Z_3 + \text{etc.} \tag{16.1}$$

EXAMPLE 1: What is the total impedance when $Z_1 = 60$ ohms$/\underline{+60°}$ and $Z_2 = 80$ ohms$/\underline{-45°}$ are connected in series?

*Solution:*

*Step I.* Always draw a circuit diagram on which can be shown all pertinent data for ready reference and a fairly accurate freehand impedance diagram to indicate the approximate solution.

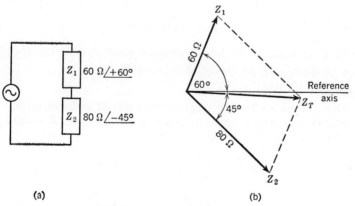

(a)                                             (b)

**Fig. 16.1.** Impedances in series.

335

*Step II.* Express the impedances in rectangular form so that their coordinates can be added.

$$Z_1 = 60 \cos 60° + j60 \sin 60° = 30 \quad + j52$$
$$Z_2 = 80 \cos 45° - j80 \sin 45° = \underline{56.5 - j56.5}$$

Adding gives $\qquad\qquad\qquad\qquad\qquad Z_T = 86.5 - \phantom{5}j4.5$ ohms

*Step III.* Convert the total impedance into polar form.

$$\theta = \arctan \frac{-4.5}{86.5} = -3°$$

$$Z_T = \sqrt{86.5^2 + 4.5^2} = 86.6 \text{ ohms}$$

$$\therefore \quad Z_T = 86.6 \text{ ohms}\underline{/-3°}$$

## 2. Impedances in Parallel

In working with resistances in parallel in Chapter 5, we found that the *more* resistors we connect in parallel, the *less* is the total resistance. We therefore found it to our advantage to switch our point of view in dealing with parallel circuits and to think in terms of the ability of the various parallel branches to *conduct* electric current. Therefore the solution of parallel circuits is a bit more involved than the solution of series circuits, since we must first make this conversion from *opposition* into *ability to conduct*. In solving parallel a-c circuits, we can use the same procedures we used with parallel resistances: the total current method and the total admittance method.

$$Z_T = \frac{E}{I_T}$$

where $\qquad\qquad\qquad I_T = I_1 + I_2 + I_3 + \text{etc.} \qquad\qquad\qquad (16.2)$

$$Z_T = \frac{1}{Y_T}$$

where $\qquad\qquad\qquad Y_T = Y_1 + Y_2 + Y_3 + \text{etc.} \qquad\qquad\qquad (16.3)$

EXAMPLE 2: What is the total impedance when $Z_1 = 60$ ohms$\underline{/+60°}$ and $Z_2 = 80$ ohms$\underline{/-45°}$ are connected in parallel?

*Solution 1:*

    *Step I.* Draw a schematic diagram and a current vector diagram.

    *Step II.* Assume a convenient value of applied emf; e.g., $E = 240$ v$\underline{/0°}$.

    *Step III.* Determine the branch currents.

$$I_1 = \frac{E}{Z_1} = \frac{240\underline{/0°}}{60\underline{/+60°}} = 4 \text{ amp}\underline{/-60°}$$

$$I_2 = \frac{E}{Z_2} = \frac{240\underline{/0°}}{80\underline{/-45°}} = 3 \text{ amp}\underline{/+45°}$$

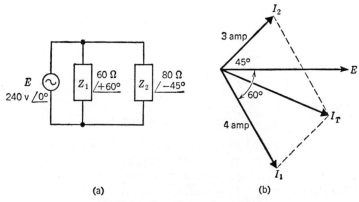

(a)                                    (b)

**Fig. 16.2.** Impedances in parallel.

*Step IV.* Express the branch currents in rectangular coordinates so they can be added.

$$I_1 = 4 \cos 60° - j4 \sin 60° = 2 \quad\ - j3.46$$
$$I_2 = 3 \cos 45° + j3 \sin 45° = 2.12 + j2.12$$

Adding gives                          $I_T = 4.12 - j1.34$ amp

*Step V.* Convert the total current into polar form.

$$\phi = \arctan \frac{-1.34}{4.12} = -18°$$

$$I_T = \sqrt{4.12^2 + 1.34^2} = 4.33 \text{ amp}$$

$$\therefore\ \ I_T = 4.33 \text{ amp}\underline{/-18°}$$

*Step VI.*

$$\therefore\ \ Z_T = \frac{E}{I_T} = \frac{240\underline{/0°}}{4.33\underline{/-18°}} = 55.5 \text{ ohms}\underline{/+18°}$$

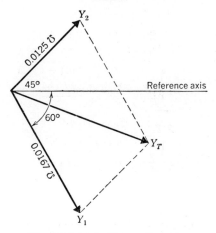

**Fig. 16.3.** Admittance diagram.

*Solution 2:*

  *Step I.*

$$Y_1 = \frac{1}{Z_1} = \frac{1}{60 / +60°} = 0.0167 \text{ mho} / -60°$$

$$Y_2 = \frac{1}{Z_2} = \frac{1}{80 / -45°} = 0.0125 \text{ mho} / +45°$$

  *Step II.*

$$Y_1 = 0.0167 \cos 60° - j0.0167 \sin 60°$$

$$Y_2 = 0.0125 \cos 45° + j0.0125 \sin 45°$$

$$Y_1 = 0.0083 - j0.0144$$
$$Y_2 = \underline{0.0088 + j0.0088}$$

Adding gives $\qquad Y_T = 0.0171 - j0.0056$

  *Step III.*

$$\phi = \arctan \frac{-0.0056}{0.0171} = -18°$$

$$Y_T = \sqrt{0.0171^2 + 0.0056^2} = 0.018 \text{ mho}$$

$$\therefore \quad Y_T = 0.018 \text{ mho} / -18°$$

  *Step IV.*

$$Z_T = \frac{1}{Y_T} = \frac{1}{0.018 / -18°} = 55.5 \text{ ohms} / +18°$$

In the special case of only *two* impedances in parallel, Equation (16.3) reduces to

$$Z_T = \frac{Z_1 Z_2}{Z_1 + Z_2} \qquad\qquad (16.4)$$

*Solution 3:*

  *Step I.* Solving the numerator,

$$Z_1 Z_2 = 60 / +60° \times 80 / -45° = 4800 / +15°$$

  *Step II.* Solving the denominator,

$$Z_1 = 60 \text{ ohms} / +60° = 30 \quad + j52$$
$$Z_2 = 80 \text{ ohms} / -45° = \underline{56.5 - j56.5}$$

Adding gives $\qquad\qquad\qquad\qquad 86.5 - \quad j4.5$

from which $\qquad Z_1 + Z_2 = 86.6 \text{ ohms} / -3°$

  *Step IV.*

$$\frac{Z_1 Z_2}{Z_1 + Z_2} = \frac{4800 / +15°}{86.6 / -3°}$$

$$\therefore \quad Z_T = 55.5 \text{ ohms} / +18°$$

## 3. Equivalent Circuits

We will encounter many a-c circuits which can be solved more readily if we can replace an elaborate impedance network by a simple equivalent network. This is particularly true in any analysis of electronic circuitry. In working with resistance networks in d-c circuits in Chapter 6, we used Thévenin's theorem and the wye-delta transformation to replace the original network with ones which were easier to solve. Since impedances are vector quantities, and therefore require more mathematical manipulation in their solution, equivalent circuits assume even greater significance in solving a-c circuits.

In Chapter 14 we found that the impedance of a resistance and reactance in series is

$$Z = R + jX \tag{14.4}$$

with the resistance and reactance forming the rectangular coordinates of the impedance. Therefore whenever we express an impedance in rectangular coordinates, we are automatically specifying an equivalent circuit

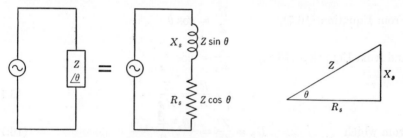

**Fig. 16.4.** Series equivalent circuit of an impedance.

consisting of a resistance and reactance in *series* as shown in Fig. 16.4. Applying basic trigonometry functions to the impedance diagram,

$$R_s = Z \cos \theta \tag{16.5}$$

$$X_s = Z \sin \theta \tag{16.6}$$

We found also that the admittance of a conductance and susceptance in parallel is

$$Y = G - jB \tag{14.17}$$

Therefore whenever we express an admittance in rectangular coordinates, we automatically specify an equivalent circuit consisting of a conductance and susceptance in *parallel* as shown in Fig. 16.5.

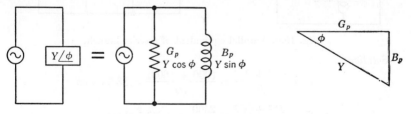

**Fig. 16.5.** Parallel equivalent circuit of an admittance.

From the admittance diagram,

$$G_p = Y \cos \theta \qquad (16.7)$$

But $\qquad G = \dfrac{1}{R}$ and $Y = \dfrac{1}{Z}$

$$\therefore \quad R_p = \dfrac{Z}{\cos \theta} \qquad (16.8)$$

Similarly $\qquad\qquad B_p = Y \sin \theta \qquad (16.9)$

$$X_p = \dfrac{Z}{\sin \theta} \qquad (16.10)$$

In order for a parallel circuit to be the exact equivalent of a given series circuit as far as the generator is concerned, their impedances must be exactly the same both in magnitude and angle.

From Equation (16.5), $\qquad \dfrac{R_s}{Z} = \cos \theta$

and from Equation (16.8), $\qquad \dfrac{Z}{R_p} = \cos \theta$

$$\therefore \quad \dfrac{R_s}{Z} = \dfrac{Z}{R_p} \qquad (16.11)$$

from which $\qquad R_p = \dfrac{Z^2}{R_s} = \dfrac{(R_s{}^2 + X_s{}^2)}{R_s} \qquad (16.12)$

Similarly, $\qquad X_p = \dfrac{Z^2}{X_s} = \dfrac{(R_s{}^2 + X_s{}^2)}{X_s} \qquad (16.13)$

EXAMPLE 3: An a-c circuit consists of two parallel branches, one consisting of a 30 ohm resistance and a 40 ohm inductive reactance in series. The other branch consists of a 50 ohm capacitive reactance. Find the equivalent parallel circuit.

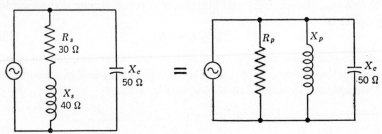

Fig. 16.6. Parallel equivalent of a series branch.

Solution:

$$R_p = \dfrac{R_s{}^2 + X_s{}^2}{R_s} = \dfrac{(900 + 1600)}{30} = 83.3 \text{ ohms}$$

$$X_p = \dfrac{R_s{}^2 + X_s{}^2}{X_s} = \dfrac{2500}{40} = +j62.5 \text{ ohms}$$

The equivalent susceptance of the parallel inductance and capacitance branches of the equivalent circuit of Fig. 16.6(b) is

$$B_{eq} = B_C - B_L = \frac{1}{X_C} - \frac{1}{X_p} = \frac{1}{50} - \frac{1}{62.5} = 0.02 - 0.016$$

$$= 0.004 \text{ mho} \quad \text{(capacitive)}$$

$$\therefore \quad X_{eq} = \frac{1}{B_{eq}} = \frac{1}{0.004} = -j250 \text{ ohms}$$

Therefore the equivalent parallel circuit consists of an 83.3 ohm resistance in parallel with a 250 ohm capacitive reactance.

We will find this type of conversion very useful in dealing with practical parallel resonant circuits in the next chapter.

Returning to Equation (16.11), we can derive the following equations for the series equivalent components of a given parallel circuit.

$$R_s = \frac{R_p X_p{}^2}{(R_p{}^2 + X_p{}^2)} \tag{16.14}$$

$$X_s = \frac{R_p{}^2 X_p}{(R_p{}^2 + X_p{}^2)} \tag{16.15}$$

## 4. Kirchhoff's Laws

Kirchhoff's current and voltage laws state two of the fundamental relationships that must exist in all electric circuits. We have used these laws to set up equations by which we can solve elaborate resistance networks in d-c circuits. We have also used Kirchhoff's laws to establish the behavior of inductance and capacitance in both d-c and a-c circuits. To apply Kirchhoff's laws to impedance networks, all that is necessary is to realize that the voltages and currents involved are *vector* quantities.

**Kirchhoff's voltage law:** In any complete electric circuit, the vector sum of the emf's must equal the vector sum of the voltage drops.

**Kirchhoff's current law:** At any junction point in an electric circuit, the vector sum of the currents entering the point must equal the vector sum of the currents leaving the point.

EXAMPLE 4: Two 60 c alternators are connected in parallel to feed a load whose impedance is 20 ohms$\underline{/+15°}$. Alternator #1 develops an open-circuit emf of 120 v and has an internal impedance of 10 ohms$\underline{/+30°}$. Alternator #2 has an open-circuit emf of 117 v which lags the emf of alternator #1 by a constant 15°. Alternator #2 has an internal impedance of 8 ohms$\underline{/+45°}$. Find the load current.

Review Example 1 in Chapter 6.

*Solution:* After we have prepared a detailed schematic diagram, the next step is to establish sufficient tracing loops to include all the components of the circuit. Since the current in a d-c circuit always flows in the same direction, establishing the direction of these tracing loops in a d-c circuit presents no problem. We simply assumed that the direction was from the + terminal of the source of emf, through the circuit, and back to the − terminal of the source. However in an a-c circuit, the instantaneous current reverses its direction twice each cycle. Nevertheless we must have some way of marking the direction of an a-c source of emf, since reversing the leads of an a-c source will change the angle of the emf by 180° just as reversing the leads of a d-c source will invert the polarity of the source.

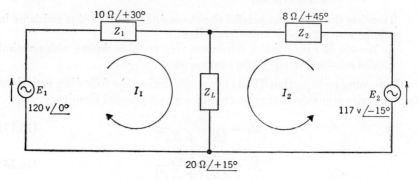

**Fig. 16.7.**

In Fig. 16.7, the bottom terminals of both generators are common. According to the given data, the emf appearing at the top terminal of alternator #2 (with respect to the bottom terminal) lags the emf appearing at the top terminal of alternator #1 by 15°. To show that this angle depends on our thinking in terms of the voltage at the *top* terminal *with respect to* the bottom terminal in each case, many textbooks would mark the top terminals in this example with + signs and the bottom terminals with − signs. Other textbooks indicate that we are expressing the emf in terms of the top terminals with respect to the bottom terminals by placing an arrow alongside the source of emf as we have done in Fig. 16.7. This arrow indicates that the angle given for the emf is expressed in terms of the emf at the terminal indicated by the head of the arrow with respect to the other terminal. We can now use these arrows to indicate the directions for our tracing loops.

*Step I.* From Kirchhoff's voltage law,

$$E_1 = I_1 Z_1 + (I_1 + I_2) Z_L = I_1(Z_1 + Z_L) + I_2 Z_L$$

$$\therefore \quad I_1 = \frac{E_1}{Z_1 + Z_L} - \frac{I_2 Z_L}{Z_1 + Z_L}$$

$$Z_1 + Z_L = 10\underline{/+30°} + 20\underline{/+15°} = (8.66 + j5) + (19.32 + j5.18)$$

$$= 27.98 + j10.18 = 29.7 \text{ ohms}\underline{/+20°}$$

$$\therefore \quad I_1 = \frac{120\underline{/0°}}{29.7\underline{/+20°}} - \frac{I_2 \times 20\underline{/+15°}}{29.7\underline{/+20°}} = 4.04\underline{/-20°} - I_2 \times 0.674\underline{/-5°} \quad (1)$$

*Step II.* Also from Kirchhoff's voltage law,

$$E_2 = I_2Z_2 + (I_1 + I_2)Z_L = I_1Z_L + I_2(Z_2 + Z_L)$$

$$= I_1 \times 20\underline{/+15°} + I_2(8\underline{/+45°} + 20\underline{/+15°})$$

$$\therefore \quad 117\underline{/-15°} = I_1 \times 20\underline{/+15°} + I_2 \times 27.2\underline{/+23.5°}$$

Substituting from Equation (1),

$$117\underline{/-15°} = 20\underline{/+15°}\,(4.04\underline{/-20°} - I_2 \times 0.674\underline{/-5°}) + I_2 \times 27.2\underline{/+23.5°}$$

$$117\underline{/-15°} = 80.8\underline{/-5°} - I_2 \times 13.48\underline{/+10°} + I_2 \times 27.2\underline{/+23.5°}$$

from which

$$I_2 = \frac{117\underline{/-15°} - 80.8\underline{/-5°}}{27.2\underline{/+23.5°} - 13.48\underline{/+10°}} = \frac{(112.4 - j30.3) - (80.5 - j7.04)}{(24.98 + j10.84) - (13.25 + j2.34)}$$

$$= \frac{31.9 - j23.96}{11.63 + j8.5} = \frac{39.8\underline{/-34°}}{14.4\underline{/+36°}} = 2.77 \text{ amp}\underline{/-70°}$$

*Step III.* Substituting in Equation (1),

$$I_1 = 4.04\underline{/-20°} - 2.77\underline{/-70°} \times 0.674\underline{/-5°} = 4.04\underline{/-20°} - 1.87\underline{/-75°}$$

$$= (3.8 - j1.39) - (0.48 - j1.8) = 3.32 + j0.41 = 3.34 \text{ amp}\underline{/+7°}$$

*Step IV.*

$$I_1 + I_2 = 3.34\underline{/+7°} + 2.77\underline{/-70°} = (3.32 + j0.41) + (0.95 - j2.61)$$

$$\therefore \quad I_L = 4.27 - j2.2 = 4.8 \text{ amp}\underline{/-27.3°}$$

## 5. The Superposition Theorem

In circuits containing more than one source of emf, we can avoid equations with more than one unknown, as was the case in Example 4, by applying the **superposition theorem.**

The current that flows in any branch of a network of impedances resulting from the simultaneous application of a number of emf's distributed in any manner throughout the network is the vector sum of the component currents in that branch that would be caused by each source of emf acting independently in turn while the others are replaced in the network by their respective internal impedances.

EXAMPLE 4A: Two 60 c alternators are connected in parallel to feed a load whose impedance is 20 ohms$\underline{/+15°}$. Alternator #1 develops an open-circuit emf of 120 v and has an internal impedance of 10 ohms$\underline{/+30°}$. Alternator #2 has an open-circuit emf of 117 v which lags the emf of alternator #1 by a constant 15°. Alternator #2 has an internal impedance of 8 ohms$\underline{/+45°}$. Find the load current.

Review Example 1A in Chapter 6.

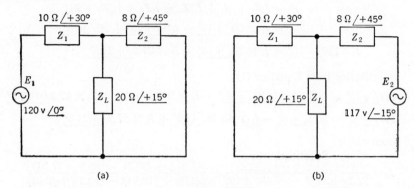

**Fig. 16.8.**

*Solution:*

*Step I.* Considering $E_1$ to be acting alone in the network thus giving the circuit of Fig. 16.8(a):

$$Z_T = Z_1 + \frac{Z_2 Z_L}{Z_2 + Z_L}$$

$$= (8.66 + j5) + \frac{(5.66 + j5.66)(19.32 + j5.18)}{(5.66 + j5.66) + (19.32 + j5.18)}$$

$$= (8.66 + j5) + \frac{80.2 + j138.8}{24.98 + j10.84}$$

$$= (8.66 + j5) + (4.72 + j3.5) = 13.38 + j8.5 = 15.85 \text{ ohms}/\underline{+32.4°}$$

$$\therefore \quad I_1 = \frac{E_1}{Z_T} = \frac{120/\underline{0°}}{15.85/\underline{32.4°}} = 7.57 \text{ amp}/\underline{-32.4°}$$

From Kirchhoff's voltage law,

$$E_L = E_1 - I_1 Z_1$$

$$= 120/\underline{0°} - 7.57/\underline{-32.4°} \times 10/\underline{+30°}$$

$$= (120 + j0) - (75.6 - j3.17) = 44.6 \text{ v}/\underline{+4.1°}$$

Therefore the first component of the load current is

$$I_L = \frac{E_L}{Z_L} = \frac{44.6/\underline{+4.1°}}{20/\underline{+15°}} = 2.23 \text{ amp}/\underline{-10.9°}$$

*Step II.* Now considering $E_2$ to be acting alone in the network and giving the circuit of Fig. 16.8(b):

$$Z_T = Z_2 + \frac{Z_1 Z_L}{Z_1 + Z_L}$$

$$= (5.66 + j5.66) + \frac{(8.66 + j5)(19.32 + j5.18)}{(8.66 + j5) + (19.32 + j5.18)}$$

$$= (5.66 + j5.66) + \frac{141.6 + j141.3}{27.98 + j10.18}$$

$$= (5.66 + j5.66) + (6.11 + j2.85)$$

$$= 11.77 + j8.51 = 14.5 \text{ ohms}\underline{/+36°}$$

$$\therefore \quad I_2 = \frac{E_2}{Z_T} = \frac{117\underline{/-15°}}{14.5\underline{/+36°}} = 8.07 \text{ amp}\underline{/-51°}$$

From Kirchhoff's voltage law,

$$E_L = E_2 - I_2 Z_2$$

$$= 117\underline{/-15°} - 8.07\underline{/-51°} \times 8\underline{/+45°}$$

$$= (112.4 - j30.3) - (64.1 - j6.7)$$

$$= 48.3 - j23.6 = 54 \text{ v}\underline{/-26°}$$

Therefore the second component of the load current is

$$I_L = \frac{E_L}{Z_L} = \frac{54\underline{/-26°}}{20\underline{/+15°}} = 2.7 \text{ amp}\underline{/-41°}$$

*Step III.*

$$I_L = 2.23\underline{/-10.9°} + 2.7\underline{/-41°}$$

$$= (2.2 - j0.42) + (2.04 - j1.77)$$

$$= 4.24 - j2.19 = 4.8 \text{ amp}\underline{/-27.3°}$$

## 6. Thévenin's Theorem

A frequently used type of radio circuit consists of a signal source feeding through a four-terminal coupling network to a load. Thévenin's theorem allows us to replace the signal source and the coupling network

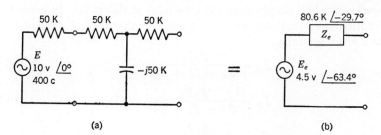

(a)                                      (b)

**Fig. 16.9.** A-c circuit simplification by Thévenin's theorem.

as in Fig. 16.9(a) with a simple equivalent series circuit as in Fig. 16.9(b). Applied to a-c circuits, Thévenin's theorem may be stated as follows:

Any two-terminal network of fixed impedances and sources of emf may be replaced by a single source of emf having an equivalent emf equal to the open circuit emf at the terminals of the original network and having an internal impedance equal to the impedance looking back into the network from the two terminals with all sources of emf replaced by their internal impedances.

EXAMPLE 5: Given the signal source and four-terminal network of Fig. 16.9(a), determine the Thévenin equivalent source.

*Solution:*

*Step I.* Load on the source with no load connected to the output terminals is

$$Z = 50,000 + 50,000 - j50,000 = 112 \text{ kilohms}/{-26.6°}$$

$$I = \frac{E}{Z} = \frac{10/0°}{112,000/{-26.6°}} = 89.5 \ \mu\text{a}/{+26.6°}$$

Therefore the open circuit voltage is

$$E_e = E_C = IX_C = 89.5 \times 10^{-6}/{+26.6°} \times 50,000/{-90°} = 4.5 \text{ v}/{-63.4°}$$

*Step II.* Looking back into the source from the output terminals,

$$Z_e = (50,000 + j0) + \frac{(100,000 + j0)(0 - j50,000)}{(100,000 + j0) + (0 - j50,000)}$$

$$= (50,000 + j0) + \frac{0 - j5 \times 10^9}{100,000 - j50,000}$$

$$= (50,000 + j0) + (20,000 - j40,000)$$

$$= 70,000 - j40,000 = 80.6 \text{ kilohms}/{-29.7°}$$

## 7. Delta-Wye Transformation

By substituting the impedance symbol for the resistance symbol, the equations we developed in Chapter 6 for converting a given delta network into an equivalent wye network and vice versa can be applied to a-c circuits. Since the derivation of these equations is the same as for resistance networks, we shall simply state the equations at this point. In using these transformation equations, we must remember that each $Z$ symbol represents a *vector* quantity.

$$Z_A = \frac{Z_Y Z_Z}{Z_X + Z_Y + Z_Z} \tag{16.16}$$

$$Z_B = \frac{Z_X Z_Z}{Z_X + Z_Y + Z_Z} \tag{16.17}$$

$$Z_C = \frac{Z_X Z_Y}{Z_X + Z_Y + Z_Z} \tag{16.18}$$

$$Z_X = \frac{Z_A Z_B + Z_B Z_C + Z_C Z_A}{Z_A} \tag{16.19}$$

$$Z_Y = \frac{Z_A Z_B + Z_B Z_C + Z_C Z_A}{Z_B} \tag{16.20}$$

$$Z_Z = \frac{Z_A Z_B + Z_B Z_C + Z_C Z_A}{Z_C} \tag{16.21}$$

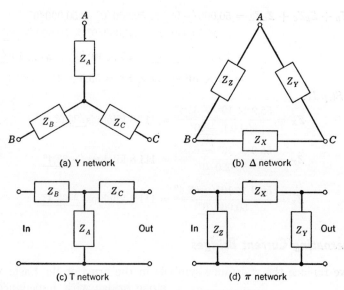

Fig. 16.10. Delta-wye transformation.

We derived these transformation equations to apply to the three-terminal wye network of Fig. 16.10(a) and the three-terminal delta network of Fig. 16.10(b). In this form these transformations are quite useful in solving three-phase networks. In communications circuitry we often have to deal with four-terminal passive* networks connected between a source of emf and a load. Since one terminal is common to both the input and output in the circuits of Figs. 16.10(c) and 16.10(d), the T network of Fig. 16.10(c) is the same as the Y network of Fig. 16.10(a), and the $\pi$ network of Fig. 16.10(d) is the same as the $\Delta$ network of Fig. 16.10(b). Therefore the wye-delta transformation equations may also be used to determine the $\pi$ network equivalent of a given T network and vice versa.

EXAMPLE 6: Find the $\pi$ equivalent of the T network shown in Fig. 16.11(a).

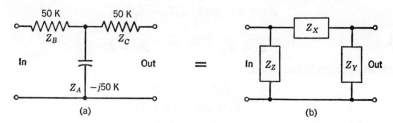

Fig. 16.11. T-network to $\pi$-network transformation.

*Solution:*

    *Step I.* Solving first for the common numerator used in all three equations,

* A passive network is one which contains no source of emf.

$$Z_A Z_B + Z_B Z_C + Z_C Z_A = 50,000\underline{/-90°} \times 50,000\underline{/0°} + 50,000\underline{/0°}$$
$$\times\ 50,000\underline{/0°} + 50,000\underline{/0°} \times 50,000\underline{/-90°}$$
$$= 25 \times 10^8\underline{/-90°} + 25 \times 10^8\underline{/0°} + 25 \times 10^8\underline{/-90°}$$
$$= 25 \times 10^8 - j50 \times 10^8 = 55.9 \times 10^8\underline{/-63.4°}$$

*Step II.*

$$Z_X = \frac{55.9 \times 10^8\underline{/-63.4°}}{50,000\underline{/-90°}} = 111.8 \text{ kilohms}\underline{/26.6°}$$

$$Z_Y = \frac{55.9 \times 10^8\underline{/-63.4°}}{50,000\underline{/0°}} = 111.8 \text{ kilohms}\underline{/-63.4°}$$

$$Z_Z = \frac{55.9 \times 10^8\underline{/-63.4°}}{50,000\underline{/0°}} = 111.8 \text{ kilohms}\underline{/-63.4°}$$

## 8. Alternating Current Bridges

If we replace the resistance symbols in the arms of the basic Wheatstone bridge with impedance symbols, we obtain the general a-c bridge circuit of Fig. 16.12. A brief consideration of a-c bridges at this point will serve the dual purpose of acquainting us with the method by which we can obtain precision measurement of a-c circuit parameters, and second, providing us with a source of practical a-c network problems.

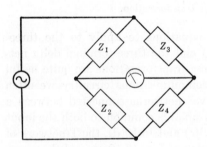

Fig. 16.12. The general form of an a-c bridge.

In order for the null indicator in Fig. 16.12 to read zero, the voltage across its terminals must be zero. For this to be so, the voltage across $Z_1$ and $Z_3$ must be exactly the same both in magnitude and phase. Therefore

$$E_1 = E_3 \quad \text{and} \quad I_1 Z_1 = I_3 Z_3$$

But

$$I_1 = \frac{E}{Z_1 + Z_2} \quad \text{and} \quad I_3 = \frac{E}{Z_3 + Z_4}$$

when the bridge is balanced.

$$\therefore \quad \frac{E Z_1}{Z_1 + Z_2} = \frac{E Z_3}{Z_3 + Z_4}$$

from which

$$Z_1 Z_4 = Z_2 Z_3 \tag{16.22}$$

This is known as the **general bridge equation** and must hold true for all special forms of an a-c bridge when it is properly balanced to give zero voltage across the null indicator.

The bridge arrangement of Fig. 16.13 is called a **capacitance comparison bridge** since the unknown capacitance $C_x$ and its loss resistance $R_x$ are to be balanced against the standard capacitor $C_s$. In this particular case, the terms of the general bridge equation become

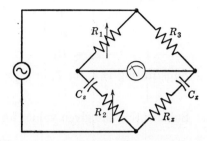

$$Z_1 = R_1, \qquad Z_2 = R_2 - j\,\frac{1}{\omega C_s}$$

$$Z_3 = R_3, \qquad Z_4 = R_x - j\,\frac{1}{\omega C_x}$$

Substituting in Equation (16.22) gives

**Fig. 16.13.** The capacitance comparison bridge.

$$R_1 R_x - j R_1/\omega C_x = R_2 R_3 - j R_3/\omega C_s$$

As an impedance diagram will show, altering the magnitude of a reactance can have no effect on the magnitude of the total resistance of the circuit, since these two quantities are at right angles. Therefore the $j$ term on the left of the above equation must equal the $j$ term on the right of the equation. Similarly the two horizontal or *real* components must be equal. Therefore, we can separate equations expressed in rectangular coordinates into two equations.

$$R_1 R_x = R_2 R_3$$

from which

$$R_x = \frac{R_2 R_3}{R_1} \qquad (16.23)$$

and

$$\frac{R_1}{\omega C_x} = \frac{R_3}{\omega C_s}$$

from which

$$C_x = C_s R_1/R_3 \qquad (16.24)$$

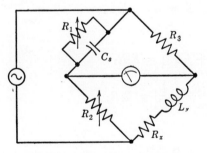

**Fig. 16.14.** The Maxwell bridge.

Note that in deriving Equations (16.23) and (16.24), the angular velocity term disappeared. Therefore the accuracy of the capacitance comparison bridge is not dependent on the accuracy of the frequency of the source of emf. None of the a-c bridges is dependent on the magnitude of the applied emf for an accurate reading when balanced, since this term disappeared in deriving Equation (16.22).

Although we can construct a similar inductance comparison bridge to determine accurately an unknown inductance, standard inductors are expensive and bulky. The **Maxwell bridge** circuit of Fig. 16.14 allows us to balance the bridge by using a standard capacitance for comparison purposes. In this case branch #1 contains parallel components. Therefore it is more convenient to identify the four arms thus:

$$Y_1 = \frac{1}{R_1} + j\omega C_s \qquad Z_2 = R_2$$

$$Z_3 = R_3 \qquad\qquad Z_4 = R_x + j\omega L_x$$

Substituting $1/Y_1$ for $Z_1$ in Equation (16.22) gives

$$Z_4 = Y_1 Z_2 Z_3$$

Substituting the given values for the Maxwell bridge gives

$$R_x + j\omega L_x = \frac{R_2 R_3}{R_1} + j\omega C_s R_2 R_3$$

Again separating the real and $j$ terms into separate equations,

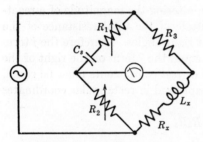

$$R_x = \frac{R_2 R_3}{R_1} \qquad (16.25)$$

$$L_x = C_s R_2 R_3 \qquad (16.26)$$

The Maxwell bridge is best suited to coils in which $R_x$ is an appreciable fraction of $\omega L_x$. As Equation (16.25) indicates, if $R_x$ is very small, $R_1$ must be very large in order to obtain balance. For such coils the Hay bridge of Fig. 16.15 is preferred even though

**Fig. 16.15.** The Hay bridge.

the equations turn out to be frequency dependent.

In this case,

$$Z_1 = R_1 - j\frac{1}{\omega C_s} \qquad Z_2 = R_2$$

$$Z_3 = R_3 \qquad\qquad Z_4 = R_x + j\omega L_x$$

Substituting in Equation (16.22),

$$\left(R_1 - j\frac{1}{\omega C_s}\right)(R_x + j\omega L_x) = R_2 R_3$$

$$R_1 R_x + j\omega L_x R_1 - \frac{jR_x}{\omega C_s} + \frac{L_x}{C_s} = R_2 R_3$$

Separating the real and $j$ terms,

$$R_1 R_x + \frac{L_x}{C_s} = R_2 R_3 \qquad (1)$$

$$\omega L_x R_1 = \frac{R_x}{\omega C_s} \qquad (2)$$

From Equation (2),            $R_x = \omega^2 L_x C_s R_1 \qquad (3)$

Substituting in Equation (1) gives

$$\omega^2 L_x C_s R_1^2 + \frac{L_x}{C_s} = R_2 R_3$$

from which
$$L_x = \frac{C_s R_2 R_3}{1 + \omega^2 C_s^2 R_1^2} \qquad (16.27)$$

Substituting Equation (16.27) in Equation (3) gives

$$R_x = \frac{\omega^2 C_s^2 R_1 R_2 R_3}{1 + \omega^2 C_s^2 R_1^2} \qquad (16.28)$$

EXAMPLE 7: The Maxwell bridge of Fig. 16.14 balances when $C_s = 0.01 \ \mu f$, $R_1 = 470$ kilohms, $R_2 = 5.1$ kilohms, and $R_3 = 100$ kilohms. Determine the inductance and resistance of the inductor being measured.

*Solution:*
$$L_x = C_s R_2 R_3 = 10^{-8} \times 5.1 \times 10^3 \times 10^5 = 5.1 \text{ h}$$
$$R_x = \frac{R_2 R_3}{R_1} = \frac{5.1 \times 10^3 \times 10^5}{4.7 \times 10^5} = 1{,}085 \text{ ohms}$$

## 9. Circle Diagrams

Since the current in a series circuit is common to all components, we have been using current as the reference vector for series circuit vector diagrams as in Fig. 16.16(b). We then draw the total voltage as the resultant of the voltages across the resistance and the reactance of the circuit.

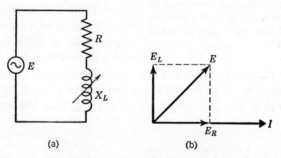

Fig. 16.16. A simple series a-c circuit.

But in practice the applied emf is a constant, and as either the resistance or the reactance of the circuit is changed, the current (the dependent variable of most electric circuits) must change in such a manner that

$$E_R + jE_L = E$$

We can redraw the vector diagram with the applied emf as the reference vector as shown in Fig. 16.17.

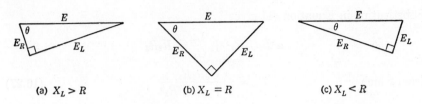

**Fig. 16.17.** Effect of varying $X_L$ in a series circuit connected to a fixed source of EMF.

Since the applied emf is constant, and since the voltage across the inductance must always lead the voltage across the resistance by exactly 90°, this vector diagram will always be in the form of a right-angled triangle with a constant hypotenuse. We can show that, under these circumstances, the junction of the $E_R$ and $E_L$ vectors must be on the circumference of a circle with the $E$ vector as a diameter.*

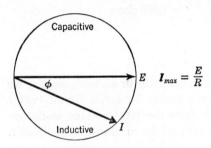

**Fig. 16.19.** Circle diagram for current in a series circuit with a fixed resistance and variable reactance.

In the circuit of Fig. 16.16(a), the resistance remains constant but the inductive reactance can change. Since $I = E_R/R$, and since $R$ is constant, the current vector in Fig. 16.17 will have the same angle and same proportionate magnitude as the $E_R$ vector. Therefore in a series circuit containing a fixed resistance and a variable reactance, the tip of the current vector must lie on the circumference of a circle having the applied emf as the reference vector and a diameter of $I_{max} = E/R$ since the current will be greatest when the reactance drops to zero, as shown in Fig. 16.19. Such is the situation when the source of emf has a constant magnitude but a variable frequency. Realizing that the current vector

* In $\triangle ABC$,

$$\angle CAB + \angle ABC + \angle BCA = 180°$$
$$\therefore \ \angle CAB + \angle ABD + \angle DBC + \angle BCA = 180°$$

But since $AD = DB = DC$,

$$\angle CAB = \angle ABD$$

Similarly                 $\angle BCA = \angle DBC$

$$\therefore \ 2(\angle ABD + \angle DBC) = 180°$$

from which                 $\angle ABC = 90°$

Conversely, whenever $\angle ABC = 90°$,

$$AD = DB = DC = \text{radii of a circle}$$

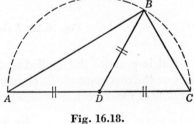

**Fig. 16.18.**

must follow a circular locus as the frequency changes can be used to advantage in the analysis of resonant circuits and transmission lines.

Figure 16.20 shows a simple series circuit in which the inductive reactance remains constant and the resistance varies. This condition will be encountered in analyzing the operating characteristics of induction motors as the mechanical load on the motor is changed. The current will be maximum when the resistance is zero. Therefore $I_{max} = E/X_L$, lagging the applied emf by 90° as shown. As the resistance increases, the current decreases and at the same time the phase angle decreases. Again since the applied emf is constant, and since $E_R$ and $E_L$ must always be at right angles, the tip of the current vector must be on the circumference of a circle with $E/X_L$ as the diameter.

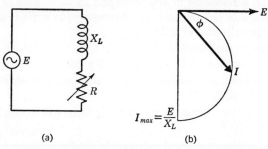

(a)                                      (b)

**Fig. 16.20.** Circle diagram for current in a series circuit with a fixed inductive reactance and a variable resistance.

Therefore from Fig. 16.20(b),

$$\frac{I}{I_{max}} = \cos(90° - \phi) = \sin\phi$$

Therefore when the resistance is the variable in the circuit,

$$I_{max} = \frac{I}{\sin\phi} \qquad (16.29)$$

EXAMPLE 8: A series circuit with a fixed reactance draws a 10 amp current from a 120 v, 60 c source at 0.5 lagging power factor. What is the maximum true power for this circuit?

*Solution:*

$$\phi = \arccos 0.5 = 60°$$

$$I_{max} = \frac{I}{\sin 60°} = \frac{10}{0.866} = 11.5 \text{ amp}$$

$$P = EI \cos\phi$$

where $E$ is the applied emf and $I \cos\phi$ is the in phase rectangular coordinate of the current. As the circle diagram of Fig. 16.20(b) shows, $I \cos\phi$ will be maximum when $\phi = 45°$. Therefore, when $\phi = 45°$,

$$I = I_{max} \sin\phi = 11.5 \times 0.707 = 8.14 \text{ amp}$$

$$\therefore \quad P_{max} = EI \cos\phi = 120 \times 8.14 \times 0.707 = 691 \text{ w}$$

## Problems

Draw schematic and vector diagrams where ever applicable.

1. What is the total impedance when 400 ohms$/+15°$ and 800 ohms$/+60°$ are connected in series?

2. What is the total impedance when
$Z_1 = 5$ kilohms$/+30°$, $Z_2 = 4.7$ kilohms$/-45°$, and $Z_3 = 2.2$ kilohms$/+75°$
are connected in series?

3. What is the total admittance when the two components of Problem 1 are connected in parallel?

4. What is the total impedance when the three impedances of Problem 2 are connected in parallel?

5. A coil having a resistance of 100 ohms and an inductance of 0.5 h, a 60 $\mu f$ capacitor, and a 30 ohm resistor are all connected in series to a 60 c source of emf whose open-circuit emf is 208 v$/0°$.

   (a) What are the magnitude and phase of the current through the coil?
   (b) What are the magnitude and phase of the voltage across the coil?

6. What is the over-all power factor when the three components of Problem 5 are connected in parallel?

7. What values of capacitance and resistance in series will form a 1 kc impedance of 600 ohms$/-30°$?

8. What values of capacitance and resistance in parallel will form a 1 kc impedance of 600 ohms$/-30°$?

9. What values of pure inductance and resistance in parallel will be equivalent at 60 c to a 0.5 h inductance and a 120 ohm resistance in series?

10. What values of capacitance and resistance in series will be equivalent at 400 c to a 0.02 $\mu f$ capacitor and 680 ohm resistor in parallel?

11. What value of impedance must be connected in series with a 60 ohms$/+45°$ impedance in order for the current drawn from a 120 v source of emf to be 1 amp lagging the source emf by 30°?

12. What value of impedance must be connected in parallel with a 10 kilohm$/-60°$ impedance for the current from a 1.5 v, 100 kc source to be 150 $\mu a/0°$?

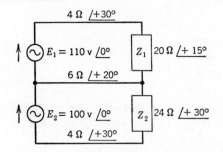

13. Find the current in the common neutral lead of the three-wire single-phase system shown in Fig. 16.21.

**Fig. 16.21.**

14. The three-wire single-phase circuit of Problem 13 can be converted into a two-

phase system by making $E_2 = 110 \text{ v}\underline{/90°}$. Find the current in $Z_1$ under these circumstances.

15. A $26\frac{1}{2}$ $\mu f$ capacitor is connected in series with a 100 ohm resistor to a 120 v, 60 c source. What value of resistance must be connected in parallel with the capacitor to make the current in the capacitor have a magnitude of 0.5 amp?

16. If the two capacitors in the circuit of Fig. 16.22 are equal, what must their capacitance be for the output voltage of this network to be 90° out of phase with the input voltage at 60 cps?

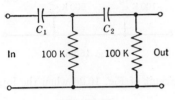

Fig. 16.22.

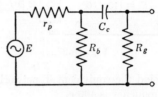

Fig. 16.23.

17. A vacuum tube amplifier and its $CR$ output coupling circuit represent the source of emf shown in Fig. 16.23. $E = 10v\underline{/180°}$; $r_p = 20,000$ ohms; $R_b = 80,000$ ohms; $C_c = 0.02$ $\mu f$; $R_g = 470,000$ ohms. Using 1 kc as a reference frequency, by how many degrees will the phase of the output voltage shift as the frequency decreases to 100 c?

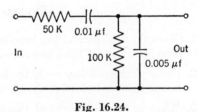

18. At what frequency will the output voltage of the network in Fig. 16.24 be in phase with the input voltage?

Fig. 16.24.

19. The circuit of Fig. 16.12 balances when $Z_1 = 470$ ohms$\underline{/0°}$, $Z_2$ is a 0.01 $\mu f$ capacitor in series with an 860 kilohm resistor, $Z_3 = 5$ kilohms$\underline{/0°}$, and $f = 1$ kc. Determine the components that constitute $Z_4$.

20. The circuit of Fig. 16.12 balances when $Z_2 = 10$ kilohms$\underline{/0°}$, $Z_3 = 5.6$ kilohms$\underline{/0°}$, $Z_4$ consists of a 0.01 $\mu f$ capacitor in parallel with a 1.23 megohm resistor and $f = 1$ kc. Determine the components that constitute $Z_1$.

21. The circuit of Fig. 16.12 balances when $Z_1 = 10$ kilohms$\underline{/0°}$, $Z_3$ is a 0.01 $\mu f$ capacitor in series with a 27 ohm resistor, $Z_4 = 2700$ ohms$\underline{/0°}$ and $f = 1$ kc. Determine the value of $Z_2$ in rectangular coordinates.

22. The circuit of Fig. 16.12 balances when $Z_1 = 475$ ohms$\underline{/0°}$, $Z_2 = 1780$ ohms$\underline{/+75°}$, $Z_3 = 1000$ ohms$\underline{/0°}$, and $f = 1$ kc. Determine the components that constitute $Z_4$.

23. In the circuit of Fig. 16.12, $Z_1 = 200$ ohms$\underline{/-45°}$, $Z_2 = 1000$ ohms$\underline{/0°}$, $Z_3 = 10$ kilohms$\underline{/0°}$, and $Z_4 = 500$ ohms$\underline{/+60°}$. The null indicator has an impedance of 5 kilohms$\underline{/0°}$. What is the total current if $E = 50$ v, 1 kc?

24. Solve for the ammeter reading in the circuit of Fig. 16.25, using the wye-delta transformation equations.

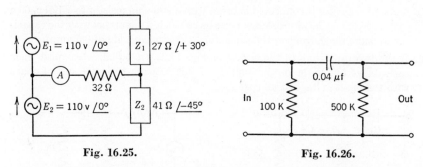

Fig. 16.25.                                 Fig. 16.26.

25. Find the equivalent T network for the circuit of Fig. 16.26 when the input frequency is 400 c.

26. A circuit consisting of a $\frac{3}{4}$ h inductance, a 40 ohm resistance, and a $26\frac{1}{2}$ $\mu f$ capacitance in series is connected to a source of emf which remains constant at 120 v rms, but whose frequency can vary from 25 c to 60 c. Draw an accurate circle diagram showing the manner in which the magnitude and phase of the current vary as the frequency is varied through its range.

## Review Questions

1. Given the magnitude of two impedances in ohms, why can we not calculate the total impedance of these two impedances in series?

2. Under what conditions could the total impedance of two impedances in series be less than that of either one by itself?

3. What is the advantage of thinking in terms of total **admittance** when dealing with parallel a-c circuits?

4. Show how Equation (16.4) is derived.

5. What conditions must be fulfilled for a series circuit to be the exact equivalent of a given parallel circuit?

6. What is the significance of equivalent circuits in the analysis of electric and electronic circuits?

7. Given a resistance and reactance in series with $R_s = 4X_s$, in the equivalent parallel circuit $X_p = 4R_p$. Explain.

8. A coil and capacitor connected in series to a given source of emf represent an inductive impedance. When the same two components are connected in parallel to the same source, the total impedance becomes capacitive. Explain.

9. In applying Kirchhoff's laws to a-c circuits with more than one source of emf, why is it necessary to identify which generator terminal is which?

10. Compare the relative merits of Kirchhoff's law equations and the superposition theorem for solving a-c networks containing more than one source of emf.

11. What is the main advantage of Thévenin's theorem as a means of solving a-c circuits?

12. To be quite precise in stating Thévenin's theorem, we should have specified a network of fixed *linear, bilateral* impedances. In an a-c system, what is the significance of (a) a *linear* impedance and (b) a *bilateral* impedance?

13. What is meant by a *passive* network?

14. Why is it possible to apply the equations we developed for wye-delta transformation in converting a four-terminal T network into a $\pi$ network?

15. Why do we not need to take the impedance of the null indicator into account in a balanced bridge circuit?

16. Why does a variation in the magnitude of the source emf not affect the accuracy of a balanced bridge measurement?

17. How will the sensitivity of the null indicator affect the accuracy of an a-c bridge measurement?

18. Why can we split the general bridge Equation (16.22) into two separate equations in deriving equations for the unknown components in the various a-c bridge circuits?

19. After assembling a bridge in the form shown in Fig. 16.27, we find that it cannot be balanced. Show why by deriving equations for $L_x$ and $R_x$ from the general bridge equation.

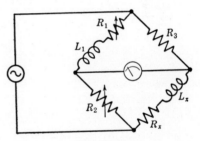

Fig. 16.27.

20. Why is the Hay bridge more suitable than the Maxwell bridge for measuring coils with a very low resistance?

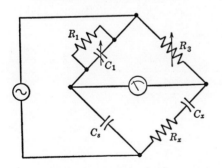

Fig. 16.28. Schering bridge.

21. Derive equations for $C_x$ and $R_x$ in the Schering bridge of Fig. 16.28.

22. Why do we refer to the current as the dependent variable in most electric circuits?

23. Why does the tip of the current vector move around the circumference of a circle when the resistance alone is varied in an a-c circuit containing resistance and reactance in series?

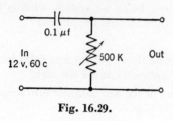

In
12 v, 60 c

0.1 μf

500 K          Out

**Fig. 16.29.**

24. Draw a circle diagram for the output voltage of the phase shifter of Fig. 16.29 as the variable resistance is increased from zero to 500 kilohms.

# Chapter 17

# RESONANCE

~~~~~~~~~~~~~~~~~~~~~~~~~~~~~~~~~~~~~~~~~~~~~~~~~~~~~~~~~~~~~~~~~~~

## 1. Effect of Varying Frequency in a Series RLC Circuit

In most of the examples we have considered, the frequency of the source of emf has remained constant. This is the case in electric power systems. The standard frequency in North America is 60 c, although there are a few areas in which the power line frequency is 25 c. The standard frequency in Europe is 50 c. In radio circuitry however, frequency is an important variable. Therefore we must now devote our attention to the behavior of electric circuits connected to sources of emf in which we can consider the rms voltage to remain constant but the frequency to be variable.

If the circuit connected to a variable frequency source is a pure resistance, the frequency of the source will have no effect on the magnitude or phase of the current drawn from the source, since $I = E/R$. But if a pure inductance is connected to a variable frequency source, since $X_L = 2\pi f L$, the inductive reactance is directly proportional to the frequency. Similarly the reactance of a capacitor *decreases* as the frequency increases.

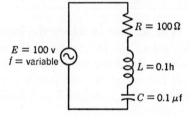

**Fig. 17.1.** A series $RLC$ circuit connected to a variable frequency source.

In the circuit of Fig. 17.1, resistance, inductance, and capacitance are all connected in series to a variable-frequency source. When the frequency is quite low, the inductive reactance is quite small and the capacitive reactance is quite large. Therefore the net reactance is a large capacitive reactance, much greater than the resistance, and therefore the impedance of the circuit is practically the same as the reactance of the capacitance of

359

the circuit. As the frequency is increased, not only does the capacitive reactance become smaller, but the inductive reactance increases. Therefore the net reactance decreases considerably as the frequency is increased until a frequency is reached at which $X_L = X_C$. The net reactance at this frequency is zero and therefore the impedance is simply the resistance of the circuit. As the frequency is increased past this point, the inductive reactance exceeds the capacitive reactance and the impedance becomes inductive, approaching the condition of being practically the same as the inductive reactance of the circuit when the frequency is quite high.

Table I. Effect of Varying Frequency in a Series $RLC$ Circuit

| $f$ c | $R$ ohms | $X_L$ ohms | $X_C$ ohms | $X_L - X_C$ ohms | $Z$ $\sqrt{R^2 + X^2}$ | $\theta$ arctan $X/R$ | $I = E/Z$ |
|---|---|---|---|---|---|---|---|
| 159 | 100 | 100 | 10 K | $-j9900$ | 9900 | $-89.4°$ | 0.0101 |
| 660 | 100 | 415 | 2415 | $-j2000$ | 2002 | $-87.2°$ | .0499 |
| 985 | 100 | 618 | 1618 | $-j1000$ | 1005 | $-84.3°$ | .0995 |
| 1,245 | 100 | 781 | 1281 | $-j500$ | 509 | $-78.7°$ | .1965 |
| 1,440 | 100 | 905 | 1105 | $-j200$ | 223 | $-63.4°$ | .448 |
| 1,515 | 100 | 952 | 1052 | $-j100$ | 141 | $-45°$ | .707 |
| 1,590 | 100 | 1,000 | 1000 | 0 | 100 | $0°$ | 1.00 |
| 1,675 | 100 | 1,052 | 952 | $+j100$ | 141 | $+45°$ | .707 |
| 1,760 | 100 | 1,105 | 905 | $+j200$ | 223 | $+63.4°$ | .448 |
| 2,040 | 100 | 1,281 | 781 | $+j500$ | 509 | $+78.7°$ | .1965 |
| 2,575 | 100 | 1,618 | 618 | $+j1000$ | 1005 | $+84.3°$ | .0995 |
| 3,840 | 100 | 2,415 | 415 | $+j2000$ | 2002 | $+87.3°$ | .0499 |
| 15,900 | 100 | 10,000 | 100 | $+j9900$ | 9900 | $+89.4°$ | 0.0101 |

The manner in which the impedance of the series circuit of Fig. 17.1 changes as the frequency of the source of emf is increased is recorded in Table I. In order to get a better picture of the variation in impedance with frequency, we can plot a graph of impedance *vs* frequency as shown in Fig. 17.2. (Note the logarithmic scales used for such graphs.)

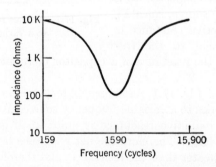

Fig. 17.2. Effect of varying frequency on the impedance of a series $RLC$ circuit.

If the emf of the source remains at 100 v rms in spite of the frequency variation, the magnitude of the current is inversely proportional to the impedance. Therefore, whereas the impedance becomes minimum at 1590 c, the current will be maximum at this frequency. Again we can plot data from Table I in graph form to show the manner in which the current in the series circuit of Fig. 17.1 depends on the frequency of the source as shown in Fig. 17.3.

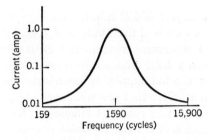

**Fig. 17.3.** Effect of varying frequency on the current in a series *RLC* circuit.

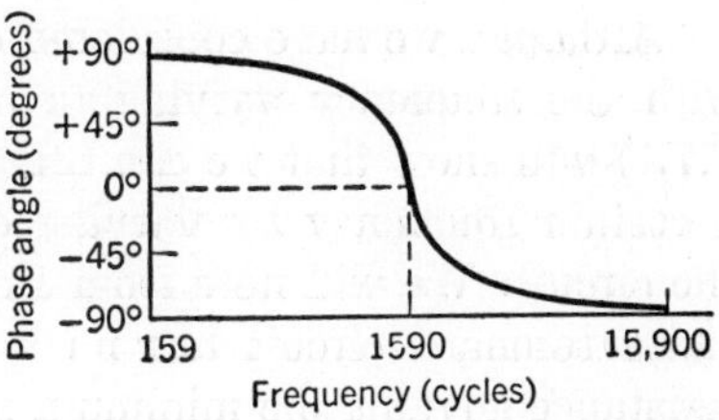

**Fig. 17.4.** Effect of varying frequency on the phase angle of the current in a series *RLC* circuit.

As we have noted, at very low frequencies the impedance of the series *RLC* circuit of Fig. 17.1 is almost pure capacitive reactance, and therefore the angle of the impedance is almost $-90°$. Therefore at these low frequencies the current would lead the applied emf by almost 90°. At 1590 c the net reactance becomes zero and the impedance is simply the resistance of the circuit with a 0° angle. Then at very high frequencies the impedance becomes almost pure inductive reactance, under which circumstances the current lags the applied emf by almost 90°. Again we can show the effect of frequency on the phase angle of the current in the circuit with respect to the applied emf, by transferring data from Table I to the graph of Fig. 17.4. If we wish to show the effect of frequency on both the magnitude and the phase of the current, we can prepare a circle diagram similar to Fig. 16.19.

## 2. Series Resonance

In the series *RLC* circuit of Fig. 17.1, when the frequency of the source of emf is 1590 c:

1. The inductive reactance and the capacitive reactance of the circuit are equal.
2. Therefore the impedance is minimum and is equal to the resistance of the circuit.
3. Therefore the current in the circuit is maximum and is equal to $E/R$.
4. The current through the circuit is in phase with the applied emf.

This condition is known as **resonance.** The series circuit of Fig. 17.1 is called a **resonant circuit** and the frequency at which resonance occurs is called the **resonant frequency** of the circuit.

The letter symbol for **resonant frequency** is $f_r$ (or $f_0$).

Since at resonance $X_L = X_C$, then $2\pi fL = 1/2\pi fC$, from which

$$f_r = \frac{1}{2\pi\sqrt{LC}} \tag{17.1}$$

where $f_r$ is in cycles per second, $L$ is in henrys and $C$ is in farads.

Although we have considered only the case of fixed values of $L$ and $C$ with the frequency varying to obtain resonance, rearranging Equation (17.1) will show that we can bring a given $RLC$ circuit into resonance at a certain frequency by varying either the inductance or capacitance of the circuit. We will note from Equation (17.1) that the resistance of the series resonant circuit has no bearing on the resonant frequency. The resistance governs the minimum impedance of the circuit which occurs at resonance. As a result, the resistance governs the steepness of the "skirts" of the resonance curve. In the series resonant circuit of Fig. 17.5(a) the

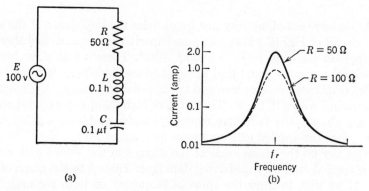

(a)

(b)

**Fig. 17.5.** Effect of resistance on the shape of the resonance curve.

inductance and capacitance are the same as in the circuit of Fig. 17.1. Therefore its resonant frequency is still 1590 c. However, the resistance has been reduced from 100 ohms to 50 ohms. If we prepare a table similar to Table I for the circuit of Fig. 17.5(a), we can then plot the resonance curve shown in Fig. 17.5(b). Off resonance the total impedance has not been affected very much by the change in resistance. But at the resonant frequency the impedance is only half that of the circuit of Fig. 17.1, and therefore the circuit current at resonance is twice as great.

We will also note from Equation (17.1) that as long as the product of $L$ and $C$ is constant, the resonant frequency of a series resonant circuit will remain constant. In the circuit of Fig. 17.6(a) we have doubled the inductance and cut the capacitance in half. Therefore the $LC$ product and the resonant frequency are unchanged. However we have increased the $L/C$ ratio by a factor of 4 : 1. This means that at resonance, $X_L =$

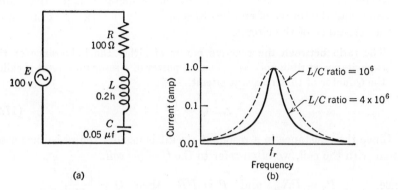

**Fig. 17.6.** Effect of $L/C$ ratio on the shape of the resonance curve.

$X_C = 2000$ ohms instead of 1000 ohms as in the circuit of Fig. 17.1. Therefore at a frequency of 1515 c, $X_L - X_C = 200$ ohms instead of 100 ohms as in the circuit of Fig. 17.1. This increase in the $L/C$ ratio will therefore steepen the skirts of the resonance curve as shown in Fig. 17.6(b).

> EXAMPLE 1: A coil in a tuned circuit in a radio receiver has an inductance of 300 $\mu$h and a resistance of 15 ohms. What value of capacitance must be connected in series with the coil for the circuit to be series resonant at 840 kc?
>
> *Solution:*
>
> $$X_L = 2\pi f L = 2 \times 3.14 \times 840 \times 10^3 \times 300 \times 10^{-6} = 1580 \text{ ohms}$$
>
> At resonance, $\qquad X_C = X_L = 1580$ ohms
>
> $$\therefore \quad C = \frac{10^{12}}{2 \times 3.14 \times 840 \times 10^3 \times 1580} = 120 \ \mu\mu\text{f}$$

## 3. Q of Resonant Circuits

Decreasing the resistance in a series resonant circuit and increasing the $L/C$ ratio both had the effect of steepening the skirts of the resonance curve. Perhaps we can combine both these variables into a single factor relating to resonant circuits. As we noted when we considered power factor correction in Chapter 15, in an a-c circuit containing both inductance and capacitance, the capacitance *stores* energy while the inductance *returns* energy stored in its magnetic field and vice versa. Therefore a-c circuits containing both inductance and capacitance *exchange* reactive power between the inductance and capacitance. Therefore the source of emf is required to supply only the difference between the reactive power of the inductance and the reactive power of the capacitance. This accounts for the net reactance of a series circuit being the *difference* between the inductive and capacitive reactance, and the reactive voltage of a series circuit being the *difference* between $E_L$ and $E_C$.

At resonance the reactive power of the inductance and capacitance are equal and the source of emf has to supply only the true power required by the resistance of the circuit.

The **ratio between the reactive power** of either the inductance or the capacitance at resonance and the **true power** of a resonant circuit is called the $Q$ factor of that resonant circuit.

$$\therefore \quad Q = \frac{P_q}{P} \tag{17.2}$$

Since the resistance in a resonant circuit is usually the resistance associated with the coil, we often refer to the $Q$ *of the coil*.

Since $\qquad P_q = I^2 X_L \quad$ and $\quad P = I^2 R, \quad$ then $\quad Q = \dfrac{I^2 X_L}{I^2 R}.$

But the current is common to all components in a series circuit.

$$\therefore \quad Q = \frac{X_L}{R} = \frac{\omega L}{R} \tag{17.3}$$

Equation (17.3) provides us with a simpler form for the calculation of $Q$ than Equation (17.2). It is sometimes given as a definition of $Q$.

Since $\omega L = 2\pi f L$ and since $f_r = 1/2\pi\sqrt{LC}$,

$$\therefore \quad Q = \frac{1}{R}\sqrt{\frac{L}{C}} \tag{17.4}$$

The $Q$ factor of a resonant circuit is therefore the single factor which takes into account the effect of both the resistance and the $L/C$ ratio on the shape of a resonance curve. The higher the $Q$, the steeper the skirts of the resonance curve.

EXAMPLE 2: A series resonant circuit consists of a 50 $\mu$h inductance whose resistance is 5 ohms, and a 200 $\mu\mu$f capacitor. What is its $Q$?

*Solution I:*

$$Q = \frac{1}{R}\sqrt{\frac{L}{C}} = \frac{1}{5}\sqrt{\frac{50 \times 10^{-6}}{200 \times 10^{-12}}} = \frac{1}{5} \times 500 = 100$$

*Solution II:* Since it is quite likely that we will need to know the resonant frequency of a circuit, this solution may be quicker in the long run.

$$f_r = \frac{1}{2\pi\sqrt{LC}} = \frac{1}{6.28\sqrt{50 \times 10^{-6} \times 200 \times 10^{-12}}} = 1.59 \text{ megacycles}$$

$$X_L = 2\pi f L = 6.28 \times 1.59 \times 10^6 \times 50 \times 10^{-6} = 500 \text{ ohms}$$

$$Q = \frac{X_L}{R} = \frac{500}{5} = 100$$

## 4. Resonant Rise of Voltage

We have not as yet considered the effect on the voltage distribution in a series resonant circuit of varying the frequency of the source of emf. With respect to the circuit of Fig. 17.1 we can prepare Table II.

Table II. RESONANT RISE OF VOLTAGE

| $f$ (c) | $E_R = IR$ | $E_L = IX_L$ | $E_C = IX_C$ |
|---|---|---|---|
| 159 | 1.01 v | 1.01 v | 101     v |
| 660 | 4.99 | 20.7 | 120 |
| 985 | 9.95 | 61.5 | 161 |
| 1,245 | 19.65 | 153.5 | 252 |
| 1,440 | 44.8 | 406 | 495 |
| 1,515 | 70.7 | 675 | 747 |
| 1,590 | 100 | 1,000 | 1,000 |
| 1,675 | 70.7 | 747 | 675 |
| 1,760 | 44.8 | 495 | 406 |
| 2,040 | 19.65 | 252 | 153.5 |
| 2,575 | 9.95 | 161 | 61.5 |
| 3,840 | 4.99 | 120 | 20.7 |
| 15,900 | 1.01 | 101 | 1.01 |

Plotting the manner in which varying the frequency of the source affects the voltage across the capacitance in graph form, we find that at frequencies well below the resonant frequency of the circuit the voltage across the capacitor is practically the same as the applied emf, since the total impedance of the circuit at these frequencies is mainly the reactance of the capacitance. As the frequency approaches the resonant frequency, even though the reactance of the capacitor is decreasing, the increasing current due to the decreasing total impedance causes the voltage across the capacitance to exceed the applied emf. Since $E_L$ and $E_C$ are equal but 180° out of phase at resonance, $E_R$ is the same as the applied emf, and $E_C$ is much greater than the applied emf. As the frequency is increased to many times the resonant frequency, the impedance of the circuit is practically the same as the inductive reactance of the circuit and the voltage across the capacitance become very small.

Since capacitive reactance decreases as frequency increases, the product $IX_C$ reaches a maximum at a frequency just slightly *lower* than the resonant frequency of the circuit as shown in Fig. 17.7. This frequency difference is usually so small that it can be neglected. In Table II the frequency readings are not close enough to show the exact frequency at which $E_C$ is maximum. We can plot a similar graph showing the rise in the voltage across the inductance of the series resonant circuit as the frequency of the source is varied through resonance. In this case the exact frequency at

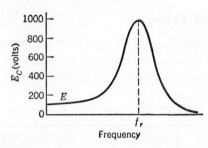

Fig. 17.7. Effect of varying frequency on the voltage across the capacitance of a series resonant circuit.

which $E_L$ is a maximum is slightly higher than the resonant frequency of the circuit. This increase in the voltage across the capacitance (and the inductance) of a series resonant circuit at resonance as shown in Fig. 17.7 is called **resonant rise of voltage.**

$$E_C = IX_C$$

But $I = E/Z$ and at resonance, $Z = R$.

$$\therefore \quad E_C = \frac{EX_C}{R}$$

But $X_C/R = Q$. Therefore, the resonant rise of voltage in a series resonant circuit is

$$E_C = QE \tag{17.5}$$

where $E$ is the emf of the source at the resonant frequency. Since $Q$ is usually much greater than unity, a voltage much greater than the source voltage appears across the capacitance and inductance of a series resonant circuit at resonance. However, since the voltage drops across the inductance and capacitance are equal and opposite at resonance and the voltage drop across the resistance is equal to the applied voltage, the vector sum of the voltage drops does equal the applied emf as required by Kirchhoff's voltage law. Equation (17.5) is sometimes given as a definition of $Q$.

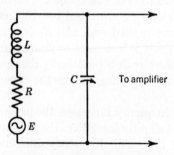

Fig. 17.8. Resonant rise of voltage.

Resonant rise of voltage can be put to practical use in radio receivers as a means of increasing the voltage of a desired signal to which the circuit is tuned. The generator symbol in Fig. 17.8 represents the signal coupled into the tuned circuit from the antenna. As Equation (17.5) indicates, the higher the $Q$ of the tuned circuit, the greater the **sensitivity.**

## 5. Selectivity

Since the capacitance of the circuit of Fig. 17.8 is variable, we can *select* the frequency at which the resonant rise of voltage provides us with a voltage gain of $Q$ times the input voltage. The shape of the resonance curve of Fig. 17.7 is such that frequencies close to the resonant frequency receive just about as great an increase in voltage as the resonant frequency itself. Therefore we can say that a resonant circuit selects a certain *band* of frequencies. This is desirable in radio communications since, according to Hartley's bandwidth law, any signal carrying intelligence requires a band of frequencies whose bandwidth is directly proportional to the rate at which intelligence is transmitted.

However, the skirts of the resonance curve are not steep enough for us to be able to draw a definite boundary between those frequencies which will be selected and those frequencies which will be rejected. We must therefore arbitrarily select a point on the resonance curve on either side of the resonant frequency which we will consider to be the practical boundary between selected and rejected frequencies.

Since the current is common to all components in a series circuit, we will return to the graph of current *vs* frequency in a series resonant circuit to determine the bandwidth of a tuned circuit. As the frequency of the source is decreased from the resonant frequency of a given tuned circuit, the impedance of the circuit will increase and the current will decrease as

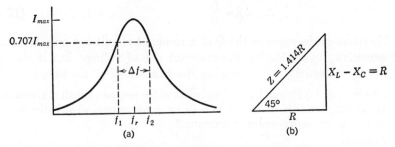

**Fig. 17.9.** The bandwidth of a resonant circuit.

shown in Fig. 17.9a. We will consider the frequency $f_1$ at which the current is diminished to $1/\sqrt{2}$, or 0.707, of its value at resonance as the limit of the band of frequencies below the resonant frequency which the tuned circuit will accept. Similarly, the frequency $f_2$ in Fig. 17.9(a) at which the current is again diminished to 0.707 of the maximum current at resonance is considered to be the limit of the band of frequencies above the resonant frequency which the tuned circuit will accept. Therefore the total bandwidth is

$$\Delta f = f_2 - f_1 \tag{17.6}$$

Since $P = I^2R$, the true power input to the tuned circuit at frequencies $f_1$ and $f_2$ is

$$P = (0.707I_m)^2R = 0.5P_m$$

Therefore the frequencies $f_1$ and $f_2$ on a resonance curve are referred to as the **half-power points**.

In order for the current to drop to 0.707 of the current at resonance, the impedance of the tuned circuit must be $1/0.707$ or 1.414 times the impedance at resonance. Since at resonance $Z = R$, the circuit impedance at the half-power frequencies must be $1.414R$. As indicated by Fig. 17.9(b), the net reactance at the half-power points must be equal to the resistance of the tuned circuit for this to be the case. Since inductive reactance is directly proportional to frequency and capacitive reactance is inversely proportional to frequency, at frequency $f_2$, the value of $X_L$ must have increased by an amount approximately equal to $\frac{1}{2}R$, and $X_C$ must have decreased by an amount approximately equal to $\frac{1}{2}R$. From this it follows that

$$2\pi f_2 L - 2\pi f_1 L = R, \quad \text{or} \quad 2\pi L(f_2 - f_1) = R$$

$$\therefore \quad \Delta f = \frac{R}{2\pi L} \tag{17.7}$$

Dividing both sides of Equation (17.7) by $f_r$,

$$\frac{\Delta f}{f_r} = \frac{R}{2\pi f_r L} = \frac{R}{X_L} = \frac{1}{Q}$$

$$\therefore \quad \Delta f = \frac{f_r}{Q} \tag{17.8}$$

Therefore an increase in the $Q$ of a resonant circuit not only increases the **sensitivity** by increasing the resonant rise of voltage, but it also increases the **selectivity** by decreasing the bandwidth of the tuned circuit.

EXAMPLE 3: (a) Determine the bandwidth of the resonant circuit of Example 2. (b) If this circuit is connected to a 40 $\mu v$ signal source, what is the voltage across the tuning capacitor at resonance?

Solution:

(a)      $\Delta f = \dfrac{f_r}{Q} = \dfrac{1,590,000}{100} = 15.9$ kc

(b)           $E_C = QE = 100 \times 40 \ \mu v = 4$ mv

## 6. The Theoretical Parallel Resonant Circuit

The theoretical parallel resonant circuit of Fig. 17.10 consists of a pure inductance, a capacitance, and a *high* resistance connected in parallel to a source of emf. Since the current in the inductive branch lags the emf by 90° and the current in the capacitive branch leads by 90°,

$$I_T = \sqrt{I_{Rp}^2 + (I_L - I_C)^2}$$

Since $I_L = E/X_L$ and $I_C = E/X_C$, the current in the inductive branch will decrease and the current in the capacitive branch will increase as the frequency of the source increases. Therefore there will be a particular frequency at which $I_L = I_C$. At this frequency the current drawn from the source will be a minimum and will be equal to the current in the resistance branch of the theoretical parallel resonant circuit.

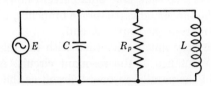

**Fig. 17.10.** The theoretical parallel resonant circuit.

If we carefully plot a graph of total current *vs* frequency for the circuit of Fig. 17.10, we will note [Fig. 17.11(a)] that we produce a resonance curve which has the same shape but is inverted in comparison with the current *vs* frequency graph for a series resonant circuit. But by now we should be accustomed to the "similar but opposite" characteristics of parallel and series circuits. Similarly then, the total impedance *vs* frequency

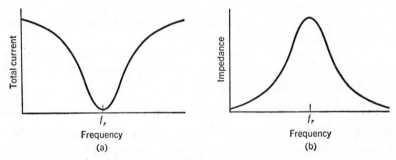

**Fig. 17.11.** Parallel resonance curves.

resonance curve of Fig. 17.11(b) is inverted in comparison with the impedance *vs* frequency graph for a series resonant circuit. Because of these inverted characteristics, parallel resonance is sometimes referred to as **antiresonance.**

Since the current in the pure inductance branch and the current in the capacitance branch are equal at resonance, it follows that the resonant frequency of the theoretical parallel resonant circuit is, as in the case of series resonance,

$$f_r = \frac{1}{2\pi\sqrt{LC}} \qquad (17.1)$$

Although the *total* current in a parallel resonant circuit is minimum at resonance, if the reactances of the inductive and capacitive branches are considerably less than the resistance of the high-resistance branch, the current in the inductance and capacitance is many times as great as the line current. Remembering that the capacitance is charging when the magnetic field around the inductance is collapsing and vice versa, we can consider this current as being the medium which carries the energy back and forth between the capacitance and the inductance. Therefore at resonance we can say that a considerable **tank current** flows in the closed loop consisting of the inductance and capacitance branches, while the resistance branch draws current from the source of emf.

Again we will be very much concerned with the relationship between the resistance and reactance of the resonant circuit. And again we will define the $Q$ factor of the parallel resonant circuit as the ratio between the reactive power of either the inductance or the capacitance at resonance and the true power of the resistance. Therefore

$$Q = \frac{P_q}{P} = \frac{E^2/X_L}{E^2/R_p}$$

and

$$Q = \frac{R_p}{X_L} \tag{17.9}$$

Note that this results in a ratio between resistance and reactance which is inverted as compared with the $Q$ of a series resonant circuit. But note also that the *parallel* resistance is quite high, 100,000 ohms or so, whereas the *series* resistance is only a few ohms.

At resonance the tank current in the theoretical parallel resonant circuit will be the same as $I_L$ or $I_C$ and the total current will be the same as $I_{Rp}$. Since $E = I_R R_p = I_L X_L$,

$$\text{tank current} = Q \times \text{line current} \tag{17.10}$$

We can think of Equation (17.10) as representing a **resonant rise of tank current** similar to the resonant rise of voltage in a series resonant circuit.

The bandwidth of a parallel resonant circuit would be the range of frequencies between the points on the resonance curve where the total impedance drops to 0.707 of the value of the parallel resistance. This would again result in a bandwidth of

$$\Delta f = \frac{f_r}{Q} \tag{17.8}$$

## 7. Practical Parallel Resonant Circuits

The losses in the dielectric of a practical capacitor are usually so small that we can neglect them. If we are required to take these losses into consideration, we can represent them as a high resistance in parallel with the capacitance. But since capacitor losses are so small in comparison to coil losses, the parallel resistance can be omitted from the schematic diagram for the practical parallel resonant circuit of Fig. 17.12. The resistance of the coil must be represented as acting in *series* with the inductance of the coil.

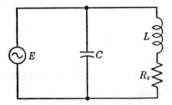 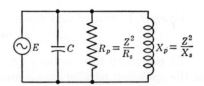

**Fig. 17.12.** A practical parallel resonant circuit.       **Fig. 17.13.** Parallel equivalent of a practical parallel resonant circuit.

Since the practical parallel resonant circuit is not a simple parallel circuit, we must be careful how we define its resonant frequency. We can define the resonant frequency of a practical parallel resonant circuit by any of the following statements, all of which specify essentially the same conditions. The resonant frequency of a practical parallel resonant circuit is the frequency at which (1) the reactive power of the inductance and capacitance are equal; (2) the circuit has unity power factor; (3) the total impedance is a pure resistance; (4) the line current is in phase with the emf of the source.

If we assume that the frequency applied to the circuit of Fig. 17.12 is such that $X_L = X_C$, the impedance of the inductive branch will be slightly greater than the reactance of the capacitive branch due to the resistance in series with the inductive reactance. Therefore the frequency of the source must be *decreased* slightly to allow sufficient current to flow in the inductive branch to make the reactive power of the inductance equal the reactive power of the capacitance. To assist us in solving for the actual resonant frequency of a practical parallel resonant circuit, we can apply a technique we developed in Chapter 16. We can replace the series $LR$ branch by an equivalent parallel circuit as in Fig. 17.13, where

$$R_p = \frac{Z^2}{R_s} = \frac{R_s^2 + X_s^2}{R_s} \tag{16.12}$$

$$X_p = \frac{Z^2}{X_s} = \frac{R_s^2 + X_s^2}{X_s} \tag{16.13}$$

We determined that the $Q$ of a parallel resonant circuit is

$$Q = \frac{R_p}{X_L} \tag{17.9}$$

$$\therefore \quad Q = \frac{Z^2}{R_s} \times \frac{X_s}{Z^2} = \frac{X_s}{R_s}$$

Therefore the $Q$ of the practical resonant circuit is the same as the $Q$ of the coil itself.

At resonance the impedance of the parallel resonant circuit is

$$Z_p = R_p = \frac{R_s^2 + X_s^2}{R_s} = R_s + QX_s \qquad (17.11)$$

Since $R_s$ is usually very small compared to $QX_s$,

$$\therefore \quad Z_p \approx QX_L \qquad (17.12)$$

At resonance the reactances of the inductive and capacitive branches of the *equivalent* parallel circuit must be equal.

$$\therefore \quad \frac{1}{2\pi f_r C} = \frac{R_s^2 + (2\pi f_r L)^2}{2\pi f_r L} \qquad (17.13)$$

$$\frac{L}{C} = R_s^2 + (2\pi f_r L)^2$$

from which
$$f_r^2 = \frac{L - CR_s^2}{4\pi^2 L^2 C}$$

$$\therefore \quad f_r = \frac{1}{2\pi\sqrt{LC}} \times \sqrt{1 - \frac{CR_s^2}{L}} \qquad (17.14)$$

By substituting $2\pi f_r L/Q = R_s$ in Equation (17.13),

$$\frac{1}{2\pi f_r C} = \frac{(2\pi f_r L/Q)^2 + (2\pi f_r L)^2}{2\pi f_r L} = 2\pi f_r L \left(\frac{1 + Q^2}{Q^2}\right)$$

from which
$$f_r = \frac{1}{2\pi\sqrt{LC}} \times \sqrt{\frac{Q^2}{1 + Q^2}} \qquad (17.15)$$

There are several important observations we can make from Equations (17.14) and (17.15).

1. The resonant frequency of a practical parallel resonant circuit is slightly lower than the frequency given by Equation (17.1).
2. Unlike series resonant circuits or theoretical parallel resonant circuits, the resonant frequency of a practical parallel resonant circuit *is* dependent on the resistance of the circuit.
3. If $CR_s^2/L > 1$, there is no parallel resonant frequency for that particular circuit.
4. If the $Q$ of the coil is reasonably high ($Q > 10$), the difference between Equations (17.14) and (17.15) and Equation (17.1) is so small that we can consider the resonant frequency of the parallel resonant circuit to be

$$f_r = \frac{1}{2\pi\sqrt{LC}} \qquad (17.1)$$

Since $R_p$ in Fig. 17.13 is dependent on frequency, the impedance of a practical resonant circuit is not a maximum at the resonant frequency.

Since solving for maximum impedance involves calculus, we shall simply state that the frequency at which the impedance of a parallel resonant circuit is a maximum is

$$f = \frac{\sqrt{1 - (1/4Q^2)}}{2\pi\sqrt{LC}} \tag{17.16}$$

This frequency is between the actual resonant frequency of the practical parallel resonant circuit and the frequency given by Equation (17.1). Equation (17.16) shows that if the $Q$ of a tuned circuit is reduced to $\frac{1}{2}$, there is no particular frequency at which the total impedance is a maximum. Purposely reducing the $Q$ of a tuned circuit is called **damping** and when $Q = \frac{1}{2}$, the result is **critical damping**. Just as we damp meter movements to keep the pointers from oscillating, we add resistance to peaking coils in television receivers to keep them from **ringing** at a frequency determined by their inductance and distributed capacitance.

Although in most examples the $Q$ of parallel tuned circuits is high enough that we can neglect the effect of resistance on the resonant frequency, we have taken the time to investigate the effect of $Q$ on the practical parallel resonant circuit so that we can appreciate the effect that loading has on a parallel tuned circuit. In most cases such frequency instability is undesirable.

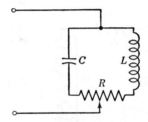

**Fig. 17.14.** A resistance tuned parallel resonant circuit.

However it is possible for a designer to capitalize on these characteristics of parallel resonant circuits in order to use a variable resistance to tune the circuit to resonance as shown in Fig. 17.14.

EXAMPLE 4: A coil in a tuned circuit of a radio receiver has an inductance of 50 $\mu$h and a resistance of 50 ohms. It forms a parallel resonant circuit with a 200 $\mu\mu$f capacitor.
(a) At what frequency is the total impedance a pure resistance?
(b) What is the magnitude of the impedance at this frequency?
(c) What is the bandwidth of the tuned circuit?

*Solution:*

(a) $\quad\quad f_r = \dfrac{1}{2\pi\sqrt{LC}} \times \sqrt{1 - \dfrac{CR_s^2}{L}}$

$\quad\quad\quad = \dfrac{1}{6.28\sqrt{50 \times 10^{-6} \times 200 \times 10^{-12}}} \times \sqrt{1 - \dfrac{CR_s^2}{L}}$

$\quad\quad\quad = 1.59 \sqrt{1 - \dfrac{200 \times 10^{-12} \times 2500}{50 \times 10^{-6}}}$

$\therefore \quad f_r = 1.59 \times 0.995 = 1.582 \text{ megacycles}$

(b)   $X_L = 2\pi f L = 6.28 \times 1.582 \times 10^6 \times 50 \times 10^{-6} \approx 500$ ohms

$$Q = \frac{X_L}{R_s} \approx \frac{500}{50} \approx 10$$

$\therefore \quad Z_p \approx QX_L \approx 10 \times 500 \approx 5 \text{ kilohms}$

(c)                    $\Delta f = \frac{f_r}{Q} \approx \frac{1.59 \times 10^6}{10} \approx 159 \text{ kc}$

## 8. Filter Networks

So far we have considered resonant circuits only in terms of their ability to select a certain band of frequencies centered about the resonant frequency of the circuit and to reject all other frequencies. We can also use resonant circuits to reject a specific frequency without affecting the response of the circuit to all other frequencies. Such an application is called

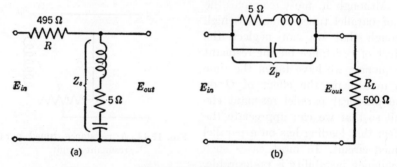

Fig. 17.15. Wavetraps.

a **wavetrap.** Figure 17.15 illustrates two wavetrap circuits. In both cases the four-terminal network forms a voltage divider across the input. If we assume a very high-impedance load connected to the output terminals, then the output voltage of the circuit of Fig. 17.15(a) will be

$$E_{out} = E_{in} \times \frac{Z_s}{R + Z_s} \qquad (17.17)$$

At resonance, $Z_s$ will be equal to the resistance of the coil, which is quite small compared with the resistance $R$. With the values given in Fig. 17.15(a), the output voltage will be only 1% of the input voltage at the resonant frequency. With a high-$Q$ tuned circuit, at frequencies other than the resonant frequency $Z_s$ will be much greater than $R$ and the fraction $Z_s/(R + Z_s)$ will approach 100%.

In the wavetrap circuit of Fig. 17.15(b), the load voltage will be

$$E_{out} = E_{in} \times \frac{R_L}{R_L + Z_p} \qquad (17.18)$$

At resonance the impedance of the parallel resonant circuit will be many times as great as the resistance of the load. This results in a very small voltage across the load at this frequency. At frequencies off resonance, $Z_p$ becomes quite small, and therefore $R_L/(R_L+Z_p)$ approaches 100%.

In many communications circuits it is desirable to include the selection of one frequency and the rejection of another frequency into a combined **double resonant** circuit such as that shown in Fig. 17.16.

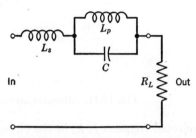

Fig. 17.16. A double resonant circuit.

EXAMPLE 5: If the capacitance in the circuit of Fig. 17.16 is 200 $\mu\mu f$, determine the inductances of $L_p$ and $L_s$ in order to reject a signal at 456 kc and to accept a signal at 1200 kc.

*Solution:*

Step I. $L_p$ and $C$ form a parallel resonant circuit which will represent a high impedance in series with $R_L$ at resonance. Therefore $L_p$ and $C$ form a wavetrap and must be tuned to the frequency which is to be rejected, 456 kc.

$$X_C = \frac{1}{2\pi fC} = \frac{10^{12}}{6.28 \times 456 \times 10^3 \times 200} = 1750 \text{ ohms}$$

$$L_p = \frac{X_L}{2\pi f} = \frac{1750}{6.28 \times 456 \times 10^3} = 612 \text{ } \mu h$$

Step II. At 1200 kc,

$$B_C = 2\pi fC = 6.28 \times 1.2 \times 10^6 \times 200 \times 10^{-12} = 15.07 \times 10^{-4} \text{ mho}$$

$$B_{L_p} = \frac{1}{2\pi fL} = \frac{1}{6.28 \times 1.2 \times 10^6 \times 612 \times 10^{-6}} = 2.17 \times 10^{-4} \text{ mho}$$

Therefore the net susceptance of the parallel circuit at 1.2 megacycles is

$$B = 0.001507 - 0.000217 = 0.00129 \text{ mho capacitive}$$

$$\therefore \quad X = \frac{1}{B} = \frac{1}{0.00129} = 775 \text{ ohms capacitive}$$

For the whole circuit to be *series* resonant at 1.2 megacycles

$$X_{L_s} = 775 \text{ ohms}$$

$$\therefore \quad L_s = \frac{X_L}{2\pi f} = \frac{775}{6.28 \times 1.2} = 103 \text{ } \mu h$$

Figure 17.17 illustrates an alternate circuit arrangement to achieve the results required in Example 5. Here $L_s$ and $C$ are selected first to form a series resonant circuit at the desired frequency of 1200 kc, thus forming a low impedance in series with $R_L$ at 1200 kc. At 456 kc this series branch has a net capacitive reactance which can be tuned with $L_p$ to form a parallel resonant circuit at 456 kc. If the selected frequency is lower than the

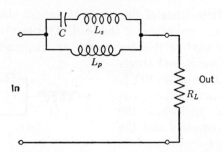

**Fig. 17.17.** Alternate arrangement of double resonant circuit.

rejected frequency, $L_s$ in the circuit of Fig. 17.16 and $L_p$ in the circuit of Fig. 17.17 must be replaced with capacitors.

## Problems

1. At what frequency is a circuit consisting of a 40 $\mu\mu f$ capacitor and a 90 $\mu h$ coil with a $Q$ of 80 series resonant?

2. What is the bandwidth of the circuit in Problem 1?

3. If the circuit of Problem 1 is connected to a 500 $\mu v$ source of emf, what voltage will appear across the capacitor at resonance?

4. What current will flow through the circuit at resonance?

5. What value of capacitance is required to tune a 500 $\mu h$ coil to series resonance at 465 kc?

6. What is the value of an inductance which in series with a 12 $\mu\mu f$ capacitor forms a series resonant circuit at 45 megacycles?

7. A tuned circuit consisting of a 40 $\mu h$ inductance and a 100 $\mu\mu f$ capacitance in series has a bandwidth of 25 kc. What is its $Q$?

8. What is the resistance of the coil in the tuned circuit of Problem 7?

9. What is the resonant frequency of a tuned circuit consisting of the coil and capacitor of Problem 1 connected in parallel?

10. What is the impedance of the parallel tuned circuit of Problem 9 at resonance?

11. If the resonant circuit of Problem 9 is connected to a 500 $\mu v$ source, what is the tank current at resonance?

12. What will the parallel resonant frequency be if loading the inductive branch reduces the $Q$ of the tuned circuit of Problem 9 to 20?

13. A variable tuning capacitor in a radio receiver has a maximum capacitance of 365 $\mu\mu f$ and a minimum capacitance of 30 $\mu\mu f$.
    (a) What inductance is required for the lowest frequency to which the circuit can tune to be 540 kc?
    (b) What is the highest frequency to which this circuit can be tuned?

14. A coil with a $Q$ of 90 and a capacitor form a parallel resonant circuit tuned to 4.5 megacycles. The total impedance of the circuit at resonance is 60 kilohms. Find (a) the inductance of the coil, and (b) the capacitance of the capacitor.

15. A 4 h filter choke with a resistance of 20 ohms is connected in series with a pulsating d-c source of emf and a resistive load. What value of capacitance must be connected across the choke to provide the most effective filtering of a 120 c ripple component in the output of the pulsating source?

16. An audio filter for reducing the 10 kc heterodyne between broadcast stations contains a parallel resonant circuit whose capacitance branch is 0.02 $\mu$f. The inductance branch has a resistance of 100 ohms. What inductance should this branch possess?

17. Solve Example 5 with reference to the circuit of Fig. 17.17.

18. Design a filter which can be used to pass the output of a 200 kc power line carrier transmitter whose bandwidth is 6 kc but reject any third harmonic content in the transmitter output. This filter will contain an 0.5 mh coil.

## Review Questions

1. What is meant by the general term **resonance?**

2. What property of electric circuits makes resonance possible?

3. Why does the resistance in a series resonant circuit have no bearing on the resonant frequency?

4. What is the significance of the resistance in a series resonant circuit?

5. What is the significance of the term $L/C$ **ratio** in resonant circuits?

6. What is the significance of the $Q$ factor of resonant circuits?

7. Prepare a table similar to Table I for the circuit of Fig. 17.5.

8. Prepare a table similar to Table I for the circuit of Fig. 17.6.

9. What is the significance of the term **resonant rise of voltage** in discussing resonant circuits?

10. What is the significance of the term **half-power points** in discussing resonant circuits?

11. How does a parallel resonant circuit differ in circuit behavior from a series resonant circuit?

12. Why are parallel resonant circuits capacitive at frequencies above the resonant frequency whereas series resonant circuits are inductive at frequencies above the resonant frequency?

13. Why does *decreasing* the resistance of the coil of a parallel resonant circuit *increase* the total impedance at resonance?

14. Why does a change in the resistance of a coil in a parallel resonant circuit affect the resonant frequency?

15. If a resistor were placed in parallel with the capacitor of a series resonant circuit, would the resonant frequency be affected? Explain.

16. Why does the impedance of a parallel resonant circuit not become maximum right at the frequency at which the circuit has unity power factor?

17. What is the significance of the term **tank current** in discussing resonant circuits?

18. What is the significance of the answer to *Problem* 16?

19. Representing the portion of the resistance in series with the inductance as $R_L$ and the portion in series with the capacitance as $R_C$ in the circuit of Fig. 17.14, derive an equation for the resonant frequency.

20. In constructing the filter circuit of Fig. 17.17, $L_p$ and $L_s$ are both made variable to allow the filter to be tuned. In which order must these inductances be adjusted? Why?

# Chapter 18

# TRANSFORMER ACTION AND MUTUAL INDUCTANCE

## 1. Mutual Induction

We encountered mutual induction briefly in Chapter 9. Figure 9.2 showed a circuit in which *changing* the current in one winding (primary) induced an emf in another winding (secondary) which was *linked* by the magnetic lines of force created by the current in the primary winding. The generation of an emf in one winding by a *changing* current in another winding is called **mutual induction.** In Chapter 9 we considered mutual induction only to the extent that it illustrated Faraday's and Lenz's laws. Since mutual induction is based on *changing* current, we did not pursue its application to d-c circuits. However, since the current in an a-c circuit is continually changing, mutual induction plays a very important role in a-c circuits.

## 2. Transformer Action

A practical device which depends on mutual induction for its operation is the **transformer.** In schematic diagrams it is customary to connect the source of emf to the *left*-hand coil (primary) and the load to the *right*-hand coil (secondary) as in Fig. 18.1. For the moment we will assume that the secondary terminals are left open circuit as shown.

According to Kirchhoff's voltage law, a voltage must appear across the primary coil such that it is exactly equal to the applied emf at every instant in time. As we discovered in Chapter 12, if the resistance of the primary coil is negligible, this voltage must be induced into the coil by a changing flux in the core. Since the applied emf is a sine wave and since, according

379

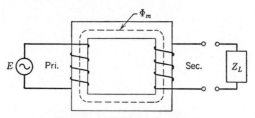

**Fig. 18.1.** Transformer action.

to Faraday's law, the induced emf is proportional to the *rate of change* of flux, the flux in the transformer core must be a sine wave lagging the applied emf by 90°.

Since the **weber** is defined as the magnetic flux which must cut (or link) an electric conductor in one second in order to induce an average emf of one volt, and since *each* turn of a coil is linked by the same field, it follows that

$$E_{av} = \frac{N\Phi_m}{t} \tag{18.1}$$

where $E_{av}$ is the average emf induced into a coil, $N$ is the number of turns in the coil, and $t$ is the time (seconds) it takes the flux to rise from zero to $\Phi_m$ webers.

Since the flux in the transformer must be a sine wave, it must rise from zero to $\Phi_m$ in one-quarter of a cycle.

$$\therefore \quad E_{av} = \frac{N\Phi_m}{1/4f} = 4fN\Phi_m$$

But the *average* value of a sine wave is 0.637 of the peak value, and since the *effective* value of a sine wave is 0.707 of the peak value,

$$E = 1.11E_{av} \tag{18.2}$$

$$\therefore \quad E = 4.44fN\Phi_m \tag{18.3}$$

where $f$ is the frequency of the applied emf, $N$ is the number of turns in the coil, and $\Phi_m$ is the peak value of the flux in webers. (Remember that 1 weber $= 10^8$ lines of force.) Equation (18.3) is called the **general transformer equation.** Applying this equation to the simple transformer of Fig. 18.1,

$$E_p = 4.44fN_p\Phi_m \tag{18.4}$$

EXAMPLE 1: The iron core of a transformer has a cross-sectional area of 1.5 sq in. If the peak flux density in the core is to be 80 kilolines per sq in. (see the **BH** curves of Fig. 7.15), how many turns are required on a primary winding that is to be connected to a 120 v, 60 c source of emf?

*Solution:*

$$\Phi_m = 1.5 \times 80{,}000 \times 10^{-8} = 0.0012 \text{ weber}$$

$$N_p = \frac{E_p}{4.44f\Phi_m} = \frac{120}{4.44 \times 60 \times 0.0012} = 375 \text{ turns}$$

To create this sine wave of flux in the core, an alternating current must flow in the primary winding. And since

$$\Phi_p = \frac{\mathfrak{F}}{\mathfrak{R}} = \frac{N_p I_p}{\mathfrak{R}} \qquad \text{(7.1 and 7.2)}$$

it follows that the peak value of the primary current is

$$I_{p_m} = \Phi_m \frac{\mathfrak{R}}{N_p}$$

from which
$$I_p = \frac{\Phi_m}{\sqrt{2}} \times \frac{\mathfrak{R}}{N_p} \qquad \text{(18.5)}$$

If for the moment we can neglect core losses and assume that $\mathfrak{R}$ remains constant, even though the secondary of the transformer is open circuit, there must be a sine wave of primary current in phase with the flux and lagging the applied emf by 90°. This primary current is called the **exciting** or **magnetizing** current of the transformer. In good transformers this magnetizing current is usually less than 5% of the current which the primary winding can be expected to pass when full load is connected to the secondary.

## 3. Transformation Ratio

In the ideal transformer, all the flux created by primary current will link the secondary winding. Therefore an emf will be induced in the secondary winding,

$$E_s = 4.44 f N_s \Phi_m \qquad \text{(18.6)}$$

Dividing Equation (18.6) into Equation (18.4) gives

$$\frac{E_p}{E_s} = \frac{N_p}{N_s} = a \qquad \text{(18.7)}$$

Therefore when all the primary flux links the secondary winding, the ratio of the primary induced emf to the secondary induced emf is the same as the ratio of the number of primary turns to the number of secondary turns. These ratios are called the **transformation ratio**, which is represented by the letter symbol $a$.

Equation (18.7) shows us why transformers are so widely used in power systems. They provide a means of transforming a given source of alternating emf into any desired voltage with minimum loss. If we arrange to produce a secondary voltage higher than the source voltage, we have a **step-up** transformer. Similarly, a **step-down** transformer is one in which the secondary voltage is less than the primary voltage.

EXAMPLE 2: The secondary of the transformer of Example 1 is to be wound to supply 6.3 v for vacuum tube filaments. How many turns must there be on the secondary winding?

*Solution:*

$$a = \frac{E_p}{E_s} = \frac{120}{6.3} = 19, \qquad N_s = \frac{N_p}{a} = \frac{375}{19} \approx 20 \text{ turns}$$

If we now connect the load impedance to the secondary winding in the simple transformer circuit of Fig. 18.1, the emf induced into the secondary winding by the primary flux will cause current to flow in the secondary circuit. This current flowing in the secondary winding will create a magnetomotive force of $N_s I_s$ ampere turns, which according to Lenz's law, tends to reduce the amplitude of the sine wave of flux in the core. But in a lossless transformer the amplitude of the flux sine wave must not change since it is responsible for always inducing an emf equal to the applied emf into the primary winding. Therefore when a load is connected to the secondary, *additional* primary current must flow in order to develop a primary mmf component which exactly cancels the secondary mmf. Therefore

$$N_p I'_p = N_s I_s \tag{18.8}$$

where $I'_p$ is the additional or load component of the primary current. Equation (18.8) may be rearranged to give

$$\frac{I_s}{I'_p} = \frac{N_p}{N_s} = a \tag{18.9}$$

When we connect a load to the secondary of the simple transformer of Fig. 18.1, an additional primary current component $I'_p$ appears. As far as the source of emf is concerned, we can treat this additional current as if an extra load impedance were now connected in *parallel* with the original primary impedance. This load appears to have an impedance of

$$Z_p = \frac{E_p}{I'_p}$$

From Equation (18.7),        $E_p = \dfrac{N_p}{N_s} E_s = a E_s$

and from Equation (18.9)     $I'_p = \dfrac{N_s}{N_p} I_s = \dfrac{I_s}{a}$

$$\therefore \quad Z_p = \frac{E_s}{I_s} \left( \frac{N_p}{N_s} \right)^2$$

But $E_s/I_s$ is dependent on the total impedance of the secondary circuit. In a good transformer the impedance of the secondary winding will be small compared with the load impedance.

$$\therefore \quad Z_p \approx \left( \frac{N_p}{N_s} \right)^2 Z_L \approx a^2 Z_L \tag{18.10}$$

where $Z_p$ is called the **reflected impedance**. It is approximately equal to the *square* of the turns ratio times the load impedance. Therefore we can use transformers as a means of transforming a given load impedance into a different value with minimum loss. There are many circuit applications in which a transformer is used as an impedance **matching** device. One example is in coupling a given load to a vacuum tube amplifier which requires a specific value of load impedance for maximum power output with minimum distortion as illustrated in the following example.

EXAMPLE 3: An audio transformer has 1200 turns in the primary winding. How many turns must be wound in the secondary winding to make a 4 ohm loudspeaker appear as a 5 kilohm load to the vacuum tube amplifier connected to the primary?

*Solution:*

$$a^2 = \frac{Z_p}{Z_L} = \frac{5000}{4} = 1250$$

$$\therefore \quad a = 35.3$$

$$N_s = \frac{N_p}{a} = \frac{1200}{35.3} = 34 \text{ turns}$$

EXAMPLE 4: The audio output transformer of Fig. 18.2 presents the correct load impedance to a vacuum tube amplifier when *either* an 8 ohm load is connected to terminals $A$ and $B$ or a 16 ohm load is connected to terminals $A$ and $C$. What load may be connected to terminals $B$ and $C$ alone to present the same reflected load?

*Solution:* We can solve this problem either by assuming convenient values for the number of primary turns and reflected impedance or with algebraic symbols. Let $N_1$ represent the number of secondary turns between terminals $A$ and $B$, and $N_2$ the total number of turns between terminals $A$ and $C$.

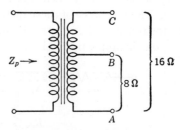

Fig. 18.2. A tapped audio output transformer.

Then

$$Z_p = 8 \left(\frac{N_p}{N_1}\right)^2 = 16 \left(\frac{N_p}{N_2}\right)^2 = Z_x \left(\frac{N_p}{N_2 - N_1}\right)^2$$

from which

$$\frac{\sqrt{8}}{N_1} = \frac{\sqrt{16}}{N_2} = \frac{\sqrt{Z_x}}{N_2 - N_1}$$

from which $\quad \sqrt{Z_x} = \sqrt{16} - \sqrt{8}, \quad$ and $\quad Z_x = (\sqrt{16} - \sqrt{8})^2 = 1.38$ ohms

Note that the required impedance is *not* simply the difference between the two given loads.

## 4. Leakage Reactance

In establishing the transformation ratio in the preceding section, we assumed that *all* the flux created by the magnetizing current in the primary linked the secondary winding. However, since there is no magnetic in-sulator, even in the best transformers some of the magnetic lines of force produced by the magnetizing current do not link the secondary. These lines of force are called the primary **leakage flux** as shown in Fig. 18.3.

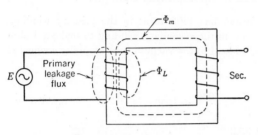

**Fig. 18.3.** Leakage flux.

The remainder of the total primary flux does link the secondary and is called the **mutual flux.** Similarly when load current flows in the secondary, some of the sec-ondary magnetic lines of force do not link the pri-mary. These lines of force are called the secondary leakage flux.

The effect of leakage flux is the same as if $\Phi_m/\Phi_p$ of the total primary turns were developing lines of force that link the secondary winding and $\Phi_L/\Phi_p$ of the primary turns act as a self inductance in series with the pri-mary. The reactance of these ineffective primary turns is called the primary **leakage reactance.** As far as the source of emf is concerned, the transformer takes on the appearance shown in Fig. 18.4.

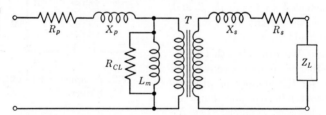

**Fig. 18.4.** Effect of leakage reactance. $R_{CL}$ represents core losses; $L_m$, primary induc-tance governing magnetizing current; $R_p$, primary winding resistance; $X_p$, primary winding leakage reactance; $T$, a perfect transformer of trans-formation ratio $a$; $X_s$, secondary winding leakage reactance; $R_s$, secondary winding resistance; $Z_L$, secondary winding load impedance.

In most iron-core transformers, the primary and secondary leakage reactances represent approximately the same percentage of their respective windings; therefore the transformation ratio of the perfect transformer portion of the equivalent circuit of Fig. 18.4 is still essentially $N_p/N_s$. Since this represents a perfect transformer, looking into its primary the source of emf sees a reflected load of

$$Z_{ref} = a^2(R_s + jX_s + Z_L) \qquad (18.11)$$

We can therefore reduce the transformer still further to the equivalent circuit of Fig. 18.5(a). If the transformer is fully loaded, the magnetizing

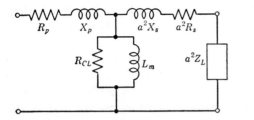

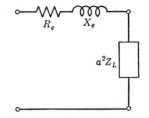

(a) Complete equivalent network for Fig. 18.4          (b) Simplified equivalent network.

**Fig. 18.5.** Equivalent networks for an iron core transformer.
$$R_e = R_p + a^2 R_s \text{ and } X_e = X_p + a^2 X_s.$$

current in the branch of the equivalent circuit of Fig. 18.5(a) containing $R_{CL}$ and $L_m$ is so small compared with the load current that it creates negligible voltage drop across $R_p$ and $X_p$. Therefore when we wish to determine the effects of loading a transformer, we can omit the $R_{CL}$ and $L_m$ branch and simplify the equivalent circuit still further to the simple series circuit of Fig. 18.5(b).

## 5. The Open-Circuit and Short-Circuit Tests

The transformer constants for the equivalent networks of Fig. 18.5 are readily determined experimentally from two simple tests. If we leave the secondary terminals open, $Z_L$ is infinitely large and current will flow only in the $R_{CL}$ and $j\omega L_m$ branch of the equivalent circuit of Fig. 18.5(a). We now feed the rated value of source emf to the primary through a group of instruments consisting of voltmeter, ammeter, and wattmeter. Since the magnetizing current is only a very small fraction of the full load primary current, we can assume that the $I^2 R$ loss due to magnetizing current alone in the primary is negligible. Therefore the wattmeter shows the core losses. These core losses are due to eddy currents in the core and to the hysteresis loop of the core material. The eddy currents produce a small counterflux in the core just as if we had connected a resistor across the secondary winding. The hysteresis loop of the iron causes the exciting current to lag the applied emf by slightly less than 90°. The in-phase component of the magnetizing current contributes to the true power reading of the watt-meter.

From the voltmeter and ammeter readings we can determine the total impedance of the magnetizing current and core loss branch of the equivalent network of Fig. 18.5(a). As this diagram indicates, an increase in the load current will slightly increase the voltage drop across $R_p$ and $X_p$. This in turn will slightly reduce the current in the $R_{CL}$ and $L_m$ branch. Therefore there is a slight reduction in the magnetizing current as the transformer is fully loaded.

We now short-circuit the low-voltage winding of the transformer. In the case of the step-down transformer this will be the secondary winding. This is equivalent to making $Z_L$ zero in Fig. 18.5(b). Since $R_e + jX_e$ is fairly small, the source of emf connected to the high-voltage winding is greatly reduced to keep the currents in the transformer windings from exceeding their rated values. The choice of the low-voltage winding for the short circuit reduces the danger to both the personnel performing the test and to the transformer itself. It is customary to adjust the emf of the source to a value which will cause rated current to flow in the short-circuited winding. This requires an applied emf of less than 5% of the rated voltage for the winding being used as the primary. Since reducing the applied emf reduces the exciting current to less than 5% of its normal value, the core losses are now less than 0.25% of their normal value and we can assume that the wattmeter is showing only the copper losses from which we can determine the value of $R_e$.

EXAMPLE 5: When the secondary of a small step-down transformer is short-circuited, the applied primary voltage is 6 v, the primary current is 4 amp, and the wattmeter reading is 12 w. Determine $R_e$ and $X_e$.

*Solution:*

$$R_e = \frac{P}{I^2} = \frac{12}{16} = 0.75 \text{ ohm}$$

$$Z_e = \frac{E}{I} = \frac{6}{4} = 1.5 \text{ ohms}$$

$$\therefore \quad X_e = \sqrt{Z_e{}^2 - R_e{}^2} = \sqrt{2.25 - 0.56} = +j1.3 \text{ ohms}$$

## 6. Effect of Loading a Transformer

One important effect of the leakage reactance and the resistance of the windings in Fig. 18.4 is that the load voltage $V_L$ is not the same as the voltage induced into the secondary since, to satisfy Kirchhoff's voltage law,

$$E_s = I_s R_s + jI_s X_s + V_L$$

Similarly the voltage induced into the primary by the mutual flux must be slightly less than the total applied voltage $V_p$. Therefore as the current drawn by the load is changed, the voltage across the load will also change, even though the applied emf may remain constant.

We can show the effect of load current on the load voltage by preparing vector diagrams for the equivalent circuit of Fig. 18.5(b). The current flowing in this equivalent circuit is the primary load current which is $1/a$ times the actual load current. Similarly the voltage across $a^2 Z_L$ in Fig. 18.5 is $a$ times the actual load voltage. Since the current is common to all components, we will use it as a reference vector in the vector diagrams of Fig. 18.6. The total applied primary voltage will be the vector sum of three voltages: $aV_L$, which will have an angle with respect to the current depending on the power factor of the load (power factor angle), $I_p R_e$ or $I_L/a \times R_e$,

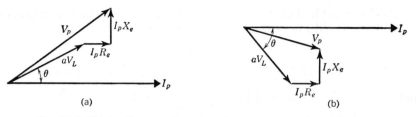

**Fig. 18.6.** Vector diagrams for a transformer under load. (a) Lagging power factor load. (b) Leading power factor load.

which will be in phase with the current, and $I_pX_e$ or $I_L/a \times X_e$, which will lead the current by 90°.

Although we could add these vector voltages by the customary geometrical construction we learned in Chapter 12, in which all vectors are drawn with a common origin, the vector diagrams will be less confusing if we add each vector with its proper direction and magnitude to the tip of the preceding vector somewhat as we did in preparing power triangles. Such vectors are referred to as **funicular** (chain-like) vectors.

When the load is disconnected, $I_pR_e$ and $I_pX_e$ become zero, and $aV_L$ and $V_p$ in Fig. 18.6 are identical. But as shown in Fig. 18.6(a), when the load has a lagging power factor so that $V_L$ leads the current, the load voltage will drop appreciably under load. However, with a leading power factor load as in Fig. 18.6(b), the full-load voltage and no-load voltage are almost the same.

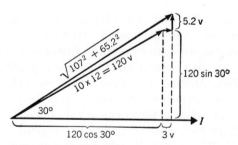

**Fig. 18.7.** Vector diagram for Example 6.

EXAMPLE 6: The transformer tested in Example 5 has a transformation ratio of 10 and develops a load voltage of 12 v when the load current is 40 amp at 0.866 lagging power factor. What is the open-circuit secondary voltage?
*Solution:*

$$aV_L = 10 \times 12 = 120 \text{ v}$$

Since the power factor is 0.866 lagging, this voltage will lead the current by arccos 0.866 or 30° as shown in Fig. 18.7.

$$I_pR_e = \frac{40}{10} \times 0.75 = 3 \text{ v}, \qquad I_pX_e = \frac{40}{10} \times 1.3 = 5.2 \text{ v}$$

As shown in Fig. 18.7, we must express the load voltage in rectangular coordinates in order to carry out the vector addition.

$$\therefore \quad aV_L = 120 \cos 30° + j120 \sin 30° = 104 + j60$$

$$V_p = (104 + 3) + j(60 + 5.2) = \sqrt{107^2 + 65.2^2} = 125 \text{ v}$$

and
$$\text{No load } V_L = \frac{V_p}{a} = \frac{125}{10} = 12.5 \text{ v}$$

## 7. Audio Transformers

We have already noted that transformers are very useful for **matching** a given load impedance to the output resistance of vacuum tube amplifiers. In such applications the frequency of the source of emf can vary from 20 c to 20 kc. To determine the effect of this range of input frequencies on the performance of an audio transformer, we must consider two additional circuit parameters in the equivalent circuit of Fig. 18.8; the internal re-

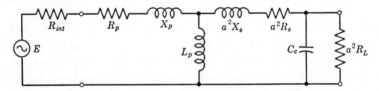

Fig. 18.8. Equivalent circuit of an audio transformer.

sistance of the source $R_{int}$, and at the higher frequencies, the equivalent shunt capacitance $C_e$ of the distributed capacitance between the turns.

As the frequency of the source decreases from a reference frequency of 1 kc, the primary exciting current must increase in order to maintain the required mutual flux. Another way of saying the same thing is that, as the frequency of the source decreases, the reactance of the primary inductance decreases. This means that as the frequency decreases there will be more of the source voltage lost across $R_{int}$ and less applied to the equivalent transformer circuit. We can consider the low-frequency limit of the transformer to be at the frequency at which the inductive reactance of the primary drops to the same value as the internal resistance of the source. Good low-frequency response therefore requires sources with low internal resistance and transformers with high primary inductance.

As the frequency increases, the voltage across the equivalent leakage reactance increases, which tends to reduce the output voltage as shown by the dashed curve of Fig. 18.9. But if the transformer is designed so that the equivalent capacitance and the leakage inductance are resonant at approximately 20 kc, the resonant rise of voltage across this capacitance can be used to advantage to offset the natural roll-off at the high-frequency end of the audio spectrum. Excessive resonant rise would be undesirable,

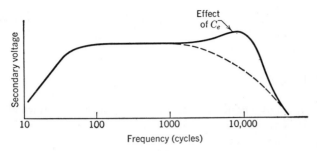

**Fig. 18.9.** Frequency response of a typical audio transformer.

but this can be controlled in the transformer design by choosing the proper ratio between the reactance and resistance. At frequencies above the resonant frequency of $X_e$ and $C_e$, the output voltage is very small.

## 8. Coefficient of Coupling

Since leakage reactance has such a major effect on the performance of magnetically coupled circuits, we are interested in knowing the fraction of the total primary flux that actually links the secondary winding. This fraction is called the **coefficient of coupling.**

The letter symbol for **coefficient of coupling** is $K$. Therefore, by definition,

$$K = \frac{\Phi_m}{\Phi_p} \qquad (18.12)$$

The value of $K$ can range from unity when all the primary flux links the secondary as in the ideal transformer of Fig. 18.1 down to zero when the secondary winding is completely outside the magnetic field of the primary or is purposely positioned at right angles to the primary flux [Fig. 18.10(c)]. The physical arrrangement of Fig. 18.10(c) is used in radio cir-

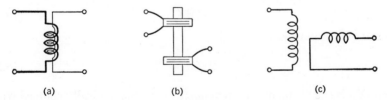

(a)                    (b)                    (c)

**Fig. 18.10.** Variations in magnetic coupling. (a) Tight coupling. (b) Loose coupling. (c) Minimum coupling.

cuits where magnetic coupling between tuned circuits is to be kept to a minimum and the physical dimensions are rather restricted. In order to obtain *tight* coupling with $K$ close to unity in radio frequency coils where iron cores are not practical, the two strands of wire are interwound on the coil form as a **bifilar** winding [Fig. 18.10(a)]. Magnetic coupling of tuned coils requires a very *loose* coupling with a coefficient of coupling of approximately 0.01 as shown by the physical placement of the two coils on the coil form of Fig. 18.10(b).

## 9. Mutual Inductance

The equivalent circuit we developed for iron-core power and audio transformers is valid only because the coefficient of coupling is very close to unity. In the case of magnetically coupled circuits which are loosely coupled we must use a different approach.

In Chapter 9 we found that a coil has a self-inductance of one henry when current in that coil *changing* at the rate of one ampere per second induces a cemf of one volt in the coil. Applying the same line of thought to the process of mutual induction, we can say that

> a pair of magnetically coupled coils has a **mutual inductance** of one henry when current changing at the rate of one ampere per second in one coil induces an average emf of one volt in the other coil.

The letter symbol for **mutual inductance** is $M$. Therefore by definition,

$$E_{s_{av}} = \frac{M I_{pm}}{t} \tag{18.13}$$

Since the instantaneous current must rise from zero to maximum in one quarter of a cycle of a sine wave,

$$E_{s_{av}} = \frac{M I_{pm}}{1/4f} = 4fM I_{pm}$$

But
$$E_{av} = \frac{2}{\pi} E_m \tag{11.4}$$

Therefore
$$\frac{2}{\pi} E_{s_m} = 4fM I_{pm}$$

from which
$$E_s = 2\pi fM I_p \tag{18.14}$$

Rearranging Equation (18.14) gives

$$\frac{E_s}{I_p} = 2\pi fM = X_M \tag{18.15}$$

where $X_M$ is called the **mutual reactance** of the magnetically coupled windings.

> EXAMPLE 7: 120 v, 60 c is applied to the primary of a transformer whose primary inductance is 5 h. The open-circuit secondary voltage is 40 v. Neglecting losses, what is the mutual inductance between the two windings?
>
> *Solution:*
> $$E_s = \omega M I_p$$

But $$I_p = \frac{E_p}{\omega L_p}$$

$$\therefore \quad E_s = \frac{M}{L_p} E_p$$

$$M = L_p \frac{E_s}{E_p} = 5 \times \frac{40}{120} = 1.67 \text{ h}$$

Combining Equations (18.1) and (18.13),

$$\frac{N\Phi_m}{t} = \frac{MI_{pm}}{t}$$

But from Equation (18.12),     $\Phi_m = K\Phi_p$

$$\therefore \quad MI_{pm} = N_s K\Phi_p \tag{1}$$

If we now reverse the windings and use the original secondary winding as the primary and vice versa, it follows that

$$MI_{sm} = N_p K\Phi_s \tag{2}$$

Multiplying Equations (1) and (2),

$$M^2 = K^2 \left(\frac{N_p\Phi_p}{I_{pm}}\right)\left(\frac{N_s\Phi_s}{I_{sm}}\right) \tag{3}$$

But from the definition of self-inductance,

$$E_{av} = \frac{LI_m}{t}$$

and from the definition of the weber,

$$E_{av} = \frac{N\Phi}{t}$$

$$\therefore \quad L = \frac{N\Phi}{I_m}$$

Substituting in Equation (3) gives

$$M = K\sqrt{L_p L_s} \tag{18.16}$$

EXAMPLE 8: If the secondary winding of the transformer of Example 7 has a self-inductance of 0.8 h, what is the coefficient of coupling between the windings?

Solution:

$$K = \frac{M}{\sqrt{L_p L_s}} = \frac{1.67}{\sqrt{5 \times 0.8}} = 0.83$$

One method for experimentally determining mutual inductance is shown in Fig. 18.11. We can measure the total inductance of the series connected coils on an inductance bridge. Connecting the windings as shown and checking by our hand rule, the flux produced by the current in one winding

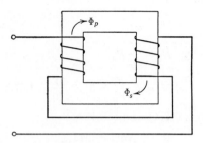

**Fig. 18.11.** Determining mutual inductance.

is in the same direction around the core as the flux produced by the current in the other winding. This increases the total flux, thus increasing the emf induced by a given alternating current; thus increasing the total inductance. All the induced emf's will be in phase. There are four induced emf's: the self-induced emf in the primary, the emf mutually induced in the primary by current in the secondary, the emf mutually induced in the secondary by current in the primary and the self induced emf in the secondary.

$$\therefore \quad E = I(\omega L_p + \omega M + \omega M + \omega L_s)$$

from which $L_T = L_p + L_s + 2M$.

If, however, we reverse the leads to the secondary, the mutually induced emf's in each coil are 180° out of phase with the self-induced emf's resulting in

$$L_T = L_p + L_s - 2M$$

Therefore we can extend our original Equation (9.5) for two inductances in series to include magnetic coupling between them.

$$\therefore \quad L_T = L_p + L_s \pm 2M \tag{18.17}$$

Therefore the mutual inductance of the magnetically coupled coils in Fig. 18.11 will be one-quarter of the difference between the total inductance readings with the coils connected series aiding and then series opposing.

## 10. Coupled Impedance

The voltage across the primary of a pair of magnetically coupled coils will be made up of two components: the self-induced emf due to primary current and the mutually induced emf due to secondary current. Therefore according to Kirchhoff's voltage law,

$$E = I_p Z_p + I_s \omega M \tag{1}$$

where $Z_p$ is the impedance of the primary circuit by itself. This impedance is mostly the inductive reactance of the primary winding along with a small amount of resistance. Similarly according to Kirchhoff's voltage law,

$$E_s = I_p \omega M = I_s (Z_s + Z_L) \tag{2}$$

where $Z_s$ is the impedance of the secondary winding by itself, again mainly inductive reactance. Solving for $I_s$ in Equation (2),

$$I_s = \frac{I_p \omega M}{Z_s + Z_L}$$

and substituting in Equation (1),

$$E = I_p Z_p + I_p \frac{(\omega M)^2}{Z_s + Z_L}$$

from which $$Z_T = Z_p + \frac{(\omega M)^2}{Z_s + Z_L} \tag{18.18}$$

where $(\omega M)^2/(Z_s + Z_L)$ is called the **coupled impedance.** As Equation (18.18) indicates, it is considered to be in *series* with the primary impedance (unlike the expression we developed for the reflected impedance which is in *parallel* with the primary impedance in iron-core transformers). When we consider the effect of Lenz's law on the direction of the emf's induced in the primary, the + sign joining the two impedances in Equation (18.18) is based on considering $(\omega M)^2$ to be a vector quantity with a 0° angle. [If we consider $\omega M$ as a $+j$ quantity, $(\omega M)^2$ becomes a $-$ quantity requiring the two impedances of Equation (18.18) to be joined by a $-$ sign.] We can check Equation (18.18) by considering the effect of loading the secondary winding of a pair of magnetically coupled coils. If the secondary is left open circuit, $Z_L$ is infinitely large and therefore the coupled impedance in Equation (18.18) becomes zero. Therefore the total impedance is simply the primary impedance alone as we would expect.

If we connect a resistance across the secondary winding, $Z_L$ will have a 0° angle. Since $Z_s$ is largely the inductive reactance of the secondary winding, the total secondary circuit impedance is inductive. Therefore when we carry out the vector division, dividing an impedance with a + angle into $(\omega M)^2$ with its 0° angle results in a *capacitive* coupled impedance. Since $Z_p$ is largely *inductive*, the *capacitive* impedance coupled into the primary circuit via the mutual inductance adds the coupled resistance component in series with the primary resistance component but *reduces* the total primary reactance. As a result, the total impedance becomes smaller as the secondary is loaded with a resistance, thus allowing more primary current to flow in order to transfer energy to the secondary circuit. This method then checks with our first approach to transformer action in which we discovered that primary current must increase when a transformer is loaded in order to keep the amplitude of the mutual flux sine wave constant.

EXAMPLE 9: If the resistance of the windings can be neglected, determine the total input impedance to the transformer of Examples 7 and 8, (a) with the secondary open circuit, and (b) with a 50 ohm resistance connected to the secondary.

*Solution:*

(a) $$Z_T = Z_p = \omega L_p = 377 \times 5 = +j1885 \text{ ohms}$$

(b) Coupled $Z = \dfrac{(\omega M)^2}{Z_s + Z_L} = \dfrac{(377 \times 1.67)^2}{+j(377 \times 0.8) + 50}$

$$= \frac{396000\underline{/0°}}{304\underline{/80.5°}} = 1300\underline{/-80.5°} = 213 - j1284 \text{ ohms}$$

$$\therefore \quad Z_T = (+j1885) + (213 - j1284) = 213 + j601$$
$$= 636 \text{ ohms } \underline{/+70.5°}$$

## 11. Tuned Transformers

The most important application of loose coupling is the use of tuned transformers in radio circuitry. If we consider the source of emf to be a constant voltage source as in Fig. 18.12, the primary winding is designed

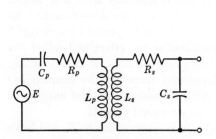

Fig. 18.12. A tuned transformer.

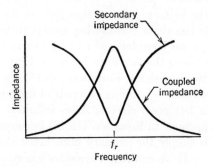

Fig. 18.13. Effect of a tuned secondary circuit.

to form a series resonant circuit with the capacitive reactance of $C_p$ equal to the inductive reactance of the primary winding at the desired resonant frequency. This will result in maximum current in the primary winding at resonance (neglecting for the moment any coupled impedance due to secondary current).*

Considering now the effect of tuning the secondary circuit, the total secondary circuit impedance [$Z_s + Z_L$ in Equation (18.18)] will be minimum and equal to $R_s$ at resonance. Therefore the secondary circuit behaves like a series resonant circuit. Since $(\omega M)^2$ is essentially constant over the small range of frequencies near resonance, when $Z_s + Z_L$ becomes a *minimum*, the coupled impedance becomes a *maximum* as shown in Fig. 18.13.

---

* If a vacuum tube amplifier is used to feed the primary of a tuned transformer, the vacuum tube represents a constant *current* source providing a signal current equal to the mutual conductance of the tube times the signal input voltage to its grid. Hence $C_p$ must then be connected in *parallel* with the primary winding to obtain maximum primary current (resonant rise of current) at resonance.

And when the source frequency is slightly lower than the resonant frequency, $X_{C_s}$ is greater than $X_{L_s}$ and the secondary impedance becomes capacitive. But dividing a *capacitive* impedance into $(\omega M)^2$ with its $0°$ angle results in an *inductive* coupled impedance. Therefore as far as the signal source is concerned, the secondary behaves as if it were a *parallel* resonant circuit in series with the primary winding.

The primary impedance by itself in the circuit of Fig. 18.12 is attempting to become a minimum at resonance in order to allow maximum primary current to flow. But the coupled impedance is attempting to raise the primary impedance at resonance, thus limiting the maximum primary current. The extent to which the coupled secondary tuned circuit affects the primary resonance curve depends on the degree of coupling between the coils. When the coupling is very loose, the mutual inductance is very small and even at resonance the coupled impedance is *smaller* than the resistance of the primary circuit. Under these circumstances, the only effect that the coupled secondary has on the shape of the primary current resonance curve is to limit its peak value slightly. The secondary current tends to have the usual series resonance curve. But with loose coupling, since the primary current rises to a maximum at resonance and since the secondary induced emf depends on the primary current, the secondary resonance curve is much sharper than that of a single tuned circuit having the same $Q$.*

We will recall from earlier studies that maximum transfer of energy occurs when the load resistance is equal to the resistance of the source. Applying this to magnetically coupled tuned circuits, maximum energy transfer will take place when the coupled resistance is equal to the primary circuit resistance. Since the coupled resistance depends on the mutual inductance which in turn depends on the coefficient of coupling, there is a **critical coupling** for a given pair of tuned circuits at which maximum energy transfer from primary to secondary takes place.

At resonance, $$Z_p = R_p$$

and the coupled $$Z = \frac{(\omega M)^2}{R_s}$$

Therefore for critical coupling, $$M^2 = R_p R_s / \omega^2.$$

But $$M^2 = K^2 L_p L_s \qquad (18.16)$$

Therefore $$K^2 = \frac{R_p}{\omega L_p} \times \frac{R_s}{\omega L_s}$$

from which $$K_c = \frac{1}{\sqrt{Q_p Q_s}} \qquad (18.19)$$

With critical coupling, the secondary current attains its greatest value. But with the coupled impedance rising at resonance, the primary current

* The bandwidth is approximately $\Delta f \approx K f_r$.

is no longer maximum at resonance. As we have already noted, at a frequency slightly below resonance the coupled impedance is *inductive*, whereas the impedance of the series tuned primary is *capacitive*. Therefore there are two frequencies, one slightly above the resonant frequency and one slightly below where the coupled reactance tunes the primary reactance to give minimum total primary impedance and therefore maximum primary current. This double hump in the primary current tends to flatten the peak of the secondary current response curve since the emf induced into the secondary at the resonant frequency is not quite as great as at the two hump frequencies either side of resonance.

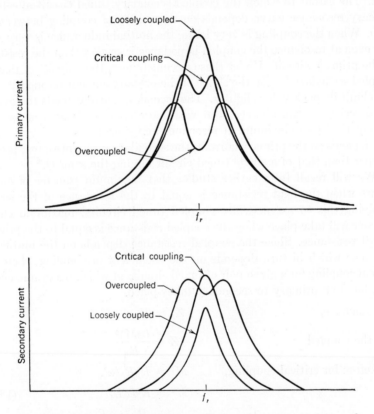

**Fig. 18.14.** Effect of coefficient of coupling on the resonance curves of a tuned transformer.

If the tuned circuits are overcoupled, the increase in coupled impedance moves the primary current humps further apart. This in turn causes such a decrease in primary current at resonance that the secondary current also starts to show a double humped curve as shown in Fig. 18.14. In practice a coefficient of coupling of 1.5 times the critical coefficient of coupling produces such a slight dip in the secondary current at resonance that the resulting secondary current resonance curve has a very desirable flat top with steep skirts.

## Problems

1. What is the transformation ratio of a transformer having 40 turns on the secondary winding and 680 turns on the primary?

2. What is the transformation ratio of a transformer which has an open-circuit secondary voltage of 300 v rms when the primary is connected to a 120 v, 60 c source?

3. What rms voltage must be applied to the primary of the transformer in Problem 1 to develop an open-circuit secondary voltage of 6.3 v?

4. What is the load component of the primary current when a 2 kilohm resistor is connected across the secondary winding of the transformer in Problem 2?

5. The secondary of the transformer in Problem 2 has 1400 turns. How many primary turns are required?

6. The primary of a certain transformer has 2.7 turns per volt of applied emf. How many turns must there be on a 5 v secondary winding?

7. A small filament transformer has a laminated sheet steel core whose average path length is 8 in. and whose cross-sectional area is 0.8 sq in. How many turns must there be on a primary winding to be connected to a 120 v, 60 c source if the flux density must not exceed 80 kilolines per sq in.?

8. How many turns would there be on a $7\frac{1}{2}$ v secondary winding on the transformer of Problem 7?

9. Assuming the magnetizing current to be a pure sine wave, what is the rms value of the primary current in the transformer of Problem 7 when the secondary is open circuit? (Use the **BH** curves of Fig. 7.15.)

10. The primary of the transformer of Problem 7 is connected to a 110 v, 25 c source of emf. What is the rms value of the exciting current?

11. An audio output transformer has 1500 primary turns and 40 secondary turns. What is the reflected value of a 4 ohm load connected to its secondary?

12. An audio transformer is listed as 7 kilohm primary reflected impedance with a 4 ohm load at 1000 c. This transformer is to be used with a tube requiring a 4500 ohm load. What value of load must be connected to the transformer secondary?

13. An audio output transformer has 1200 primary turns and two secondary windings of 50 turns each. If the circuit feeding the transformer must see a reflected load of 5 kilohms, what load must be connected to the secondary windings when they are connected (a) in series? (b) in parallel?

14. An audio transformer has a 6 kilohm primary winding and an 8 ohm secondary with a tap at 4 ohms with respect to a common secondary terminal. Through error a 4 ohm load is connected from the 4 ohm tap to the 8 ohm terminal. What is the reflected impedance?

15. The transformer of Fig. 18.4 has a transformation ratio of 0.2, a primary winding resistance of 1.2 ohms, a primary leakage reactance of 2.5 ohms, a secondary winding resistance of 7 ohms, and a secondary leakage reactance of 13 ohms. This transformer develops 550 v rms across a 100 ohm, 0.707 leading power factor load. What is the open-circuit secondary voltage of the transformer?

16. An a-c ammeter with negligible resistance and reactance is connected across the secondary of the transformer of Problem 15. What voltage must be applied to the primary in order to have the ammeter read 10 amp?

17. What is the mutual inductance of the transformer in Problems 7, 8, and 9?

18. Two coils wound on a common core have self-inductances of 1.6 and 3.2 h, respectively. When connected in series their total inductance is 8 h. (a) What is the coefficient of coupling? (b) What is the total inductance when the leads of one of the coils are reversed?

19. An air-core transformer has a primary inductance of 200 mh, a secondary inductance of 50 mh, and a coefficient of coupling of 0.1. If the resistance of the windings can be neglected, what is the coupled impedance at 100 kc when a 10 kilohm resistor is connected across the secondary?

20. The primary and secondary windings of an intermediate frequency transformer in a radio receiver each have a self-inductance of 2 mh. The total equivalent primary circuit series resistance is 200 ohms and the total equivalent secondary circuit series resistance is 100 ohms.
    (a) What value of tuning capacitors are required to tune each winding to 456 kc?
    (b) What is the critical coupling coefficient?
    (c) What is the approximate bandwidth of the IF transformer if its coils are critically coupled?

## Review Questions

1. Why is mutual induction more significant in a-c circuits than in d-c circuits?
2. What is a **transformer?**
3. What is the purpose of an iron core in power and audio transformers?
4. What problems would be encountered in using iron cores in radio frequency transformers?
5. What is meant by the **general transformer equation?** What is its application?
6. What is meant by **exciting current?**
7. The exciting current in a certain transformer lags the applied emf by 87°. Account for this angle.
8. Account for the results obtained in Problem 10 and relate these results to a practical transformer.
9. What would be the effect of operating a 110 v, 25 c transformer on a 120 v, 60 c supply?

10. What is the relationship between the turns ratio of a transformer and its transformation ratio?

11. What is the relationship between the load current ratio and the turns ratio of a transformer?

12. By combining Equations (18.7) and (18.9), determine the power input to power output ratio of a transformer.

13. What is meant by **reflected impedance?**

14. Why is the impedance ratio of an audio transformer equal to the *square* of the turns ratio?

15. What is the significance of impedance ratio in practical transformers?

16. Complete the individual steps in reducing the initial equation in Example 4 to its final form.

17. What is meant by **mutual flux** and **leakage flux?**

18. Define **leakage reactance.**

19. Why is the total core loss of a transformer essentially independent of load current?

20. Why can we assume that the wattmeter reading on an open-circuit transformer test is essentially only the core loss?

21. Why is the core loss on a short-circuit transformer test less than 1/400 of its normal value?

22. Explain why we can state that $R_e = R_p + a^2 R_s$ and $X_e = X_p + a^2 X_s$ in Fig. 18.5(b).

23. Draw a vector diagram showing the relationship between primary terminal voltage and secondary terminal voltage for a unity power factor load.

24. **Voltage regulation** is defined as no load voltage minus full load voltage divided by full load voltage. What is the voltage regulation in Example 6 (in per cent)?

25. What factor is primarily responsible for the difference between the no-load and-full load secondary voltages of a power transformer?

26. Why does a leading power factor load give better voltage regulation than an equivalent lagging power factor load?

27. What factors limit the lowest frequency that an audio transformer can handle satisfactorily?

28. What factors limit the highest frequency that an audio transformer can handle satisfactorily?

29. Define **coefficient of coupling.**

30. What is meant by **loose** coupling and **tight** coupling?

31. Express coefficient of coupling in terms of mutual flux and leakage flux.

32. What effect has the coefficient of coupling on the mutual inductance of a pair of magnetically coupled coils?

33. What is meant by **mutual reactance?**

34. What would be the effect on the reflected impedance in Problem 12 of con-

necting the secondary winding (a) in series opposing, and (b) in parallel opposing?

35. How does the coupled impedance of loose coupled coils differ from the reflected impedance of an audio transformer?

36. How is the coupled impedance related to the coefficient of coupling?

37. Why does an inductive secondary circuit appear as a capacitive coupled impedance?

38. Define **critical coupling.**

39. Why is the secondary current greater at frequencies slightly off resonance than at the resonant frequency in an overcoupled tuned transformer?

40. Why does increasing the coupling between two tuned circuits increase their bandwidth?

# Chapter 19

# THREE-PHASE SYSTEMS

## 1. Advantages of Polyphase System

In the a-c networks we have considered up to this point, we have encountered only one source of alternating emf. Such circuits are referred to as **single-phase** circuits. In Chapter 11 we were introduced to the sinusoidal nature of alternating emf's by considering the instantaneous emf induced in an electric conductor rotating at a constant angular velocity in a uniform magnetic field. We also noted that most of our electric energy is generated at the expense of mechanical energy by **alternators** based on the principle of the rotating loop in a magnetic field. However, when we consider practical systems for the generation and distribution of large amounts of electric energy, the single-phase system has several disadvantages.

If we add a second loop to the simple alternator of Chapter 11, as shown in Fig. 19.1(a), two separate sine wave emf's will be induced in the

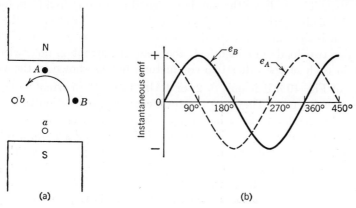

(a)                                    (b)

**Fig. 19.1.** A simple two phase generator.

401

one machine. Since both loops are mounted on the same rotor assembly, both rotate at the same angular velocity. Therefore both emf's have the same frequency. If both loops have the same number of turns, both emf's will have the same effective value. But what is most important is that loop $A$ is mounted on the rotor 90° ahead (in the direction of rotation) of loop $B$. Therefore loop $A$ always cuts a certain magnetic line of force 90° ahead (in time) of loop $B$. Therefore although we can use the two emf's separately if we wish as in Fig. 19.2(a), the emf in loop $A$ is always 90° out of phase with the emf in loop $B$ as shown in Fig. 19.1(b). This simple alternator is referred to as a **two-phase** alternator.

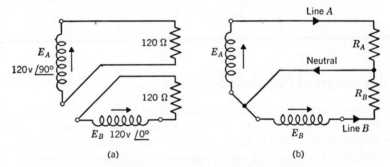

**Fig. 19.2.** A simple two phase system.

In Fig. 19.2 we have connected identical loads to the two windings of the simple two-phase alternator. Note the customary procedure of using a coil to represent the alternator winding rather than the general a-c generator symbol. This enables us to draw the coils at right angles in a circuit diagram to indicate that their emf's are 90° out of phase. Although we can connect each winding independently to its load as in Fig. 19.2(a), it is customary to use a common or **neutral** lead for the two circuits as in Fig. 19.2(b). This reduces the number of conductors required from four to three. Although, as the circuit diagram of Fig. 19.2(b) indicates, the neutral current is the sum of the two load currents, this is a *vector* sum. Therefore if the two loads are identical, the neutral current is not twice the current in each of the other two conductors, but as shown in the vector diagram of Fig. 19.3 it is only $\sqrt{2}$, or 1.414, times the current in each of the other conductors. Therefore the total copper cross section to feed the two 120 ohm loads at 120 v in the two-phase system is only the copper cross section required to handle 1 amp, 1.414 amp, and 1 amp, a total of 3.414 amp. The equivalent single-phase system to supply the two 120 ohm loads in parallel at 120 v would require two conductors each carrying 2 amp, or a total copper cross section to handle 4 amp. This then is the first advantage of any polyphase system. **Less copper is required to supply a** given load power at a given voltage with a polyphase system than with a single-phase system.

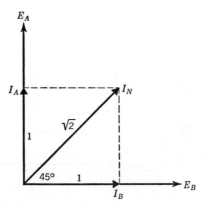

**Fig. 19.3.** Vector diagram for the neutral current in a simple two phase system.

We can illustrate the second advantage of a polyphase system by plotting the graphs of the instantaneous power to the two identical loads in the circuits of Fig. 19.2 on a common graph as in Fig. 19.4. The total

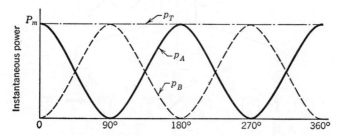

**Fig. 19.4.** Instantaneous power in a balanced two phase system.

instantaneous power supplied by the alternator at any instant is the sum of the instantaneous power to the two loads at that instant. Since the two emf's are 90° out of phase, the instantaneous power to one load becomes maximum as the other becomes zero. Even though the instantaneous power in each load is the customary pulsating sine squared wave, if we check carefully we will find that at every instant in time the sum of the two instantaneous powers is constant. Therefore **if the load on each phase of a polyphase source is identical, the instantaneous power output of the alternator is constant.** This is an important advantage in large machines since it allows a steady conversion of mechanical energy into electric energy.

The third advantage can be demonstrated by connecting the two-phase

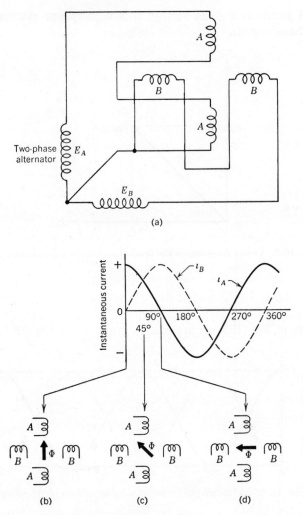

**Fig. 19.5.** Producing a rotating magnetic field in a two phase system.

alternator to a set of coils placed at right angles as shown in Fig. 19.5(a). Each coil will pass a sine wave of current but the current in coil $B$ will be 90° out of phase with the current in coil $A$. We will now consider the total flux at various instants during a cycle of current. Starting at the 0° position, the current in coil $B$ is zero and the current in coil $A$ is maximum in the positive direction. This produces a magnetic field in which the direction of the magnetic lines of force is that indicated by the arrow in Fig. 19.5(b). At 45° both coils pass $0.707 I_m$, resulting in a net flux which is the *vector* sum of these two components. This results in a total flux with the *same* total flux density but with the direction of the magnetic lines of force

being that shown in Fig. 19.5(c). At the 90° point in the cycle, coil $A$
current is zero and coil $B$ current is maximum positive resulting in a magnetic field which is now at right angles to its original direction at 0° in
the cycle.

If we continue the diagrams commenced in Fig. 19.5 we will find that
the coil arrangement of Fig. 19.5(a) connected to a two-phase source of
emf develops **a magnetic field which has a constant flux density and rotates
at the frequency of the applied sine wave.** If we place a compass needle
in the center of the coils in Fig. 19.5(a), it will rotate with the magnetic
field at a **synchronous speed** which in this case is the same as the frequency
of the two-phase sine wave. This rotating magnetic field, which is characteristic of all polyphase systems, greatly simplifies a-c motor construction.
A single-phase system can produce only a magnetic field which increases
and decreases in flux density and *reverses* its direction each 180° but does
*not* rotate.

## 2. Generation of a Three-Phase emf

The simple two-phase system that we used to show the advantages of
polyphase electric power generation has been used to a limited extent in
the distribution of electric energy.
However its main application in
present day equipment is in servo-
mechanisms. The auto pilot of an
aircraft is an example of a servo-
mechanism. If the aircraft deviates
from its course, a gyrocompass
senses this error and develops voltages which operate a servomotor,
which in turn operates the rudder
to bring the aircraft back on course.
Two-phase motors are ideal for
servosystem applications since their
rotation depends on the presence of

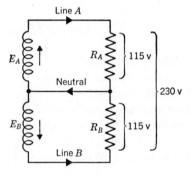

Fig. 19.6. The Edison three-wire single
phase system.

an error voltage and their direction of rotation depends on whether this
sine wave error voltage leads or lags a reference voltage by 90°.

In search of an improvement on the two-phase system for the distribution of electric energy, let us suppose that we place two coils 180° apart
on the rotor of a simple a-c generator and connect them to two identical
loads with a common neutral lead as shown in Fig. 19.6. The neutral current is now the vector sum of two equal currents which are 180° out of
phase. Therefore with identical loads the neutral current in this system
is zero. Therefore this system requires less copper than the two-phase
system of Fig. 19.2(b) to supply each load with 115 v at a given power.

However the total voltage from line $A$ to line $B$ is greater than in the two-phase system. But the instantaneous power in each coil of the generator in Fig. 19.6 reaches its peak at the *same* instant and therefore the total instantaneous power *is* pulsating in nature. Also with two currents 180° out of phase we cannot produce a rotating magnetic field. Therefore this system is *not* a two-phase system. It is called the Edison three-wire single-phase system, and is widely used for distributing electric energy to residences because of the reduction in line current (and the resulting reduction in wire size required) for a given load power and voltage as compared with the simple two-wire single-phase system.

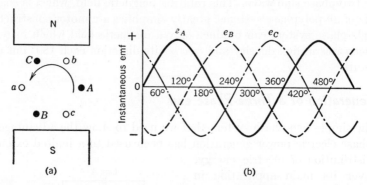

Fig. 19.7. A simple three phase generator.

The system which is universally used for electric power distribution is a *three*-phase system based on the simple generator of Fig. 19.7(a) which has three coils mounted on the rotor at 120° intervals. This alternator generates three sine wave emf's which are 120° out of phase with one another as shown in Fig. 19.7(b). Figure 19.8(a) shows the method of connecting these coils to a load which follows the same pattern as for the two-phase system of Fig. 19.2(b). With a **balanced** load the currents in each arm of the load

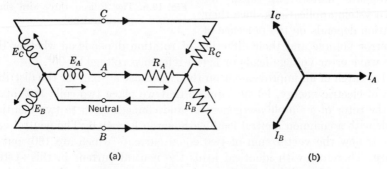

Fig. 19.8. A simple three phase system.

will be equal in magnitude and 120° out of phase with one another as shown in the vector diagram of Fig. 19.8(b).* The neutral current is the vector sum of these three load currents. As the vector diagram of Fig. 19.8(b) indicates, this neutral current will be zero with a balanced load. As a result, with a balanced load, even less copper is required to convey energy at a given rate and given voltage in the three-phase system than in an equivalent two-phase system.

With identical load resistors in Fig. 19.8(a),

$$p_T = \frac{e_A{}^2 + e_B{}^2 + e_C{}^2}{R}$$

Careful inspection of Fig. 19.7(b) will show us that $e_A{}^2 + e_B{}^2 + e_C{}^2$ is always constant. Therefore the instantaneous power in a balanced three-phase system is a constant. We will also find that we can use the emf's generated by a three-phase alternator to produce a rotating magnetic field of constant flux density just as we did with the two-phase system. Therefore the three-phase system has all the advantages of the two-phase system plus others that we will discover as we investigate the behavior of three-phase circuits.

## 3. Double Subscript Notation

The 3$\phi$ circuit of Fig. 19.8 represents an impedance network with three sources of emf acting simultaneously. As we noted in Example 4 of Chapter 16, reversing the leads to one of the coils in an a-c generator has the same effect on an a-c circuit as reversing the leads to a battery in a d-c circuit containing several sources of direct emf. Therefore we cannot take the six leads from the coils in Fig. 19.8(a), connect them in a random manner, and then assume that we will obtain the current relationships shown by the vector diagram of Fig. 19.8(b). When we consider that the leads to each coil of the simple 3$\phi$ generator can be reversed, thus changing the angle of the emf by 180°, there are quite a few possible combinations that can be obtained.

In the circuit of Fig. 19.8(a) we indicated the manner in which we had connected the leads to each winding by drawing an arrow alongside the symbol representing the alternator winding. Using the angle given with the emf, we must consider the tracing direction around the loop to be in the direction indicated by the arrow. However, the arrow system by itself does not allow us to show the connection of the leads to each coil when we write a Kirchhoff's voltage law equation for the loop. Neither does the letter symbol $E_A$ give us any indication of which lead is which.

---

* A balanced load is one in which the impedance of each arm of the load is identical both in magnitude and phase (power factor) angle. A balanced load need not be a pure resistance.

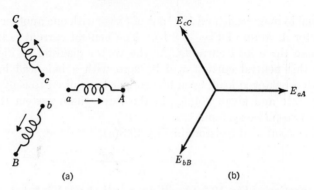

**Fig. 19.9.** Double subscript notation for three phase EMF's.

This problem can be solved by using a **double subscript notation.** In one of the common systems of double subscript notation one end of each coil is indicated by a lower case letter and the other by an upper case letter as in Fig. 19.9(a). In any complete electric circuit, these coils will be included in tracing loops around the circuit. If as we follow one of these tracing loops, it enters coil $A$ by the terminal marked with the lower case letter and leaves by the terminal marked with the upper case letter, we would represent the emf of that coil as $E_{aA}$. **The first of the two subscripts always represents the end of a circuit component at which the tracing loop enters the component, and the second subscript represents the end of the component from which the tracing loop leaves the component.**

If we reverse the leads to coil $A$ so that the tracing loop in a given circuit layout enters at end $A$ and leaves at end $a$, we would represent the emf in the Kirchhoff's voltage law equation as $E_{Aa}$, where $E_{Aa}$ has the same rms magnitude as $E_{aA}$ but its angle is displaced by an additional 180°. Referring to our consideration of vector subtraction in Chapter 13, since $E_{Aa}$ is 180° out of phase with $E_{aA}$,

$$\therefore \quad E_{Aa} = -E_{aA} \qquad (19.1)$$

In the following discussions of three-phase systems, we must make sure that when we write a letter symbol for a voltage or current, we write the subscripts in the same order as the tracing loop in which these voltages and currents appear.

## 4. The Four-Wire Wye Connected System

We can assume that in winding the coils on the simple $3\phi$ generator of Fig. 19.7 we were methodical enough that if we take the tracing direction from the lower case letter to the upper case letter in each coil, the three emf's will be 120° out of phase. We shall assume that these three generated emf's for the alternator of Fig. 19.7 are:

$$E_{aA} = 120 \text{ v } \underline{/0°}$$

$$E_{bB} = 120 \text{ v } \underline{/-120°}$$

$$E_{cC} = 120 \text{ v } \underline{/+120°}$$

Since one of the reasons for using a three-phase system is to cut down on the conductors required to carry electric energy to a load, we can connect one end of each generator coil to a common neutral. Since **it is conventional to consider the tracing direction as going out from the generator to the load along the individual lines and returning along the common neutral lead,** we shall connect the lower case letter ends of the three windings to the neutral as shown in Fig. 19.10. In order to show that points

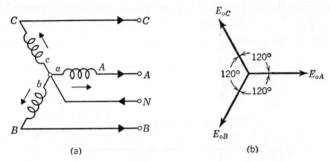

(a)                                 (b)

**Fig. 19.10.** Wye connected alternator windings.

$a$, $b$, and $c$ are all connected to the neutral, we can replace these lower case letters with the letter $o$ when we express the voltage on the three lines with respect to the common neutral. Therefore $E_{oA} = E_{aA}$, $E_{oB} = E_{bB}$, and $E_{oC} = E_{cC}$. The voltage measured from line to neutral in the wye connected source is called the **phase voltage** of the source. Connecting the alternator coils in this manner produces a **wye (Y)** connected three-phase source, so called because of the physical appearance of the circuit diagram and the vector diagram of the phase voltages.*

We could also form a wye connected $3\phi$ source by connecting all the upper case letter ends of the coils to the common neutral. However we must avoid the situation shown in Fig. 19.11. Coils $A$ and $C$ have their lower case letter ends connected to the neutral, but coil $B$ leads have been reversed. Since the tracing direction must be out along the line and back along the neutral, we must reverse the subscripts and represent the emf in coil $B$ as $E_{Bb}$ in Fig. 19.11(b) which is 180° displaced from $E_{bB}$ in Fig. 19.10(b). If we connect such a source to three equal resistors, as the vector

---

   * A system in which one terminal of each phase is connected to a common point (star point) can also be called a **star** connected system.

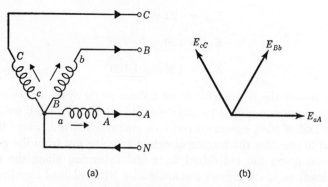

(a)　　　　　　　　　　　　　(b)

**Fig. 19.11.** Incorrect wye connection.

diagram of Fig. 19.11(b) suggests, there will be considerable neutral current.

Figure 19.12 shows three impedances connected as a four-wire wye load. If we trace the wiring carefully we will note that $Z_A$ is connected directly

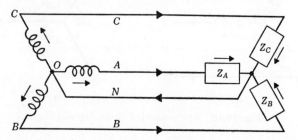

**Fig. 19.12.** Four-wire wye connected load.

across coil $A$ of the generator. We will also find that the current in $Z_A$, the current in line $A$ and the current in coil $A$ must all be the same since they are all part of the same series loop. Since it is conventional to consider the tracing direction as outward from the alternator along the individual lines and back toward the alternator along the neutral, we do not need double subscripts to represent the current in a 4-wire wye system. Therefore $I_A$ represents the current in $Z_A$, line $A$, and generator coil $A$. Therefore

$$\therefore \quad I_A = \frac{E_{oA}}{Z_A}, \quad I_B = \frac{E_{oB}}{Z_B}, \quad \text{and} \quad I_C = \frac{E_{oC}}{Z_C} \tag{19.2}$$

$$I_N = I_A + I_B + I_C \tag{19.3}$$

The three load impedances of the 4-wire wye load may be independent single-phase loads. For example, $Z_A$ may be a bank of lamps, $Z_B$ may be a heater, and $Z_C$ a single-phase motor. It is customary in dividing the total single-phase load among the three phases to make the line currents as nearly equal in magnitude as possible. Also $Z_A$, $Z_B$, and $Z_C$ may represent the windings of a 3$\phi$ motor in which case $Z_A = Z_B = Z_C$ and the load is a balanced load. In such cases the three line currents will be equal in magnitude and the neutral current will be zero.

$$\therefore \quad I_L = \frac{E_p}{Z} \tag{19.4}$$

where $I_L$ is the magnitude of the current in each line, $E_p$ is the magnitude of the phase voltage, and $Z$ is the impedance from each line to neutral.

EXAMPLE 1: In the circuit of Fig. 19.12, $Z_A = Z_B = Z_C = 30$ ohms $\underline{/+30°}$ and the alternator emf's are those listed with Fig. 19.10.
(a) Find the current in each line.
(b) Find the neutral current.
(c) Draw a vector diagram showing phase voltages and line currents.

*Solution:*

(a)        $I_A = \dfrac{E_{oA}}{Z_A} = \dfrac{120\underline{/0°}}{30\underline{/+30°}} = 4 \text{ amp } \underline{/-30°}$

           $I_B = \dfrac{E_{oB}}{Z_B} = \dfrac{120\underline{/-120°}}{30\underline{/+30°}} = 4 \text{ amp } \underline{/-150°}$

           $I_C = \dfrac{E_{oC}}{Z_C} = \dfrac{120\underline{/+120°}}{30\underline{/+30°}} = 4 \text{ amp } \underline{/+90°}$

(b)    $I_N = I_A + I_B + I_C = 4\underline{/-30°} + 4\underline{/-150°} + 4\underline{/+90°}$

       $= (3.46 - j2) + (-3.46 - j2) + (0 + j4) = 0 + j0 = 0 \text{ amp}$

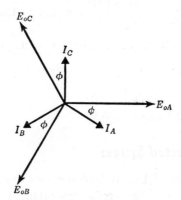

**Fig. 19.13.** Vector diagram.

Once we realize that the neutral current with a balanced wye load is zero, it is not necessary to go through the calculations of Step (b). Note that each load current lags the voltage applied to that load by 30°. This is called the **power factor angle,** $\phi$ (also $\theta$).

EXAMPLE 2: In the circuit of Fig. 19.12, $Z_A$ is a 360 w lamp, $Z_B$ passes a current of 4 amp at a 0.966 lagging power factor and $Z_C = 60$ ohms $\underline{/-30°}$. Find the neutral current.

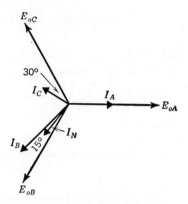

**Fig. 19.14.** Vector diagram.

*Solution:* Since the lamp is a pure resistance, $I_A = P_A/E_{oA} = 360/120 = 3$ amp in phase with $E_{oA}$.

$$\therefore \quad I_A = 3 \text{ amp } \underline{/0°}$$

Since $Z_B$ has a 0.966 lagging power factor, the power factor angle is arccos $0.966 = 15°$. Therefore $I_B$ lags $E_{oB}$ by 15° and

$$\therefore \quad I_B = 4 \text{ amp } \underline{/-135°}$$

$$I_C = \frac{E_{oC}}{Z_C} = \frac{120\underline{/+120°}}{60\underline{/-30°}} = 2 \text{ amp } \underline{/+150°}$$

$$I_N = I_A + I_B + I_C = 3\underline{/0°} + 4\underline{/-135°} + 2\underline{/+150°}$$

$$= (3 + j0) + (-2.83 - j2.83) + (-1.73 + j1)$$

$$= -1.56 - j1.83 \text{ amp}$$

$$\therefore \quad I_N = 2.4 \text{ amp } \underline{/-130.5°}$$

## 5. The Delta Connected System

The vector diagram of Fig. 19.9(b) suggests that, when properly connected, the **vector sum of the emf's generated in the three coils of a three-phase source is zero.**[*] To add voltages by circuit connection we connect the coils in series (like adding batteries in series). We will start by connecting end $b$ of coil $B$ to end $A$ of coil $A$ and end $c$ of coil $C$ to end $B$

---

[*] The three-phase source need not be a rotating machine. The secondary windings of three transformers fed from a three-phase system can be considered as representing the coils of a three-phase source of emf.

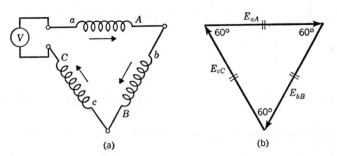

**Fig. 19.15.** Delta connection of a three phase source.

of coil $B$ as shown in Fig. 19.15(a). A voltmeter is connected between the remaining two terminals to read the vector total voltage.

When we are required to add several vectors diagrammatically, we can cut down on the geometrical construction and also obtain a less cluttered vector diagram by switching to funicular vectors (Chapter 18). Since the head end of the vector for $E_{aA}$ represents the upper case letter end of the coil [Fig. 19.15(a)], we can duplicate the circuit connection of Fig. 19.15(a) by drawing the vector $E_{bB}$ with its proper magnitude and direction from the tip of the vector $E_{aA}$. Similarly, the vector for $E_{cC}$ is constructed from the tip of the vector $E_{bB}$. This returns the tip of the vector $E_{cC}$ back to the origin, forming an equilateral triangle. Therefore if we have actually connected the coils as we have specified, the voltmeter in Fig. 19.15(a) will read zero. Therefore, it is safe to connect terminal $C$ to terminal $a$ without any short-circuit current flowing around the loop. In practice we would always check with a voltmeter before making this final connection, since reversing the leads to any one of the coils (coil $C$ in Fig. 19.16) results in a voltmeter reading of twice the phase voltage. This would cause a very

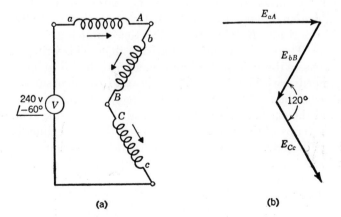

**Fig. 19.16.** Incorrect delta connection.

heavy current, limited only by the impedance of the three coils, to flow around the loop.

Since we can connect the windings of a three-phase source into a delta without any short-circuit current flowing, we require only three wires to connect the three sets of emf to a load which can also be connected in delta fashion as in Fig. 19.17. In the delta connected system, each arm of the

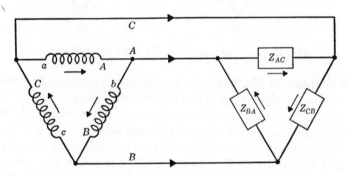

**Fig. 19.17.** Delta connected load.

load is connected directly across one of the generator coils. We can label the three lines according to the *upper* case or second subscript letters of the various phase emf's connected to each line. Therefore $E_{aA}$ becomes $E_{CA}$, $E_{bB}$ becomes $E_{AB}$, and $E_{cC}$ becomes $E_{BC}$.

In the wye connected load where each arm of the load is connected from line to neutral, we found that a single subscript for each impedance was quite satisfactory. In the delta load, each arm is connected from line to line. Therefore to identify each impedance properly, we will use two subscripts, these being the two lines between which the arm in question is connected. The order in which we write the subscripts is taken from the tracing direction around each loop. Let us examine carefully the loop between lines $A$ and $B$. The tracing direction through generator coil $B$ is from $b$ to $B$. Therefore the emf generated in that coil is written $E_{AB}$. This loop then passes through the load impedance from line $B$ to line $A$. Therefore the impedance is identified as $Z_{BA}$. Note the reversal of subscript letters. To avoid confusion between the current direction in the source (line $A$ to line $B$) and the current direction in the load (line $B$ to line $A$), instead of thinking in terms of the emf generated in coil $B$, we can think in terms of the voltage drop across $Z_{BA}$. According to our convention, this would be written $V_{BA}$. According to Kirchhoff's voltage law, the emf of the source and the voltage drop across the load are equal. Therefore $E_{AB} = V_{BA}$. Therefore when working with delta connected loads, it will be less confusing if we work with the letter symbol $V$ rather than with the emf at the source, since this will permit the voltage, current, and impedance subscripts at the load to be written all with the same order.

The phase current of the source is defined as the current flowing in a particular coil of the source of emf and the phase current of a load is the current flowing in a particular arm of the load. In the wye connected system, the source phase current, load phase current, and line current are all one and the same. But careful inspection of the delta system of Fig. 19.17 shows us that each line has to carry current for *two* arms of the load. Closer inspection shows us that the tracing direction for one of these currents is *away* from the source and the other is *toward* the source. Therefore the line current to a delta load must be the vector *difference* between the two load phase currents flowing in that line. (However if two vector quantities have an angle between them of greater than 90°, their vector difference is *greater* than either one by itself.)

Therefore, the load phase currents in Fig. 19.17 are

$$I_{AC} = \frac{V_{AC}}{Z_{AC}} = \frac{E_{CA}}{Z_{AC}} \tag{19.5a}$$

$$I_{CB} = \frac{V_{CB}}{Z_{CB}} = \frac{E_{BC}}{Z_{CB}} \tag{19.5b}$$

$$I_{BA} = \frac{V_{BA}}{Z_{BA}} = \frac{E_{AB}}{Z_{BA}} \tag{19.5c}$$

Even in a three-wire system it is conventional to consider the direction of the line current as being *outward* along all *three* lines *away* from the source as shown in Fig. 19.17. Therefore with reference to Fig. 19.17,

$$I_A = I_{AC} - I_{BA} \tag{19.6a}$$

$$I_B = I_{BA} - I_{CB} \tag{19.6b}$$

$$I_C = I_{CB} - I_{AC} \tag{19.6c}$$

In a $3\phi$, 3-wire system, there is no neutral for a return tracing direction from the load back to the generator. Therefore, even with an unbalanced load, in any $3\phi$, 3-wire system the vector sum of the three line currents must be zero. We can show this by adding the three Equations (19.6).

$$\therefore \quad I_A + I_B + I_C = 0 \tag{19.7}$$

This relationship is useful in checking the solution of $3\phi$, 3-wire a-c circuit problems.

EXAMPLE 3: Assuming the emf's as given with Fig. 19.10, the impedances of the branches of the delta load in Fig. 19.17 are $Z_{AC} = 60$ ohms $\underline{/0°}$, $Z_{CB} = 30$ ohms $\underline{/-30°}$, and $Z_{BA} = 30$ ohms $\underline{/+45°}$. Determine the three line currents.

*Solution:*

*Step I.* Start to prepare a vector diagram, adding vectors as their data are determined.

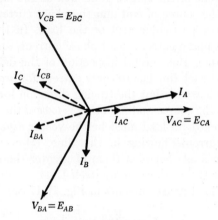

**Fig. 19.18.** Vector diagram.

*Step II.* Determine the phase currents.

$$I_{AC} = \frac{V_{AC}}{Z_{AC}} = \frac{120\underline{/0°}}{60\underline{/0°}} = 2 \text{ amp } \underline{/0°}$$

$$I_{CB} = \frac{V_{CB}}{Z_{CB}} = \frac{120\underline{/+120°}}{30\underline{/-30°}} = 4 \text{ amp } \underline{/+150°}$$

$$I_{BA} = \frac{V_{BA}}{Z_{BA}} = \frac{120\underline{/-120°}}{30\underline{/+45°}} = 4 \text{ amp } \underline{/-165°}$$

*Step III.* Determine the line currents.

$$I_A = I_{AC} - I_{BA} = 2\underline{/0°} - 4\underline{/-165°}$$
$$= (2 + j0) - (-3.86 - j1.04) = 5.86 + j1.04 = 6 \text{ amp } \underline{/+10°}$$

$$I_B = I_{BA} - I_{CB} = 4\underline{/-165°} - 4\underline{/+150°}$$
$$= (-3.86 - j1.04) - (-3.46 + j2) = -0.4 - j3.04 = 3.07 \text{ amp } \underline{/-97.5°}$$

$$I_C = I_{CB} - I_{AC} = 4\underline{/+150°} - 2\underline{/0°}$$
$$= (-3.46 + j2) - (2 + j0) = -5.46 + j2 = 5.8 \text{ amp } \underline{/+159.9°}$$

*Check.*

$$I_A + I_B + I_C = (5.86 + j1.04) + (-0.4 - j3.04) + (-5.46 + j2) = 0 + j0$$

Perhaps we will appreciate the relationship between line current and phase current in a delta system better if we carry out the vector subtraction by geometrical construction. From the solution for Example 3,

$$I_B = I_{BA} - I_{CB} = 4\underline{/-165°} - 4\underline{/+150°}$$

As we noted in Chapter 13, we can draw a vector for $-I_{CB}$ in the vector diagram of Fig. 19.19 by drawing a vector equal in length to the $I_{CB}$ vector but in the opposite direction from the origin. Having constructed the $-I_{CB}$ vector, we can now add the $I_{BA}$ vector and the $-I_{CB}$ vector by the usual geometrical construction to complete the parallelogram.

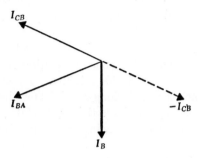

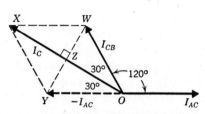

Fig. 19.19. Vector subtraction of phase currents.

Fig. 19.20. Showing the relationship between line current and phase current with a balanced delta load.

In a balanced delta load, the impedances of all three arms are equal in magnitude and angle. Since the phase voltages are equal and 120° out of phase, it follows that the phase currents will also be equal and 120° out of phase as shown in Fig. 19.20. Therefore $I_{CB}$ and $-I_{AC}$ are equal in magnitude and have a 60° angle between them.

Labeling the parallelogram by which we constructed the line current vector as shown in Fig. 19.20, since $I_{CB}$ and $-I_{AC}$ are equal in magnitude and have a 60° angle between them, $OWY$ is an equilateral triangle which is bisected by the diagonal $OX$ which bisects $WY$ at right angles at point $Z$.

$$\therefore \quad OW = 2WZ$$

From Pythagoras' theorem,

$$OZ = \sqrt{OW^2 - WZ^2} = WZ\sqrt{2^2 - 1^2} = \sqrt{3}WZ = \frac{\sqrt{3}}{2}OW$$

Since the diagonals of a parallelogram bisect each other,

$$OX = 2OZ = \sqrt{3}OW$$

Therefore the **line current to a balanced delta load** has a magnitude of $\sqrt{3}$ times the phase current in each arm of the load and is displaced 30° from the phase current.

## 6. The Wye-Delta System

In discussing the 4-wire wye connected three-phase system, we considered only the emf's as measured from line to neutral. Since the coils of the wye connected source are connected from line to neutral, this emf is the phase voltage of the wye connected source. However, in working with three-phase systems, it is customary to work in terms of the voltage measured between lines and called the **line voltage.** In fact, unless it is specified otherwise, the voltages given for a three-phase system are **line** voltages. When the source of emf is delta connected this poses no problem. Since the coils of the source of emf are connected from line to line, the phase voltage and line voltage of a delta connected source are one and the same thing.

In the wye connected source of Fig. 19.21 each voltmeter reads a line voltage which depends on the emf generated in *two* coils. In writing the subscripts for the three line voltages, we must decide whether to read clockwise or counterclockwise around the source. As long as we follow the same direction for all three line voltages, they will have the same relative angular positions. In Fig. 19.21 we have drawn the tracing arrows for the

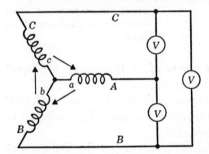
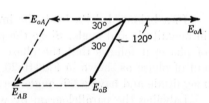

**Fig. 19.21.** The line voltages of a wye connected three phase source of EMF.

**Fig. 19.22.** Determining the line voltage of a wye connected source by geometrical construction.

source in the direction which will give us the same subscripts for the line voltages in this wye connected source as we had for the delta connected source of Fig. 19.17.

Following the tracing arrow from line $A$ to line $B$ through the wye connected source of emf in Fig. 19.21 shows us that

$$E_{AB} = E_{Aa} + E_{bB} = -E_{aA} + E_{bB} \tag{19.8a}$$

Therefore the line voltage in a wye connected source is the vector *difference* between two phase voltages. Since the angle between the phase voltages is greater than 90°, this vector difference is greater than either phase voltage by itself. Using the values given with Fig. 19.10,

$$E_{AB} = -120 \text{ v } \underline{/0°} + 120 \text{ v } \underline{/-120°}$$

$$= -(120 + j0) + (-60 - j104)$$

$$= -180 - j104 \text{ v } = 208 \text{ v } \underline{/-150°}$$

We can also solve for $E_{AB}$ by geometrical construction as shown in Fig. 19.22. First we construct vectors for the given phase voltages $E_{oA}$ and

$E_{oB}$. Then we construct the vector for $-E_{oA}$ by reversing the direction of the $E_{oA}$ vector. $E_{AB}$ then becomes the vector sum of $-E_{oA}$ and $E_{oB}$.

If the coils of the wye connected source are properly connected, the phase voltages are always equal in magnitude and 120° out of phase. Therefore, just as in the case of the line current to a balanced delta load, the line voltage from a wye must be

$$E_L = \sqrt{3}E_p = 1.73E_p \qquad (19.9)$$

For the phase voltages given with the wye connected source of emf of Fig. 19.10, the three line voltages are

$$E_{AB} = E_{Aa} + E_{bB} = E_{bB} - E_{aA} = 208 \text{ v } \underline{/-150°} \qquad (19.8a)$$

$$E_{BC} = E_{Bb} + E_{cC} = E_{cC} - E_{bB} = 208 \text{ v } \underline{/+90°} \qquad (19.8b)$$

$$E_{CA} = E_{Cc} + E_{aA} = E_{aA} - E_{cC} = 208 \text{ v } \underline{/-30°} \qquad (19.8c)$$

The complete vector diagram for both line and phase voltages of a wye connected three-phase source is shown in Fig. 19.23(a). The geometrical construction lines have been omitted in order to keep the diagram as simple as possible. Note that the line voltages are always displaced 30° from the phase voltages. Since these are generated emf's, changes in the load connected to a wye connected source of emf cannot alter the vectors of Fig. 19.23.

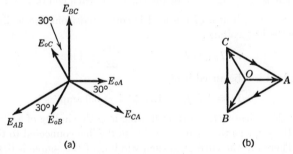

**Fig. 19.23.** Vector diagrams for a wye connected three phase source of EMF.

Since the opposite sides of a parallelogram are equal in length and parallel, a line joining the tips of the $E_{oA}$ and $E_{oB}$ vectors in Fig. 19.22 would have the same magnitude and direction as $E_{AB}$. Therefore we can check rapidly for the magnitude and direction of the line voltage vectors with respect to the phase voltage vectors for a wye connected three-phase source of emf without special geometrical construction, by joining the tips of the phase voltage vectors as in Fig. 19.23(b).

An important feature of the wye connected three-phase source is that two different values of three-phase emf are available in the one system. This is why a 3$\phi$ source consisting of wye connected transformer secondary windings rated at 120/208 v is probably the most widely used distribution system in North America. If we wish to apply 120 v, 3$\phi$ to the load, we connect $Z_A$, $Z_B$, and $Z_C$ as a four wire wye load as in Fig. 19.12. But if we wish to operate the same load from a 208 v, 3$\phi$ source, we can connect the three arms of the load in delta fashion as shown in Fig. 19.24. Since the various load impedances are connected from line to line, we use the same double subscript identification that we used with the simple delta connected system.

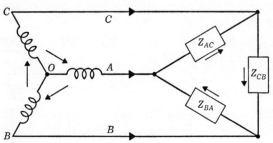

**Fig. 19.24.** A wye connected source feeding a delta connected load.

EXAMPLE 4: A balanced load each arm of which has an impedance of 52 ohms $\underline{/+45°}$ is delta connected to a 120/208 v, 3$\phi$ wye connected source as Fig. 19.24. What is the magnitude of the current in each coil of the source?

*Solution:* Since each arm of the load is connected from line to line, the load voltage is the line voltage.

$$\therefore \quad I_{BA} = I_{CB} = I_{AC} = \frac{208}{52} = 4 \text{ amp}$$

Since the load is a balanced load,

$$I_L = 1.73I_p = 1.73 \times 4 = 6.9 \text{ amp}$$

As Fig. 19.24 indicates, the current flowing in each winding of a wye connected source is the same as the current flowing in the line connected to that particular coil. Therefore the current in each winding of the source is 6.9 amp.

When a delta load is connected to a wye connected source as in Fig. 19.24, the phase voltages of the *source* are not used. Therefore, once we have determined the line voltages, we can disregard the phase voltages completely. Therefore the procedure for solving an unbalanced wye-delta circuit is exactly the same as that given in Example 3.

## 7. Power in a Balanced Three-Phase System

In a balanced three-phase load, the power in each of the three arms will be identical. Therefore the total power is three times the power in each phase. Since as far as the load is concerned, *phase* voltage is the voltage across each arm of the load and *phase* current is the current through each arm of the load,

$$P_T = 3E_pI_pF_p \tag{19.10a}$$

Since the junction points on three-phase loads such as three-phase motors are not always accessible, it is more convenient to express the total power in terms of *line* voltage and *line* current, which can be readily measured. In the wye connected system of Fig. 19.12,

$$E_L = \sqrt{3}E_p \quad \text{and} \quad I_L = I_p$$

In the balanced delta connected load of Fig. 19.17,

$$E_L = E_p \quad \text{and} \quad I_L = \sqrt{3}I_p$$

In both cases substitution in Equation (19.10a) gives

$$P_T = \sqrt{3}E_L I_L F_p \tag{19.10b}$$

EXAMPLE 5: What is the total power input to the load in Example 4?

*Solution:* Since each impedance has a power factor angle of $+ 45°$,

$$F_p = \cos 45° = 0.707 \text{ lagging}$$

$$\therefore \quad P_T = 1.73 E_L I_L F_p = 1.73 \times 208 \times 6.9 \times 0.707 = 1750 \text{ w}$$

EXAMPLE 6: A 550 v, $3\phi$ motor is delivering 15 hp to a mechanical load with an 80% efficiency. If the power factor of the motor is 0.9 lagging, what is the line current?

*Solution:*
$$P_T = \frac{\text{hp} \times 746}{\text{eff}} = \frac{15 \times 746}{0.8} = 14 \text{ kw}$$

From Equation (19.10),

$$I_L = \frac{P_T}{1.73 E_L F_p} = \frac{14,000}{(1.73 \times 550 \times 0.9)} = 16.35 \text{ amp}$$

## 8. Measuring Power in a Three-Phase System

One method of measuring the total power in a three-phase load is to connect three wattmeters so that each meter measures the voltage across

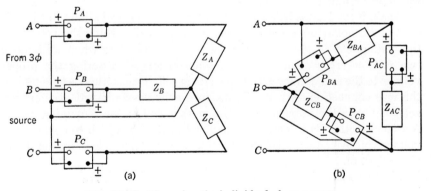

Fig. 19.25. Measuring the individual phase powers.

and the current through one of the arms of the load as in Fig. 19.25. The total power is therefore the sum of the three individual phase powers. This system applies to either balanced or unbalanced loads. However, if we know that the load is balanced (all wattmeters read the same), we can leave out two of the meters and take the total power as three times the reading of the remaining wattmeter.

However, with many three-phase loads, the junction points in both wye and delta connected loads are not accessible for measuring phase currents and phase voltages independently. We can therefore switch to the connections shown in Fig. 19.26 to measure the total power to either a wye or

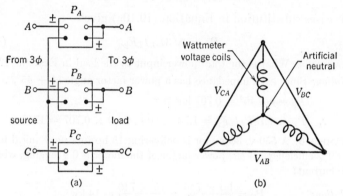

**Fig. 19.26.** Three wattmeter measurement of three phase power.

a delta connected load. By connecting the identical voltage coils of the three wattmeters as a wye load, each wattmeter will have a voltage equivalent to the phase voltage of a wye connected system $(E_L/\sqrt{3})$ as shown in Fig. 19.26(b). On this basis, regardless of load connections, the line current will appear to the wattmeters as if it were the phase current of a wye connected load. Therefore the total power is the sum of the three wattmeter readings.

Again if the load is balanced, all wattmeters will read alike. But in this case we cannot remove two wattmeters without disturbing the voltage to the voltage coil of the remaining wattmeter. Therefore when we remove two wattmeters, we must provide some means of restoring the proper voltage to the remaining wattmeter voltage coil. One method is to complete the wye connection with two impedance coils whose impedances are exactly equal to the impedance of the voltage coil of the remaining meter. A second method is to create an artificial neutral to which to connect the voltage coil by connecting three equal resistors as a wye load on the three-phase system.

Another method of using a single wattmeter to indicate the total power in a balanced three-phase load is shown in Fig. 19.27. The voltage coil of the wattmeter is returned to a center-tapped resistor across the two lines not containing the current coil. With this connection, the voltage coil receives a voltage of

$$V_M = V_{AB} + 0.5V_{BC}$$

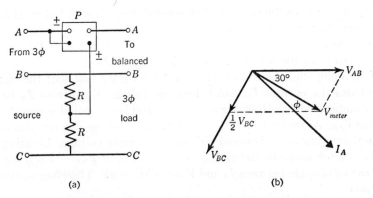

(a)                   (b)

**Fig. 19.27.** Single wattmeter measurement of three phase power in a balanced load.

Constructing the resultant vector in Fig. 19.27(b), we find that the voltage coil receives a voltage having the same phase position as if it were connected to a neutral (phase voltage for an equivalent wye system). But instead of the voltage being $E_L/\sqrt{3}$, as Fig. 19.27(b) shows, the wattmeter voltage is $E_L \cos 30°$ which is $(\sqrt{3}/2)E_L$. Therefore since $P_T = \sqrt{3}E_L I_L F_p$, the wattmeter reads *one-half* of the total power to a balanced three-phase load.

## 9. Two-Wattmeter Measurement of Three-Phase Power

The most widely used method of measuring three-phase power is based on the two-wattmeter connections of Figs. 19.28 and 19.29. Its advantages are: (1) the same connections apply to both wye and delta connected loads; (2) it shows the total power in both balanced and unbalanced circuits with

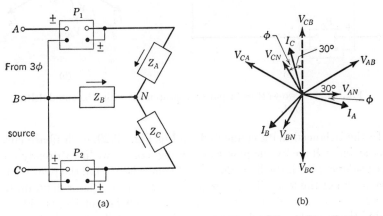

(a)                   (b)

**Fig. 19.28.** Two-wattmeter power measurement with a balanced wye load.

one less meter than the three-wattmeter systems; (3) with balanced loads, load power factor can be determined from the two-wattmeter readings. In order to determine what each wattmeter reads we will consider first the lagging power factor balanced wye load of Fig. 19.28.

Examining the connections to wattmeter $P_1$, we find that the current coil carries the current $I_A$, which lags the voltage $V_{AN}$ across $Z_A$ by the power factor angle $\phi$. However the voltage coil is connected across the *line* voltage $V_{AB}$. As we have already noted, the line voltage in a wye connected three-phase system is displaced $30°$ from the phase voltage. Locating $V_{AB}$ on the vector diagram (from $V_{AB} = V_{AN} + V_{NB} = V_{AN} - V_{BN}$), we find that the total angle between $I_A$ and $V_{AB}$ is $(30° + \phi)$. Therefore wattmeter $P_1$ reads

$$P_1 = V_{AB}I_A \cos (30° + \phi)$$

The current coil of wattmeter $P_2$ carries the current $I_C$. But note that the voltage coil is connected to read $V_{CB}$ rather than $V_{BC}$ (the systematically arranged line voltage). Therefore, locating $V_{CB}$ on the vector diagram (dashed line), we find that the angle between $I_C$ and $V_{CB}$ is $(30° - \phi)$. Therefore in general terms,

$$P_1 = E_L I_L \cos (30° + \phi) \tag{19.11}$$

$$P_2 = E_L I_L \cos (30° - \phi) \tag{19.12}$$

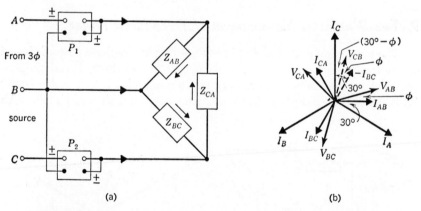

**Fig. 19.29.** Two-wattmeter power measurement with a balanced delta load.

In the balanced delta connected load of Fig. 19.29, each phase current lags the line voltage by the power factor angle $\phi$. As we have already noted, with a *balanced* load, the line current is displaced $30°$ from the phase current in each arm of the load. Therefore locating $I_A$ on the vector diagram (from $I_A = I_{AB} - I_{CA}$), we find that the angle between $I_A$ and $V_{AB}$ is $(30° + \phi)$. To find the angle between $I_C$ and the dashed vector $V_{CB}$, we can draw in the

$-I_{BC}$ vector. With a balanced load there is a 30° angle between $-I_{BC}$ and $I_C$. The angle between $V_{CB}$ and $-I_{BC}$ is the same as the angle between $V_{BC}$ and $I_{BC}$, the power factor angle $\phi$. Therefore the angle between $I_C$ and $V_{CB}$ is $(30° - \phi)$ and

$$P_1 = E_L I_L \cos(30° + \phi) \tag{19.11}$$

$$P_2 = E_L I_L \cos(30° - \phi) \tag{19.12}$$

Adding Equations (19.11) and (19.12) gives

$$P_1 + P_2 = E_L I_L[\cos(30 + \phi) + \cos(30 - \phi)]$$

To expand the terms in brackets we substitute the trigonometric expansion for $\cos(A + B)$ and $\cos(A - B)$. Therefore,

$$P_1 + P_2 = E_L I_L(\cos 30 \cos \phi - \sin 30 \sin \phi + \cos 30 \cos \phi + \sin 30 \sin \phi)$$

$$= E_L I_L(2 \cos 30 \cos \phi)$$

But $2 \cos 30° = \sqrt{3}$.

$$\therefore \quad P_1 + P_2 = \sqrt{3} E_L I_L \cos \phi$$

*which is the total power in a balanced 3φ system.*

We can also show that the sum of the two wattmeter readings is the total power for an unbalanced load by returning to the circuit of Fig. 19.29(a) and considering *instantaneous* power values. In the delta connected load,

$$p_t = (v_{AB} i_{AB}) + (v_{BC} i_{BC}) + (v_{CA} i_{CA}) \tag{1}$$

But as we noted when we delta connected a 3φ source of emf,

$$v_{AB} + v_{BC} + v_{CA} = 0 \tag{2}$$

from which

$$v_{CA} = -v_{AB} - v_{BC}$$

Substituting in Equation (1) gives

$$p_t = (v_{AB} i_{AB}) + (v_{BC} i_{BC}) - (v_{AB} i_{CA}) - (v_{BC} i_{CA})$$

Collecting the voltage terms and substituting $-v_{CB}$ for $v_{BC}$,

$$p_t = v_{AB}(i_{AB} - i_{CA}) + v_{CB}(i_{CA} - i_{BC}) = (v_{AB} i_A) + (v_{CB} i_C)$$

Inspection of the circuit of Fig. 19.29(a) shows us that this expression indicates precisely what the two wattmeters are connected to read. By a similar algebraic procedure we can show that the total instantaneous power in *any* wye connected load can also be reduced to the sum of the two wattmeter readings. Therefore with the two wattmeters connected as in Figs. 19.28 and 19.29, **the total power input to any three phase load, balanced or unbalanced, is the algebraic sum of the two wattmeter readings.**

The third advantage we claimed for the two-wattmeter system of three-phase power measurement was that with balanced loads we can determine the load power factor from the two wattmeter readings. First let us consider the effect of various load power factors on the meter readings. With unity power factor, Equations (19.11) and (19.12) both become

$$P_1 = P_2 = E_L I_L \cos 30° = \frac{\sqrt{3}}{2} E_L I_L$$

Therefore, **each wattmeter reads half of the total power.**

If the power factor angle is $+30°$,

$$P_1 = E_L I_L \cos 60° = 0.5 E_L I_L$$

$$P_2 = E_L I_L \cos 0° = E_L I_L$$

One wattmeter reads one-third of the total power and the other reads two-thirds. A power factor angle of $-30°$ simply reverses the wattmeter readings.

If the power factor angle is $60°$,

$$P_1 = E_L I_L \cos 90° = 0$$

$$P_2 = E_L I_L \cos - 30° = \frac{\sqrt{3}}{2} E_L I_L$$

One wattmeter reads zero and the other then registers the total power. Since this represents a power factor of 0.5, note that the total power is half that at unity power factor for the same line voltages and currents.

If the power factor drops below 50%, the angle $(30° + \phi)$ exceeds 90° and the cosine becomes a negative quantity. Therefore in the wattmeter movement, the counterclockwise torque exceeds the clockwise torque and the meter tries to read off scale to the left. To read the total true power to this low power factor load, we must reverse the wattmeter current coil leads to bring the reading onto the scale and then *subtract* this reading from that of the other meter.

When we know the power factor of a balanced load, we can express the ratio between the two wattmeter readings by dividing Equation (19.12) into Equation (19.11). This gives

$$\frac{P_1}{P_2} = \frac{\cos (30° + \phi)}{\cos (30° - \phi)} \qquad (19.13)$$

To use the two wattmeter readings to determine the load power factor, we start by subtracting Equation (19.11) from Equation (19.12).

$$\therefore \quad P_2 - P_1 = E_L I_L \cos (30° - \phi) - E_L I_L \cos (30° + \phi)$$

Substituting the trigonometric expansions for $\cos (30° - \phi)$ and $\cos (30° + \phi)$ and simplifying,

$$P_2 - P_1 = E_L I_L (2 \sin 30° \sin \phi)$$

But $\sin 30° = 0.5$.

$$\therefore \quad P_2 - P_1 = E_L I_L \sin \phi$$

Dividing this expression by the sum of Equations (19.11) and (19.12),

$$\frac{P_2 - P_1}{P_2 + P_1} = \frac{E_L I_L \sin \phi}{\sqrt{3} E_L I_L \cos \phi} = \frac{\tan \phi}{\sqrt{3}}$$

$$\therefore \quad \tan \phi = \sqrt{3} \frac{P_2 - P_1}{P_2 + P_1} \tag{19.14}$$

Knowing the two wattmeter readings, we can solve for the power factor angle $\phi$ and then determine the power factor of the load from $F_p = \cos \phi$.

EXAMPLE 7: The total power input to the load in Example 4 is measured by the two-wattmeter method. What are the two wattmeter readings?

*Solution:*

$$P_1 = E_L I_L \cos (30° + 45°) = 208 \times 6.9 \times \cos 75° = 370 \text{ w}$$
$$P_2 = E_L I_L \cos (30° - 45°) = 208 \times 6.9 \times \cos -15° = 1380 \text{ w}$$

## 10. Phase Sequence

In the three-phase circuit problems we have encountered so far, we have been given data from which we could determine the exact angle (with respect to the reference axis) of all the phase and line voltages. When a three-phase service is supplied by an electrical utility company, we know that all three line voltages have the same magnitude and are displaced from one another by a 120° angle. We can measure the *magnitude* of the voltages quite readily. However this does not tell us whether $E_{oB}$ lags $E_{oA}$ by 120° or *leads* $E_{oA}$ by 120°. This information is called the **phase sequence** (or phase rotation) of a three-phase system. It is important information, since it governs the direction of rotation of three-phase motors and also governs the division of the current among the three lines feeding an unbalanced load. It is also important that the electrical utility maintain the same phase sequence.

In the 3$\phi$ source of Fig. 19.30a, we are given information that shows that $E_{oB}$ lags $E_{oA}$ by 120° and $E_{oC}$ lags $E_{oB}$ by 120°. Therefore the instantaneous voltage to line $A$ passes through its positive peak value first, the instantaneous voltage to line $B$ passes through its positive peak value second, followed by the instantaneous voltage to line $C$. Therefore we say that the system in Fig. 19.30(a) has an $ABC$ phase sequence. If we reverse the leads to two of the generator coils as in Fig. 19.30(b), $E_{oB}$ now *leads* $E_{oA}$ by 120° and $E_{oC}$ *leads* $E_{oB}$ by 120°. Therefore the phase sequence has been reversed and is stated as a $CBA$ phase sequence since the instantaneous voltage to line $C$ passes a certain point in its cycle 120° before the instantaneous voltage to line $B$, which in turn is 120° ahead of the instantaneous voltage to line $A$.

Once we have prepared a vector diagram for the voltages in a 3$\phi$ system, we can read the phase sequence from the vector diagram quite readily.

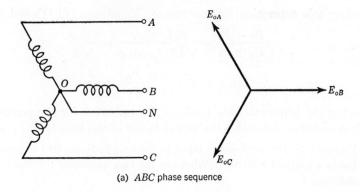

(a) *ABC* phase sequence

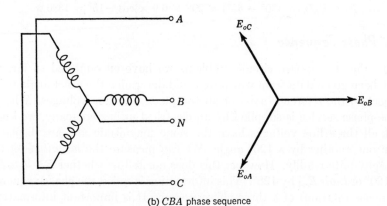

(b) *CBA* phase sequence

**Fig. 19.30.** Phase sequence of a three phase source.

Remembering that the direction of rotation of a vector is counterclockwise, the phase sequence is the order in which the voltage vectors would pass the reference axis if they were rotated in a counterclockwise direction. If we prefer to leave the vectors stationary, we can read the phase sequence from a vector diagram by reading *clockwise* around the diagram.

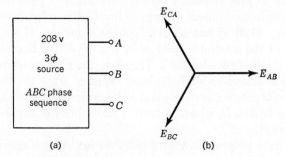

**Fig. 19.31.** Determining phase sequence from a vector diagram.

When we are given the line voltage and phase sequence of a three-phase source as in Fig. 19.31(a), we can prepare a vector diagram by placing one vector (usually $E_{AB}$) along the reference axis. In identifying the other two voltage vectors, reading *clockwise* around the vector diagram of Fig. 19.31(b), *either* all first subscript letters *or* all second subscript letters must agree with the specified phase sequence.

We can show the effect of phase sequence on the line currents to an unbalanced load by considering the following example.

EXAMPLE 8: $Z_{AB} = 52$ ohms $\underline{/-30°}$, $Z_{BC} = 52$ ohms $\underline{/+45°}$, and $Z_{CA} = 104$ ohms $\underline{/0°}$, are connected as a delta load to a 208 v, $3\phi$ source. Find the magnitude of the current in each line if the phase sequence of the source is (a) $ABC$, (b) $CBA$.

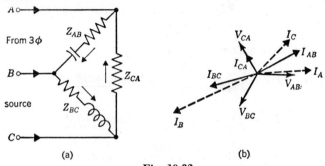

(a)                                          (b)

**Fig. 19.32.**

*Solution:* With $ABC$ phase sequence:

Step I. $\quad I_{AB} = \dfrac{V_{AB}}{Z_{AB}} = \dfrac{208\underline{/0°}}{52\underline{/-30°}} = 4$ amp $\underline{/+30°}$

$\qquad\quad I_{BC} = \dfrac{V_{BC}}{Z_{BC}} = \dfrac{208\underline{/-120°}}{52\underline{/45°}} = 4$ amp $\underline{/-165°}$

$\qquad\quad I_{CA} = \dfrac{V_{CA}}{Z_{CA}} = \dfrac{208\underline{/120°}}{104\underline{/0°}} = 2$ amp $\underline{/+120°}$

Step II. From the circuit diagram of Fig. 19.32(a),

$\quad I_A = I_{AB} - I_{CA} = 4$ amp $\underline{/+30°} - 2$ amp $\underline{/+120°}$

$\qquad = (3.46 + j2) - (-1 + j1.73) = 4.46 + j0.27$ amp

$\therefore\quad I_A = 4.5$ amp

$\quad I_B = I_{BC} - I_{AB} = 4$ amp $\underline{/-165°} - 4$ amp $\underline{/+30°}$

$\qquad = (-3.86 - j1.035) - (3.46 + j2) = -7.32 - j3.035$ amp

$\therefore\quad I_B = 7.9$ amp

$\quad I_C = I_{CA} - I_{BC} = 2$ amp $\underline{/+120°} - 4$ amp $\underline{/-165°}$

$\qquad = (-1 + j1.73) - (-3.86 - j1.035) = 2.86 + j2.765$ amp

$\therefore\quad I_C = 4$ amp

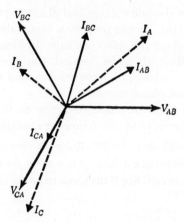

Fig. 19.33.

With $CBA$ phase sequence

Step I.  $I_{AB} = \dfrac{V_{AB}}{Z_{AB}} = \dfrac{208\underline{/0°}}{52\underline{/-30°}} = 4 \text{ amp } \underline{/+30°}$

$I_{BC} = \dfrac{V_{BC}}{Z_{BC}} = \dfrac{208\underline{/+120°}}{52\underline{/+45°}} = 4 \text{ amp } \underline{/+75°}$

$I_{CA} = \dfrac{V_{CA}}{Z_{CA}} = \dfrac{208\underline{/-120°}}{104\underline{/0°}} = 2 \text{ amp } \underline{/-120°}$

Step II.

$I_A = I_{AB} - I_{CA} = 4 \text{ amp } \underline{/+30°} - 2 \text{ amp } \underline{/-120°}$
$= (3.46 + j2) - (-1 - j1.73) = 4.46 + j3.73 \text{ amp}$

$\therefore \quad I_A = 5.8 \text{ amp}$

$I_B = I_{BC} - I_{AB} = 4 \text{ amp } \underline{/+75°} - 4 \text{ amp } \underline{/+30°}$
$= (1.035 + j3.86) - (3.46 + j2) = -2.425 + j1.86 \text{ amp}$

$\therefore \quad I_B = 3.06 \text{ amp}$

$I_C = I_{CA} - I_{BC} = 2 \text{ amp } \underline{/-120°} - 4 \text{ amp } \underline{/+75°}$
$= (-1 - j1.73) - (1.035 + j3.86) = -2.035 - j5.59 \text{ amp}$

$\therefore \quad I_C = 6 \text{ amp}$

## 11. Unbalanced Three-Wire Wye Loads

We have been able to solve unbalanced 4-wire wye loads and delta loads with no particular difficulty since in both cases we know the phase voltage across each arm of the load. But with the unbalanced 3-wire wye load of Fig. 19.34, we do not know what these phase voltages will be, since the wye junction point is *floating*. There are two fairly straightforward procedures based on the a-c network solutions we studied in Chapter 16.

The first is based on writing Kirchhoff's voltage law equations for the wye load of Fig. 19.34.

Following the conventional tracing arrows through the wye load
in Fig. 19.34,

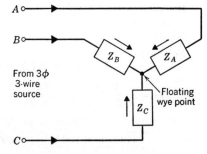

$$E_{BA} = V_{AB} = I_A Z_A - I_B Z_B \quad (1)$$

$$E_{CB} = V_{BC} = I_B Z_B - I_C Z_C \quad (2)$$

$$E_{AC} = V_{CA} = I_C Z_C - I_A Z_A \quad (3)$$

Since there is no neutral lead to
this wye load,

$$I_A + I_B + I_C = 0 \quad (4)$$

**Fig. 19.34.** The three-wire wye load.

From Equation (4), $I_B = -I_A - I_C$. Substituting in Equation (1) gives

$$V_{AB} = I_A Z_A + I_A Z_B + I_C Z_B \quad (5)$$

Multiplying Equation (5) by $Z_C$:

(5) × $Z_C$:      $V_{AB} Z_C = I_A(Z_C Z_A + Z_B Z_C) + I_C Z_B Z_C$

(3) × $Z_B$:      $V_{CA} Z_B = -I_A Z_A Z_B \qquad\qquad + I_C Z_B Z_C$

Subtracting gives

$$V_{AB} Z_C - V_{CA} Z_B = I_A(Z_C Z_A + Z_B Z_C + Z_A Z_B)$$

$$\therefore \quad I_A = \frac{V_{AB} Z_C - V_{CA} Z_B}{Z_A Z_B + Z_B Z_C + Z_C Z_A} \quad (19.15a)$$

Similarly

$$I_B = \frac{V_{BC} Z_A - V_{AB} Z_C}{Z_A Z_B + Z_B Z_C + Z_C Z_A} \quad (19.15b)$$

$$I_C = \frac{V_{CA} Z_B - V_{BC} Z_A}{Z_A Z_B + Z_B Z_C + Z_C Z_A} \quad (19.15c)$$

EXAMPLE 9: The phase sequence tester shown in Fig. 19.35 is connected to a 208 v, 3$\phi$, 60 c source whose phase sequence is $ABC$. The choke has an in-

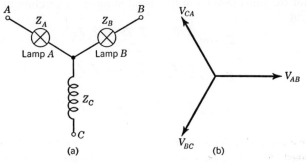

**Fig. 19.35.** A phase sequence tester.

ductance of 0.5 h with negligible resistance and the lamps each have a resistance of 100 ohms. (We will assume that the resistance remains constant even though the current through the lamp changes.) Using the equations developed from Kirchhoff's laws, determine the magnitude of the current in each of the lamps.

*Solution:*

$$Z_C = \omega L = 377 \times 0.5 = 188.5 \text{ ohms } \underline{/+90°}$$

$$I_A = \frac{V_{AB}Z_C - V_{CA}Z_B}{Z_A Z_B + Z_B Z_C + Z_C Z_A}$$

$$= \frac{(208\underline{/0°} \times 188.5\underline{/+90°}) - (208\underline{/+120°} \times 100\underline{/0°})}{(100\underline{/0°} \times 100\underline{/0°}) + (100\underline{/0°} \times 188.5\underline{/90°}) + (188.5\underline{/90°} \times 100\underline{/0°})}$$

$$= \frac{39,208\underline{/+90°} - 20,800\underline{/120°}}{10,000\underline{/0°} + 18,850\underline{/+90°} + 18,850\underline{/+90°}}$$

$$= \frac{(0 + j39,208) - (-10,400 + j18,013)}{10,000 + j37,700}$$

$$\therefore \quad I_A = \frac{23,600}{39,000} = 0.6 \text{ amp}$$

Similarly,

$$I_B = \frac{(208\underline{/-120°} \times 100\underline{/0°}) - (208\underline{/0°} \times 188.5\underline{/+90°})}{39,000}$$

$$= \frac{20,800\underline{/-120°} - 39,208\underline{/+90°}}{39,000}$$

$$= \frac{(-10,400 - j18,013) - (0 + j39,208)}{39,000} = \frac{58,300}{39,000} = 1.5 \text{ amp}$$

Therefore, with an $ABC$ phase sequence, lamp $B$ is brighter than lamp $A$.

The appearance of Equations (19.15a), (19.15b), and (19.15c) may suggest to us the second method for solving three-phase circuits with an unbalanced 3-wire wye load. In Chapter 16 we set down equations which would allow us to substitute an equivalent delta circuit for the original wye connected load. Once we know the impedance of the delta arms, we can solve for the line currents in the usual manner. Therefore in the circuit of Fig. 19.36,

$$Z_{BC} = \frac{Z_A Z_B + Z_B Z_C + Z_C Z_A}{Z_A} \tag{16.19}$$

$$Z_{CA} = \frac{Z_A Z_B + Z_B Z_C + Z_C Z_A}{Z_B} \tag{16.20}$$

$$Z_{AB} = \frac{Z_A Z_B + Z_B Z_C + Z_C Z_A}{Z_C} \tag{16.21}$$

EXAMPLE 10: If the phase sequence of the 208 v, $3\phi$, 60 c source in Example 9 is changed to $CBA$, determine the magnitude of the current in each lamp, using the wye-delta transformation equations.

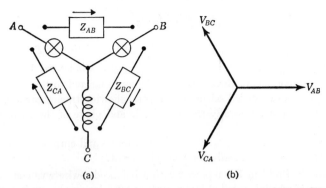

**Fig. 19.36.** Using wye-delta transformation to solve unbalanced three-wire wye loads.

*Solution:* Since we have already solved the numerator of the wye-delta transformation equations in solving Example 9,

$$\text{Step I:} \quad Z_{AB} = \frac{39,000\underline{/+75.15°}}{188.5\underline{/+90°}} = 207 \text{ ohms } \underline{/-14.85°}$$

$$Z_{BC} = \frac{39,000\underline{/+75.15°}}{100\underline{/°}} = 390 \text{ ohms } \underline{/+75.15°}$$

$$Z_{CA} = \frac{39,000\underline{/+75.15°}}{100\underline{/0°}} = 390 \text{ ohms } \underline{/+75.15°}$$

$$\text{Step II:} \quad I_{AB} = \frac{V_{AB}}{Z_{AB}} = \frac{208\underline{/0°}}{207\underline{/-14.85°}} = 1 \text{ amp } \underline{/+14.85°}$$

$$I_{BC} = \frac{V_{BC}}{Z_{BC}} = \frac{208\underline{/+120°}}{390\underline{/+75.15°}} = 0.534 \text{ amp } \underline{/+44.85°}$$

$$I_{CA} = \frac{V_{CA}}{Z_{CA}} = \frac{208\underline{/-120°}}{390\underline{/+75.15°}} = 0.534 \text{ amp } \underline{/+164.85°}$$

*Step III:* From Fig. 19.36,

$I_A = I_{AB} - I_{CA} = 1 \text{ amp } \underline{/+14.85°} - 0.534 \text{ amp } \underline{/+164.85°}$

$\quad = (0.967 + j0.256) - (-0.516 + j0.1395) = 1.481 + j0.1165 \text{ amp}$

$\therefore \quad I_A = \mathbf{1.5 \ amp}$

and $I_B = I_{BC} - I_{AB} = 0.534\underline{/+44.85°} - 1\underline{/+14.85°}$

$\quad = (0.378 + j0.376) - (0.967 + j0.256) = -0.589 + j0.12 \text{ amp}$

$\therefore \quad I_B = \mathbf{0.6 \ amp}$

Therefore with a *CBA* phase sequence, lamp *A* is brighter than lamp *B*.

Once we have solved for line currents we can return to the original wye connected circuit and solve for the various phase voltages on the basis that $V_{AN} = I_A Z_A$.

# Problems

1. Given a 60 c, $3\phi$, 4-wire wye connected source consisting of $E_{oA} = 120$ v $\underline{/0°}$, $E_{oB} = 120$ v $\underline{/+120°}$, and $E_{oC} = 120$ v $\underline{/-120°}$. A balanced 4-wire wye connected load consists of three 10 ohm resistors connected to this source.
   (a) Draw a fully labeled schematic diagram showing tracing arrows.
   (b) Determine algebraically the magnitude and phase of the current in each line.
   (c) Draw a vector diagram of the phase voltages and currents.
   (d) Determine algebraically the neutral current.

2. The load in Problem 1 is replaced with a balanced 4-wire wye connected load each arm of which is rated at 200 w with an 80% lagging power factor. Repeat all four sections of Problem 1. What will the neutral current be if line $A$ becomes open circuit?

3. The load in Problem 1 is replaced with a 4-wire wye connected load consisting of $Z_A = 30$ ohms $\underline{/+30°}$, $Z_B = 40$ ohms $\underline{/-30°}$, and $Z_C = 50$ ohms $\underline{/-90°}$. Repeat all four sections of Problem 1.

4. The load in Problem 1 is replaced with an unbalanced 4-wire wye connected load in which $Z_A$ is a 30 ohm heater, $Z_B$ is a 150 w lamp and $Z_C$ is an 0.1 h inductance whose resistance is 5 ohms. Repeat all four sections of Problem 1.

5. Given a 60 c, $3\phi$ delta connected source in which $E_{CA} = 550$ v $\underline{/0°}$, $E_{AB} = 550$ v $\underline{/+120°}$, and $E_{BC} = 550$ v $\underline{/-120°}$. A balanced delta connected load consisting of three 11 ohm resistors is connected to this source.
   (a) Draw a fully labeled schematic diagram showing tracing arrows.
   (b) Determine the phase currents algebraically.
   (c) Draw a vector diagram of the phase voltages and currents.
   (d) Determine the line currents by geometrical construction on a vector diagram.
   (e) Determine the line currents by vector algebra.

6. The load in Problem 5 is replaced by a balanced delta load which has a total power rating of 15 kw at 96.6% leading power factor. Repeat all five sections of Problem 5.

7. The load in Problem 5 is replaced by a delta load consisting of $Z_{AC} = 5$ ohms $\underline{/+45°}$, $Z_{CB} = 10$ ohms $\underline{/-36.9°}$, and $Z_{BA} = 11$ ohms $\underline{/0°}$. Repeat all five sections of Problem 5.

8. The load in Problem 5 is replaced by a delta connected load in which $Z_{AC} = 10$ kilohms $\underline{/0°}$, $Z_{CB}$ consists of a 10 h choke with a resistance of 50 ohms, and $Z_{BA}$ is a 0.5 $\mu$f capacitor. Repeat all five sections of Problem 5.

9. The load of Problem 5 is connected to the source of Problem 1.
   (a) Draw a fully labeled schematic diagram showing tracing arrows.
   (b) Determine the line voltages by vector construction.
   (c) Determine the line voltages by vector algebra.
   (d) Determine the phase currents.
   (e) Determine the line currents by vector algebra.
   (f) Draw a complete vector diagram for the circuit.

10. The load of Problem 6 is connected to the source of Problem 1. Repeat all six sections of Problem 9.

11. The load of Problem 7 is connected to the source of Problem 1. Repeat all sections of Problem 9.

12. The load of Problem 8 is connected to the source of Problem 1. Repeat all sections of Problem 9.

13. What is the total power input to the load in Problem 1?

14. What is the total power input to the load in Problem 5?

15. What is the total power input to the load in Problem 3?

16. What is the total power input to the load in Problem 7?

17. What is the phase sequence of the source in Problem 1?

18. What is the phase sequence of the source in Problem 5?

19. A wattmeter is connected with its current coil in line $B$ and its voltage coil from line $A$ to line $B$ in the circuit of Problem 1. What is its reading?

20. A wattmeter is connected with its current coil in line $C$ and its voltage coil from line $A$ to line $B$ in the circuit of Problem 7. What is its reading?

21. If the phase sequence of Problem 19 is reversed, what is the wattmeter reading?

22. If the phase sequence of Problem 20 is reversed, what is the wattmeter reading?

23. The total power input to the load in Problem 5 is checked by the two-watt-meter method. What is the reading on each wattmeter?

24. The total power input to the load in Problem 2 is checked by the two watt-meter method. What is the reading on each wattmeter.

25. A balanced delta load connected to a 208 v, $3\phi$ source is checked by the two-wattmeter method whose readings are 2 kw and 1 kw, respectively.
    (a) What is the total three-phase power?
    (b) What is the power factor of the load?
    (c) What is the magnitude of the line current?
    (d) What is the impedance (magnitude and angle) of each arm of the load?
    (e) What is the angle between the line voltage and the line current?

26. Repeat the five sections of Problem 25 when one wattmeter reads 3 kw and the other reads zero.

27. The load of Problem 1 is connected to the source of Problem 5. Repeat the four sections of Problem 1.

28. The neutral lead in Problem 3 becomes open circuit. Determine the current in each line.

29. Determine the three line currents in Problem 28 if the phase sequence of the source is reversed.

30. The load of Problem 7 is connected to a 208 v, $3\phi$ source of emf with a $CBA$ phase sequence through three conductors each of which has an impedance of $2 + j1$ ohms. Determine the magnitude of the current in each line.

## Review Questions

1. What are the three main advantages of a polyphase system compared to a single-phase power distribution system?

2. Why is it desirable to arrange that the total instantaneous power input to a polyphase system is free from the customary sine squared fluctuations?

3. Draw a graph of the total instantaneous power if one of the resistors in Fig. 19.2 is changed to 180 ohms.

4. Continue the vector representation of the magnetic flux in Fig. 19.5 at 45° intervals for the remainder of the cycle.

5. Why does the flux density of the rotating magnetic field in Fig. 19.5 remain constant?

6. What is the significance of the term **synchronous speed?**

7. How could we reverse the direction of rotation of the magnetic field in Fig. 19.5?

8. Why can we not produce a rotating magnetic field with the Edison three-wire system of Fig. 19.6?

9. What is the advantage of using the system shown in Fig. 19.6 for electric power distribution?

10. What voltage would appear across a load connected between line $A$ and line $B$ in the two-phase system of Fig. 19.2(b)?

11. What is meant by a **balanced load** in a polyphase system?

12. Why does a load not have to have unity power factor to be classed as a balanced load?

13. Draw a graph showing that the total instantaneous power input to a balanced three-phase load is constant.

14. Why can we state that in a balanced three-phase load, the currents in the three arms are equal in magnitude and displaced 120° in phase from one another regardless of the power factor of the load?

15. Show (with diagrams) how a rotating magnetic field can be produced when a three phase source of emf is available.

16. What is meant by the terms **phase voltage** and **line voltage** in a three-phase system? How do these terms apply to: (a) A wye connected source? (b) A delta connected source?

17. What is meant by the terms **phase current** and **line current** in a three-phase system? How do these terms apply to: (a) A wye connected load? (b) A delta connected load?

18. Draw a vector diagram for a wye connected source in which the upper case letter ends of the windings in Fig. 19.10 are connected to the neutral.

19. What is the function of the voltmeter when delta connecting the coils of a three phase source?

20. How would you test for incorrect wye connection of a three-phase source of emf with an a-c voltmeter?

21. Three transformers whose primary windings are fed from a three phase source of emf have the following secondary voltages: $E_{aA} = 240$ v$\underline{/0°}$, $E_{bB} = 240$ v $\underline{/-120°}$, and $E_{cC} = 240$ v $\underline{/+120°}$. Each secondary is center-tapped and these center taps are connected to a common neutral as shown in Fig. 19.37. Draw a fully labeled vector diagram for the six-phase source of emf available from these **star** connected secondary windings.

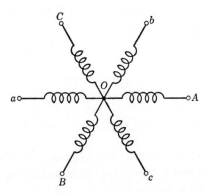

**Fig. 19.37.** Star connection of three phase transformer secondary windings.

22. Show with a vector diagram why the line current to a balanced delta load is greater than the phase current even though we *subtract* one phase current from the other to obtain the line current.

23. Why must the vector sum of the three line currents in any three-phase, three-wire system be zero?

24. Show with a vector diagram that the line voltage from a wye connected source is $\sqrt{3}$ times the voltage generated in each winding and displaced 30° from the emf's in the windings.

25. $I_L = \sqrt{3}I_p$ in a delta connected load depends on the load being a balanced load. However $E_L = \sqrt{3}E_p$ in a wye connected source is not dependent on a balanced load. Explain.

26. What is the advantage of expressing power input to a balanced three phase load in terms of *line* voltage and current rather than *phase* voltage and current?

27. Why do the wattmeters in Fig. 19.25 read the *true* power of each arm of the load?

28. What advantage does the three-wattmeter system of Fig. 19.26 have over that of Fig. 19.25?

29. What is meant by an **artificial neutral** with respect to Fig. 19.26?

30. What advantage does the two-wattmeter system of three-phase power measurement have over a single wattmeter?

31. With the two-wattmeter system of three-phase power measurement, why can the two wattmeters have different readings even though a balanced load is used?

32. Show that the total instantaneous power in *any* **wye** connected load is equal to the sum of the two wattmeter readings in Fig. 19.28.

33. Using Equation (19.13), plot an accurate graph of the power factor of a balanced load *vs* the ratio of the smaller of the two wattmeter readings to the larger. This ratio ranges from unity when both meters read the same, through zero when one wattmeter reads zero, to *minus* one when both wattmeters read the same *after it has been necessary to reverse the leads to the voltage coil of one of*

*the wattmeters.* If accurately prepared, this graph can be used to solve for the power factor of balanced loads.

34. Why is it necessary for an electrical utility company to maintain the same phase sequence?

35. What effect will reversing the tracing arrows when writing the emf subscripts in the wye connected source of Fig. 19.21 have on the phase sequence of the source? Explain.

36. Why are we instructed to read *clockwise* around a vector diagram when determining the phase sequence?

37. Explain the principle of operation of the phase sequence tester of Fig. 19.35(a).

38. Account for the changes in load phase voltages when the neutral lead becomes open circuit in Problem 28.

39. What is meant by a **floating wye point** in a three-phase system?

40. Derive Equation (19.15b) from the basic Kirchhoff's laws equations.

# Chapter 20

# HARMONICS

## 1. Nonsinusoidal Waves

In Chapter 11 we were introduced to the basic waveform in an a-c system by considering the rotation of a loop of wire in a uniform magnetic field. Applying Faraday's law to this demonstration we found that the instantaneous induced emf was directly proportional to the sine of the angle through which the loop had rotated. Therefore we called the continuously changing nature of the instantaneous emf in an a-c system a **sine wave.**

In developing the behavior of a-c circuits we have taken for granted that the sources of emf we have used do produce pure sine wave emf's. For the distribution of electric power, pure sine waves of voltage and current are very desirable, and in designing a-c machinery we strive to obtain such waveforms. But in practice it is not always possible to produce an alternating emf which has a perfectly sinusoidal form. For example, in the simple alternator of Chapter 11 a pure sine wave of emf depended on a uniform magnetic field. If the flux density is not uniform, the induced emf will not be a pure sine wave.

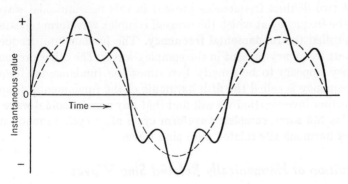

**Fig. 20.1.** Nonsinusoidal waveform from a musical instrument.

439

In audio reproducing equipment, the waveforms are seldom sinusoidal. The musical note created by feeding a sine wave from an audio oscillator to a loudspeaker is very uninteresting to listen to. If we play a single note on a musical instrument and examine the waveform of the instantaneous emf generated in a microphone, we will discover a very complex, non-sinusoidal alternating emf as shown in Fig. 20.1. But cycle after cycle of this complex wave will have exactly the same shape as the preceding cycle.

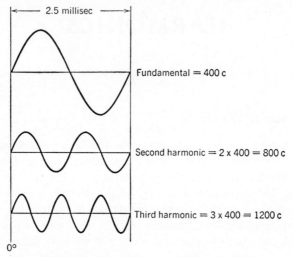

Fig. 20.2. Harmonically related sine waves.

Examining the complex waveform of Fig. 20.1 closely, we will notice that there appears to be a component, somewhat sinusoidal in shape, which seems to be going through five complete cycles during one cycle of the over-all waveform. This becomes more noticeable when we draw in a dotted line which cuts across the complex wave halfway between the peaks of the minor excursions in instantaneous emf. It would seem then that there are at least two distinct frequencies present in this nonsinusoidal waveform. One is the frequency at which the over-all complex waveform repeats itself. This is called the **fundamental frequency.** The fundamental frequency is the lowest frequency present in the complex wave. The other predominant frequency appears to be exactly five times the fundamental frequency. This frequency is called the **fifth harmonic** of the fundamental frequency. With further investigation we will find that **any nonsinusoidal wave which maintains the same complex waveform cycle after cycle is made up of a series of harmonically related pure sine waves.**

## 2. Addition of Harmonically Related Sine Waves

In order to determine the behavior of a-c circuits in the presence of nonsinusoidal waveforms, we must be able to determine the fundamental frequency, which harmonics are present, their relative amplitudes, and their phase relationship with respect to the fundamental. One method for determining the harmonic content of a nonsinusoidal wave is based on a mathematical analysis originally suggested by Joseph Fourier. A second method is based on the principle of reciprocity. *If we can exactly duplicate a given nonsinusoidal wave by adding together certain harmonically related sine waves with proper magnitudes and phase relationships, it follows that the complex wave must contain this same series of harmonically related sine waves.* Since this latter method is more in keeping with our undertaking to *understand* what goes on in electric circuits, we shall limit our discussions in this chapter to this approach. It is interesting to note that this principle is used in the Hammond electronic organ to duplicate the tone quality of various musical instruments.

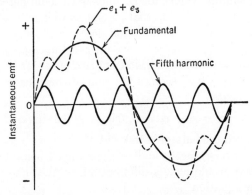

**Fig. 20.3.** Duplicating the complex wave of Fig. 20.1 by adding a fifth harmonic to the fundamental sine wave.

We can add harmonics to a fundamental sine wave in our pencil and paper complex waveform synthesis by adding instantaneous values on a linear graph as we did in Chapter 13. On the graph of Fig. 20.3 we have drawn a fundamental sine wave and a fifth harmonic with an amplitude of about 30% of that of the fundamental. We say that this harmonic is shown in phase with the fundamental since both sets of instantaneous values are zero at the origin of the graph and both start out in a positive direction. If we wish to show the harmonic 180° out of phase with the fundamental we simply invert the harmonic waveform on the graph. It would start with an instantaneous value of zero at the origin but would proceed first to a *negative* peak whereas the fundamental is proceeding first to a positive peak. If we wish to phase the harmonic so that it lags the fundamental by 90°, we must draw it on the graph so that at the same instant that the instantaneous value of the fundamental is passing through zero and proceeding in a positive direction, the instantaneous value of the harmonic is at its negative peak. Note that the 180° and 90° are considered on the basis of one cycle of the *harmonic* being 360°.

Adding the instantaneous values of these two sine waves in Fig. 20.3 from instant to instant along the horizontal axis of the graph, we obtain the resultant waveform shown by the dashed line. The resultant no longer is a sine wave as it is when we add sine waves of the same frequency; it resembles the complex wave of Fig. 20.1. Since the fifth harmonic is an exact multiple of the fundamental frequency, the succeeding cycles will have exactly the same shape as the one cycle we have plotted.

When we are discussing the *shape* of an a-c waveform, we are thinking in terms of the instantaneous values of voltage or current. In Chapter 11 we described the shape of a sine wave alternating emf by writing the general equation for the sine wave emf thus:

$$e = E_m \sin \omega t \tag{11.3}$$

By substituting suitable values for $E_m$ and $\omega$, we could determine the amplitude and frequency of the alternating emf as well as its shape. We can therefore follow a similar procedure and describe the shape of a complex wave by writing its equation. Since we formed the complex wave in Fig. 20.3 by adding the instantaneous values of two pure sine waves, the equation for the complex wave becomes the sum of the equations for the two sine wave components.

$$\therefore \quad e_t = e_1 + e_5 = E_m(\sin \omega t + 0.3 \sin 5\omega t) \tag{20.1}$$

If we had phased the harmonic 180° out of phase with the fundamental, it would simply reverse the + and − signs for all instantaneous values. The complex wave would have a different appearance and would then be described by the equation

$$e_t = E_m(\sin \omega t - 0.3 \sin 5\omega t) \tag{20.2}$$

Examining the tables of trigonometrical functions will show us that the cosine of an angle starts at plus one at 0° and decreases to zero at 90°, whereas the sine of an angle is zero at 0° and increases to plus one at 90°. Therefore a *cosine* wave has the same shape as a sine wave but *leads* the sine wave by 90° (since the cosine reached plus one 90° ahead of the sine). This then gives us a convenient way of expressing a 90° phase difference between a harmonic and the fundamental when we write the equation of a complex wave. If we wished to draw the fifth harmonic in the graph of Fig. 20.3 with its *negative* peak coinciding with the instant when the instantaneous value of the fundamental is passing through zero proceeding in a positive direction, we would write the equation describing the complex wave thus:

$$e_t = E_m(\sin \omega t - \cos 5\omega t) \tag{20.3}$$

In practice most nonsinusoidal waves do not consist of a fundamental and a single harmonic as in Fig. 20.3. Most complex waves consist of a *series* of harmonically related sine waves with the amplitude of each harmonic diminishing as the multiple of the fundamental frequency becomes higher. However we can get a fair approximation of the shape of the complex waveform by adding together the instantaneous values of only the first few harmonics in the series. On analyzing the harmonic content of some of the more common nonsinusoidal waveforms, we will discover that there are two series of harmonics which govern the general appearance of nonsinusoidal waves. Complex waves such as that of Fig. 20.1 in which the positive and negative half cycles are *symmetrical* are composed mainly of the *odd* order harmonics (third, fifth, seventh, ninth, etc.). The *even* order series of harmonics produces a symmetrical complex waveform if all the even harmonics are exactly in phase or 180° out of phase with the fundamental. For a harmonic to be in phase with the fundamental, when the instantaneous value of the fundamental is passing through zero going in a positive direction, the instantaneous value of the harmonic must be passing through zero, going in a positive direction as shown in Figs. 20.2 and 20.3. When a complex wave is composed of an even order series of harmonics, one or more of which is *not* exactly in phase or 180° out of phase with the fundamental, the positive and negative half cycles of the nonsinusoidal wave are quite different in appearance as shown in Fig. 20.5(b).

EXAMPLE 1: Determine the shape of the complex wave whose equation is $e = 60 \sin 2512t + 20 \cos 7536t$.

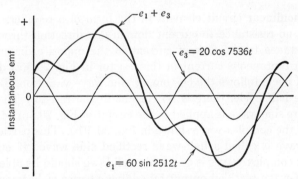

**Fig. 20.4.** Complex waveform.

*Solution:*

$$\omega = 2\pi f, \tag{11.4}$$

fundamental      $f = \dfrac{\omega}{2\pi} = \dfrac{2512}{6.28} = 400 \text{ c}$

and harmonic     $f = \dfrac{7536}{6.28} = 1200 \text{ c} = 3\text{rd harmonic}$

Draw as accurately as possible on a sheet of graph paper a sine wave representing the fundamental. Select the number of degrees per horizontal scale division in such a manner that the third harmonic can be accurately located in phase.

Draw a third harmonic sine wave with 20/60 or $\frac{1}{3}$ the amplitude of the funda-mental. Since this is a positive cosine component, start with the positive peak value phased to match the zero instantaneous value of the fundamental.

Add instantaneous values every few degrees by counting the sum of the vertical scale divisions on the graph. Mark these plots on the graph and join them to show the waveform of the complex wave as in Fig. 20.4.

## 3. Generation of Harmonics

In stating the a-c network theorems in Chapter 16 we were assuming that the impedance of every circuit component remained constant through-out the cycle of the sine wave voltage and current waveforms. Such an im-pedance is called a **linear** impedance. However, the circuit of Fig. 20.5(a)

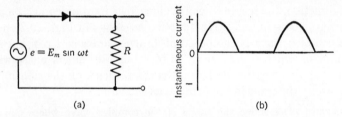

(a)                                              (b)

**Fig. 20.5.** Complex waveform created by a half-wave rectifier.

contains a **nonlinear** circuit element in the form of a rectifier. The ideal rectifier has no resistance to current flow in one direction through it but infinite resistance to the flow of current in the opposite direction. As a result the instantaneous current in the resistor in Fig. 20.5(a) during the positive half cycle follows the customary sine wave variation. But during the negative half cycle, there is no current in the resistor. Therefore al-though a pure sine wave is applied to the circuit of Fig. 20.5(a), the output waveform is the complex wave shown in Fig. 20.5(b). This particular non-sinusoidal wave is called a **half-wave rectified sine wave.** If our method of analyzing complex waves is to remain valid, we should be able to dupli-cate the half-wave rectified output by adding a series of harmonics to the input sine wave. Since the waveform of Fig. 20.5(b) is quite unsymmetrical, the series of harmonics required will be the even order series. Their phasing will have to be such that the peaks of these even harmonics coincide with the peak of the fundamental. To achieve this all the harmonics must lag the fundamental by 90° and therefore all the harmonics will be minus cosine terms.

Examining the complex waveform of Fig. 20.5(b), we will also note that all the instantaneous values are positive quantities. Therefore when we average the *complete* cycle, instead of an average value of zero, for this particular waveform we obtain an average value of 0.318 of the peak in-stantaneous value. Whenever the average of a complete cycle of a wave-form is not zero, it is an indication that there is a d-c component present in addition to the harmonically related sine waves. Its presence in this waveform is due to the characteristic of the rectifier that allows current to flow in one direction through $R$ but not in the other. This is usually the one component of this particular complex waveform that we are interested in when we construct the circuit of Fig. 20.5(a) in practical equipment. When we remove the parentheses in Equation (20.4), the first term gives us the magnitude of this d-c component.

Writing an equation combining all these specifications, the equation for the half-wave rectified sine wave developed by an ideal rectifier becomes

$$e = \frac{E_m}{\pi}\left(1 + \frac{\pi}{2}\sin \omega t - \frac{2}{3}\cos 2\omega t - \frac{2}{15}\cos 4\omega t - \frac{2}{35}\cos 6\omega t - \frac{2\cos n\omega t}{n^2 - 1}\right)$$

$$(20.4)$$

where $n$ is an even number.

The significance of Equation (20.4) in so far as this chapter is concerned is that **harmonics not contained in the input waveform are generated whenever an a-c waveform is applied to a nonlinear circuit element.**

## 4. Generation of Harmonics in a Vacuum Tube Amplifier

In an ideal vacuum tube amplifier, varying the grid voltage 10 v either side of its quiescent (no signal) value should swing the plate current the same number of milliamperes either side of its quiescent value. This would

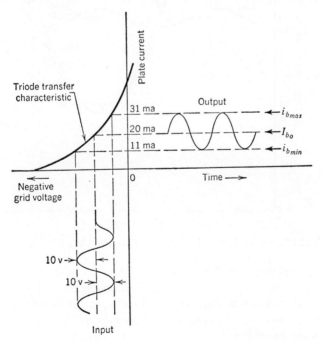

**Fig. 20.6.** Nonlinear transfer characteristic of a triode amplifier.

be indicated by using a straight line for the transfer characteristic on the graph of Fig. 20.6. But the average triode type vacuum tube amplifier has a slightly curved transfer characteristic as shown in Fig. 20.6. As a result, a 10 v swing of the grid voltage in one direction results in an 11 ma change in plate current, whereas a 10 v swing of the grid voltage in the other direction produces only a 9 ma change in plate current.

We will note that, with respect to the quiescent value of the plate current, the positive and negative half cycles of the wave form are unsymmetrical. Therefore we can assume that the tube has added a series of even order harmonics, neither in phase nor 180° out of phase, to the input sine wave. Most significant of this series is the second harmonic, and we can approximately duplicate the output waveform by considering that it consists of a sine wave fundamental with a peak amplitude of 10 ma and a second harmonic with a peak value of 1 ma superimposed on the quiescent d-c component as shown in Fig. 20.7.

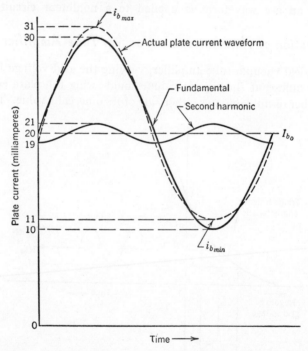

**Fig. 20.7.** Second harmonic content in the output of a triode amplifier.

Careful examination of Fig. 20.7 will show us how we can determine the magnitude of this second harmonic distortion from the measurement of the peak deviations in the actual plate current (dashed curve) from the quiescent (no signal) plate current $I_{b_0}$. Since the positive peaks of the second harmonic coincide with the peaks of the fundamental, the *peak to peak* amplitude of the fundamental is the same as the peak to peak deviation in plate current. And since the effective value of a sine wave is $1/\sqrt{2}$ of the peak value, therefore the effective value of the sine wave fundamental is $1/2\sqrt{2}$ of the peak to peak value of the sine wave.

$$\therefore \quad I_{pfund} = \frac{i_{b_{max}} - i_{b_{min}}}{2\sqrt{2}} \tag{20.5}$$

Again from Fig. 20.7, the peak to peak amplitude of the second harmonic is the difference in deviations of the instantaneous plate current from its quiescent value. Therefore

$$\text{peak to peak 2nd harmonic} = (i_{b_{max}} - I_{b_0}) - (I_{b_0} - i_{b_{min}})$$

$$I_p \text{ (2nd harmonic)} = \frac{i_{b_{max}} + i_{b_{min}} - 2I_{b_0}}{2\sqrt{2}} \tag{20.6}$$

## 5. Generation of Harmonics in an Iron-Core Transformer

In Chapter 18 we noted that when we connect the primary of a transformer across a sine wave source of emf, in order for the primary to develop a sine wave cemf the flux in the core must also be a sine wave. If the permeability of the core were constant, this would require a sine wave of

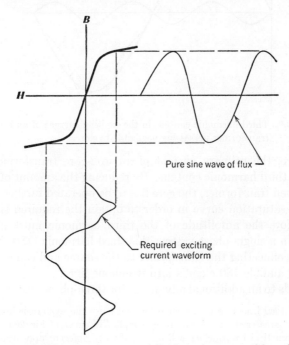

**Fig. 20.8.** Producing a sine wave of flux in an iron core with negligible hysteresis.

exciting current in the primary winding. However with an iron core, because of saturation effect, the permeability decreases as the flux density approaches its maximum value. This requires a greater than normal increase in the instantaneous primary current in order to maintain the sine wave shape for the total flux waveform.

We can use the **BH** curve of Fig. 20.8 as a transfer curve to determine the nature of the exciting current waveform.* We will note that the peaks of the exciting current waveform are narrower and greater in amplitude than those of a pure sine wave. Since both half cycles of the exciting current waveform are identical, we can expect that odd order harmonics will be present. Since the third harmonic is the predominant harmonic of this series, we can approximate the waveform of the exciting current in an iron-core transformer possessing negligible hysteresis by adding a third harmonic to the fundamental as shown in Fig. 20.9.

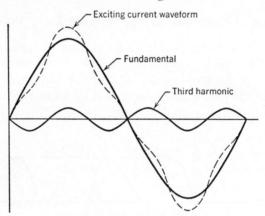

**Fig. 20.9.** Third harmonic content in the exciting current of an iron-core transformer possessing negligible hysteresis.

Therefore, the primary current of an iron-core transformer contains appreciable third harmonic content. By reducing the amount of iron in the core of a given transformer, the core has to be operated further around the knee of the saturation curve in order to obtain the required sine wave of flux. Therefore the amplitude of the third harmonic must increase appreciably. In a single-phase system this third harmonic (180 c) must flow in the lines connecting the transformer to the source and can cause trouble by inducing audible 180 c emf's into telephone lines.

This leads to an additional advantage for three-phase systems of electric

* In a practical iron-core transformer, we must use the hysteresis loop of the iron as a transfer characteristic rather than the simple **BH** curve of Fig. 20.8. The exciting current in a practical transformer will have a slightly different appearance from that shown in Fig. 20.8. This is due to a shift in the phase relationships among the component sine waves.

power distribution. If we connect the primary windings of a three-phase transformer bank as a delta, the line current is the difference between the phase currents. Since with a balanced load the fundamental frequency components of the phase currents are 120° out of phase, the fundamental current in the line is $\sqrt{3}I_p$. However, as we can see from examining Fig. 20.2, a 120° phase shift at the fundamental frequency is the same as three times 120°, or a 360°, phase shift for the third harmonic. Therefore subtracting the third harmonic components of the transformer primary phase currents results in complete cancellation of any third harmonic current in the line. The third harmonic current necessary to operate the iron-core transformer properly flows around the delta and not in the transmission lines. However the phase difference between the fifth harmonic components of the primary phase currents is five times 120°, which is the same as −120°. Therefore there will be a fifth harmonic component in the line current with a magnitude which is the customary $\sqrt{3}$ times the fifth harmonic content of the phase current.

## 6. Effective Value of a Nonsinusoidal Wave

In Chapter 11 we found that in order to obtain the effective value of a sine wave of voltage or current, we had to determine the average power. The effective voltage then became $E = \sqrt{P_{av}R}$. We have already noted that a regularly recurring nonsinusoidal wave consists of a fundamental sine wave plus a series of harmonic sine waves. Applying the principle of the superposition theorem, we can think of a nonsinusoidal source of emf as consisting of the harmonically related sine wave sources all acting independently to contribute to the total power.

$$\therefore \quad P_T = \frac{E_1^2}{R} + \frac{E_2^2}{R} + \frac{E_3^2}{R} + \text{etc.}$$

Since each of these terms is based on a sine wave of voltage, we can apply the definition for effective value to the total power. Therefore the effective value of a nonsinusoidal wave becomes

$$E = \sqrt{P_T R} = \sqrt{E_1^2 + E_2^2 + E_3^2 + \text{etc.}} \tag{20.7}$$

where $E_1$, $E_2$, and $E_3$ are the effective values of the fundamental, second, and third harmonics, respectively.

EXAMPLE 2: The emf of a three-phase wye connected alternator is known to possess a certain amount of third and fifth harmonic. No other harmonic content of any significance is present. The phase voltage of the alternator is measured as 122 v and the line voltage is 208 v. What is the effective value of the third harmonic emf in each alternator coil?

*Solution:* Since the fundamental phase voltages are 120° out of phase, the line voltage contains a fundamental component which is $\sqrt{3}$ times the fundamental component of the phase voltage.

Since the fifth harmonic phase voltages are 600°, or −120°, out of phase, the line voltage contains a fifth harmonic component which is $\sqrt{3}$ times the fifth harmonic component of the phase voltage.

But the third harmonic phase voltages are 360° out of phase and therefore there is no third harmonic in the line voltage. Therefore

$$208\ v = 1.73\ \sqrt{E_1{}^2 + E_5{}^2} \quad \text{and} \quad 122\ v = \sqrt{E_1{}^2 + E_3{}^2 + E_5{}^2}$$

Squaring both equations, subtracting and taking the square root of both sides gives

$$E_3 = \sqrt{122^2 - 120^2} = 22\ v$$

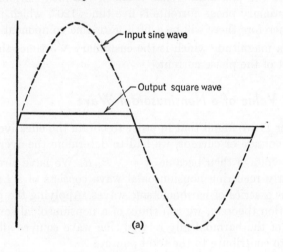

(a)

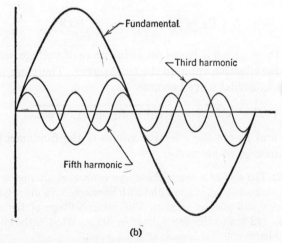

(b)

**Fig. 20.10.** Production and synthesis of a square wave.

## 7. Square Waves and Sawtooth Waves

From our discussion of the generation of harmonics in vacuum tubes and iron-core transformers, it would seem that nonlinear circuit elements should be avoided. However there are many applications in which we purposely distort an input sine wave in order to obtain a special wave shape. One such example is the **square wave** of Fig. 20.10(a). Although our method of determining the harmonic content of a nonsinusoidal wave has been to synthesize the required waveform by adding together the appropriate harmonics, we must note that in practical equipment these waveforms are usually produced by passing a sine wave through a nonlinear impedance network. Thus we can produce a square wave by passing a large amplitude sine wave through a nonlinear network which limits the peak value of the output voltage to ± a few volts. Therefore we can say that the square wave of Fig. 20.10(a) has been produced by *clipping* the peaks of the input sine wave.

Although the square wave has been produced by clipping a sine wave, the nonlinear impedance network producing this effect has added harmonics to the input sine wave. We can produce square waves in which the positive pulse is either wider or narrower than the negative pulse. However, the square wave of Fig. 20.10(a) is completely symmetrical. Therefore, as we would expect, it is made up of a fundamental sine wave plus a series of odd order harmonics. As the simple geometrical shape of the square wave suggests, this series of harmonics has a simple harmonic relationship between the amplitude and the frequency of each harmonic; the amplitude of each harmonic is inversely proportional to its frequency. And in order to contribute to the flat top and steep sides of the square wave, all harmonics are in phase with the fundamental. Therefore the equation for the instantaneous value of a symmetrical square wave becomes

$$e = E(\sin \omega t + \tfrac{1}{3} \sin 3\omega t + \tfrac{1}{5} \sin 5\omega t + \tfrac{1}{7} \sin 7\omega t + \text{etc.}) \quad (20.8)$$

The first three terms of this equation are shown superimposed on a linear graph in Fig. 20.10(b) as we would prepare to determine the shape of the waveform represented by Equation (20.8) by graphical addition of instantaneous values.

Another very common nonsinusoidal wave is the **sawtooth wave** shown in Fig. 20.11. This waveform contains the same odd order series

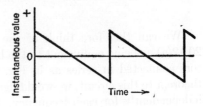

**Fig. 20.11.** A sawtooth waveform.

of harmonics as the square wave but it also includes the even order series of harmonics as well. Therefore the equation for the waveform of Fig. 20.11 becomes

$$e = E(\sin \omega t + \tfrac{1}{2} \sin 2\omega t + \tfrac{1}{3} \sin 3\omega t + \tfrac{1}{4} \sin 4\omega t$$
$$+ \tfrac{1}{5} \sin 5\omega t + \tfrac{1}{6} \sin 6\omega t + \text{etc.})  \quad (20.9)$$

## 8. Nonsinusoidal Waves in Linear Impedance Networks

We have investigated the generation of harmonics which combine to form nonsinusoidal waveforms by applying pure sine waves to networks containing nonlinear circuit elements. We must now consider how we can handle a circuit problem in which a nonsinusoidal wave is applied to a network of linear impedances.

We have noted that we can think of a nonsinusoidal wave as consisting of a pure sine wave at the fundamental frequency plus a series of harmonically related sine waves. In determining the effective value of a nonsinusoidal wave we referred to the superposition theorem. According to the superposition theorem, we can determine the net effect of several sources of emf in a network on any branch of that network by determining the effect of each source acting independently, with the other sources switched off. This provides us with the basic line of action for determining the effect of nonsinusoidal waves in linear impedance networks.

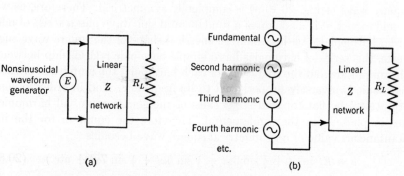

**Fig. 20.12.** Applying the superposition theorem to linear impedance networks fed from nonsinusoidal sources of EMF.

We can therefore think of the nonsinusoidal source of emf of Fig. 20.12(a) as being equivalent to the harmonically related sine wave generators connected in series as in Fig. 20.12(b). Applying the superposition theorem to this circuit, we would determine the current in the load resistor independently for each frequency. If we wish to know the rms value of the total current, we simply apply Equation (20.7) to the individual harmonic currents in the load resistor. If we wish to know the shape of the output waveform, we can plot the various harmonic components of the output on a linear graph and add their instantaneous values.

EXAMPLE 3: The nonsinusoidal waveform described as $e = 45 \sin 6280t - 15 \sin 18840t$ is applied to the circuit of Fig. 20.13.

(a) Determine the waveform of the input wave.

(b) Determine the waveform of the output wave.

(c) Determine the over-all power factor of the circuit.

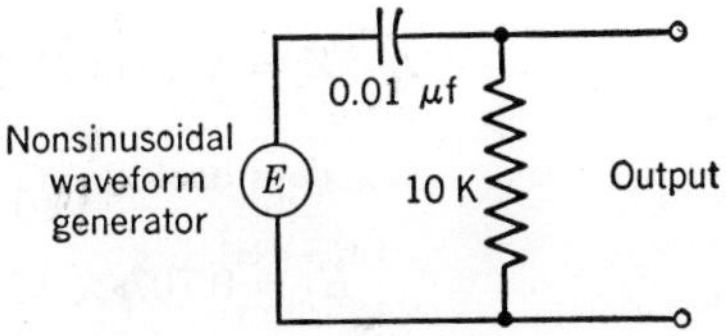

*Solution:* (a) The fundamental has a frequency of

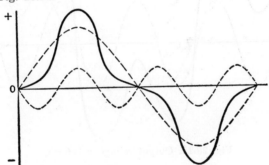

Fig. 20.13. Schematic diagram for Example 3.

$$f_f = \frac{\omega}{2\pi} = \frac{6280}{6.28} = 1 \text{ kc}$$

and the harmonic in the nonsinusoidal wave has a frequency of

$$f_h = \frac{18840}{6.28} = 3 \text{ kc}$$

which is the third harmonic.

As the equation indicates, the harmonic and the fundamental are 180° out of phase and the amplitude of the third harmonic is one-third of the amplitude of the fundamental. Therefore the input voltage has the waveform shown in Fig. 20.14.

Fig. 20.14. Input voltage waveform.

(b) $e_{out} = iR$ and since resistance is a constant, the output voltage waveform will have the same shape as the total instantaneous current waveform. At the fundamental frequency

$$X_C = \frac{1}{\omega C} = \frac{10^6}{6280 \times 0.01} = -j15.9 \text{ kilohms}$$

$$\therefore \quad Z = \sqrt{10,000^2 + 15,900^2} = 18.8 \text{ kilohms}$$

$$\phi = \arctan \frac{-15.9}{10} = -57.8°$$

$$E_f = 0.707 E_m = 0.707 \times 45 = 31.8 \text{ v}$$

$$\therefore \quad I_f = \frac{E}{Z} = \frac{31.8 \underline{/0°}}{18.8 \underline{/-57.8°}} = 1.69 \text{ ma } \underline{/+57.8°}$$

At the third harmonic

$$X_C = \frac{10^6}{18840 \times 0.01} = -j5.3 \text{ kilohms}$$

$$\therefore \quad Z = \sqrt{10{,}000^2 + 5{,}300^2} = 11.35 \text{ kilohms}$$

$$\phi = \arctan \frac{-5.3}{10} = -27.9°$$

$$E_3 = 0.707 \times 15 = 10.6 \text{ v}$$

$$\therefore \quad I_3 = \frac{E_3}{Z_3} = \frac{10.6\underline{/180°}}{11.35\underline{/-27.9°}} = 0.933 \text{ ma } \underline{/207.9°}$$

In drawing the fundamental and third harmonic current sine waves on a linear graph we must note first of all that the amplitude of the harmonic is now 55% of the amplitude of the fundamental, since the reactance of the capacitor is less at the third harmonic frequency than at the fundamental frequency. In the input wave the 180° point of the third harmonic coincides with the 0°

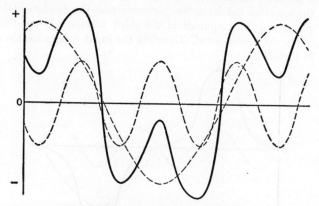

**Fig. 20.15.** Output voltage waveform.

point of the fundamental at $t = 0$ on the horizontal axis. But in the current waveform, the fundamental has been advanced 57.8° (360° to a fundamental cycle) and the third harmonic has been advanced only 27.9° (360° to a cycle of third harmonic). Therefore in drawing the output voltage waveform, the 57.8° point on the fundamental and the 207.9° point on the third harmonic must coincide as shown in Fig. 20.15.

(c) The total true power is

$$P_T = I_f^2 R + I_3^2 R = 10^4(0.00169^2 + 0.000933^2) = 37.2 \text{ mw}$$

The effective value of the nonsinusoidal input voltage is

$$E_T = \sqrt{E_f^2 + E_3^2} = \sqrt{31.8^2 + 10.6^2} = 33.6 \text{ v}$$

$$I_T = \sqrt{1.69^2 + 0.933^2} = 1.925 \text{ ma}$$

Therefore the apparent power in the network is

$$P_s = E_T I_T = 33.6 \times 1.925 = 64.6 \text{ mva}$$

And by definition the power factor is

$$F_p = \frac{P}{P_s} = \frac{37.2}{64.6} = 57.5\% \text{ leading}$$

# Problems

1. Determine graphically the shape of the complex wave described by Equation (20.2).

2. Determine graphically the shape of the complex wave described by Equation (20.3).

3. Determine graphically the shape of the complex wave based on only the fundamental and the first two harmonic terms of the equation for the square wave as shown in Fig. 20.10(b).

4. Determine graphically the shape of the complex wave described by Equation (20.4) using all terms up to and including the sixth harmonic.

5. Determine graphically the shape of the nonsinusoidal wave described by the equation

$$e = 120 \sin 1570t - 60 \sin 3140t + 40 \sin 4710t - 30 \sin 6280t + 24 \sin 7850t$$

Compare this with the waveform of Fig. 20.11.

6. Determine graphically the shape of the nonsinusoidal wave described by the equation

$$e = 100(\sin 1256t - \tfrac{1}{9} \sin 3768t + \tfrac{1}{25} \sin 6280t - \tfrac{1}{49} \sin 8792t)$$

Describe the shape of the resulting complex wave.

7. What is the rms value of the complex emf in Problem 5?

8. A wye connected three-phase source of emf has a phase voltage of 110 v and a line voltage of 188 v. The induced emf is known to contain odd order harmonics. If the amplitudes of the harmonics above the seventh are small enough that they can be neglected, what is the effective value of the third harmonic content of the phase voltage?

9. When a pure sine wave is applied to a triode vacuum tube amplifier, the plate current swings 8 ma above its quiescent value and 7 ma below. Determine the percentage second harmonic distortion by expressing the second harmonic current and the fundamental current as a ratio.

10. (a) What is the rms value of the current in a series circuit consisting of a 50 mh inductance and a 50 ohm resistance when the applied emf has the nonsinusoidal waveform of Problem 5?
    (b) What is the true power in this circuit?
    (c) What is the over-all power factor of this circuit?

11. Determine the output voltage waveform if the positions of the capacitor and resistor in Example 3 are reversed.

12. Determine the equation for the total current when an emf described by the equation

$$e = 180 \sin 377t - 60 \sin 1131t + 36 \sin 1885t$$

is applied to a circuit consisting of two parallel branches. Branch I has an impedance of 90 ohms $\underline{/-60°}$ at the fundamental frequency and Branch II has an impedance of $40 + j30$ ohms at the fundamental frequency.

## Review Questions

1. Suggest several reasons why it is desirable to obtain a pure sine wave source of emf for electric power distribution systems.

2. Define the terms **fundamental** and **harmonic**.

3. Why is it possible to describe the shape of a nonsinusoidal wave by an equation such as Equation (20.1)?

4. What is the significance of a $-$ sign in front of a term in the equation for a nonsinusoidal wave?

5. What is the significance of a cosine term in the equation for a nonsinusoidal wave?

6. How would you describe the phase relationship among the fundamental and the harmonics shown in Fig. 20.2?

7. Why is it usually possible to obtain a fairly good duplication of a nonsinusoidal wave by considering only the first five or six terms of the harmonic series?

8. What is the distinction between the odd and even order of harmonics in governing the shape of nonsinusoidal waves?

9. What is meant by a **linear bilateral** circuit element? Give several examples.

10. What is meant by a **unilateral** circuit element?

11. Give an example of a nonlinear bilateral circuit element.

12. When a vacuum tube introduces harmonic distortion into a circuit, where do these harmonics which are not present in the input wave come from?

13. If a vacuum tube amplifier is developing 8% second harmonic distortion and 6% third harmonic distortion, what is the percentage total harmonic distortion?

14. The waveforms shown for the transformer in Fig. 20.8 are based on a sine wave *voltage* source. Draw the waveforms which apply when the transformer is fed from a sine wave *current* source. What order of harmonics is introduced?

15. The **BH** curve transfer characteristic in Fig. 20.8 is based on only alternating current in the primary. Draw a similar sketch to show the appearance of the flux waveform when the transformer primary is connected in series with the plate of a pentode type vacuum tube in which the plate current varies in a sinusoidal manner about its quiescent value. What order of harmonics are introduced by such an output transformer?

16. Why does none of the third harmonic content of the exciting current in the primary windings of a three-phase delta connected transformer bank appear in the line current?

17. Why does the seventh harmonic content of the line current to a delta connected transformer bank have the customary $\sqrt{3}$ relationship to the seventh harmonic current in the transformer primary windings?

18. Suggest why the harmonic content of an alternator emf contains odd order harmonics rather than even order harmonics.

19. What percentage of the ninth harmonic induced into an alternator winding will appear in the line voltage of a wye connected three-phase source?

20. A symmetrical square wave of voltage has a peak value of 100 v. What is its effective value?

21. What effect does reversing the sign in front of the even order harmonic terms of Equation (20.9) have on the shape of the complex wave?

22. A certain amplifier advances the phase of a 500 c sine wave by 2°. In order to pass a complex wave without changing its shape, this amplifier must have a 4° phase advance at 1 kc, a 6° phase advance at 1.5 kc, etc. Explain.

23. Explain the significance of the superposition theorem in solving linear a-c networks which are fed from nonsinusoidal sources of emf.

24. The output waveform in Example 3 is taken across a resistor whose resistance is not dependent on frequency. Why then does the output waveform not have the same shape as the input waveform?

# ANSWERS TO PROBLEMS

## CHAPTER 1

**1.** $2.5 \times 10^4$ m. **3.** $8.999 \times 10^{-28}$ g. **5.** 1.65 kg. **7.** 16.67 msec. **9.** 400 sq cm. **11.** 432 cu in. **13.** 1 mi = 1.609 km. **15.** 1 sq ft = 0.0929 sq m. **17.** 22.35 m/sec. **19.** 0.05 in.

## CHAPTER 2

**1.** $2.23 \times 10^5$ coulomb. **3.** 2.1 coulomb. **5.** 5 amp. **7.** 18 coulomb. **9.** 32 sec. **11.** 0.43 in./sec. **13.** 0.25 v. **15.** 0.3 joule. **17.** 16 joules. **19.** 150 ma.

## CHAPTER 3

**1.** 48 ohms. **3.** 22 ohms. **5.** 5 amp. **7.** 8.17 amp. **9.** 45 v. **11.** 89.6 v. **13.** 2 kilohms. **15.** 583 ohms. **17.** 25 ma. **19.** 218 $\mu$a. **21.** 4.4 v. **23.** 35.1 mv. **25.** $1.724 \times 10^{-8}$ ohm-meters. **27.** 18 kilohms. **29.** 1.25 ohms. **31.** 0.0324 ohm. **33.** $3.23 \times 10^{-5}$ ohm. **35.** 8.38 ohms. **37.** AWG 30. **39.** 4.34 ohms. **41.** 25.5 ohms. **43.** 2.38 ohms. **45.** 0.002. **47.** 8.15 ohms. **49.** tungsten.

## CHAPTER 4

**1.** $2.034 \times 10^6$ joules. **3.** $5.28 \times 10^5$ joules. **5.** 81.4%. **7.** 167 kw. **9.** 0.0784 hp. **11.** 8.8 min. **13.** 600 w. **15.** 3.78 w. **17.** 469 w. **19.** 0.04 w. **21.** 1 w rating (0.726 w). **23.** 320 w. **25.** 22.3 ma. **27.** 200 v. **29.** 120 v. **31.** 16.58 amp. **33.** 30 ohms. **35.** 5.89 w. **37.** 18 kw-hr. **39.** $66\frac{1}{4}$¢.

## CHAPTER 5

**1.** 30 ohms. **3.** 20 v; 40 v; 60 v. **5.** 0.923 ohm; 40 w. **7.** 90 ohms; 100 ohms. **9.** 3888 v. **11.** 119 ohms. **13.** (a) 4.8 v; (b) 59.5 w; (c) 75%; (d) 180w. **15.** (a) 13.8 kv; (b) 13.2 kv; (c) $7\frac{1}{2}$ ma. **17.** 0.5 ohm. **19.** 411.4 w. **21.** 44 amp. **23.** 1.333 ohms. **25.** 2.5 kilohms; 909 ohms. **27.** 30 kilohms. **29.** 9.23 ma; 6.15 ma; 4.62 ma. **37.** 600 ohms. **39.** 10.44 v (or 0.96 v). **41.** 155.35 v. **43.** 10 kilohms. **45.** 1.3 megohms; 1 megohm. **47.** $R_1 = 2.97$ kilohms, 3.04 w; $R_2 = 5$ kilohms, $4\frac{1}{2}$ w; $R_3 = 100$ ohms, $\frac{1}{4}$ w.

## CHAPTER 6

**1.** $4\frac{1}{4}$ amp.   **3.** 2.43 amp.   **5.** $I_A = 363$ ma; $I_B = 116.6$ ma.   **7.** 4 v.   **13.** 620 ohms.   **15.** $12\frac{1}{2}$ amp.   **17.** 573 v.   **19.** 235 ma.   **21.** 117.7 ma.   **23.** 3.64 ma. **25.** 48.9 v.

## CHAPTER 7

**5.** 500 AT/weber.   **7.** 480 ma.   **9.** $2.54 \times 10^8$ AT/weber.   **11.** $4 \times 10^{-4}$ mks units.   **13.** $5 \times 10^{-4}$ mks units.   **15.** $2.5 \times 10^{-3}$ mks units.   **17.** $9 \times 10^{-5}$ mks units.   **19.** $3\frac{1}{4}$ amp.   **21.** $3.69 \times 10^{-7}$ webers.   **23.** $6\frac{1}{4}$ amp.   **25.** 400 ma (approx.).   **27.** 248 lb.   **29.** 600 turns (approx.).

## CHAPTER 8

**1.** 0.59 newtons.   **3.** 0.05025 ohm.   **5.** 0.450125 ohm; 0.0451225 ohm; 0.0050026 ohm.   **7.** 199 kilohms; 800 kilohms; 1 megohm; 8 megohms.   **9.** 10.909 v.   **11.** 30 kilohms.   **13.** 120 kilohms.   **15.** 550 megohms.   **17.** 210 kilohms. **19.** 40.86 ohms.

## CHAPTER 9

**1.** $\frac{1}{4}$ h.   **3.** 333 v.   **5.** 7.888 $\mu$h.   **7.** 2.63 h.   **9.** 270 turns.   **11.** (a) 20 amp; (b) 0.1 sec.   **13.** 6.77 v.   **15.** (a) 96 ma; (b) 4.8 amp/sec; (c) 137 ma; (d) 206 ma; (e) 1/7 sec; (f) 257 v; (g) 1/15 sec; (h) 22.6 msec.

## CHAPTER 10

**1.** $8 \times 10^{-15}$ newton.   **3.** 17.8 $\mu\mu$f.   **5.** 13.9 $\mu\mu$f.   **7.** 0.0014 $\mu$f.   **9.** (a) 50 $\mu$f; (b) 4 millicoulomb; 16 millicoulomb; (c) 4 joules.   **11.** (a) 5.71 $\mu$f; (b) 2.286 millicoulomb; (c) 228.6 v, 114.3 v, 57.1 v.   **13.** 27.8 $\mu\mu$f.   **15.** (a) 1.25 ma; (b) 0 v; (c) 62.5 v/sec; (d) 4 sec; (e) 20 sec; (f) 178 v; (g) 0.76 ma; (h) 2.8 sec.

## CHAPTER 11

**1.** 106 v.   **3.** 126 v.   **5.** $-88$ v.   **7.** 8.5 v.   **9.** $e = 200 \sin 2512t$.   **11.** 325 v. **13.** 4.7 amp.   **15.** 160 v.   **17.** 41.7 min.   **19.** 4.8 v.

## CHAPTER 12

**1.** $+j29.25$ ohms.   **3.** $-j16,667$ ohms.   **5.** $+j1,508$ ohms.   **7.** $-j7,960$ ohms. **9.** 637 c.   **11.** 470 $\mu$h.   **13.** 124.5 c.   **15.** 7.96 $\mu$f.   **17.** 215 $\mu$h.

## CHAPTER 13

**1.** 280 v.   **3.** 80.5 amp.   **5.** 0 v.   **7.** 25.9 $\underline{/-5°}$.   **9.** (a) $+20 + j15$; (b) $-27.6 + j23.1$; (c) $+89 - j154$; (d) $-30 - j52$; (e) $-5.9 + j12.9$; (f) $+5.5 + j4.0$.   **11.** $26.4\underline{/+24.6°}$.   **13.** $198\underline{/+226.3°}$.   **15.** $134.3\underline{/+78.25°}$.   **17.** $0.822\underline{/-16.2°}$.   **19.** $53.3\underline{/-51°}$; $0.315\underline{/-77°}$.   **21.** 10.75 ohms $\underline{/-30°}$.

## CHAPTER 14

**1.** 100 v $\underline{/-36.9°}$.   **3.** (a) 133 ohms $\underline{/+72°}$ (b) $41.2 + j126.8$ ohms.   **5.** 842 ohms $\underline{/+53.6°}$.   **7.** (a) 411 ohms; (b) 56.8°.   **9.** 150 ohms $\underline{/+48.2°}$.   **11.** (a) 0.00133 mho $\underline{/+70°}$; (b) $256 - j703$ ohms.   **13.** 48 ohms; 0.292 h.   **15.** $6\frac{1}{2}$ $\mu$f. **17.** 2.32 $\mu$f.   **19.** 42 ohms; 1 h.

## CHAPTER 15

**1.** (a) 660 w; (b) 1320 w. **3.** 150 w. **5.** (a) 0 w; (b) 0.452 vars; (c) 0.452 w. **7.** (a) 76 va; (b) 9.6 w; (c) 12.6% lagging. **9.** 10.4 ohms; 0.0366 h. **11.** (a) 24.24 amp; (b) 2.67 kw. **13.** $147\frac{1}{2}$ v. **15.** (a) 46 $\mu$f; (b) 6 amp, 3.6 amp, 4.8 amp. **17.** 99.8% leading. **19.** 682 w.

## CHAPTER 16

**1.** 1119 ohms $\underline{/+45.3°}$. **3.** 0.0035 mho $\underline{/-29.6°}$. **5.** (a) 1.07 amp $\underline{/-48°}$; (b) 228 v $\underline{/+14°}$. **7.** 519 ohms; 0.53 $\mu$f. **9.** 416 ohms; 0.703 h. **11.** 64.2 ohms $\underline{/+15.9°}$. **13.** .092 amp $\underline{/+18°}$. **15.** 84.5 ohms. **17.** 8.4°. **19.** 940 $\mu\mu$f; 9.15 megohm. **21.** $2.88 + j1695$ ohms. **23.** 54.5 ma. **25.** 1.67 kilohms $\underline{/-89.1°}$, 8.33 kilohms $\underline{/-89.1°}$, 83.3 kilohms $\underline{/+0.9°}$.

## CHAPTER 17

**1.** 2.66 megacycles. **3.** 40 mv. **5.** 234 $\mu\mu$f. **7.** 101. **9.** 2.66 megacycles. **11.** 0.333 $\mu$a. **13.** (a) 239 $\mu$h; (b) 1.89 megacycles. **15.** 0.44 $\mu$f. **17.** 88 $\mu$h; 523 $\mu$h.

## CHAPTER 18

**1.** 17. **3.** 107 v. **5.** 560 turns. **7.** 705 turns. **9.** 144 ma. **11.** 5620 ohms. **13.** (a) 34.7 ohms; (b) 8.7 ohms. **15.** 953 v. **17.** 0.138 h. **19.** 1200 ohms $\underline{/-72.3°}$.

## CHAPTER 19

**1.** (b) 12 amp $\underline{/0°}$, 12 amp $\underline{/+120°}$, 12 amp $\underline{/-120°}$; (d) zero. **3.** (b) 4 amp $\underline{/-30°}$, 3 amp $\underline{/+150°}$, 2.4 amp $\underline{/-30°}$; (d) 3.4 amp $\underline{/-30°}$. **5.** (b) 50 amp $\underline{/0°}$, 50 amp $\underline{/+120°}$, 50 amp $\underline{/-120°}$; (e) 86.5 amp $\underline{/-30°}$, 86.5 amp $\underline{/+90°}$, 86.5 amp $\underline{/-150°}$. **7.** (b) 110 amp $\underline{/-45°}$, 55 amp $\underline{/-83.1°}$, 50 amp $\underline{/+120°}$; (e) 159 amp $\underline{/-49.6°}$, 103 amp $\underline{/+107.9°}$, 75 amp $\underline{/+162°}$. **9.** (c) 208 v $\underline{/+30°}$, 208 v $\underline{/-90°}$, 208 v $\underline{/+150°}$; (d) 18.9 amp $\underline{/+30°}$, 18.9 amp $\underline{/-90°}$, 18.9 amp $\underline{/+150°}$; (e) 32.7 amp $\underline{/0°}$, 32.7 amp $\underline{/-120°}$, 32.7 amp $\underline{/120°}$. **11.** (a) 208 v $\underline{/30°}$, 208 v $\underline{/-90°}$, 208 v $\underline{/+150°}$; (b) 41.6 amp $\underline{/-15°}$, 20.8 amp $\underline{/-53.1°}$, 18.9 amp $\underline{/+150°}$; (e) 60 amp $\underline{/-19.7°}$, 39 amp $\underline{/+137.9°}$, 28.3 amp $\underline{/-168°}$. **13.** 4.32 kw. **15.** 728 w. **17.** *CBA*. **19.** 2.16 kw. **21.** 2.16 kw. **23.** 41.25 kw. **25.** (a) 3 kw; (b) 86.6%; (c) 9.6 amp; (d) 37.5 ohms $\underline{/30°}$; (e) 60°. **27.** 31.8 amp $\underline{/-30°}$, 31.8 amp $\underline{/+90°}$, 31.8 amp $\underline{/-150°}$. **29.** 5.9 amp $\underline{/+12.6°}$, 1.31 amp $\underline{/-167.4°}$, 4.58 amp $\underline{/-167.4°}$.

## CHAPTER 20

**7.** 102.5 v. **8.** 17.3 v. **9.** 6.67%. **10.** (a) 957 ma; (b) 46 w; (c) 47% lagging.

# APPENDICES

## GREEK ALPHABET

BECAUSE physicists, mathematicians, and engineers invariably use certain letters of the Greek alphabet as symbols to denote particular physical and geometrical quantities, we follow this convenient practice. For reference, the letters of the Greek alphabet, in lower and upper case, together with their names, are given below:

| | | | | | | | |
|---|---|---|---|---|---|---|---|
| $\alpha$ | A | alpha | $\iota$ | I | iota | $\rho$ P | rho |
| $\beta$ | B | beta | $\kappa$ | K | kappa | $\sigma$ $\Sigma$ | sigma |
| $\gamma$ | $\Gamma$ | gamma | $\lambda$ | $\Lambda$ | lambda | $\tau$ T | tau |
| $\delta$ | $\Delta$ | delta | $\mu$ | M | mu | $\upsilon$ $\Upsilon$ | upsilon |
| $\epsilon$ | E | epsilon | $\nu$ | N | nu | $\phi$ $\Phi$ | phi |
| $\zeta$ | Z | zeta | $\xi$ | $\Xi$ | xi | $\chi$ X | chi |
| $\eta$ | H | eta | $o$ | O | omicron | $\psi$ $\Psi$ | psi |
| $\theta$ | $\Theta$ | theta | $\pi$ | $\Pi$ | pi | $\omega$ $\Omega$ | omega |

461

# TABLE OF EXPONENTIALS
$$e^{-x}$$

| x | | 0 | 1 | 2 | 3 | 4 | 5 | 6 | 7 | 8 | 9 |
|---|---|---|---|---|---|---|---|---|---|---|---|
| 0.0 | | 1.000 | .9900 | .9802 | .9704 | .9608 | .9512 | .9418 | .9324 | .9231 | .9139 |
| 0.1 | | .9048 | .8958 | .8869 | .8781 | .8694 | .8607 | .8521 | .8437 | .8353 | .8270 |
| 0.2 | | .8187 | .8106 | .8025 | .7945 | .7866 | .7788 | .7711 | .7634 | .7558 | .7483 |
| 0.3 | | .7408 | .7334 | .7261 | .7189 | .7118 | .7047 | .6977 | .6907 | .6839 | .6771 |
| 0.4 | | .6703 | .6637 | .6570 | .6505 | .6440 | .6376 | .6313 | .6250 | .6188 | .6126 |
| 0.5 | | .6065 | .6005 | .5945 | .5886 | .5827 | .5769 | .5712 | .5655 | .5599 | .5543 |
| 0.6 | | .5488 | .5434 | .5379 | .5326 | .5273 | .5220 | .5169 | .5117 | .5066 | .5016 |
| 0.7 | | .4966 | .4916 | .4868 | .4819 | .4771 | .4724 | .4677 | .4630 | .4584 | .4538 |
| 0.8 | | .4493 | .4449 | .4404 | .4360 | .4317 | .4274 | .4232 | .4190 | .4148 | .4107 |
| 0.9 | | .4066 | .4025 | .3985 | .3946 | .3906 | .3867 | .3829 | .3791 | .3753 | .3716 |
| 1.0 | | .3679 | .3642 | .3606 | .3570 | .3535 | .3499 | .3465 | .3430 | .3396 | .3362 |
| 1.1 | | .3329 | .3296 | .3263 | .3230 | .3198 | .3166 | .3135 | .3104 | .3073 | .3042 |
| 1.2 | | .3012 | .2982 | .2952 | .2923 | .2894 | .2865 | .2837 | .2808 | .2780 | .2753 |
| 1.3 | | .2725 | .2698 | .2671 | .2645 | .2618 | .2592 | .2567 | .2541 | .2516 | .2491 |
| 1.4 | | .2466 | .2441 | .2417 | .2393 | .2369 | .2346 | .2322 | .2299 | .2276 | .2254 |
| 1.5 | | .2231 | .2209 | .2187 | .2165 | .2144 | .2122 | .2101 | .2080 | .2060 | .2039 |
| 1.6 | | .2019 | .1999 | .1979 | .1959 | .1940 | .1920 | .1901 | .1882 | .1864 | .1845 |
| 1.7 | | .1827 | .1809 | .1791 | .1773 | .1755 | .1738 | .1720 | .1703 | .1686 | .1670 |
| 1.8 | | .1653 | .1637 | .1620 | .1604 | .1588 | .1572 | .1557 | .1541 | .1526 | .1511 |
| 1.9 | | .1496 | .1481 | .1466 | .1451 | .1437 | .1423 | .1409 | .1395 | .1381 | .1367 |
| 2.0 | | .1353 | .1340 | .1327 | .1313 | .1300 | .1287 | .1275 | .1262 | .1249 | .1237 |
| 2.1 | | .1225 | .1212 | .1200 | .1188 | .1177 | .1165 | .1153 | .1142 | .1130 | .1119 |
| 2.2 | | .1108 | .1097 | .1086 | .1075 | .1065 | .1054 | .1043 | .1033 | .1023 | .1013 |
| 2.3 | | .1003 | *9926 | *9827 | *9730 | *9633 | *9537 | *9442 | *9348 | *9255 | *9163 |
| 2.4 | 0.0 | 9072 | 8982 | 8892 | 8804 | 8716 | 8629 | 8544 | 8458 | 8374 | 8291 |
| 2.5 | 0.0 | 8208 | 8127 | 8046 | 7966 | 7887 | 7808 | 7730 | 7654 | 7577 | 7502 |
| 2.6 | 0.0 | 7427 | 7353 | 7280 | 7208 | 7136 | 7065 | 6995 | 6925 | 6856 | 6788 |
| 2.7 | 0.0 | 6721 | 6654 | 6587 | 6522 | 6457 | 6393 | 6329 | 6266 | 6204 | 6142 |
| 2.8 | 0.0 | 6081 | 6020 | 5961 | 5901 | 5843 | 5784 | 5727 | 5670 | 5613 | 5558 |
| 2.9 | 0.0 | 5502 | 5448 | 5393 | 5340 | 5287 | 5234 | 5182 | 5130 | 5079 | 5029 |
| 3.0 | 0.0 | 4979 | 4929 | 4880 | 4832 | 4783 | 4736 | 4689 | 4642 | 4596 | 4550 |
| 3.1 | 0.0 | 4505 | 4460 | 4416 | 4372 | 4328 | 4285 | 4243 | 4200 | 4159 | 4117 |
| 3.2 | 0.0 | 4076 | 4036 | 3996 | 3956 | 3916 | 3877 | 3839 | 3801 | 3763 | 3725 |
| 3.3 | 0.0 | 3688 | 3652 | 3615 | 3579 | 3544 | 3508 | 3474 | 3439 | 3405 | 3371 |
| 3.4 | 0.0 | 3337 | 3304 | 3271 | 3239 | 3206 | 3175 | 3143 | 3112 | 3081 | 3050 |

| x | | .0 | .1 | .2 | .3 | .4 | .5 | .6 | .7 | .8 | .9 |
|---|---|---|---|---|---|---|---|---|---|---|---|
| 3 | 0.0 | 4979 | 4505 | 4076 | 3688 | 3337 | 3020 | 2732 | 2472 | 2237 | 2024 |
| 4 | 0.0 | 1832 | 1657 | 1500 | 1357 | 1228 | 1111 | 1005 | *9095 | 2237 | *7447 |
| 5 | 0.00 | 6738 | 6097 | 5517 | 4992 | 4517 | 4087 | 3698 | 3346 | *8230 | 2739 |
| 6 | 0.00 | 2479 | 2243 | 2029 | 1836 | 1662 | 1503 | 1360 | 1231 | 1114 | 1008 |
| 7 | 0.000 | 9119 | 8251 | 7466 | 6755 | 6112 | 5531 | 5004 | 4528 | 4097 | 3707 |
| 8 | 0.000 | 3355 | 3035 | 2747 | 2485 | 2249 | 2035 | 1841 | 1666 | 1507 | 1364 |
| 9 | 0.000 | 1234 | 1117 | 1010 | *9142 | *8272 | *7485 | *6773 | *6128 | *5545 | *5017 |
| 10 | 0.0000 | 4540 | 4108 | 3717 | 3363 | 3043 | 2754 | 2492 | 2254 | 2040 | 1846 |

$$\log_{10}e^{-x} = -x\log_{10}e = -0.43429\,x$$

# NATURAL TRIGONOMETRIC FUNCTIONS: SINE

## Angles from 0°0 to 44°9

|  | .0 | .1 | .2 | .3 | .4 | .5 | .6 | .7 | .8 | .9 |
|---|---|---|---|---|---|---|---|---|---|---|
| 0° | .0000 | .0017 | .0035 | .0052 | .0070 | .0087 | .0105 | .0122 | .0140 | .0157 |
| 1° | .0175 | .0192 | .0209 | .0227 | .0244 | .0262 | .0279 | .0297 | .0314 | .0332 |
| 2° | .0349 | .0366 | .0384 | .0401 | .0419 | .0436 | .0454 | .0471 | .0488 | .0506 |
| 3° | .0523 | .0541 | .0558 | .0576 | .0593 | .0610 | .0628 | .0645 | .0663 | .0680 |
| 4° | .0698 | .0715 | .0732 | .0750 | .0767 | .0785 | .0802 | .0819 | .0837 | .0854 |
| 5° | .0872 | .0889 | .0906 | .0924 | .0941 | .0958 | .0976 | .0993 | .1011 | .1028 |
| 6° | .1045 | .1063 | .1080 | .1097 | .1115 | .1132 | .1149 | .1167 | .1184 | .1201 |
| 7° | .1219 | .1236 | .1253 | .1271 | .1288 | .1305 | .1323 | .1340 | .1357 | .1374 |
| 8° | .1392 | .1409 | .1426 | .1444 | .1461 | .1478 | .1495 | .1513 | .1530 | .1547 |
| 9° | .1564 | .1582 | .1599 | .1616 | .1633 | .1650 | .1668 | .1685 | .1702 | .1719 |
| 10° | .1736 | .1754 | .1771 | .1788 | .1805 | .1822 | .1840 | .1857 | .1874 | .1891 |
| 11° | .1908 | .1925 | .1942 | .1959 | .1977 | .1994 | .2011 | .2028 | .2045 | .2062 |
| 12° | .2079 | .2096 | .2113 | .2130 | .2147 | .2164 | .2181 | .2198 | .2215 | .2233 |
| 13° | .2250 | .2267 | .2284 | .2300 | .2317 | .2334 | .2351 | .2368 | .2385 | .2402 |
| 14° | .2419 | .2436 | .2453 | .2470 | .2487 | .2504 | .2521 | .2538 | .2554 | .2571 |
| 15° | .2588 | .2605 | .2622 | .2639 | .2656 | .2672 | .2689 | .2706 | .2723 | .2740 |
| 16° | .2756 | .2773 | .2790 | .2807 | .2823 | .2840 | .2857 | .2874 | .2890 | .2907 |
| 17° | .2924 | .2940 | .2957 | .2974 | .2990 | .3007 | .3024 | .3040 | .3057 | .3074 |
| 18° | .3090 | .3107 | .3123 | .3140 | .3156 | .3173 | .3190 | .3206 | .3223 | .3239 |
| 19° | .3256 | .3272 | .3289 | .3305 | .3322 | .3338 | .3355 | .3371 | .3387 | .3404 |
| 20° | .3420 | .3437 | .3453 | .3469 | .3486 | .3502 | .3518 | .3535 | .3551 | .3567 |
| 21° | .3584 | .3600 | .3616 | .3633 | .3649 | .3665 | .3681 | .3697 | .3714 | .3730 |
| 22° | .3746 | .3762 | .3778 | .3795 | .3811 | .3827 | .3843 | .3859 | .3875 | .3891 |
| 23° | .3907 | .3923 | .3939 | .3955 | .3971 | .3987 | .4003 | .4019 | .4035 | .4051 |
| 24° | .4067 | .4083 | .4099 | .4115 | .4131 | .4147 | .4163 | .4179 | .4195 | .4210 |
| 25° | .4226 | .4242 | .4258 | .4274 | .4289 | .4305 | .4321 | .4337 | .4352 | .4368 |
| 26° | .4384 | .4399 | .4415 | .4431 | .4446 | .4462 | .4478 | .4493 | .4509 | .4524 |
| 27° | .4540 | .4555 | .4571 | .4586 | .4602 | .4617 | .4633 | .4648 | .4664 | .4679 |
| 28° | .4695 | .4710 | .4726 | .4741 | .4756 | .4772 | .4787 | .4802 | .4818 | .4833 |
| 29° | .4848 | .4863 | .4879 | .4894 | .4909 | .4924 | .4939 | .4955 | .4970 | .4985 |
| 30° | .5000 | .5015 | .5030 | .5045 | .5060 | .5075 | .5090 | .5105 | .5120 | .5135 |
| 31° | .5150 | .5165 | .5180 | .5195 | .5210 | .5225 | .5240 | .5255 | .5270 | .5284 |
| 32° | .5299 | .5314 | .5329 | .5344 | .5358 | .5373 | .5388 | .5402 | .5417 | .5432 |
| 33° | .5446 | .5461 | .5476 | .5490 | .5505 | .5519 | .5534 | .5548 | .5563 | .5577 |
| 34° | .5592 | .5606 | .5621 | .5635 | .5650 | .5664 | .5678 | .5693 | .5707 | .5721 |
| 35° | .5736 | .5750 | .5764 | .5779 | .5793 | .5807 | .5821 | .5835 | .5850 | .5864 |
| 36° | .5878 | .5892 | .5906 | .5920 | .5934 | .5948 | .5962 | .5976 | .5990 | .6004 |
| 37° | .6018 | .6032 | .6046 | .6060 | .6074 | .6088 | .6101 | .6115 | .6129 | .6143 |
| 38° | .6157 | .6170 | .6184 | .6198 | .6211 | .6225 | .6239 | .6252 | .6266 | .6280 |
| 39° | .6293 | .6307 | .6320 | .6334 | .6347 | .6361 | .6374 | .6388 | .6401 | .6414 |
| 40° | .6428 | .6441 | .6455 | .6468 | .6481 | .6494 | .6508 | .6521 | .6534 | .6547 |
| 41° | .6561 | .6574 | .6587 | .6600 | .6613 | .6626 | .6639 | .6652 | .6665 | .6678 |
| 42° | .6691 | .6704 | .6717 | .6730 | .6743 | .6756 | .6769 | .6782 | .6794 | .6807 |
| 43° | .6820 | .6833 | .6845 | .6858 | .6871 | .6884 | .6896 | .6909 | .6921 | .6934 |
| 44° | .6947 | .6959 | .6972 | .6984 | .6997 | .7009 | .7022 | .7034 | .7046 | .7059 |

# NATURAL TRIGONOMETRIC FUNCTIONS: SINE

## Angles from 45°.0 to 89°.9

| | .0 | .1 | .2 | .3 | .4 | .5 | .6 | .7 | .8 | .9 |
|---|---|---|---|---|---|---|---|---|---|---|
| 45° | .7071 | .7083 | .7096 | .7108 | .7120 | .7133 | .7145 | .7157 | .7169 | .7181 |
| 46° | .7193 | .7206 | .7218 | .7230 | .7242 | .7254 | .7266 | .7278 | .7290 | .7302 |
| 47° | .7314 | .7325 | .7337 | .7349 | .7361 | .7373 | .7385 | .7396 | .7408 | .7420 |
| 48° | .7431 | .7443 | .7455 | .7466 | .7478 | .7490 | .7501 | .7513 | .7524 | .7536 |
| 49° | .7547 | .7559 | .7570 | .7581 | .7593 | .7604 | .7615 | .7627 | .7638 | .7649 |
| 50° | .7660 | .7672 | .7683 | .7694 | .7705 | .7716 | .7727 | .7738 | .7749 | .7760 |
| 51° | .7771 | .7782 | .7793 | .7804 | .7815 | .7826 | .7837 | .7848 | .7859 | .7869 |
| 52° | .7880 | .7891 | .7902 | .7912 | .7923 | .7934 | .7944 | .7955 | .7965 | .7976 |
| 53° | .7986 | .7997 | .8007 | .8018 | .8028 | .8039 | .8049 | .8059 | .8070 | .8080 |
| 54° | .8090 | .8100 | .8111 | .8121 | .8131 | .8141 | .8151 | .8161 | .8171 | .8181 |
| 55° | .8192 | .8202 | .8211 | .8221 | .8231 | .8241 | .8251 | .8261 | .8271 | .8281 |
| 56° | .8290 | .8300 | .8310 | .8320 | .8329 | .8339 | .8348 | .8358 | .8368 | .8377 |
| 57° | .8387 | .8396 | .8406 | .8415 | .8425 | .8434 | .8443 | .8453 | .8462 | .8471 |
| 58° | .8480 | .8490 | .8499 | .8508 | .8517 | .8526 | .8536 | .8545 | .8554 | .8563 |
| 59° | .8572 | .8581 | .8590 | .8599 | .8607 | .8616 | .8625 | .8634 | .8643 | .8652 |
| 60° | .8660 | .8669 | .8678 | .8686 | .8695 | .8704 | .8712 | .8721 | .8729 | .8738 |
| 61° | .8746 | .8755 | .8763 | .8771 | .8780 | .8788 | .8796 | .8805 | .8813 | .8821 |
| 62° | .8829 | .8838 | .8846 | .8854 | .8862 | .8870 | .8878 | .8886 | .8894 | .8902 |
| 63° | .8910 | .8918 | .8926 | .8934 | .8942 | .8949 | .8957 | .8965 | .8973 | .8980 |
| 64° | .8988 | .8996 | .9003 | .9011 | .9018 | .9026 | .9033 | .9041 | .9048 | .9056 |
| 65° | .9063 | .9070 | .9078 | .9085 | .9092 | .9100 | .9107 | .9114 | .9121 | .9128 |
| 66° | .9135 | .9143 | .9150 | .9157 | .9164 | .9171 | .9178 | .9184 | .9191 | .9198 |
| 67° | .9205 | .9212 | .9219 | .9225 | .9232 | .9239 | .9245 | .9252 | .9259 | .9265 |
| 68° | .9272 | .9278 | .9285 | .9291 | .9298 | .9304 | .9311 | .9317 | .9323 | .9330 |
| 69° | .9336 | .9342 | .9348 | .9354 | .9361 | .9367 | .9373 | .9379 | .9385 | .9391 |
| 70° | .9397 | .9403 | .9409 | .9415 | .9421 | .9426 | .9432 | .9438 | .9444 | .9449 |
| 71° | .9455 | .9461 | .9466 | .9472 | .9478 | .9483 | .9489 | .9494 | .9500 | .9505 |
| 72° | .9511 | .9516 | .9521 | .9527 | .9532 | .9537 | .9542 | .9548 | .9553 | .9558 |
| 73° | .9563 | .9568 | .9573 | .9578 | .9583 | .9588 | .9593 | .9598 | .9603 | .9608 |
| 74° | .9613 | .9617 | .9622 | .9627 | .9632 | .9636 | .9641 | .9646 | .9650 | .9655 |
| 75° | .9659 | .9664 | .9668 | .9673 | .9677 | .9681 | .9686 | .9690 | .9694 | .9699 |
| 76° | .9703 | .9707 | .9711 | .9715 | .9720 | .9724 | .9728 | .9732 | .9736 | .9740 |
| 77° | .9744 | .9748 | .9751 | .9755 | .9759 | .9763 | .9767 | .9770 | .9774 | .9778 |
| 78° | .9781 | .9785 | .9789 | .9792 | .9796 | .9799 | .9803 | .9806 | .9810 | .9813 |
| 79° | .9816 | .9820 | .9823 | .9826 | .9829 | .9833 | .9836 | .9839 | .9842 | .9845 |
| 80° | .9848 | .9851 | .9854 | .9857 | .9860 | .9863 | .9866 | .9869 | .9871 | .9874 |
| 81° | .9877 | .9880 | .9882 | .9885 | .9888 | .9890 | .9893 | .9895 | .9898 | .9900 |
| 82° | .9903 | .9905 | .9907 | .9910 | .9912 | .9914 | .9917 | .9919 | .9921 | .9923 |
| 83° | .9925 | .9928 | .9930 | .9932 | .9934 | .9936 | .9938 | .9940 | .9942 | .9943 |
| 84° | .9945 | .9947 | .9949 | .9951 | .9952 | .9954 | .9956 | .9957 | .9959 | .9960 |
| 85° | .9962 | .9963 | .9965 | .9966 | .9968 | .9969 | .9971 | .9972 | .9973 | .9974 |
| 86° | .9976 | .9977 | .9978 | .9979 | .9980 | .9981 | .9982 | .9983 | .9984 | .9985 |
| 87° | .9986 | .9987 | .9988 | .9989 | .9990 | .9990 | .9991 | .9992 | .9993 | .9993 |
| 88° | .9994 | .9995 | .9995 | .9996 | .9996 | .9997 | .9997 | .9997 | .9998 | .9998 |
| 89° | .9998 | .9999 | .9999 | .9999 | .9999 | 1.000 | 1.000 | 1.000 | 1.000 | 1.000 |

# NATURAL TRIGONOMETRIC FUNCTIONS: COSINE

## Angles from 0°.0 to 44°.9

|  | .0 | .1 | .2 | .3 | .4 | .5 | .6 | .7 | .8 | .9 |
|---|---|---|---|---|---|---|---|---|---|---|
| 0° | 1.0000 | 1.0000 | 1.0000 | 1.0000 | 1.0000 | 1.0000 | .9999 | .9999 | .9999 | .9999 |
| 1° | .9998 | .9998 | .9998 | .9997 | .9997 | .9997 | .9996 | .9996 | .9995 | .9995 |
| 2° | .9994 | .9993 | .9993 | .9992 | .9991 | .9990 | .9990 | .9989 | .9988 | .9987 |
| 3° | .9986 | .9985 | .9984 | .9983 | .9982 | .9981 | .9980 | .9979 | .9978 | .9977 |
| 4° | .9976 | .9974 | .9973 | .9972 | .9971 | .9969 | .9968 | .9966 | .9965 | .9963 |
| 5° | .9962 | .9960 | .9959 | .9957 | .9956 | .9954 | .9952 | .9951 | .9949 | .9947 |
| 6° | .9945 | .9943 | .9942 | .9940 | .9938 | .9936 | .9934 | .9932 | .9930 | .9928 |
| 7° | .9925 | .9923 | .9921 | .9919 | .9917 | .9914 | .9912 | .9910 | .9907 | .9905 |
| 8° | .9903 | .9900 | .9898 | .9895 | .9893 | .9890 | .9888 | .9885 | .9882 | .9880 |
| 9° | .9877 | .9874 | .9871 | .9869 | .9866 | .9863 | .9860 | .9857 | .9854 | .9851 |
| 10° | .9848 | .9845 | .9842 | .9839 | .9836 | .9833 | .9829 | .9826 | .9823 | .9820 |
| 11° | .9816 | .9813 | .9810 | .9806 | .9803 | .9799 | .9796 | .9792 | .9789 | .9785 |
| 12° | .9781 | .9778 | .9774 | .9770 | .9767 | .9763 | .9759 | .9755 | .9751 | .9748 |
| 13° | .9744 | .9740 | .9736 | .9732 | .9728 | .9724 | .9720 | .9715 | .9711 | .9707 |
| 14° | .9703 | .9699 | .9694 | .9690 | .9686 | .9681 | .9677 | .9673 | .9668 | .9664 |
| 15° | .9659 | .9655 | .9650 | .9646 | .9641 | .9636 | .9632 | .9627 | .9622 | .9617 |
| 16° | .9613 | .9608 | .9603 | .9598 | .9593 | .9588 | .9583 | .9578 | .9573 | .9568 |
| 17° | .9563 | .9558 | .9553 | .9548 | .9542 | .9537 | .9532 | .9527 | .9521 | .9516 |
| 18° | .9511 | .9505 | .9500 | .9494 | .9489 | .9483 | .9478 | .9472 | .9466 | .9461 |
| 19° | .9455 | .9449 | .9444 | .9438 | .9432 | .9426 | .9421 | .9415 | .9409 | .9403 |
| 20° | .9397 | .9391 | .9385 | .9379 | .9373 | .9367 | .9361 | .9354 | .9348 | .9342 |
| 21° | .9336 | .9330 | .9323 | .9317 | .9311 | .9304 | .9298 | .9291 | .9285 | .9278 |
| 22° | .9272 | .9265 | .9259 | .9252 | .9245 | .9239 | .9232 | .9225 | .9219 | .9212 |
| 23° | .9205 | .9198 | .9191 | .9184 | .9178 | .9171 | .9164 | .9157 | .9150 | .9143 |
| 24° | .9135 | .9128 | .9121 | .9114 | .9107 | .9100 | .9092 | .9085 | .9078 | .9070 |
| 25° | .9063 | .9056 | .9048 | .9041 | .9033 | .9026 | .9018 | .9011 | .9003 | .8996 |
| 26° | .8988 | .8980 | .8973 | .8965 | .8957 | .8949 | .8942 | .8934 | .8926 | .8918 |
| 27° | .8910 | .8902 | .8894 | .8886 | .8878 | .8870 | .8862 | .8854 | .8846 | .8838 |
| 28° | .8829 | .8821 | .8813 | .8805 | .8796 | .8788 | .8780 | .8771 | .8763 | .8755 |
| 29° | .8746 | .8738 | .8729 | .8721 | .8712 | .8704 | .8695 | .8686 | .8678 | .8669 |
| 30° | .8660 | .8652 | .8643 | .8634 | .8625 | .8616 | .8607 | .8599 | .8590 | .8581 |
| 31° | .8572 | .8563 | .8554 | .8545 | .8536 | .8526 | .8517 | .8508 | .8499 | .8490 |
| 32° | .8480 | .8471 | .8462 | .8453 | .8443 | .8434 | .8425 | .8415 | .8406 | .8396 |
| 33° | .8387 | .8377 | .8368 | .8358 | .8348 | .8339 | .8329 | .8320 | .8310 | .8300 |
| 34° | .8290 | .8281 | .8271 | .8261 | .8251 | .8241 | .8231 | .8221 | .8211 | .8202 |
| 35° | .8192 | .8181 | .8171 | .8161 | .8151 | .8141 | .8131 | .8121 | .8111 | .8100 |
| 36° | .8090 | .8080 | .8070 | .8059 | .8049 | .8039 | .8028 | .8018 | .8007 | .7997 |
| 37° | .7986 | .7976 | .7965 | .7955 | .7944 | .7934 | .7923 | .7912 | .7902 | .7891 |
| 38° | .7880 | .7869 | .7859 | .7848 | .7837 | .7826 | .7815 | .7804 | .7793 | .7782 |
| 39° | .7771 | .7760 | .7749 | .7738 | .7727 | .7716 | .7705 | .7694 | .7683 | .7672 |
| 40° | .7660 | .7649 | .7638 | .7627 | .7615 | .7604 | .7593 | .7581 | .7570 | .7559 |
| 41° | .7547 | .7536 | .7524 | .7513 | .7501 | .7490 | .7478 | .7466 | .7455 | .7443 |
| 42° | .7431 | .7420 | .7408 | .7396 | .7385 | .7373 | .7361 | .7349 | .7337 | .7325 |
| 43° | .7314 | .7302 | .7290 | .7278 | .7266 | .7254 | .7242 | .7230 | .7218 | .7206 |
| 44° | .7193 | .7181 | .7169 | .7157 | .7145 | .7133 | .7120 | .7108 | .7096 | .7083 |

# NATURAL TRIGONOMETRIC FUNCTIONS: COSINE

## Angles from 45°.0 to 89°.9

| | .0 | .1 | .2 | .3 | .4 | .5 | .6 | .7 | .8 | .9 |
|---|---|---|---|---|---|---|---|---|---|---|
| 45° | .7071 | .7059 | .7046 | .7034 | .7022 | .7009 | .6997 | .6984 | .6972 | .6959 |
| 46° | .6947 | .6934 | .6921 | .6909 | .6896 | .6884 | .6871 | .6858 | .6845 | .6833 |
| 47° | .6820 | .6807 | .6794 | .6782 | .6769 | .6756 | .6743 | .6730 | .6717 | .6704 |
| 48° | .6691 | .6678 | .6665 | .6652 | .6639 | .6626 | .6613 | .6600 | .6587 | .6574 |
| 49° | .6561 | .6547 | .6534 | .6521 | .6508 | .6494 | .6481 | .6468 | .6455 | .6441 |
| 50° | .6428 | .6414 | .6401 | .6388 | .6374 | .6361 | .6347 | .6334 | .6320 | .6307 |
| 51° | .6293 | .6280 | .6266 | .6252 | .6239 | .6225 | .6211 | .6198 | .6184 | .6170 |
| 52° | .6157 | .6143 | .6129 | .6115 | .6101 | .6088 | .6074 | .6060 | .6046 | .6032 |
| 53° | .6018 | .6004 | .5990 | .5976 | .5962 | .5948 | .5934 | .5920 | .5906 | .5892 |
| 54° | .5878 | .5864 | .5850 | .5835 | .5821 | .5807 | .5793 | .5779 | .5764 | .5750 |
| 55° | .5736 | .5721 | .5707 | .5693 | .5678 | .5664 | .5650 | .5635 | .5621 | .5606 |
| 56° | .5592 | .5577 | .5563 | .5548 | .5534 | .5519 | .5505 | .5490 | .5476 | .5461 |
| 57° | .5446 | .5432 | .5417 | .5402 | .5388 | .5373 | .5358 | .5344 | .5329 | .5314 |
| 58° | .5299 | .5284 | .5270 | .5255 | .5240 | .5225 | .5210 | .5195 | .5180 | .5165 |
| 59° | .5150 | .5135 | .5120 | .5105 | .5090 | .5075 | .5060 | .5045 | .5030 | .5015 |
| 60° | .5000 | .4985 | .4970 | .4955 | .4939 | .4924 | .4909 | .4894 | .4879 | .4863 |
| 61° | .4848 | .4833 | .4818 | .4802 | .4787 | .4772 | .4756 | .4741 | .4726 | .4710 |
| 62° | .4695 | .4679 | .4664 | .4648 | .4633 | .4617 | .4602 | .4586 | .4571 | .4555 |
| 63° | .4540 | .4524 | .4509 | .4493 | .4478 | .4462 | .4446 | .4431 | .4415 | .4399 |
| 64° | .4384 | .4368 | .4352 | .4337 | .4321 | .4305 | .4289 | .4274 | .4258 | .4242 |
| 65° | .4226 | .4210 | .4195 | .4179 | .4163 | .4147 | .4131 | .4115 | .4099 | .4083 |
| 66° | .4067 | .4051 | .4035 | .4019 | .4003 | .3987 | .3971 | .3955 | .3939 | .3923 |
| 67° | .3907 | .3891 | .3875 | .3859 | .3843 | .3827 | .3811 | .3795 | .3778 | .3762 |
| 68° | .3746 | .3730 | .3714 | .3697 | .3681 | .3665 | .3649 | .3633 | .3616 | .3600 |
| 69° | .3584 | .3567 | .3551 | .3535 | .3518 | .3502 | .3486 | .3469 | .3453 | .3437 |
| 70° | .3420 | .3404 | .3387 | .3371 | .3355 | .3338 | .3322 | .3305 | .3289 | .3272 |
| 71° | .3256 | .3239 | .3223 | .3206 | .3190 | .3173 | .3156 | .3140 | .3123 | .3107 |
| 72° | .3090 | .3074 | .3057 | .3040 | .3024 | .3007 | .2990 | .2974 | .2957 | .2940 |
| 73° | .2924 | .2907 | .2890 | .2874 | .2857 | .2840 | .2823 | .2807 | .2790 | .2773 |
| 74° | .2756 | .2740 | .2723 | .2706 | .2689 | .2672 | .2656 | .2639 | .2622 | .2605 |
| 75° | .2588 | .2571 | .2554 | .2538 | .2521 | .2504 | .2487 | .2470 | .2453 | .2436 |
| 76° | .2419 | .2402 | .2385 | .2368 | .2351 | .2334 | .2317 | .2300 | .2284 | .2267 |
| 77° | .2250 | .2233 | .2215 | .2198 | .2181 | .2164 | .2147 | .2130 | .2113 | .2096 |
| 78° | .2079 | .2062 | .2045 | .2028 | .2011 | .1994 | .1977 | .1959 | .1942 | .1925 |
| 79° | .1908 | .1891 | .1874 | .1857 | .1840 | .1822 | .1805 | .1788 | .1771 | .1754 |
| 80° | .1736 | .1719 | .1702 | .1685 | .1668 | .1650 | .1633 | .1616 | .1599 | .1582 |
| 81° | .1564 | .1547 | .1530 | .1513 | .1495 | .1478 | .1461 | .1444 | .1426 | .1409 |
| 82° | .1392 | .1374 | .1357 | .1340 | .1323 | .1305 | .1288 | .1271 | .1253 | .1236 |
| 83° | .1219 | .1201 | .1184 | .1167 | .1149 | .1132 | .1115 | .1097 | .1080 | .1063 |
| 84° | .1045 | .1028 | .1011 | .0993 | .0976 | .0958 | .0941 | .0924 | .0906 | .0889 |
| 85° | .0872 | .0854 | .0837 | .0819 | .0802 | .0785 | .0767 | .0750 | .0732 | .0715 |
| 86° | .0698 | .0680 | .0663 | .0645 | .0628 | .0610 | .0593 | .0576 | .0558 | .0541 |
| 87° | .0523 | .0506 | .0488 | .0471 | .0454 | .0436 | .0419 | .0401 | .0384 | .0366 |
| 88° | .0349 | .0332 | .0314 | .0297 | .0279 | .0262 | .0244 | .0227 | .0209 | .0192 |
| 89° | .0175 | .0157 | .0140 | .0122 | .0105 | .0087 | .0070 | .0052 | .0035 | .0017 |

# NATURAL TRIGONOMETRIC FUNCTIONS: TANGENT

## Angles from 0°.0 to 44°.9

| | .0 | .1 | .2 | .3 | .4 | .5 | .6 | .7 | .8 | .9 |
|---|---|---|---|---|---|---|---|---|---|---|
| 0° | .0000 | .0017 | .0035 | .0052 | .0070 | .0087 | .0105 | .0122 | .0140 | .0157 |
| 1° | .0175 | .0192 | .0209 | .0227 | .0244 | .0262 | .0279 | .0297 | .0314 | .0332 |
| 2° | .0349 | .0367 | .0384 | .0402 | .0419 | .0437 | .0454 | .0472 | .0489 | .0507 |
| 3° | .0524 | .0542 | .0559 | .0577 | .0594 | .0612 | .0629 | .0647 | .0664 | .0682 |
| 4° | .0699 | .0717 | .0734 | .0752 | .0769 | .0787 | .0805 | .0822 | .0840 | .0857 |
| 5° | .0875 | .0892 | .0910 | .0928 | .0945 | .0963 | .0981 | .0998 | .1016 | .1033 |
| 6° | .1051 | .1069 | .1086 | .1104 | .1122 | .1139 | .1157 | .1175 | .1192 | .1210 |
| 7° | .1228 | .1246 | .1263 | .1281 | .1299 | .1317 | .1334 | .1352 | .1370 | .1388 |
| 8° | .1405 | .1423 | .1441 | .1459 | .1477 | .1495 | .1512 | .1530 | .1548 | .1566 |
| 9° | .1584 | .1602 | .1620 | .1638 | .1655 | .1673 | .1691 | .1709 | .1727 | .1745 |
| 10° | .1763 | .1781 | .1799 | .1817 | .1835 | .1853 | .1871 | .1890 | .1908 | .1926 |
| 11° | .1944 | .1962 | .1980 | .1998 | .2016 | .2035 | .2053 | .2071 | .2089 | .2107 |
| 12° | .2126 | .2144 | .2162 | .2180 | .2199 | .2217 | .2235 | .2254 | .2272 | .2290 |
| 13° | .2309 | .2327 | .2345 | .2364 | .2382 | .2401 | .2419 | .2438 | .2456 | .2475 |
| 14° | .2493 | .2512 | .2530 | .2549 | .2568 | .2586 | .2605 | .2623 | .2642 | .2661 |
| 15° | .2679 | .2698 | .2717 | .2736 | .2754 | .2773 | .2792 | .2811 | .2830 | .2849 |
| 16° | .2867 | .2886 | .2905 | .2924 | .2943 | .2962 | .2981 | .3000 | .3019 | .3038 |
| 17° | .3057 | .3076 | .3096 | .3115 | .3134 | .3153 | .3172 | .3191 | .3211 | .3230 |
| 18° | .3249 | .3269 | .3288 | .3307 | .3327 | .3346 | .3365 | .3385 | .3404 | .3424 |
| 19° | .3443 | .3463 | .3482 | .3502 | .3522 | .3541 | .3561 | .3581 | .3600 | .3620 |
| 20° | .3640 | .3659 | .3679 | .3699 | .3719 | .3739 | .3759 | .3779 | .3799 | .3819 |
| 21° | .3839 | .3859 | .3879 | .3899 | .3919 | .3939 | .3959 | .3979 | .4000 | .4020 |
| 22° | .4040 | .4061 | .4081 | .4101 | .4122 | .4142 | .4163 | .4183 | .4204 | .4224 |
| 23° | .4245 | .4265 | .4286 | .4307 | .4327 | .4348 | .4369 | .4390 | .4411 | .4431 |
| 24° | .4452 | .4473 | .4494 | .4515 | .4536 | .4557 | .4578 | .4599 | .4621 | .4642 |
| 25° | .4663 | .4684 | .4706 | .4727 | .4748 | .4770 | .4791 | .4813 | .4834 | .4856 |
| 26° | .4877 | .4899 | .4921 | .4942 | .4964 | .4986 | .5008 | .5029 | .5051 | .5073 |
| 27° | .5095 | .5117 | .5139 | .5161 | .5184 | .5206 | .5228 | .5250 | .5272 | .5295 |
| 28° | .5317 | .5340 | .5362 | .5384 | .5407 | .5430 | .5452 | .5475 | .5498 | .5520 |
| 29° | .5543 | .5566 | .5589 | .5612 | .5635 | .5658 | .5681 | .5704 | .5727 | .5750 |
| 30° | .5774 | .5797 | .5820 | .5844 | .5867 | .5890 | .5914 | .5938 | .5961 | .5985 |
| 31° | .6009 | .6032 | .6056 | .6080 | .6104 | .6128 | .6152 | .6176 | .6200 | .6224 |
| 32° | .6249 | .6273 | .6297 | .6322 | .6346 | .6371 | .6395 | .6420 | .6445 | .6469 |
| 33° | .6494 | .6519 | .6544 | .6569 | .6594 | .6619 | .6644 | .6669 | .6694 | .6720 |
| 34° | .6745 | .6771 | .6796 | .6822 | .6847 | .6873 | .6899 | .6924 | .6950 | .6976 |
| 35° | .7002 | .7028 | .7054 | .7080 | .7107 | .7133 | .7159 | .7186 | .7212 | .7239 |
| 36° | .7265 | .7292 | .7319 | .7346 | .7373 | .7400 | .7427 | .7454 | .7481 | .7508 |
| 37° | .7536 | .7563 | .7590 | .7618 | .7646 | .7673 | .7701 | .7729 | .7757 | .7785 |
| 38° | .7813 | .7841 | .7869 | .7898 | .7926 | .7954 | .7983 | .8012 | .8040 | .8069 |
| 39° | .8098 | .8127 | .8156 | .8185 | .8214 | .8243 | .8273 | .8302 | .8332 | .8361 |
| 40° | .8391 | .8421 | .8451 | .8481 | .8511 | .8541 | .8571 | .8601 | .8632 | .8662 |
| 41° | .8693 | .8724 | .8754 | .8785 | .8816 | .8847 | .8878 | .8910 | .8941 | .8972 |
| 42° | .9004 | .9036 | .9067 | .9099 | .9131 | .9163 | .9195 | .9228 | .9260 | .9293 |
| 43° | .9325 | .9358 | .9391 | .9424 | .9457 | .9490 | .9523 | .9556 | .9590 | .9623 |
| 44° | .9657 | .9691 | .9725 | .9759 | .9793 | .9827 | .9861 | .9896 | .9930 | .9965 |

# NATURAL TRIGONOMETRIC FUNCTIONS: TANGENT

## Angles from 45°.0 to 89°.9

| | .0 | .1 | .2 | .3 | .4 | .5 | .6 | .7 | .8 | .9 |
|---|---|---|---|---|---|---|---|---|---|---|
| 45° | 1.000 | 1.003 | 1.007 | 1.011 | 1.014 | 1.018 | 1.021 | 1.025 | 1.028 | 1.032 |
| 46° | 1.036 | 1.039 | 1.043 | 1.046 | 1.050 | 1.054 | 1.057 | 1.061 | 1.065 | 1.069 |
| 47° | 1.072 | 1.076 | 1.080 | 1.084 | 1.087 | 1.091 | 1.095 | 1.099 | 1.103 | 1.107 |
| 48° | 1.111 | 1.115 | 1.118 | 1.122 | 1.126 | 1.130 | 1.134 | 1.138 | 1.142 | 1.146 |
| 49° | 1.150 | 1.154 | 1.159 | 1.163 | 1.167 | 1.171 | 1.175 | 1.179 | 1.183 | 1.188 |
| 50° | 1.192 | 1.196 | 1.200 | 1.205 | 1.209 | 1.213 | 1.217 | 1.222 | 1.226 | 1.230 |
| 51° | 1.235 | 1.239 | 1.244 | 1.248 | 1.253 | 1.257 | 1.262 | 1.266 | 1.271 | 1.275 |
| 52° | 1.280 | 1.285 | 1.289 | 1.294 | 1.299 | 1.303 | 1.308 | 1.313 | 1.317 | 1.322 |
| 53° | 1.327 | 1.332 | 1.337 | 1.342 | 1.347 | 1.351 | 1.356 | 1.361 | 1.366 | 1.371 |
| 54° | 1.376 | 1.381 | 1.387 | 1.392 | 1.397 | 1.402 | 1.407 | 1.412 | 1.418 | 1.423 |
| 55° | 1.428 | 1.433 | 1.439 | 1.444 | 1.450 | 1.455 | 1.460 | 1.466 | 1.471 | 1.477 |
| 56° | 1.483 | 1.488 | 1.494 | 1.499 | 1.505 | 1.511 | 1.517 | 1.522 | 1.528 | 1.534 |
| 57° | 1.540 | 1.546 | 1.552 | 1.558 | 1.564 | 1.570 | 1.576 | 1.582 | 1.588 | 1.594 |
| 58° | 1.600 | 1.607 | 1.613 | 1.619 | 1.625 | 1.632 | 1.638 | 1.645 | 1.651 | 1.658 |
| 59° | 1.664 | 1.671 | 1.678 | 1.684 | 1.691 | 1.698 | 1.704 | 1.711 | 1.718 | 1.725 |
| 60° | 1.732 | 1.739 | 1.746 | 1.753 | 1.760 | 1.767 | 1.775 | 1.782 | 1.789 | 1.797 |
| 61° | 1.804 | 1.811 | 1.819 | 1.827 | 1.834 | 1.842 | 1.849 | 1.857 | 1.865 | 1.873 |
| 62° | 1.881 | 1.889 | 1.897 | 1.905 | 1.913 | 1.921 | 1.929 | 1.937 | 1.946 | 1.954 |
| 63° | 1.963 | 1.971 | 1.980 | 1.988 | 1.997 | 2.006 | 2.014 | 2.023 | 2.032 | 2.041 |
| 64° | 2.050 | 2.059 | 2.069 | 2.078 | 2.087 | 2.097 | 2.106 | 2.116 | 2.125 | 2.135 |
| 65° | 2.145 | 2.154 | 2.164 | 2.174 | 2.184 | 2.194 | 2.204 | 2.215 | 2.225 | 2.236 |
| 66° | 2.246 | 2.257 | 2.267 | 2.278 | 2.289 | 2.300 | 2.311 | 2.322 | 2.333 | 2.344 |
| 67° | 2.356 | 2.367 | 2.379 | 2.391 | 2.402 | 2.414 | 2.426 | 2.438 | 2.450 | 2.463 |
| 68° | 2.475 | 2.488 | 2.500 | 2.513 | 2.526 | 2.539 | 2.552 | 2.565 | 2.578 | 2.592 |
| 69° | 2.605 | 2.619 | 2.633 | 2.646 | 2.660 | 2.675 | 2.689 | 2.703 | 2.718 | 2.733 |
| 70° | 2.747 | 2.762 | 2.778 | 2.793 | 2.808 | 2.824 | 2.840 | 2.856 | 2.872 | 2.888 |
| 71° | 2.904 | 2.921 | 2.937 | 2.954 | 2.971 | 2.989 | 3.006 | 3.024 | 3.042 | 3.060 |
| 72° | 3.078 | 3.096 | 3.115 | 3.133 | 3.152 | 3.172 | 3.191 | 3.211 | 3.230 | 3.251 |
| 73° | 3.271 | 3.291 | 3.312 | 3.333 | 3.354 | 3.376 | 3.398 | 3.420 | 3.442 | 3.465 |
| 74° | 3.487 | 3.511 | 3.534 | 3.558 | 3.582 | 3.606 | 3.630 | 3.655 | 3.681 | 3.706 |
| 75° | 3.732 | 3.758 | 3.785 | 3.812 | 3.839 | 3.867 | 3.895 | 3.923 | 3.952 | 3.981 |
| 76° | 4.011 | 4.041 | 4.071 | 4.102 | 4.134 | 4.165 | 4.198 | 4.230 | 4.264 | 4.297 |
| 77° | 4.331 | 4.366 | 4.402 | 4.437 | 4.474 | 4.511 | 4.548 | 4.586 | 4.625 | 4.665 |
| 78° | 4.705 | 4.745 | 4.787 | 4.829 | 4.872 | 4.915 | 4.959 | 5.005 | 5.050 | 5.097 |
| 79° | 5.145 | 5.193 | 5.242 | 5.292 | 5.343 | 5.396 | 5.449 | 5.503 | 5.558 | 5.614 |
| 80° | 5.671 | 5.730 | 5.789 | 5.850 | 5.912 | 5.976 | 6.041 | 6.107 | 6.174 | 6.243 |
| 81° | 6.314 | 6.386 | 6.460 | 6.535 | 6.612 | 6.691 | 6.772 | 6.855 | 6.940 | 7.026 |
| 82° | 7.115 | 7.207 | 7.300 | 7.396 | 7.495 | 7.596 | 7.700 | 7.806 | 7.916 | 8.028 |
| 83° | 8.144 | 8.264 | 8.386 | 8.513 | 8.643 | 8.777 | 8.915 | 9.058 | 9.205 | 9.357 |
| 84° | 9.514 | 9.677 | 9.845 | 10.02 | 10.20 | 10.39 | 10.58 | 10.78 | 10.99 | 11.20 |
| 85° | 11.43 | 11.66 | 11.91 | 12.16 | 12.43 | 12.71 | 13.00 | 13.30 | 13.62 | 13.95 |
| 86° | 14.30 | 14.67 | 15.06 | 15.46 | 15.89 | 16.35 | 16.83 | 17.34 | 17.89 | 18.46 |
| 87° | 19.08 | 19.74 | 20.45 | 21.20 | 22.02 | 22.90 | 23.86 | 24.90 | 26.03 | 27.27 |
| 88° | 28.64 | 30.14 | 31.82 | 33.69 | 35.80 | 38.19 | 40.92 | 44.07 | 47.74 | 52.08 |
| 89° | 57.29 | 63.66 | 71.62 | 81.85 | 95.49 | 114.6 | 143.2 | 191.0 | 286.5 | 573.0 |

# INDEX